SWITCHING CIRCUITS
AND LOGICAL DESIGN

JOHN WILEY & SONS, INC., NEW YORK

Chapman & Hall Limited, London

SWITCHING CIRCUITS
AND LOGICAL DESIGN

SAMUEL H. CALDWELL

Professor of Electrical Engineering

Massachusetts Institute of Technology

To Betty

Preface

Many of the world's existing switching circuits were designed and built without the aid of any appreciable body of switching-circuit theory. The men who designed them developed and organized their experience into creative skills of high order without benefit of theory. Why, then, is it important to have a theoretical basis for designing switching circuits? What are these circuits and what do they do?

Probably the earliest switching "circuit"—invented more than a century ago—was the railway signal interlocking system. By means of it the designer sought, primarily, to expedite railway traffic, but he also wanted to do so without the risk of accidents. When traffic is light the switch and signal operators can readily expedite its movement with safety. But under heavy traffic conditions, with a complex variety of traffic patterns to consider, the operator's ability to make decisions becomes overloaded, and he becomes prone to error. Using the signal interlocking system the operator is not permitted to make incorrect decisions. The machine does not initiate action; its function is merely to respond to whatever action the operator attempts by either permitting it or not permitting it.

We are witnessing today a similar development in the control of air traffic at and between terminals. No longer is there a light stream of traffic. Worse yet, air traffic occupies a third dimension. Man now seeks further assistance in adding a "third dimension" to his ability to make decisions. In the century since the invention of the railway signal interlocking system nature has not had sufficient time to improve man's ability to make decisions rapidly.

So, we have the same problem as that of a century ago—the problem of making decisions. But we are evolving better solutions to that problem through those assemblages of switching circuits which constitute the modern digital computer or data-processing machine.

Inevitably the solutions to the problem of air-traffic control must contain the means for increasing man's ability to make safe decisions while under stress. That progress is necessary, but unless all the consequences of those decisions are of equal importance, it is not sufficient. Once the safety of a decision is assured we will surely ask for the "best" decision. In other words, we cannot expect to be satisfied by a mere random set of safe decisions if, by further development of the decision-making process, we can find an optimum set of decisions.

This discussion of the use of switching circuits in the control of traffic on railways and in the air is intended only to develop the fact that the basic function of a switching circuit is to help make decisions rapidly. At a relatively leisurely pace the designer of the circuit assembles its components so that each output (that is, each decision) is exactly that demanded by the input combination (the prevailing circumstances), or even by a sequence of input combinations (the history of the circumstances). He must, of course, be certain that he accounts for all combinations and sequences that can possibly occur. By this process he is able to synthesize a circuit from which the output responses are predetermined functions of the input stimuli, obtainable at high speed, either under routine conditions or in emergencies.

The work of C. E. Shannon in his classic 1938 paper, "A Symbolic Analysis of Relay and Switching Circuits" (reference 5, page 64), stimulated worldwide interest and activity in the subject. Shannon's work presented an opportunity to supplement skill with methods based on science, and thus to increase the productivity of circuit designers. Of even greater importance, though, was the possibility of developing a science which would promote deep understanding and nourish creative imagination.

Many workers since Shannon have made contributions to the scientific aspects of switching. Unfortunately these published reports are scattered and some are not readily obtainable. One of the major objectives in writing this book was to make available, both for the teacher and for the engineer at work, an integrated presentation of the fundamentals of switching circuit design, with emphasis on the scientific methods that have been developed.

This book is based on the sequence of lecture material I have presented in a two-semester treatment of the subject in the Department of Electrical Engineering of the Massachusetts Institute of Technology. Many variations of the sequence are possible, particularly by the omission or the postponement of some topics. These possibilities will be discussed more fully later.

After two chapters of introductory and descriptive material, Chapter 3 seeks first to establish switching algebra as an independent structure of ideas and concepts. This is especially important for those engineering students who have not studied the mathematical disciplines which are the sources of switching algebra. Because the algebra is applied to circuits using a variety of components, the student's understanding of it should not be based on a physical visualization of its significance in relation to any one particular component. He need not develop great skill in manipulation at this point; it is sufficient that he see clearly that the algebra needs no physical support, for it is this understanding that unifies the subsequent study of switching circuits in which many kinds of physical components are used.

The second half of Chapter 3 introduces an interpretation of switching algebra in terms of simple relay contact configurations. This is an elementary treatment, but it prepares for the final article of the chapter in which many of the theorems of the algebra are restated in terms of the contact-network transformations they describe. This process is primarily a transition from the earlier abstraction of a pencil-and-paper algebra to the physical world of materials and instruments. But the real significance of the abstract is revealed to the student in the unexpected manipulations of physical networks he discovers.

Chapters 4 to 8, inclusive, and Chapter 11 discuss combinational switching circuits in terms of relay contact networks. This use of the contact network is, of course, a teaching device. It enables us to explore many aspects of logical design without the encumbrance of engineering and physical limitations which afflicts other switching components. Moreover, it has been my experience that when the student does reach the material of Chapter 9—the use of electronic and solid-state devices—he has built up a command of the principles of logical design that enables him to understand and apply new components with ease.

Chapter 10, on the switching aspects of codes, is introduced to give some background on one of the important classes of switching-circuit problems. Chapter 11, Iterative Networks, completes the treatment of combinational circuits. Iterative circuit design presents problems of great challenge and stimulation to the student. It also becomes the vehicle for the introduction of a matrix approach to synthesis. Effectively the iterative network can be regarded as a sequence in space and designed accordingly. This concept leads directly to the study of (time) sequential circuits in the remaining chapters.

Chapters 12 and 13 develop the methods of sequential circuit design, again using relays and contact networks. A basic objective of the synthesis method is to transform the sequential problem to a combinational problem, and it is shown that a sequential circuit is really a combinational circuit with feedback loops which usually contain time delay. In Chapter 14 these concepts permit a direct attack on the problems of sequential circuit design using the non-relay components discussed in Chapter 9.

Chapter 15 concludes the book with a discussion of pulsed circuits. Against the broad background already established relatively few new concepts or procedures are needed. Various kinds of flip-flops are used in the examples, and the examples themselves are chosen to illustrate the broad scope of pulsed circuit design.

It was previously mentioned that the content of this book required two semesters for presentation by lectures. The time released from lecturing by having a text available may be used profitably in many ways. One plan is to offer a one-semester subject which will be the first semester for the student who wants to specialize in switching circuits, but which will serve also as a broad introduction to the student who wants background material for the study of computers and other data manipulation systems. This one-semester offering should contain material selected from the entire book. The basis for selection is to omit material which is of interest primarily to the specialist. Chapters 3, 4, 5, 9, 12, 14, and 15 form a suitable selection for a one-semester presentation at the fourth-year level. For graduate students Chapters 6 and 13 should be included and, depending on the time available, possibly Chapter 7 also.

Some of Chapter 7, most of Chapter 8, and all of Chapter 11 are of interest primarily to the specialist and can be deferred to a second semester. In addition, a second course offers the opportunity to introduce engineering aspects of switching-circuit design, to discuss current developments as reported in periodical literature, and to seek further integration of the subject through project studies on larger logical systems. At this level it may also be advantageous to present the material in the seminar form.

Selected problems have been included at the end of each chapter, starting with Chapter 3. The importance to the individual student of solving problems cannot be overstated. For many students this is the first encounter with the need to perform synthesis. Most problems do not have unique and tidy "answers." It usually requires an exercise of judgment to select, on some basis, a preferred result from among the many that are available. The experience required to develop good judgment is obtainable only by personal effort.

It is also desirable to supplement the classroom study of switching circuits with laboratory exercises. While combinational problems are being studied the student can examine in the laboratory the physical characteristics and switching properties of various switching-circuit components. There is no need to experiment at this time with combinational circuits, which are not particularly attractive as laboratory experiments, for the more stimulating sequential circuits contain them. And we need not make our experiments with sequential circuits complex. Most of the basic problems are revealed at a quite elementary level.

In writing this book I have tried to avoid two extremes. First, it is a temptation to use existing switching circuits as illustrative examples because they provide motivation to the student. There is no harm in discussing a useful circuit, but there can be harm if the usefulness is the only reason for discussing it.

Second, I have avoided the extreme of treating switching-circuit theory as an exercise in mathematics. It is inevitable, of course, that an engineering subject which sprang from the purest of pure mathematics must surely benefit from mathematical resources that have not even been recognized, and certainly not appreciated. But, despite the rapidly growing mathematical literacy of the engineer, the problem of good communication between the mathematician and the engineer still remains unresolved.

Most engineers are not familiar with the ideograms of symbolic logic. Some of these look to them more like the brands that identify western U. S. cattle ranches than mathematical symbols. These symbols express important subtleties which properly concern the mathematician. But there is no need for them in switching-circuit theory—certainly not at its present state of development. Shannon, in his first paper on the subject, displayed a sure instinct in his choice of symbology. Many who have followed seem not so sure about their choices. To me there is something quite illogical about insisting that Boolean addition be described by the *cup* symbol of logic, rather than by the ordinary plus sign, but at the same time relaxing to the extent of describing Boolean multiplication by the product dot, or by simple juxtaposition of terms, rather than by the *cap* symbol which is the companion of the cup symbol of symbolic logic.

The time is coming when further progress in the understanding and the design of switching circuits will require the engineer to appreciate mathematical concepts rather than mathematical operations and manipulations. But I am convinced that until engineers have a greater knowledge of switching circuits, progress in this field will depend on our ability to communicate the present state of knowledge to currently practicing engineers, with whatever diverse mathematical backgrounds and skills they may have.

In steering a course which avoids the extremes of strict utility and pure mathematics it is paradoxically true that many engineering students become either intensely, and skillfully, practical, or highly, and soundly, theoretical. It is most encouraging to the teacher when he can stimulate widely scattered and divergent interests among his students. The process of teaching is, after all, much less important than the *learning* accomplished by the student who gets personally excited about something. I have observed at first hand the challenge that the mastery of switching circuits offers to engineering students through seven years of teaching it. I hope many other teachers will enjoy a corresponding experience.

This book contains the contributions of many of my colleagues and students to which I have given bibliographical reference or other acknowledgment. There have been many other contributions, however, for which I can express my gratitude only in general terms. These have been the day-to-day items which cumulatively have given this subject much of its substance and have improved its presentation.

I have made numerous references to papers written by Dr. David A. Huffman and treating a broad expanse of switching-circuit theory and practice. Of equal importance are the contributions Professor Huffman has made in the classroom in fostering understanding based on science, and continued growth of that understanding through research.

I must also express my thanks to a group of men who have assisted in teaching this subject during the last several years and who have developed it and strengthened it in numerous ways—Dr. Edward J. McCluskey, Jr., Albert A. Mullin, Wayne G. Kellner, Leo Jedynak, Frederick C. Hennie, III, Trenchard More, Jr., Paul E. Gray, and Fred H. Irons.

To my secretary, Margaret Park, I express my appreciation for her loyal assistance through the long period during which this book was written.

SAMUEL H. CALDWELL

Watertown, Mass.
February, 1958

Contents

CHAPTER 1

Properties
and applications
of
switching circuits

This has been called the age of the machine. It might also be called the age of communication and control. The two designations are closely related, for a machine must be controlled in a prescribed manner if it is to serve a useful purpose, and a control system generally exerts its influence over some sort of machine. Taken separately, a machine or a control element has properties which may be useful, or they may be merely interesting. When appropriate combinations of these are brought together by competent design a system of enhanced worth is formed.

1.1 Control Systems

In this book we are concerned with a particular kind of control system, commonly known as a switching circuit. There are many types of switching circuits, and they perform a wide variety of functions in our complex industrial and social life. We encounter them directly when we push the buttons, spin the dials, and interrupt the beams of light which form their input mechanisms. Behind these palpable components of the automatic systems and devices which we have learned to accept as commonplace, there is a vast, unseen structure of components assembled into switching circuits of many types.

Another major type of control system—the servomechanism—makes use primarily of the feedback principle. Although switching circuits and servomechanisms can be and are used in combination, the differences between them should be clearly understood. Servomechanisms usually receive input information which is either continuous in its variations, or is discontinuous in relatively small steps. Because of the feedback which is present the output of the servomechanism inherently becomes a continuous function of the input variables. In switching circuits both the inputs and the outputs have a two-valued character, and no attempt is made to introduce continuity. There are many forms which this "two-valuedness" can take. An input or output voltage may be high or low, a pulse may be present or absent, or a circuit may be open or closed. The essential thing is that the switching circuit operates not merely upon a discrete-valued basis, but upon a two-valued basis which involves the extremes of variation.

It was noted that the continuous servomechanism and the two-valued switching circuit could be used in combination. An example of such combined operation occurs in the control of automatic elevators. The simplest form of push-button elevator is operated under the control of a switching circuit which applies power to the elevator motor so as to take the car in the desired direction. When the elevator reaches the right floor the automatic equipment opens the motor power circuit and applies a mechanical brake. Under this form of control the elevator stops with a jerk, and it is difficult to maintain an adjustment of the coasting distance such that the car stops in line with the floor under all combinations of loading and direction of travel.

An improved form of control depends again upon the action of a switching circuit, and is widely used. Instead of stopping the car in one step, this form of control reduces the speed through a series of steps. Although the final step is still discontinuous, it is much less abrupt than before, and the coasting distance is more readily adjusted and maintained. Here we appear to have an example in which a switching circuit is operating upon a somewhat continuous basis. Within the switching circuit, however, and at its inputs and outputs, the action is completely two-valued. The input mechanism is not concerned with the speed of the elevator or with its exact distance from the desired floor. It simply determines whether the car is or is not within a certain pre-determined distance, and the switching circuit components respond only when a particular input condition is reached.

A still more elaborate type of control combines the switching circuit and the servomechanism. The switching circuit starts the elevator in the right direction and keeps it operating at high speed until it approaches the desired floor. An initial step or two of speed reduction may be introduced by the switching circuit, but when the car gets near the required floor level the switching circuit shifts the control to a servomechanism. The servomechanism receives information from a position-measuring element located in the elevator shaft and uses this information to produce a gradual reduction of the elevator speed. Under this system the car is brought to a halt smoothly and with considerable precision in its final location, but the continuous control which characterizes the final stage of the process is accomplished by means of a servomechanism.

We cannot truly compare the switching circuit and the servomechanism; they can only be contrasted. The objectives of the two systems are quite different, and neither is a substitute for the other. As the above example shows, they can be brought together to accomplish results that neither system alone can achieve.

1.2 Applications of Switching Circuits

It would serve no useful purpose to attempt here to summarize, even by title, all the applications of switching circuits. Moreover, it is doubtful that the effort would succeed, for the ubiquitous push button seems to breed more push buttons at a startling pace. Our concern is not primarily with present applications of switching circuits as such, except to the extent that they provide examples of the effective use of basic principles. Nevertheless, a general appreciation of the magnitude and scope of these applications can serve to direct attention to the possibilities for future growth in this field.

One of the largest and most spectacular applications of switching circuits is the dial telephone system. It contains many individual systems ranging in size from the relatively small units which operate within the boundaries of industrial plants to the tremendous structures which serve metropolitan populations throughout the world. The torrent of traffic which pours through these systems testifies to the fact that they are reliable in spite of their size and complexity. The extension of the dial system to enable it to handle long-distance calls emphasizes the versatility of the equipment. New developments have already placed auxiliary operations of the telephone industry on an automatic basis. For many years the familiar coin-operated telephones have been collecting money from the cash customers; another development in switching circuits, known as Automatic Message Accounting, has assumed the responsibility for collecting from the charge customers.

Technically, the problem of automatic switching within the telephone plant is considerably complicated by the fact that there are three basically different types of automatic switching systems in use (within the United States). Each new type of system must contain equipment and circuits to enable it to cooperate with older types of equipment and also with a variety of manually operated switchboards which are still in use. The switching circuit has been shown to have outstanding flexibility in meeting these difficult requirements imposed by system evolution.

In the field of transportation, switching circuits have long served the railroad and rapid transit lines by helping to control the movement of trains with safety and dispatch. They are finding increasing application in the operation of airplanes, again with particular emphasis on their use in promoting safety by preventing improper operation. For example, many airplanes have reversible-pitch propellers which can be used for braking purposes after the plane has landed. The pilot has a switch which enables him to operate the pitch-reversing mechanism, but additional switches are provided on the landing gear, and a switching circuit is so arranged that the pilot cannot reverse the propeller pitch unless the weight of the plane is carried by the landing gear.

In the business world many companies use punched-card equipment to record and to analyze their statistical and financial data. The machines which perform these duties depend for their operation on a variety of switching circuits. It is doubtful whether some of our larger business enterprises could operate successfully without the aid of these computing, sorting, comparison, and classification devices which furnish management with the voluminous facts upon which decisions must be based, and which also carry on the staggering load of routine paper work involved in the day-to-day operation of the business. But productive as they are, even these machines are being overtaxed by the needs of large business organizations, and even more so by the special problems of government groups such as the Census Bureau and the armed forces. These new demands have turned attention to the possibility of using the switching techniques developed for high-speed, digital, electronic computing machines.

From the standpoint of operating speed the switching circuits of electronic digital computers represent the peak of modern development. A number of these machines are now in operation at pulse frequencies measured in megacycles per second, and they perform basic arithmetical operations in times measured in microseconds. To do this it has been necessary to develop new types of switching circuits which exploit the high operating speeds of electronic devices without becoming excessively cumbersome because of the limited switching abilities of these devices. In the world of science and engineering the high-speed computer is recognized as a major achievement and one which will have a profound influence in many fields of technology. To the social sciences it brings the hope that quantitative methods, implemented by high-speed computers, will furnish better understanding of the relations between man and his environment, and between man and man.

A most important aspect of computing machine development is the emphasis it has given to the part played by the switching circuit and to the future possibilities of switching circuit application. The foregoing discussion points out that a wide variety of switching circuits has been in use for many years. But it is the computing machine that fixes attention on the tremendous versatility of even the simplest components of switching circuits, and turns the thoughts of designers to applications in other types of machines.

1.3 Basic Concepts

In the next chapter we shall consider the nature of the components used in switching circuits. There are, however, certain properties of switching circuits which are independent of the types of components used. We may discuss these ideas in terms of the diagram shown in Fig. 1–1.

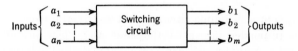

Fig. 1–1. The generalized switching circuit.

It was pointed out in Art. 1.1 that the inputs and outputs of a switching circuit are two valued in character. For example, the inputs in Fig. 1–1 could be a group of lines, a_1 to a_n, on which voltages (to ground) either appear or do not appear. On each input line there is either full voltage or no voltage, and no intermediate voltages are ever found. Likewise the outputs might consist of either grounding or not grounding the terminals to which lines b_1 to b_m are connected. When the outputs are tested it is found that each output is either grounded or is open circuited, and no intermediate impedances to ground are ever found.

It is not necessary that there be the same number of inputs and outputs, and in general their numbers are different. A highly important type of switching circuit has multiple inputs and a single output.

The fact that both the inputs and the outputs of a switching circuit are two valued implies that the circuit itself is two valued in its internal operation. If we think of a sort of "transfer function" which relates output conditions to input conditions,* it becomes apparent that in order to maintain two-valued output variations when the inputs are two valued, the circuit between inputs and outputs must not introduce gradations in the output variations. Hence the circuit itself must operate in the extreme sense that we have defined as two-valued.

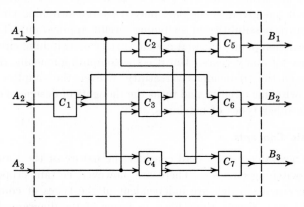

Fig. 1–2. A switching circuit formed by combining a group of smaller switching circuits.

The action of a switching circuit would be trivial if each of a number of outputs responded in exactly the same way when the input conditions varied. Actually, we can obtain any desired relation between each output and the inputs, and all the output variations can be different. Moreover, any of the outputs can be dependent upon all of the inputs, or upon any selection of inputs.

This suggests that switching circuits can be either broken down into simpler structures or combined into more complex ones. A two-valued output from one switching circuit can become a two-valued input to another switching circuit. In Fig. 1–2 the boxes $C_1, C_2, \ldots C_7$ represent individual switching circuits which are interconnected as shown. The two outputs of C_1 provide inputs to C_3 and C_6, the outputs of C_2 become inputs to C_5 and C_7, and so on. Each of the switching circuits $C_1 \ldots C_7$ may be a rather substantial structure, but the connections shown have the effect of combining them into a single switching circuit which is shown enclosed within a broken line in Fig. 1–2. The inputs to the composite circuit are on lines A_1, A_2, A_3, and the outputs are on B_1, B_2, B_3.

* This concept will be expressed more precisely in Chapter 4 when we consider switching functions.

In analogous fashion we may break down a large switching circuit into a group of smaller ones, and we can continue the process until we reach the individual switching elements. Regardless of the size or complexity of a switching circuit, its inputs and outputs are two-valued.

Sometimes it is necessary to introduce auxiliary equipment, particularly at the inputs, in order to obtain two-valued variations. For example, an input may be dependent upon a temperature, and the switching circuit may be required to take a certain action depending upon whether the temperature is above or below a specified value. Here a thermostat is introduced, and preferably one which has a snap action. By means of the thermostat contacts the necessary two-valued temperature input is provided.

1.4   Information and the Logical System

When we examine more closely the nature of the inputs and outputs of a switching circuit it becomes apparent that fundamentally it is a mechanism which receives information of one sort and delivers information of another sort. In the automatic elevator example of Art. 1.1, what information is received and delivered when someone pushes a button to call the elevator? A signal goes to the switching circuit over a line associated with the button pushed. The location of that line informs the switching circuit where the elevator is needed. By means of auxiliary contacts driven by the hoisting drum the circuit "knows" where the elevator is located at the moment, and thus it can determine the direction of motion required. Other auxiliary equipment informs the control circuit that the door must first be closed and, later, that the door is closed. When it is safe to proceed, the control system energizes the motor power contactor which it selects to cause the correct direction of travel.

There is always the possibility that contradictory signals will arrive. If someone in the car pushes a button to go down while someone else calls for the elevator at a higher floor, the control system must "know" what to do about the conflict. If someone on the sixth floor gets in the car and pushes the button to go to the first floor, and immediately afterward someone on the third floor calls for the car to stop and take him down, the control circuit must know whether or not it should make the intermediate stop.

Some of the automatic control systems designed for elevators are quite elaborate, but it is not our purpose to go into great detail in this example. What we have sought to establish is that by way of the push buttons and auxiliary devices discussed, the switching circuit receives a number of pieces of information. Some of the information is static, such as the location of a floor on which a button is pushed. Other information has a sequential aspect, and it tells the control system the order in which events occur.

It is broadly characteristic of the inputs to switching circuits that they carry information regarding either (1) a combination of events or situations which exist or do not exist, or (2) a sequence of events or situations which occur in a certain order, or (3) both combinations and sequences of events or situations.

Since the switching circuit must respond by delivering to its outputs new information which is functionally related to the input information, it becomes appropriate to regard the circuit as being fundamentally a device for processing and modifying information. It must do so in accordance with certain rules, which are built into the circuit by the designer. He in turn must establish the rules (or someone establishes them for him) by a process of thought. For each input condition, or perhaps for some class of input conditions, the designer specifies the required output conditions. It is these relations and only these relations that the switching circuit "knows," but since the designer must include all possible input conditions, the control system is by the process of design "taught" everything it needs to "know" in order to do its job.

It is customary to designate the above process of design as logical design.* Certainly it is the job of the designer to establish the kind of system of formal rules which is the hallmark of traditional logic, and, although the words "logic" and "logical" are sometimes used in a rather meaningless way by those working in this field, they do have a valid application to the subject. A correctly designed switching circuit is one which can enforce the logical relations which the designer establishes between the inputs and the outputs. It is convenient to designate a system of this type as a logical system, and it is this concept which forms the sharpest distinction between the switching circuit and the servomechanism.†

1.5   Objectives of Design

In the preceding section, two aspects of the designer's problem are discussed. He must first determine and state precisely the relations which exist between the information arriving at the inputs of the

---

* Webster's New International Dictionary (2nd edition) gives: *Logical:* "In accordance with the inferences reasonably to be drawn from preceding or surrounding events or circumstances."

† The reader should not infer that there is something illogical about the design of a servomechanism. It simply is not logical in the formal sense of relating its input and output by means of a set of strict rules for which no approximations are valid.

switching circuit and the information sent from the output or outputs of the circuit. It is only after this is done that the second stage of design can be attempted—the synthesis of the logical system.

Most of the remainder of this book will be devoted to a study of the methods used for the analysis of logical systems, and methods for synthesis which are based on the analytic principles thus established. It can readily be shown that it is always possible to synthesize a logical system which will satisfy any prescribed relations between the inputs and the outputs. The problem is hence more than merely being able to realize a desired switching function.

Probably the most sought-for objective of design is simplicity in the circuit structure. The analytic procedures available are quite powerful in eliminating superfluous elements, but there are still many areas of design in which the methods of analysis do not readily indicate the best road to take when we want to reverse the process and perform a synthesis. We know, for example, that certain circuit configurations are highly efficient in the use of switching elements. But it is not easy, by any routine procedure, to identify the situations for which such configurations are applicable. Unfortunately, the whole process of circuit simplification still requires some of the kind of skill best described as the art of design. Notable progress has been made in building up synthesis procedures which do not depend upon our ability to take advantage of subtle observations, but it is likely that there will always continue to be an irreducible minimum of such individual skill required.

Once the logical design of a system is completed there remains the task of engineering the system. The logical designer does his work in terms of functional relations and schematic diagrams. His end result is the starting point for the engineer, who must design the physical circuit and who takes into account matters of voltage levels, power ratings, operating times, and other details of actual performance. Of course, the same man frequently does both jobs—the point is that there are two distinct kinds of design required in the production of a switching circuit. In this book we shall deal only slightly with problems of circuit engineering. Logical design can be treated without regard for the physical structures involved except when the structure imposes limitations on the freedom with which we can manipulate circuit elements.

One specialized problem of design occurs rather frequently. If an existing logical system is to be modified or extended it may be necessary to establish design criteria which would not be required in a completely fresh approach. Again, there is always a way to realize the desired performance, but by the use of appropriate methods a more thrifty result is often obtainable.

As we proceed to the detailed study of this subject we shall refer frequently to steps and methods which save a pair of contact springs or which achieve a required performance with one less vacuum-tube grid. Sometimes the gain seems trivial and the effort an obsession. But the same technique at another time rewards us with substantial simplification and economy. There seems to be no ready-made law of diminishing returns which we can apply in order to learn when to stop trying to improve our methods for logical design.

CHAPTER 2

Switching components and their characteristics

The engineering of a logical system requires close attention to the details of the physical performance of the components used. To a certain extent the designer of the logical system must also keep in mind the physical characteristics of the devices he is using. They are remarkably versatile and flexible, but they do have limitations which must be respected.

In this chapter we shall discuss some of the components which the designer has available and their characteristics when used as logical elements. We shall also introduce certain symbols and schematic arrangements which are useful in preparing diagrams of switching circuits.

2.1 Types of Logical Elements

There are many natural phenomena that can be put to use in building two-valued devices. An ordinary fuse protects an electric circuit by melting if the current through it exceeds a safe value. Below that current the fuse remains intact and the circuit is kept closed; above the safe value of current the fuse material melts and thus opens the circuit.

One ingenious engineer who liked to keep his windows open whenever possible developed an automatic mechanism which would close the windows when it rained. His device for detecting the rain contained a pair of wires connected end to end by a piece of lump sugar. This arrangement was used to hold a switch open against the action of a spring. When it rained the lump of sugar dissolved, the wire link opened up, and the spring operated the switch which controlled the window-closing mechanism.

The fuse and the lump of sugar are both two-valued in their actions, but they both have the serious limitation that the change of state involved is not a reversible one. In order to be useful in a logical system, a two-valued element must be able to pass reversibly from one state to the other under the influence of an appropriate external control.

Among the many devices which have two-valued properties that are useful in the design of logical systems, the following types appear in the majority of applications:

1. RELAYS AND SWITCHES. This class includes all the equipment in which mechanical, electromagnetic, and manual actuation are used to open and close electrical contacts. The electromagnetic relay is the most versatile member of the class, but push buttons and mechanically operated contacts supply vital information in many relay circuits.

2. TUBES. Both vacuum tubes and gaseous-conduction tubes are used in logical systems. Vacuum tubes inherently are capable of operation at much higher speeds than gas tubes, and they are, therefore, more often used in high-speed switching circuits. However, the gas tube has its two-valued character more or less "built-in," because after it starts conducting current the conduction continues until it is interrupted by reducing the plate voltage. This feature has unique advantage in certain special circumstances.

3. SEMI-CONDUCTORS. In high-speed switching circuits many of the functions of vacuum tubes can be performed by rectifiers. This substitution is important for its saving in cost, space, and power. The transistor has become a powerful contender as a switching device, and is already displacing vacuum tubes in many important applications.

4. MAGNETIC STRUCTURES. Applications of the properties of magnetic materials have been largely for the purpose of storing information in two-valued form. However, magnetic cores can also be used as switching elements by appropriate circuit design. It is likely that similar properties will be available in condensers built with "ferrostatic" dielectric material.

2.2 Switches

Historically, the switching circuit began with the simple switch. It is still the basic element in the most widespread types of switching circuits. Giant electronic machines attract more attention, but most of the world's logical systems still use switches. Tens of thousands of houses and industrial plants contain a familiar arrangement of wall switches which make it possible to control a light or an electric appliance from more than one point. Later we shall learn to recognize this circuit as one example of an important class of switching circuits.

The elementary switch consists of a pair of conductors which can be either brought into contact or separated, and thus close or open an electric circuit. In logical systems switches are rarely called upon to control substantial amounts of power, and the structure can hence be relatively light. The most common switch element consists of a pair of spring blades made of a flexible material such as german silver or phosphor bronze, on which are welded or riveted pieces of metal such as silver, palladium, platinum, tungsten, or an alloy of these and other metals. When the springs are pushed together the mating pieces of contact material are forced into contact and thus establish the electric circuit. These contact materials are chosen for their ability to make satisfactory electrical contact at relatively low mechanical pressures, to resist corrosion and damage caused by electric arcs, and to operate for long periods without attention.

Switches are classified in many ways, but for the purposes of this study they will be grouped in accordance with the method of actuation used. The three principal classes of switches thus defined are:

1. Manually operated;
2. Mechanically operated;
3. Electromagnetically operated.

Manually operated switches include the push buttons, key switches, plug and jack combinations, knife switches, toggle switches, and rotary switches which are available in a profuse variety of sizes, styles, and structures. They are listed and described in many catalogs and technical advertisements, and no attempt will be made here to present particular descriptions or details. It is important to understand, however, that a manually operated switch is not necessarily an elementary switch. Later in this chapter there will be a discussion of the ways in which elementary switches are combined into groups for purposes of simultaneous operation. Composite structures of this sort are frequently found in manually operated switches.

Generally speaking, mechanically operated switches contain the same types of spring and contact assemblies that are found in manually operated versions, but they are arranged for actuation by means of mechanisms such as cams, linkages, hydraulic or pneumatic cylinders, bimetallic strips, or weights. The idea is simply to provide information to a logical system about the state of some physical quantity by actuating a contact structure at a predetermined value of that quantity. It is not necessary to limit the process to a single operating point, for by means of a group of switches the logical system can be informed when the physical quantity in question reaches any one of a succession of different values.

Many mechanically operated switches are made specially to fit the circumstances of a particular application. It will be recognized that essentially we are dealing here with transducers which convert continuous information to two-valued information. The requirements for the design of such transducers are derived in general from an understanding of the requirements of switching circuits. Some types, such as those designated as "limit switches," serve similar purposes in a variety of applications, and it is possible to obtain them as standard components. This, however, is the exception rather than the rule.

2.3 Electromagnetic Relays

Strictly speaking, the electromagnetically operated switch is within the class of mechanically operated switches, but it is placed in a separate class because the electromagnetic mode of operation makes it possible for one switch to control the operation of another. This type of switch is known as the electromagnetic relay, or simply the relay. Relays are the classical building blocks of switching circuits, and, although other types of switching components now surpass them in speed, and some are cheaper or more compact, they still have no rivals with respect to versatility and ease of circuit manipulation.

The structure of the ordinary relay is shown schematically in Fig. 2–1. It consists of three main elements: a magnetic circuit, a winding for exciting the magnetic circuit, and a group of contact springs. In a typical design the magnetic circuit consists of a frame (sometimes called the heel-piece), a core upon which the coil is located, and a movable part called the armature. When sufficient current passes through the coil, magnetic attraction moves the armature toward the core and into the position shown by the dotted lines of Fig. 2–1. The armature in moving must overcome the deflection force of the contact springs (and that of any auxiliary springs which may be present), and in doing so it opens or closes electric circuits which are connected through the contact spring structure. When the relay is not energized, the restoring force of the contact springs moves the armature away from the core and into the position shown by the solid lines of Fig. 2–1.

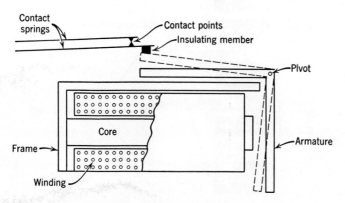

Fig. 2–1.   Structural elements of a relay.

Provision must be made for adjusting the magnetic circuit of a relay in two respects. When a relay is in the operated position it is desirable to maintain a small air gap between the armature and the core; otherwise the residual magnetism of the circuit tends to hold the armature against the core when the relay is released and the relay becomes "sticky." A residual adjustment is provided by threading a non-magnetic screw through the armature and adjusting it so that the screw strikes the core in the operated position and thus prevents the air gap from closing. It is also necessary to adjust the stroke of the relay armature. This is done by providing an adjustable abutment on the frame of the relay against which either the armature or an extension of the armature rests when the relay is not operated.

These features can be seen in Fig. 2–2, which shows a relay broken down into its components, and in Fig. 2–3, which shows the relay assembled.

The selection of specific relay coils is a matter of circuit engineering rather than of logical design. However, logical design is concerned with the kinds of coils which can be used to accomplish various purposes. Most relays are equipped with a coil having a single winding designed to operate the relay at a specified voltage. By varying the design so as to vary the power taken by the coil, the

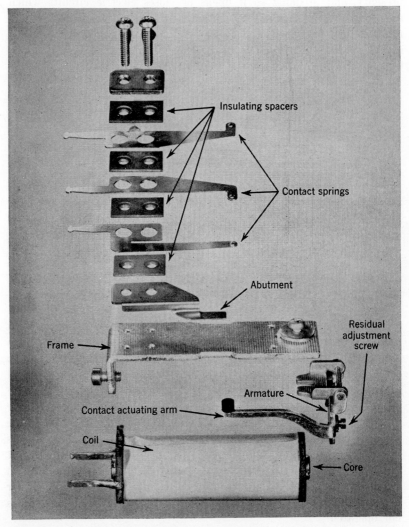

Fig. 2–2. Components of an electromagnetic relay. (*C. P. Clare and Co.*)

manufacturer can adjust either the operating speed of the relay, or the contact spring load which it is capable of handling, or both.

In specifying variations in relay coils it should be remembered that relays, like other kinds of equipment, are built to operate within certain tolerance limits. In particular, they will operate and release at certain values of current which vary slightly from one relay to another. Very close tolerance limits can be obtained by special manufacturing procedures, but it is not usually necessary to use "marginal" relays of this type.

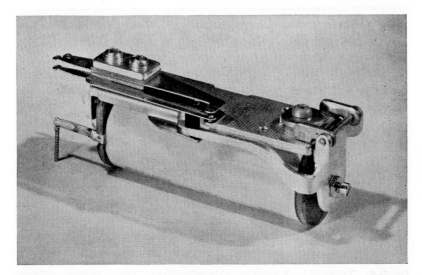

Fig. 2–3. Relay assembled from parts shown in Fig. 2-2. (*C. P. Clare and Co.*)

Multiple-winding coils are of considerable importance to the designer of the logical system. They include the following principal varieties:

1. Two or more independent windings, each of which is capable of operating the relay on normal voltage.

2. Two or more cooperative windings designed so that no one of the windings will operate the relay alone. Two or more of the windings must be energized simultaneously (with magnetomotive forces aiding) to cause operation.

3. Combinations which contain, in addition to independent or cooperative windings for operating the relay, "holding" windings which are incapable of operating the relay but can independently maintain it in the operated state.

4. Differential combinations in which either of two windings can operate the relay, but together they oppose each other and release the relay.

2.4   Arrangements of Contact Springs

An outstanding feature of the modern relay is that it enables the designer to introduce control elements at a number of points in a switching circuit.   By appropriate arrangement of contact springs and insulated actuating elements, the armature can be made to operate a relatively large number of independent contact elements simultaneously.   In a well-designed commercial relay, twenty contact springs can be assembled for operation by a single armature, and the same relay can be supplied with forty springs for use where

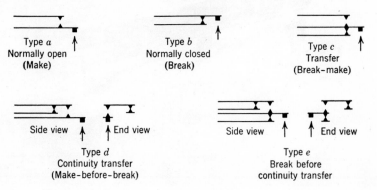

Type *a*
Normally open
(Make)

Type *b*
Normally closed
(Break)

Type *c*
Transfer
(Break–make)

Side view   End view

Type *d*
Continuity transfer
(Make–before–break)

Side view   End view

Type *e*
Break before
continuity transfer

Fig. 2–4.   Types of basic relay spring combinations.   Arrows indicate points of application and direction of armature force applied during operation of the relay.

operating conditions warrant it.   The construction permits the use of any combination of the basic contact groupings which will be discussed; when all the contacts are of the simple make or break type, somewhat larger assemblies of springs can be operated by a single armature.*

The combination of contacts used on a relay is usually called the spring pile-up, and most of the combinations normally encountered in switching circuit design can be assembled from the five types shown diagrammatically in Fig. 2–4.   Of these types, the first three—the normally open, normally closed, and the transfer—are used most frequently.   It will be found convenient, in certain kinds of circuit diagrams, to designate the contact type by the letter shown with it in Fig. 2–4.   That is, the type *a* (or form *a*) contact is always a "make"

* If all the contacts are simple make or break types the armature stroke can be made less than is required when some of the contacts are of the transfer type. For a given power input to the relay winding the armature can then exert more force and hence can deflect more springs.

contact, or normally open contact. If the relay which carries this contact is not operated, a circuit which passes through the type *a* contact will be open. When the relay operates, the type *a* contact closes. It should be noted that in the term normally open, the "normal" condition of a relay is its non-operated condition.

Similarly, the type *b* contact is always a "break" contact, or one which is normally closed. It is the exact opposite of the type *a* contact.

Frequently, it is found in circuit design that both a type *a* and a type *b* contact appear on the same relay structure. If these con-

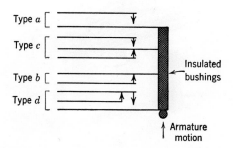

Fig. 2–5. Relay spring pile-up using basic types shown in Fig. 2–4.

tacts are separated electrically within the contact network, they must be built and used as individual circuit elements. If, however, each of them has one spring connected to the same point in the circuit, the separate make and break contacts usually may be merged into the "transfer" combination shown as type *c* in Fig. 2–4. By this means three springs can do the work which required four springs before the merger.

The type *d* contact arrangement shown in Fig. 2–4 is a special type of transfer combination which is known as the "make-before-break" contact or the "continuity transfer" contact. It is intended for use in situations where no circuit interruption during a transfer operation can be tolerated. In the type *c* contact the springs are usually adjusted so that when the relay is operated the type *b* part of the combination opens before the *a* part closes. If this "dead time" in the transfer process can cause false operation of the output circuit, it may be necessary to resort to the type *d* contact.*

By the addition of one spring to the type *d* contact, the type *e* contact of Fig. 2–4 is obtained. This arrangement provides a

* It will be shown later that sometimes a type *c* contact can be arranged to give the effect of a continuity transfer contact.

"break-before-continuity-transfer" sequence which occasionally is found to be useful.

Relays can be obtained with any mixtures of the basic contact types, subject only to the limitation on the total number of springs which can be operated by a single armature. Figure 2–5 illustrates schematically the way several contact types can be combined in a

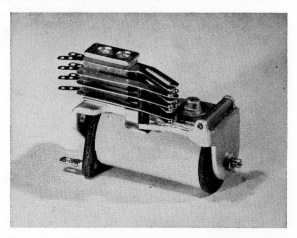

Fig. 2–6. Contact assembly contains, from top to bottom, one normally open contact, one transfer contact, one normally closed contact. (*C. P. Clare and Co.*)

pile-up and Fig. 2–6 is a photograph of a typical relay contact assembly. Note in Fig. 2–6 that each of the springs is bifurcated and equipped with two contact points. The purpose of this construction is to provide higher reliability of contact performance; the probability that both contacts will fail simultaneously is extremely low.

2.5 Special Types of Relays

Most of the requirements of logical systems are met by the general-purpose relay discussed in Arts. 2.3 and 2.4. There are, however, a number of situations which require special characteristics in one or more aspects of relay performance. This article will discuss some of the more frequently used types of special relays, but the discussion is not intended to be complete. The designer who is confronted with a special situation will find complete descriptions available in the commercial literature.

In many of the special situations encountered it is necessary to obtain relays which operate and release either much faster or much more slowly than ordinary relays. The calculation of the operate and release times of a relay is an exceedingly complex matter, and there is no simple analysis available. At present we must depend upon test results for basic data, and then apply general theoretical considerations to determine the effects of departures from test conditions.*

The ordinary relay is built to operate in 0.002 to 0.025 second and to release in 0.005 to 0.025 second. The factors which the manufacturer can vary in order to control the operate and release times are power input to the coil, spring load, armature stroke, and residual air gap. Unfortunately, the operate and release time adjustments are not independent of each other. Generally the adjustments which decrease the operating time will also increase the release time, and vice versa. High-speed operation requires that the power input be relatively large, that the inertia and friction associated with the moving parts be reduced, and that the spring load be a minimum.

It is also necessary at times to have relays which operate or release, or both, at relatively slow speeds. For this purpose it is not feasible to use the normal relay adjustments if the required delay time exceeds approximately 0.025 second. Occasionally it is possible to obtain additional delay by the use of external circuit elements. An inductance can be connected in series with the relay winding, or a capacitance can be connected across the winding. Generally speaking, however, these methods are not used because the external circuit elements are bulky and the system wiring is made more complicated. For most applications, which involve time delays up to 0.025 to 0.350 second, some form of short-circuited winding is placed on the relay magnetic circuit to retard the build-up or decay of flux.

If a relay with more than one winding is used it can be retarded both in operation and in release by using one winding for exciting the magnetic circuit and the other as a short-circuited winding. When power is applied to the operating winding the current increases quite rapidly because the effect of the short-circuited winding is to reduce the apparent inductance of the input winding and thus to decrease its time constant. The magnetic flux does not build up rapidly, however, because the currents in the two windings produce opposing magnetomotive forces, which initially are equal in magnitude, and hence cancel each other. Subsequently the current in the short-circuited winding decreases to zero value and permits the magnetomotive

* See the *Bell System Technical Journal*, Vol. 33, January 1954. This entire issue is devoted to a group of papers on "Design of Relays."

force of the operating winding to establish flux in the magnetic circuit. The rate at which flux builds up is hence determined essentially by the time constant of the short-circuited, or secondary, winding. In releasing the relay a similar action takes place. As the primary current is interrupted a current is induced in the short-circuited secondary winding in a direction such as to oppose the decay of magnetic flux, and again the rate of decay of flux is determined essentially by the time constant of the secondary winding.

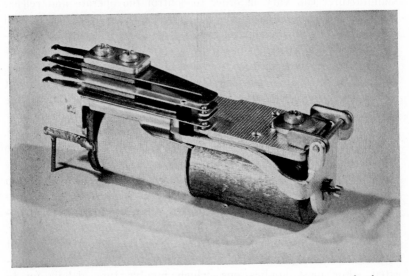

Fig. 2–7. A slow-operate relay, with copper slug at armature end of core. (*C. P. Clare and Co.*)

The same principle can be used to obtain time delay in the release of a relay having only a single winding. In Chapter 6 we shall discuss methods for controlling relays; among them, the so-called shunt control applies a short circuit across the operating winding in order to release the relay. When this is done the rate of decay of magnetic flux again depends upon the time constant of the short-circuited winding, but now it is the operating winding which is involved.

A more economical way to obtain most time delays is to use a single short-circuited turn which can be in the form of a copper cylinder, called a "slug." It has a hole drilled through its center so that it can be assembled on the core of the relay. Figures 2–7 and 2–8 illustrate two ways this method is used. It should be observed that in one relay the copper cylinder is placed at the armature end of the core, whereas in the other the cylinder is at the opposite, or "heel," end of the core. In both relays the remainder of the winding space is occupied by the operating coil.

Before we discuss these two types of delay relays there is a third type which should be understood. In this type the copper cylinder has a smaller outside diameter, and it usually extends the entire length of the core. The operating winding is then made so that it slips over the copper cylinder, and the effect is to have a single short-circuited turn which is distributed along the entire length of the core.

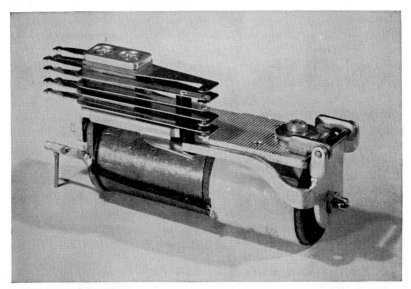

Fig. 2–8. A slow-release relay, with copper slug at "heel" end of core. (*C. P. Clare and Co.*)

A relay built in this manner operates in exactly the same way as the relay discussed earlier in which an actual winding was short circuited. The copper cylinder is a less expensive way to provide the short circuit.

When the copper cylinders are placed at one end or the other of the relay core, the action is quite different. If the slug is at the armature end of the core, as in Fig. 2–7, the relay is commonly known as a slow-operate type; if the slug is at the heel of the core, as in Fig. 2–8, the relay is designated as a slow-release type. These terms are not entirely descriptive of the action because in both cases the presence of the slug serves to retard both the increase and the decrease of magnetic flux, and hence to increase both the operate and the release times. However, when the effects of other adjustments and of flux leakage are taken into account, there is a selective action which depends upon the location of the slug.

Consider first the slow-operate type shown in Fig. 2–7. When the winding is energized, current is induced in the single turn of the copper slug, producing a magnetomotive force which opposes the build-up of flux. Because of the proximity of the slug to the armature air gap, the counter magnetomotive force is particularly effective in delaying the establishment of the air-gap flux upon which operation is entirely dependent. But the proximity effect is even more pronounced when the air gap is at its residual value, and it is often found that this type of slow-operate relay is even slower on release. By providing a large residual air gap the latter effect is reduced. If in addition a relatively heavy spring load is applied, the operate time is increased and the release time is decreased.

The slow-release type shown in Fig. 2–8 is more selective in its action. Since the copper slug is at the heel of the core, it tends to retard the build-up of flux at that point, but much of the flux through the operating winding returns to the frame by way of leakage paths, and not through the heel of the core. Hence there can be a substantial air-gap flux established to give the relay a relatively small operate time delay. After the armature moves and closes the air gap, the effect of leakage paths becomes less pronounced. On release, therefore, the short-circuit current is quite effective in delaying the decay of flux. Although there is some delay in the operation of the slow-release type of relay, it is inherently more selective than the previous type.

Among the important special types of relays the polarized relay has been the object of considerable development. Its primary property is that it responds to the polarity of the voltage across its operating winding. This is a two-valued response which is particularly useful in situations where it is necessary to detect, for example, the direction of a current. One application of this sort is found in bridge circuits where a polarized relay is used to determine the direction of bridge unbalance. It is also possible to build the polarized relay so that it has a distinct neutral position. Thus it can be used to indicate the presence or the absence of a signal, in addition to the direction of any signal which may be impressed upon it.

Historically the polarized relay was developed for use in signaling systems, beginning with the telegraph. It tended, therefore, to become a type which could operate at very low energy levels. Modern versions emphasize high-speed operation at low energy levels. One manufacturer claims reliable operation of a polarized relay in response to sinusoidal a-c signals up to 200 cycles per second, and marginal operation up to 1000 cycles per second. The excitation required is about 5 ampere-turns. Measurements at 50 cycles per second show an input of 5 millivolt-amperes, and when operated the relay takes 0.2 milliwatt.

The operation of the polarized relay can best be understood from the schematic diagram shown in Fig. 2–9. The distribution of magnetic flux in the working air gap is determined by the magnetomotive

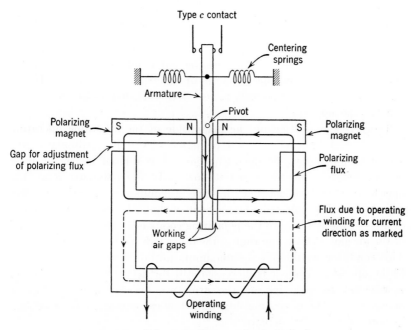

Fig. 2–9.   Schematic diagram of polarized relay.

forces of the two polarizing magnets and that of the operating coil, and is further modified by the subsequent motion of the armature. Consider the situation when the armature is centrally located in the working air gap and no current is flowing in the operating winding. Assume that the two polarizing magnets* are identical and that there is perfect symmetry of mechanical construction. Each polarizing magnet will produce the same amount of flux in the working air gap and the total combined flux of the two magnets will pass through the armature as shown by the solid flux lines in Fig. 2–9. Each com-

* Either permanent magnets, as in Fig. 2–9, or electromagnets may be used to supply the polarizing flux.

ponent of armature flux sets up a force tending to move the armature to one side of the air gap, but since the two forces are equal and opposite in direction, the armature does not move.

If a current is now applied to the operating winding in the direction shown, the resulting magnetomotive force produces another component of flux* which is indicated by the dashed line in Fig. 2–9. In the left-hand part of the working air gap the coil flux adds to the polarizing flux, whereas in the right-hand part of the gap the two components are opposite in direction. Hence the magnetic field is strengthened in the left-hand gap and weakened in the right-hand gap, so the armature moves to the left. The unbalance becomes greater when the armature moves, for in decreasing the left-hand air gap it causes further strengthening of the left-hand field, with a corresponding decrease in the strength of the right-hand field. If the current in the operating coil is reversed, the effects are, of course, exactly the opposite.

There is a limitation on the magnitude of the allowable operating current which is peculiar to the polarized relay. For ordinary relays the maximum allowable operating current is limited by the heating of the winding through which it flows. In the polarized relay the operating current must not produce a component of air-gap flux greater than the polarizing component of flux. If the coil component of flux is exactly equal to the polarizing component, the flux in one half of the air gap doubles and that in the other half of the gap goes to zero. This condition would give the maximum initial force on the armature. If the operating current is increased still further it causes a reduction in the net force acting on the armature because the coil flux is overpowering the polarizing flux, and thus causing an increase of flux in both parts of the air gap.

Figure 2–10 shows the actual construction of a modern type of polarized relay. It should be noted that the portion of the magnetic circuit which carries the flux established by the operating winding is laminated. In many applications these relays are required to respond to rapidly changing signals, and the magnetic circuit has superposed a-c and d-c excitation. Polarized relays can be built to carry groups of contacts, but they are usually employed in circumstances which capitalize on their sensitivity and speed of response. For this reason most polarized relays have only a single transfer contact arrangement (type c in Fig. 2–4).

---

* This language assumes that the effects of non-linearity in the magnetic circuit are negligible. Strictly speaking, the resultant flux cannot be obtained by superposition of component fluxes.

Many other special applications require relays which will operate with a-c excitation, but without the polarization feature. For such service the ordinary relay construction cannot be used because of excessive core losses. Furthermore, since with a-c excitation the core flux passes through zero twice during each cycle, the armature tends

Fig. 2–10.   A polarized relay.   (*C. P. Clare and Co.*)

to vibrate against the pole face at double the excitation frequency—a condition known as "chatter." To overcome these difficulties, the magnetic circuits of a-c relays are laminated for reduction of core loss, and a "shading" coil is used in the pole face which attracts the armature. The shading coil is simply a conducting loop which is set into the face of the core at the armature end, and arranged so that part of the air-gap flux passes through the loop. Since the loop is a short-circuited turn, the alternating flux through it induces a current which shifts the phase of the part of the flux passing through the shading coil, relative to the remainder of the air-gap flux. The result is that the force on the armature never goes through a zero value, and the tendency of the armature to chatter is eliminated or greatly reduced.

The types discussed are merely a sampling of a wide variety of relays built to satisfy various requirements. There are also many special types of magnetically operated switches other than relays. These will be described in connection with specific applications as they are encountered in the remainder of this book.

2.6   Relay Symbols and Schematic Diagrams

Logical systems are described almost wholly in terms of the language of circuit symbols and their arrangement in schematic diagrams. The mathematical manipulations developed in later chapters are essentially methods which enable us to reach a satisfactory circuit arrangement more elegantly than by the use of cut-and-try methods. It is important, then, that we adopt at the outset a symbology that provides vigorous expression and clear understanding. In complex diagrams there is necessarily a certain amount of circuit "tracing" which cannot be avoided, but experience indicates that the method developed in this section reduces that process to a tolerable minimum. Other types of symbols and diagrams are also included so that the reader will be equipped to analyze the operation of logical systems expressed in different schematic forms.

Figure 2–11 presents the symbols most commonly used to represent relay springs and their contacts for the contact arrangements given in Fig. 2–4. Each horizontal row shows the various ways of expressing one of the five types of contact combinations, and each column shows a particular symbology applied to each of the five types (except for columns 3 and 4). The extreme right-hand column shows the standard symbols which will be used in this book.

The first two columns of Fig. 2–11 shows two versions of a somewhat pictorial approach to the representation of switching contacts. This method is widely used in the construction of circuit diagrams in which the relay contacts are shown grouped in close association with a schematic representation of the operating windings. A typical diagram of this sort is presented in Fig. 2–12, the symbols of the first column of Fig. 2–11 being used. In reading a diagram of this type, we regard the pivoted blade of a contact as an armature which is attracted toward the electromagnet with which it is associated, when that winding carries current. The diagram always shows the contacts

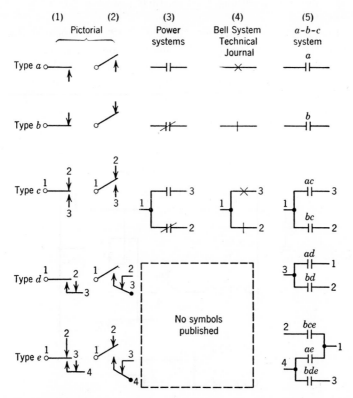

Fig. 2–11. Symbols used to represent relay contacts in circuit diagrams. Column (5) shows the symbols to be used in this book.

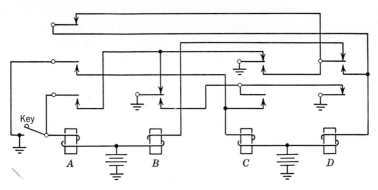

Fig. 2–12. Schematic diagram of a relay circuit. Contacts are grouped and associated with operating magnets.

in their "normal" positions, that is, their positions when the relay is not operated.

In Fig. 2–13 the connections of Fig. 2–12 are repeated, but the relay contacts are disassociated from their operating windings, and are grouped so that the contact network which controls the current in each winding becomes more clearly evident. For identification purposes each contact carries a letter or a number corresponding to that of the relay with which it is associated. Figure 2–14 is the same

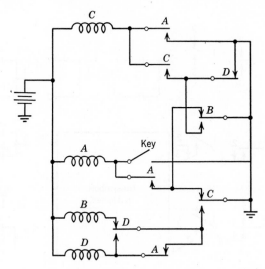

Fig. 2–13.   The circuit of Fig. 2–12 with the contacts dissociated from the relay windings.

circuit, but it is now drawn in terms of the preferred "a-b-c" system. No effort is made to arrange the contact elements in pictorial fashion, and no effort is needed to determine the nature of any particular contact or group of contacts. Each contact is again labeled with a letter or a number to identify the relay which carries it, and the relay identification symbol is followed by a lower-case designation of the type of contact, in accordance with the conventions shown in Fig. 2–4 and Fig. 2–11. Thus a contact marked Aa is a type a or normally open contact on relay A. A contact marked Db is a normally closed (type b) contact carried on relay D. When a type a and a type b contact on the same relay are both connected to the same point in the circuit, they can be combined into a transfer* (type c) contact, and

---
* The indications for the use of a continuity transfer contact (type d) will be discussed later.

this is indicated by the designation *ac* and *bc* following the relay identification symbol. It is convenient to visualize these elements as the "*a*-part" and the "*b*-part," respectively, of a *c* combination. When the normally open and the normally closed elements are not connected to the same point in the circuit, or are not parts of the same relay structure, they cannot be combined into a transfer contact.

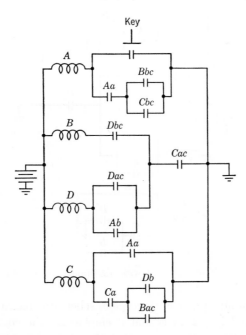

Fig. 2–14. The circuit of Fig. 2–13 showing how control paths are emphasized by using the *a-b-c* system of symbols.

The development of switching algebra has led to a further step in the evolution of simplified schematic diagrams, as is shown in Fig. 2–15. In this diagram each contact is labeled merely with the designation of its associated relay. Only the normally open and the normally closed types of contacts are shown, and these are indicated by using either an unprimed designator or a primed designator, respectively. Thus a contact marked *A* is a normally open, or "make," contact on relay *A*, whereas a contact marked *B'* is a normally closed, or "break," contact on relay *B*. For the purpose of logical design, it is not necessary to consider whether or not a make and a break contact should be combined to form a transfer. This is a step which ordinarily follows the process of logical design, except that the designer is concerned with such combinations when he counts the number of contact springs in a network to determine whether he is able to achieve simplification.

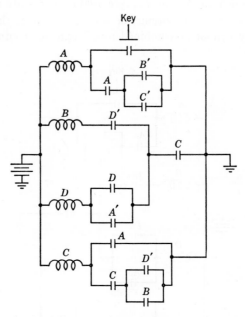

Fig. 2–15. The circuit of Fig. 2–14 with algebraic type of contact designation.

An important advantage of the type of schematic diagram illustrated in Fig. 2–14 and Fig. 2–15 is that it emphasizes the contact network aspect of relay circuit diagrams and the topological features which are present but otherwise obscured. These matters will become more evident to the individual as he uses the symbolic methods in the design of logical systems.

2.7 High-Speed Switching Components

In many vacuum-tube circuits the objective of the designer is to obtain an output voltage or current which is a continuous function of the input voltage applied to the control grid. The input signal is in general a continuous variable, and the functional relationship between the output and the input is either linear or it exhibits some particularly desirable form of non-linearity.

When used as a two-valued device the vacuum tube must be operated over a sufficiently wide range of its characteristic that the output voltage is not responsive to minor variations in the input signal. As a practical matter, tubes used for switching purposes are usually operated well into the saturation and cut-off regions of the plate characteristic. Since the input grid voltage is two-valued, and since logical design is not concerned with intermediate values, the ideal operation of a switching tube involves abrupt transitions of plate current between two extreme values. By careful circuit engineering it is possible to obtain actual operation which is sufficiently close to this ideal to permit the system designer considerable latitude in the employment of electronic switching components on a schematic basis. He does not enjoy quite the same freedom of maneuver that he has in combining relay contacts, but by observing certain physical limitations he can always achieve a required result in terms of electronic components.

It is possible to visualize and discuss the performance of a relay contact network in rather simple language. An electronic switching circuit, on the other hand, is considerably more difficult to trace out and understand by purely physical methods. The symbols and operations of switching algebra are especially helpful in manipulating electronic components of logical systems. For this reason, further discussion of the characteristics and use of tubes, rectifiers, and transistors in switching circuits will be deferred until after algebraic methods have been studied. The mathematical approach to the analysis and synthesis of switching circuits will be developed first in terms of relay contact networks. These have the advantages of great simplicity and flexibility, and the logical aspects are most readily separated from engineering considerations.

CHAPTER **3**
· · · · · · ·

Switching
algebra

Methods for the mathematical treatment of switching circuits are
of relatively recent origin. The first important contribution was made
by Shannon* in a paper published in 1938. He constructed a calculus
based on a set of postulates which described basic switching ideas; e.g.,
an open circuit in series with an open circuit is an open circuit. Then
he showed that his calculus was equivalent to certain elementary parts
of the calculus of propositions, which in turn was derived from the
algebra of logic developed by George Boole.† By a process of analogy
Shannon thus obtained a mathematical vehicle for use in the analysis
of switching circuits. In this first paper and in a later one published
in 1949, he developed other ideas and methods of importance which
will be treated in subsequent chapters. Here we are concerned only
with those algebraic ideas which have been found to be fundamental
in most of the processes of switching circuit manipulation.

* References are listed in a selected Bibliography at the end of this chapter.
† There may be confusion for the student because some writers in this field
refer to the algebra of classes rather than to the calculus of propositions. Both
derive from the work of Boole, but Shannon rejected the interpretation in terms
of classes because ". . . the variables are not limited to the two possible values
of 0 and 1." Other authorities hold that, although the algebra of classes is not
concerned with "values" as such, it is entirely proper to construct a particular
interpretation of the algebra of classes in terms of the values 0 and 1. It therefore
appears that either the algebra of classes or the calculus of propositions can be
considered as the mathematical source of switching algebra.

3.1   Switching Variables and Their Interpretations

An adequate mathematical treatment of logical systems must enable us to express the states of operation of quantities which are two valued. The output of an electronic circuit may be a voltage which is "high" or "low"; that of a relay contact network may be the presence or absence of a connection to ground. Likewise the inputs to such systems, and various elements within each system, exhibit a variation which is two-valued. The quantities we deal with are, however, strictly variables even though they can have only two different "values."

A switching variable can represent either the variation of a particular element of a switching system, or it can represent the resultant variation produced by a group of elements. In more precise terms, a given variable symbolizes the condition or state of a circuit element or a group of circuit elements; it has no numerical significance or value because there is nothing about a condition or a state which has universally measurable meaning. We can say that a circuit is turned on or that it is turned off, but we cannot answer the question, "How much is 'on' and how much is 'off'," except to say that it is all on or all off. Thus when we say that a variable is two-valued, we do not mean that it has two "values" in the usual sense, but rather that it can represent two states of operation. We infer, of course, that these two states are distinguishable in the actual circuit, but in the process of logical design we are not concerned with questions regarding how far apart the two states must be in order to become distinguishable. When we arrive at the stage of interpreting the result of an algebraic manipulation, it happens to be quite convenient to be able to assign "values" to the variables. In particular, if we assign values which represent the states of the individual elements of a system, the algebra enables us to determine the value which represents the state of the system as a whole.

For this purpose we assign "values", which are represented by the digits 0 and 1. At present we shall not attempt to say exactly what these digits mean in terms of the conditions of elements within a physical switching system, because, as we shall see later, we can apply either of two interpretations. For example, the digit 0 can represent either a closed circuit or an open circuit, and the digit 1 can then represent either the open circuit or the closed circuit, respectively. The resulting algebraic expressions appear to be quite different, but when they are interpreted in accordance with the original assignment of the meanings of the digits 0 and 1 the final interpretations are identical.

The digits 0 and 1 represent only the conditions or states of switching variables;* they do not represent any quantitive property and hence they should not be considered numbers in the ordinary arithmetic sense. In the postulates and theorems of switching algebra, the digits and the variables follow rules which for the most part are identical with the rules of ordinary algebra and arithmetic. But there are a number of expressions which do not follow ordinary rules. It is these exceptions which make it necessary to emphasize that switching algebra is not an algebra of numbers, but that it is an algebra of states, and that the digits 0 and 1 do not represent quantities.†

It was stated above that in switching algebra the digits 0 and 1 can be given two different meanings. This is our first encounter with the idea of duality—a concept which influences much of the analysis and manipulation of switching circuits. We encounter it again in the statements of the postulates and of the theorems of the algebra.

3.2   Postulates of Switching Algebra

The first postulate is merely a precise way of saying that we are dealing with two-valued variables. Let us associate a symbol, say X, with the state of a circuit element or a group of such elements. We can then write

(1) $X = 0$ if $X \neq 1$,   and

(1′) $X = 1$ if $X \neq 0$.

Note that this postulate, which is really the definition of a binary variable, is stated in two parts, (1) and (1′); the remaining postulates and most of the theorems will also have dual forms which will be stated together.

(2) $0 \cdot 0 = 0$

(2′) $1 + 1 = 1$

---

* Because they have only two values, switching variables are frequently called binary variables. We shall use the term in this book also, but the student should not confuse a binary variable with a binary number.

† The situation here is roughly parallel to that encountered by the engineer when he uses $j = \sqrt{-1}$ in the analysis of oscillatory phenomena. He learns in mathematics to call $\sqrt{-1}$ an imaginary number, but he has to learn in his engineering applications that it is being used as an extremely powerful mathematical device, and that it does not render some physical quantity "imaginary."

In the field of digital computing machines there is a mixture of concepts which can cause confusion. The control sections of such a machine form a logical system, and within that system we make use of the digits 0 and 1 in their logical, but non-numerical, sense. However, the machines operate on actual numbers which are, in most machines, expressed as binary numbers. These numbers again involve the digits 0 and 1, but here they are truly numerical in character.

(3) $1 \cdot 1 = 1$

(3′) $0 + 0 = 0$

(4) $1 \cdot 0 = 0 \cdot 1 = 0$

(4′) $0 + 1 = 1 + 0 = 1$

With the exception of postulate 2′ the above relations are exactly those of ordinary arithmetic. We shall defer any interpretation of postulate 2′ until Art. 3.6, except to note certain aspects of duality which appear.

In postulates 2, 2′ and 3, 3′ if we interchange the digits 0 and 1, we simply interchange postulates. Moreover, from 2′ and 3′ we see that $1 + 1 = 1$ and $0 + 0 = 0$, respectively—a curious sort of parallelism. These observations emphasize further the fact that the digits 0 and 1 represent states rather than numbers. But there is also at least the suggestion that the operations indicated by the plus sign and the product dot do not quite correspond with our commonly understood concepts of addition and multiplication. In fact, if we now go back and interchange in postulates 2, 2′, 3, 3′ and 4, 4′, not only the digits 0 and 1 but also the plus signs and the product dots, we find that the unprimed and primed parts of each postulate are interchanged. That is, 2 becomes 2′ and 2′ becomes 2, 3 and 3′ interchange, and so forth. The complete rule applies also to 4, 4′, whereas the results obtained from a simple interchange of digits are incorrect.

The principle of duality as developed to this point, then, is that any postulate can be converted to another postulate by interchanging both the digits 0 and 1, and the operations "add" and "multiply." Later this important working rule will be generalized to apply to any algebraic expression.

The remaining postulates of the algebra are

(5) $0′ = 1,$

(5′) $1′ = 0$

This postulate pair introduces the idea that the state opposite to the 0 state is the 1 state, and vice versa. It has been customary in many papers and books on this subject to call a primed quantity a "negative" quantity, and to speak of the operation of "negation." The terms themselves come directly from the calculus of propositions where they apply to the distinctions between "true" and "false." They are entirely appropriate in that subject, but there is considerable dissatisfaction with the terms "negative" and "negation" among those working in switching algebra. There is also a practical point involved. No confusion arises when we deal exclusively with relay contact networks, but when we apply the algebra to electronic switching circuits we become involved in the distinctions between negative electrical polarities and negative logical variables.

A more suitable designation of the operation shown in postulates 5, 5′ is "complementation." We shall hence say that the digit 1 is the complement of the digit 0, and that 0 is the complement of 1.

These postulates are the rules which govern switching algebra. Upon them we shall build the theorems which enable us to write and to manipulate the algebraic expressions of switching circuits.

3.3 Theorems Involving a Single Variable

In presenting the theorems of switching algebra, the sequence in which they are presented depends to a large degree upon whether or not the validity of each theorem is to be proved in terms of the postulates, and of theorems previously established. There is, however, another method of proof—that of perfect induction—which is entirely legitimate, and which is feasible for this algebra because each variable can have only two values. Applied to switching algebra, a proof by perfect induction means that we substitute in a given theorem all possible combinations of the values of the variables and verify that the theorem gives the correct result for all combinations.

We shall take advantage of this fact and present the theorems in a sequence which permits them to be grouped so as to emphasize the structure of the algebra rather than its formal coherence. When proofs are given, formal methods will be used if possible; otherwise the method of perfect induction will be used. The remaining proofs will be left as exercises for the student.

For the single variable X the following relations hold. Each theorem is paired with a partially dual theorem, the latter being obtained by interchanging both the digits 0 and 1, and the operations of addition and multiplication.*

(6) $$X + 0 = X$$

(6′) $$X \cdot 1 = X$$

(7) $$1 + X = 1$$

(7′) $$0 \cdot X = 0$$

---

* Partial duality here refers to the fact that in most of the theorems the letters representing variables are not replaced by their complements. However, note that the theorem pairs 9, 9′, and 10, 10′ are completely dual.

(8) $X + X = X$

(8′) $X \cdot X = X$

(9) $(X)' = X'$

(9′) $(X')' = X$

(10) $X + X' = 1$

(10′) $X'X = 0$

Theorems 6, 6′, 7, 7′, and 8, 8′ are proven by the method of perfect induction. If we substitute for X first the value 0 and then the value 1, we obtain the relations which were postulated in 2, 2′ and 3, 3′.

The statements given in theorems 6, 6′ and 7′ are familiar forms which are found in ordinary algebra, but the statements of theorems 7, 8 and 8′ are not familiar. They are direct consequences of the postulates we have taken to be true, and as such they are part of a consistent algebraic structure. Later we will show that all these forms may be given physical significance.

Theorem 7 says that if we add the variable X to the digit 1 the result is still 1. This is an important theorem in algebraic manipulation because X is a generic variable. Suppose we have the expression

$$T = A + B + C + D + E$$

If any variable in this sum has the value 1, the entire expression reduces to $T = 1$, regardless of the values of the remaining variables.

Theorem 8 has similar utility, and again the variable X represents any two-valued, or binary, variable. Its use may be illustrated by the following example.

Suppose

$$T = A + BC + CDE + F + CDE$$

Under theorem 8 the second appearance of the term CDE is redundant and the equation reduces to

$$T = A + BC + CDE + F$$

Theorem 8′ can be inferred directly from postulates 1, 1′. Since X can have only two values, there can be no new value created by raising X to a power in the ordinary algebraic sense. In fact, both theorems 8 and 8′ may be written in the extended forms

(8a) $X + X + X + \cdots = nX = X$

(8a′) $X \cdot X \cdot X \cdot \cdots = X^n = X$

Theorems 9, 9′ and 10, 10′ derive directly from postulates 5, 5′. The 10, 10′ pair are especially important in algebraic manipulation. Theorems 10, 10′ state, respectively, that the sum of any variable and its complement is the 1 state, and that the product of any variable and its complement is the 0 state.

Although these theorems contain only a single variable, they are of considerable importance in many types of algebraic manipulation. They represent simple working rules which are used repeatedly in simplifying algebraic expressions, in devising methods for designing circuits, and in modifying circuits for specific purposes.

3.4 Theorems in Two and Three Variables

Although practical problems in switching circuit design are quite likely to involve more than two or three variables, much of our algebraic manipulation is accomplished by means of the theorems given below.

(11) $X + Y = Y + X$

(11′) $X \cdot Y = Y \cdot X,$ or simply $XY = YX$

(12) $X + XY = X$

(12′) $X(X + Y) = X$

(13) $(X + Y')Y = XY$

(13′) $XY' + Y = X + Y$

(14) $X + Y + Z = (X + Y) + Z = X + (Y + Z)$

(14′) $XYZ = (XY)Z = X(YZ)$

(15) $XY + XZ = X(Y + Z)$

(15′) $(X + Y)(X + Z) = X + YZ$

(16) $(X + Y)(Y + Z)(Z + X') = (X + Y)(Z + X')$

(16′) $XY + YZ + ZX' = XY + ZX'$

(17) $(X + Y)(X' + Z) = XZ + X'Y$

Theorems 11, 11′ and 14, 14′ express the fact that the commutative and associative laws, respectively, apply in switching algebra just as they do in ordinary algebra. The operations of addition and multiplication are not dependent upon the sequential order in which the variables appear. Moreover, in a simple sum or product of variables, parentheses may be omitted without ambiguity.

Theorem 15 corresponds to the distributive law of ordinary algebra, and it is our authority for either factoring out a common term, or for any expansion which involves multiplying a group of terms by a common factor. These theorems—11, 11', 14, 14', and 15—are all readily proved by the method of perfect induction.

There remain a number of theorems for which there are no counterparts in ordinary algebra. All of them may be proved by perfect induction, but it is instructive to develop other proofs for some of them.

THEOREM 12. Factor out X from the left-hand side and then note that from theorem 7 the term $(1 + Y) = 1$.

THEOREM 12'. Carry out the indicated multiplication and note from theorem 8' that $X \cdot X = X$. The result is the same as theorem 12.

THEOREM 13. Multiply through by Y and note that $Y'Y = 0$ by theorem 10'.

THEOREM 13'. The following proof is interesting, particularly for the fact that it shows how, in switching algebra, we can use the theorems both "backwards" and "forwards" to advantage.

We note from theorem 10 that $X + X' = 1$. Hence we can write the left-hand side of theorem 13' in the form

$$XY' + Y(X + X') = XY' + XY + X'Y$$

Now in theorem 8 we see that $X + X = X$. But in this statement X is a generic variable which can stand for any binary variable. The product of two binary variables is itself a binary variable, and we can hence write, by the application of theorem 8 in the "backward" direction

$$XY = XY + XY$$

Substituting this expansion, the left-hand side of 13' becomes

$$XY' + XY + XY + X'Y$$

and this factors into the form

$$X(Y' + Y) + Y(X + X')$$

Since both the terms in parentheses become 1 by theorem 10, the proof is complete.

Although theorem 15 corresponds to the distributive law of ordinary algebra, its complementary form 15' has no counterpart in ordinary algebra. The process represented by 15' is one of absorption, and the theorem expresses the absorptive law of switching algebra. This becomes clear if we multiply out the left-hand side and obtain

$$X + XY + XZ + YZ$$

Since $(X + XY)$ and $(X + XZ)$ are both equal to X, by theorem 12, the process is one in which the XY and XZ terms are "absorbed" by the X.

Proofs of the remaining theorems in the group above are left as exercises for the student. Theorems 16, 16′ are quite powerful in eliminating redundant terms, but in actual manipulation the designer must be alert in order to recognize situations to which they apply. For theorem 17 there is no dual form, or, rather, the two sides of the equation are duals of each other.

In the proof of theorem 13′ there are some examples of the process of using the theorems of switching algebra in the backwards direction. It should be emphasized that all these theorems can be read in either direction, and there will be many situations in which this idea is found to be useful.

3.5 n-Variable Theorems

The complementary relations which are emphasized above by grouping theorems in pairs, are expressed in general form by De Morgan's theorem:

(18) $(X + Y + Z + \ldots)' = X' \cdot Y' \cdot Z' \cdot \ldots$

(18′) $(X \cdot Y \cdot Z \cdot \ldots)' = X' + Y' + Z' + \ldots$

Here we see that the complement of a sum of elements is the product of the complements of those elements, and that the complement of a product of elements is the sum of the complements of the elements. The theorem can readily be proved for two elements by the method of perfect induction. These two are then combined to form a single binary variable and another element is added, and the proof is repeated. Extension of this idea to the point where the theorem is proved for n elements, to which the $(n + 1)$ element is added, completes the proof by mathematical induction.

De Morgan's theorem does not convey completely the relations between complementary functions. Shannon has suggested a generalization of the theorem in the following form:

(19) $f(X_1, X_2, \ldots X_n, + , \cdot)' = f(X_1', X_2', \ldots X_n', \cdot, +)$

This form of De Morgan's theorem indicates that the complement of any function is obtained by replacing each variable by its complement and, at the same time, by interchanging the symbols for addition and multiplication. Care is necessary in executing the process because functions, as they are generally written, contain both explicit and implicit parentheses. These groupings must be maintained while carrying out the operations indicated by theorem 19. For example, the function

$$X'(Z + WY') + Z'Y$$

must be visualized as though it were written

$$\{X'[Z + (WY')]\} + (Z'Y)$$

When we use theorem 19 to take the complement of this function, it becomes

$$\{X + [Z'(W' + Y)]\} \cdot (Z + Y')$$

and we can then omit the superfluous brackets to obtain the final form,

$$[X + Z'(W' + Y)][Z + Y']$$

The concept of complementation is of considerable importance in the design and manipulation of switching circuits. It expresses the idea that, in two-valued systems, for every network there exists another network which has exactly complementary characteristics. Sometimes we find it easier to design a system which does the opposite of what we want, and then take its complement in order to find the desired system. At other times we use complementation during the process of simplifying a switching function, for it frequently happens that the complement is more readily manipulated than the original function. These processes will be discussed later when we apply the algebra to actual circuits.

In writing theorem 19, we used a functional form of notation without discussing its exact interpretation. Much of the work of switching algebra is concerned with switching functions. The elements X_1, X_2, $\ldots X_n$ represent generic switching variables, and all of them are binary. A switching function is an expression formed from such variables by using the operations of addition, multiplication, and complementation. For brevity, we use the form $f(X_1, X_2, \ldots X_n)$, or simply $f(X_n)$, to represent any switching function in n variables.

Any switching function in n variables may be developed into a series by means of the expansion theorem, which is expressed in the dual form:

(20) $f(X_1, X_2, \ldots X_n) = X_1 \cdot f(1, X_2, \ldots X_n) + X_1' \cdot f(0, X_2, \ldots X_n)$

(20′) $f(X_1, X_2, \ldots X_n) = [X_1 + f(0, X_2, \ldots X_n)][X_1' + f(1, X_2, \ldots X_n)]$

These equations are proved rather simply. If we substitute first $X_1 = 1$ and $X_1' = 0$, and then substitute $X_1 = 0$ and $X_1' = 1$ into each expression, they reduce to identities.

In the forms shown in 20 and 20′ the function $f(X_n)$ is said to be expanded about X_1. Similar expressions can be written to represent expansions about any of the n variables. It should also be noted that in the expansion about X_1 in theorem 20, the coefficients of X_1 and X_1' are functions of the remaining $(n-1)$ variables. These coefficients may likewise be expanded about any of the variables $(X_2, \ldots X_n)$. Similarly in theorem 20′ the additive terms on the right-hand side are functions of the variables $(X_2, \ldots X_n)$ and may be expanded about any of these variables.

If the expansion process is continued for each of the original n variables we obtain complete series expansions. Theorem 20 leads to a series expansion in the form of a sum of products, each term of which contains each of the n variables or its complement. Theorem 20′ leads to a product of sums, and in each of the sums each variable or its complement is present. The complete expansions thus formed will be called the *standard* forms of the switching function. When a function is completely expanded by the use of theorem 20, the resulting expression is the **standard sum.** If theorem 20′ is used the complete expansion leads to the **standard product.** [*]

The following theorems are useful in circuit manipulation and can be proved by application of the expansion theorem.

(21) $X_1 \cdot f(X_1, X_2, \ldots X_n) = X_1 \cdot f(1, X_2, \ldots X_n)$

(21′) $X_1 + f(X_1, X_2, \ldots X_n) = X_1 + f(0, X_2, \ldots X_n)$

(22) $X_1' \cdot f(X_1, X_2, \ldots X_n) = X_1' \cdot f(0, X_2, \ldots X_n)$

(22′) $X_1' + f(X_1, X_2, \ldots X_n) = X_1' + f(1, X_2, \ldots X_n)$

The reductions which are possible by the use of theorems 21, 21′ and 22, 22′ can also be accomplished by means of the simpler theorems discussed earlier in this chapter, but in general more steps will be required. For example, the expression

$$X + Y + (X + Z)(W + Y)$$

can be simplified by applying theorem 21′ to both the X and Y variables, and we immediately obtain

$$X + Y + (0 + Z)(W + 0) = X + Y + WZ$$

On the other hand, we could simply multiply out the product term in

---

[*] The standard sum and the standard product are probably the most compact forms available for the description of switching functions in general. The ideas expressed by them will be treated more fully in later chapters. The forms which are called "standard" in this book are identical to those which some writers call "canonical." Other terms are used by writers in the field of mathematical logic. The standard sum, for example, may be called the "alternational normal form," or the "disjunctive normal form."

the original expression and obtain

$$X + Y + XW + XY + WZ + YZ$$

By the use of theorem 12 we then have $X + XW + XY = X$, and $Y + YZ = Y$, so the same reduction is achieved without the use of theorem 21'.

Another example is useful in showing the broad application of the theorems of switching algebra. Any variable in a theorem, such as X, is a generic variable, and it may be considered to represent any binary variable. In the expression

$$W' + Z' + (X + WZ)(Y + Z)$$

the term WZ is a binary variable because both W and Z are binary variables. If we rewrite this expression in the form

$$(WZ)' + (X + WZ)(Y + Z)$$

we can immediately simplify it by the application of theorems 22' and 7, and obtain

$$(WZ)' + (X + 1)(Y + Z) = W' + Z' + Y + Z = 1$$

This is an example of extreme simplification in which an entire algebraic expression is found to have a single value.

3.6 Algebraic Expression of Basic Switching Concepts

For the reasons given at the end of Chapter 2, we shall confine ourselves at this time to an interpretation of the circuital meanings of the switching algebra in terms of networks composed of relay contacts. Furthermore, we shall deal initially with two-terminal contact networks, as shown schematically in Fig. 3–1.

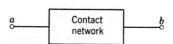

Fig. 3–1. Schematic of a two-terminal contact network.

Regardless of the size or complexity of the contact network in Fig. 3–1, it can exhibit only two conditions of conduction between its terminals. Either the circuit from a to b is closed, or it is open. We can assign the digits 0 and 1 to represent these two conditions of operation, but we can make the assignment in either of two ways. The digit 0 can be used to represent the open-circuit condition, and the digit 1 then represents the closed-circuit condition; or the digit 0 can represent a closed circuit, and the digit 1 then represents an open circuit. Since both these conventions have been used in the literature of switching circuits, it is desirable to understand both of them.

Suppose that we first consider the impedance existing between the terminals a and b of the network in Fig. 3–1.   Assuming that all the contacts and wiring in the network have negligible impedances, and that all the insulation is perfect, we would find that the network had zero impedance in the closed-circuit

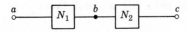

Fig. 3–2. A series connection of contact networks.

state and infinite impedance when it was in the open-circuit state.   We can represent this impedance by the binary variable X_{ab}, or simply by X.

Instead of calling the variable an impedance, however, we call it the *hindrance* of the network.   The digit 0 is used to represent the hindrance of a closed circuit, and the digit 1 represents the hindrance of an open circuit.

Now consider the system shown in Fig. 3–2 where the contact networks N_1 and N_2 are connected in series.   Let X represent the hindrance of N_1 between terminals a and b, and let Y represent the hindrance of N_2 between terminals b and c.   We can find the hindrance of the series combination from terminals a to c by means of the following tabulation, in which the series connection is closed only when both

Table 3–1

N_1	N_2	Series Connection
Open	Open	Open
Open	Closed	Open
Closed	Open	Open
Closed	Closed	Closed

N_1 and N_2 are closed.   If we substitute the digits 1 and 0 to represent the hindrances of an open and a closed circuit, respectively, the above table becomes:

Table 3–2

N_1	N_2	Series Connection	$N_1 + N_2$
1	1	1	1
1	0	1	1
0	1	1	1
0	0	0	0

Note that in Table 3–2 the hindrance of N_1 and N_2 have been allowed to take all possible combinations of values.   In a separate tabulation to the right of the main table is listed the sum of the hindrances of

N_1 and N_2, with the addition performed in accordance with the postulates of switching algebra. We now note that for each row the algebraic sum corresponds exactly with the hindrance of the series circuit. Hence, when X and Y represent hindrances connected in series, the hindrance of the series connection is given by

$$H_s = X + Y \tag{3.1}$$

The hindrance of two elements in series is itself a binary variable and may be designated as H_{2s}. If to this hindrance we connect another series element Z, the hindrance of the three elements will be

$$H_{3s} = H_{2s} + Z = (X + Y) + Z$$
$$= X + Y + Z$$

We can extend this process indefinitely, and so long as we continue to connect binary elements in series, the series hindrance is given by the sum of the elements. Expressed in general form, we have

$$H_{\text{series}} = X_1 + X_2 + \ldots + X_n$$
$$= \sum_1^n X_n. \tag{3.2}$$

By a similar procedure we now examine the behavior of contact networks which are connected in parallel, as in Fig. 3–3. Table 3–3 shows the open- and closed-circuit conditions between terminals a and b in terms of the conditions of networks N_1 and N_2. Again we assign the hindrance values 1 and 0 to the open and closed conditions, respectively, and obtain Table 3–4. A separate column at the right of Table 3–4 shows the product obtained by multiplying each pair of the hindrances of N_1 and N_2. Here we see that for each row the product corresponds exactly with the hindrance of the parallel connection, and in the table we have verified this for every possible combination of the hindrances of N_1 and N_2. Hence, if X and Y are

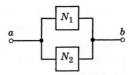

Fig. 3–3. A parallel connection of contact networks.

Table 3–3

N_1	N_2	Parallel Connection
Open	Open	Open
Open	Closed	Closed
Closed	Open	Closed
Closed	Closed	Closed

Table 3–4

N_1	N_2	Parallel Connection	N_1N_2
1	1	1	1
1	0	0	0
0	1	0	0
0	0	0	0

variables which represent the hindrances of two elements connected in parallel the hindrance of the parallel combination is given by

$$H_p = X \cdot Y \tag{3.3}$$

Since the hindrance of two elements in parallel is a binary variable, say H_{2p}, we can connect the element Z in parallel with H_{2p} and obtain

$$H_{3p} = H_{2p} \cdot Z = (X \cdot Y) \cdot Z$$
$$= XYZ$$

Again this process may be extended indefinitely and for the general case of n elements connected in parallel we write

$$H_{\text{parallel}} = X_1 \cdot X_2 \cdot \ldots \cdot X_n$$
$$= \prod_1^n X_n \tag{3.4}$$

Let us now consider these basic connections from a different point of view. Assume that in Fig. 3–1 a potential V_a is applied between terminal a and ground, and that we measure the potential V_b between terminal b and ground. Whenever the contact network is open, $V_b = 0$; and when the contact network is closed, $V_b = V_a$. If we now define a quantity T, called the *transmission*, as

$$T = \frac{V_b}{V_a} \tag{3.5}$$

we see that $T = 0$ for an open circuit, and $T = 1$ for a closed circuit. This is a basis for assigning meanings to the digits 0 and 1 which are exactly opposite to those assigned under the hindrance concept.

For the series connection of networks, Table 3–1 still applies, and for the parallel connection Table 3–3 is still valid. Under the transmission concept, however, we now assign the digit 0 to represent an open circuit and the digit 1 represents a closed circuit. Hence for the series circuit we obtain a new set of digit values, shown in Table 3–5, and for the parallel connection the digit values are shown in Table 3–6.

The separate columns to the right of each of these tables show that the transmission of series elements is given by the product of the transmissions of the elements, and that the transmission of parallel elements is given by the sum of the transmissions of the elements. Hence by a

Table 3–5

N_1	N_2	Series Connection	$N_1 N_2$
0	0	0	0
0	1	0	0
1	0	0	0
1	1	1	1

Table 3–6

N_1	N_2	Parallel Connection	$N_1 + N_2$
0	0	0	0
0	1	1	1
1	0	1	1
1	1	1	1

process similar to that used in developing the hindrance concept, we may write

$$T_{\text{series}} = X_1 \cdot X_2 \cdot \ldots \cdot X_n$$
$$= \prod_1^n X_n \qquad (3.6)$$

and

$$T_{\text{parallel}} = X_1 + X_2 + \ldots + X_n$$
$$= \sum_1^n X_n \qquad (3.7)$$

It is now apparent that the operations of addition and multiplication must be interpreted in accordance with the meanings of the switching variables. If the variables represent hindrances, addition represents a series connection and multiplication represents a parallel connection. But if the variables represent transmissions, addition represents a parallel connection and multiplication represents a series connection. The equations which describe the operation of a given network consequently can have two distinctly different forms, depending upon how the variables are interpreted. As we shall see in the next article the two kinds of equations must say exactly the same things about the overall circuit behavior.

3.7   Series-Parallel Connections

The rules derived in Art. 3.6 now enable us to treat networks which contain both series and parallel connections of networks or elements.* Consider the arrangement shown in Fig. 3–4, where the binary net-

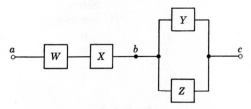

Fig. 3–4.   A series-parallel connection.

works or elements W, X, Y, Z are placed in a series-parallel connection. Between the terminals a and b we have W and X in series; between the terminals b and c we have Y and Z in parallel.

Under the hindrance concept we may write for the switching function between terminals a and b,

$$H_s = W + X$$

and for the function between terminals b and c,

$$H_p = YZ$$

Each of these functions is a binary variable, and they may therefore be combined by the series connection rule to give the hindrance between the terminals a and c:

$$H_{ac} = H_s + H_p$$
$$= W + X + YZ \qquad (3.8)$$

If we use the transmission concept, the corresponding equations are written:

$$T_s = WX$$
$$T_p = Y + Z$$
$$T_{ac} = T_s T_p$$
$$= WX(Y + Z) \qquad (3.9)$$

It is quite apparent that equations 3.8 and 3.9 do not look alike,

---

* In this book an element is a single switching component, such as a normally open or a normally closed relay contact, or a vacuum tube used for switching. A network consists of a connected group of elements.

yet, as was pointed out at the end of the last section, these two equations must express exactly the same facts about the network shown in Fig. 3–4.

The required descriptive correspondence of equations 3.8 and 3.9 may readily be demonstrated by tabulating all possible combinations of the values of W, X, Y, and Z, and then computing for each of these combinations the values of both H_{ac} and T_{ac} from their respective equations, and in accordance with the postulates and theorems of switching algebra. The result of carrying out this process is summarized in Table 3–7.

Table 3–7

W	X	Y	Z	H_{ac}	T_{ac}
0	0	0	0	0	0
0	0	0	1	0	0
0	0	1	0	0	0
0	0	1	1	1	0
0	1	0	0	1	0
0	1	0	1	1	0
0	1	1	0	1	0
0	1	1	1	1	0
1	0	0	0	1	0
1	0	0	1	1	0
1	0	1	0	1	0
1	0	1	1	1	0
1	1	0	0	1	0
1	1	0	1	1	1
1	1	1	0	1	1
1	1	1	1	1	1

In this table the first four columns merely show all the ways in which the digits 0 and 1 can be assigned* to the variables W, X, Y, and Z. These digits must be interpreted in accordance with the kind of switching function which is being computed. In the first row of Table 3–7 $(W, X, Y, Z) = (0, 0, 0, 0)$. If these are hindrances, all the variables represent closed circuits, so H_{ac} is a closed circuit. But if these digits represent transmissions, all the variables represent open circuits, and the digit 0 under T_{ac} represents an open circuit. In the last row all the digits under W, X, Y, and Z are 1; here the 1 under

* In making a table of this sort it will be found convenient to visualize each row of digits, in the $WXYZ$ columns, as a binary number, and then to write all the binary numbers from 0000 to 1111 in ascending order. The digits in Table 3–7 were thus arranged.

H_{ac} represents an open circuit, and the 1 under T_{ac} represents a closed circuit. It may be verified row by row that when the variables W, X, Y, and Z are in the states represented by the digits in Table 3–7, as interpreted by the rules given in Table 3–8, the final entries under H_{ac} and T_{ac} correctly represent the states of operation of the series-parallel network in Fig. 3–4.

Table 3–8

If you are computing:	The digit 0 means:	The digit 1 means:
Hindrance	Closed circuit	Open circuit
Transmission	Open circuit	Closed circuit

The circuit of Fig. 3–5 represents a more complex series-parallel network in which the elements are relay contacts. First assume that the letters designating the contacts represent the hindrances of the respec-

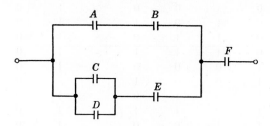

Fig. 3–5.   A series-parallel arrangement of relay contacts.

tive contacts. Then, by using addition to represent a series connection, and multiplication to represent a parallel connection, we may write the hindrance function for this network:

$$H = (A + B)(CD + E) + F$$

If we now assume that the letters represent the transmissions of the respective contacts, and if we interchange the meanings of the operations of addition and multiplication, we may write the corresponding transmission function:

$$T = [AB + (C + D)E]F$$

3.8   Duality in Series-Parallel Circuits

We have observed several examples of the fact that the algebraic forms which describe switching circuits have a quality of duality about them. It is now necessary to define more precisely what we mean when we speak of a dual element, network, or algebraic expression.

DEFINITION 1. The dual of a switching element is its complementary element. Thus the dual of a normally open contact is a normally closed contact, and vice versa. If the contact is represented by the symbol X, its dual is represented by the complementary symbol X'.

DEFINITION 2. The dual of a switching network N is the complementary network N' which is open whenever N is closed, and vice versa. For series-parallel networks the complementary network is readily obtained by the application of Shannon's extension of De Morgan's theorem (see theorem 19). According to this theorem, all the elements in a network are replaced by their complements, and the operations of addition and multiplication are interchanged. The process is exactly the same whether the system is described by a hindrance function or by a transmission function.

Consider a series connection of the elements X and Y, for which the hindrance is $H = X + Y$, and the transmission is $T = XY$. According to theorem 19, the hindrance of the complementary network is $H' = X'Y'$, and the corresponding transmission is $T' = X' + Y'$.

But, from the discussion of Arts. 3.6 and 3.7, we can recognize the latter expressions as the hindrance and transmission, respectively, of the elements X' and Y' connected in parallel.

If we had started with the elements X and Y connected in parallel, we would have in similar manner found that the hindrance and transmission functions of the complementary network represented X' and Y' connected in series.

Up to this point we have used switching algebra to write expressions which describe the performance of given networks. Here, for the first time, we have inverted the process. From the expressions for the complementary functions corresponding to simple series and parallel networks we are able to recognize the components and the structure of the complementary network.

In general, we can construct a series-parallel contact network which is a realization of any switching function by observing the following rules:

TRANSMISSION CONCEPT:
1. Addition signifies that the elements (or groups of elements) involved are connected in *parallel*.
2. A product signifies that the elements or groups involved are connected in *series*.

Hindrance concept:

3. Addition signifies that the elements or groups involved are connected in *series*.

4. A product signifies that the elements or groups involved are connected in *parallel*.

Obviously, in order to apply these rules we must know whether the function to be realized is a hindrance function or a transmission function.

It will be instructive to apply the definitions and rules discussed above to some networks of greater complexity. Thus for the network of Fig. 3–5 where the hindrance function is

$$H = (A + B)(CD + E) + F$$

the hindrance of the complementary network is

$$H' = [A'B' + (C' + D')E']F'$$

The transmission function for the network of Fig. 3–5 is

$$T = [AB + (C + D)E]F$$

and the transmission of the complementary network is

$$T' = (A' + B')(C'D' + E') + F'$$

From either the H' or the T' expression we can draw a diagram of the complementary network, as is shown in Fig. 3–6.

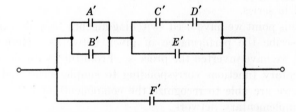

Fig. 3–6. This network is the complement of the network shown in Fig. 3–5.

A network may, of course, contain both normally open and normally closed contacts. This in no way alters the basic procedure for finding the complementary network. Consider, for example, the series-parallel network of Fig. 3–7, for which the transmission function is

$$T = A(BC' + B'C) + A'(B'C' + BC)$$

The transmission function of the complementary network, according to theorem 19, is

$$T' = [A' + (B' + C)(B + C')][A + (B + C)(B' + C')]$$

The series-parallel network represented by T' is given in Fig. 3–8.

It is now a simple matter to draw a circuit diagram which represents the complement of a given series-parallel network, without writing an

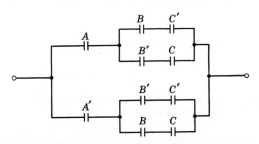

Fig. 3–7. A series-parallel network containing both normally open and normally closed contacts.

algebraic function at all. We merely draw a diagram in which all contact elements are replaced by their complements, and in which all

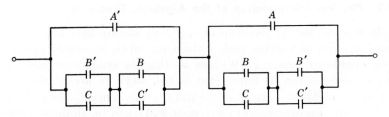

Fig. 3–8. The complement of the circuit shown in Fig. 3–7.

series connections are replaced by parallel connections, and vice versa. But by going through the algebraic step, other possibilities arise.

The transmission function for the circuit shown in Fig. 3–8 was

$$T' = [A' + (B' + C)(B + C')][A + (B + C)(B' + C')]$$

If we carry out some of the indicated multiplications in this function we obtain

$$T' = [A' + B'B + B'C' + BC + CC'][A + BB' + BC' + B'C + CC']$$

and since $BB' = CC' = 0$, the expression reduces to

$$T' = [A' + B'C' + BC][A + BC' + B'C]$$

The last function obtained represents a network which is shown in

Fig. 3–9, and which operates in exactly the same way as the network of Fig. 3–8. It also is a complement of the network in Fig. 3–7.

Since the networks of Fig. 3–8 and Fig. 3–9 do the same work, they are called equivalent networks. Although sometimes equivalent net-

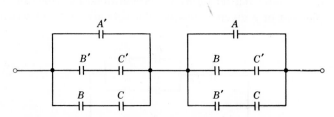

Fig. 3–9. This network is equivalent to that shown in Fig. 3–8, and is another complement of the network shown in Fig. 3–7.

works can be found by a process of inspection, the algebraic method is preferred. Likewise, the process of deriving a complementary network can be carried out without resorting to algebra, but the algebraic method is generally better because it so readily discloses the presence of equivalent networks.

3.9 Physical Interpretation of the Algebraic Theorems

In this chapter the theorems of switching algebra have been developed as a set of working tools without regard to immediate application or physical meaning. We now see that the symbols contained in these theorems can be interpreted in two ways, in accordance with either the hindrance concept or the transmission concept. As a matter of fact, with the exception of theorems 9, 9′, 17, and 19, all the theorems are arranged in pairs such that if one half of any pair is considered to be a hindrance expression, the other half of the pair is the corresponding transmission function. For example, if in the theorem pair 12, 12′, the term $X + XY$ is interpreted as a hindrance, then the term $X(X + Y)$ is the corresponding transmission.

It is also true that, if appropriate complementary variables are introduced, the theorem pairs express either the hindrances or the transmissions of complementary networks. In theorems 13, 13′, for example, if theorem 13 is considered to be a statement concerning the hindrance of a network, theorem 13′ gives the same statement about the hindrance of the complementary network, provided we replace all the variables in 13′ by their complements, and write the theorem $X′Y + Y′ = X′ + Y′$. The theorems are not written in this completely complementary form because all the variables are to be treated as generic variables. Hence it should be considered that theorem 13′ as written is representative of any of the following forms:

$$XY' + Y = X + Y$$

$$X'Y' + Y = X' + Y$$

$$XY + Y' = X + Y'$$

$$X'Y + Y' = X' + Y'$$

In other words, a systematic substitution of other variables or complementary variables does not change the meaning of a theorem.

We shall see later that these theorems have important application either for the purpose of simplifying switching networks, or for the manipulation of networks into forms which meet special requirements. A somewhat better appreciation of their utility in this respect can be derived by drawing schematic diagrams of the physical circuits

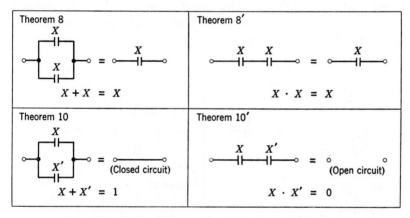

Fig. 3–10. Theorems involving one variable.

which are represented by the theorems. For purposes of this interpretation we shall assume that all the theorems are written in terms of *transmission* functions. Furthermore, we shall assume that all *unprimed* variables represent *normally open* (make) contacts, and that the *primed* variables represent *normally closed* (break) contacts. The examples shown are therefore representative of only one set of choices of the generic variables in the theorems.

Figure 3–10 shows, on the basis of the above assumptions, the circuit equivalents of theorems 8, 8′ and 10, 10′. These circuits require no further discussion except to point out an important application of the circuit shown under theorem 10′. In Fig. 3–11 the XX' circuit of theorem 10′ is connected between terminals b and c, and terminal a is connected to the junction of the elements X and X'. Terminals b and c then are connected to terminals d and e through networks N_1 and N_2 respectively. Since the transmission between terminals b and c is

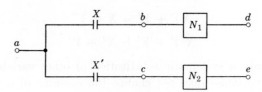

Fig. 3–11. A disjunctive circuit.

always 0, the transmission between terminals d and e must also be 0 at all times. Consequently there can never be a conducting path set up between terminals d and e, by way of the networks N_1 and N_2, which might cause false operation at some time—a condition known as a "sneak" circuit. A circuit of the type shown in Fig. 3–11 is called a disjunctive circuit, and the X–X' pair are known as disjunctive elements.

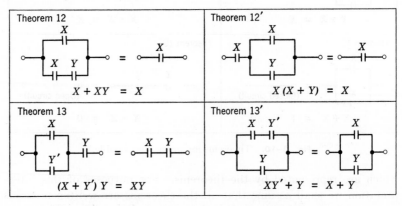

Fig. 3–12. Theorems involving two variables.

Figure 3–12 presents circuits which correspond to theorems 12, 12′ and 13, 13′. In the circuits of theorems 12, 12′ it may readily be observed that the circuit behavior is dependent only upon the operation of element X, and that the Y element is redundant. In the circuit for theorem 13 there can never be a closed path through the contacts Y and Y' connected in series, so the Y' contact is redundant.

The physical justification for the elimination of the Y' contact in the circuit for theorem 13′ is more subtle. If Y closes, Y' must open; and the circuit is closed through Y regardless of the condition of X. If Y is open, Y' is closed, and the circuit is hence closed only if X closes. This is exactly the performance of the X and Y contacts in parallel, and the Y' contact is therefore redundant.

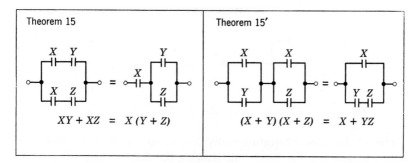

Fig. 3–13. Circuit equivalents of theorems 15, 15′.

Figure 3–13 shows the elimination of redundant contacts by means of theorems 15, 15′. These two situations arise quite frequently. They are easily recognized in physical circuits, and if they are encountered in the algebraic form the process of reduction is a routine one.

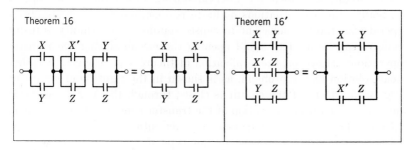

Fig. 3–14. Circuit equivalents of theorems 16, 16′.

Theorems 16, 16′ are exceedingly powerful tools for eliminating redundant contacts, but the situations to which they are applicable are frequently difficult to recognize. This is particularly true when the generic variables of the theorems actually represent groups of elements. In drawing the circuit equivalents shown in Fig. 3–14, the variables have been rearranged so as to emphasize the physical situations to which these theorems apply. It can readily be observed, in the circuit for theorem 16, that since either X or X' is always open, if the parallel pair of contacts $Y + Z$ is open, one of the other parallel pairs must be open, and the $Y + Z$ pair is not needed. In the circuit of theorem 16′ if the series YZ pair of contacts is closed, one of the other series paths must be closed, through either X or $X′$, and the YZ pair is hence not needed.

Theorem 17

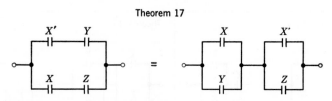

Fig. 3–15. A transfer contact that acts like a continuity transfer.

One of the most interesting equivalent circuits is that of theorem **17** which is shown in Fig. 3–15. In drawing the diagram according to the transmission concept, the left-hand side of Fig. 3–15 represents the right-hand side of theorem **17**, as it is written, and vice versa. Note that on both sides of Fig. 3–15 the contact pair X–$X′$ has a common connection, and these contacts can therefore be combined into a single transfer contact. If the Y and Z contacts are both closed and the X–$X′$ transfer changes its position, there may be, when using the left-hand circuit, a momentary interval during which the circuit opens. In many practical situations no harm is done, but in others this brief operational fault is sufficient to cause trouble. A continuity transfer contact can be used to avoid opening the circuit during the transfer operation. However, the application of theorem **17** produces a rather neat solution of the problem, as is shown in the right-hand circuit of Fig. 3–15. Here, if the circuit is closed through the Y–Z contacts, it does not open during operation of the transfer contact. In effect, then, theorem **17** transforms a transfer contact into a continuity transfer, without the necessity for using the type d (see Fig. 2–4) contact structure.

Figure 3–16 shows graphically how, by means of the expansion theorem, the occurrence of any variable in a network can be limited to a single transfer contact. This procedure can be very important, for example, where an existing network is to be extended, and the additional contact spring load on a particular relay must be kept to the minimum. By means of theorems **20, 20′** the required function can be "expanded about" any variable selected, and that variable can always be represented by means of a single transfer contact.

If a switching network N has a transmission function containing a variable, say X_1, and if the network N is connected in series or in parallel with the element X_1 (or X_1'), then the appearance of X_1 as a variable may be entirely eliminated within the network N. This is accomplished by means of theorems 21, 21' and 22, 22', and the equivalent circuits are shown in Fig. 3–17. In a new design this situation is

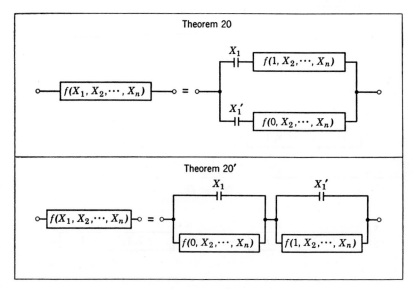

Fig. 3–16. Circuit equivalents of theorems 20, 20'.

quite unlikely to occur because switching algebra will normally avoid it. It can occur, however, in the process of extending or modifying an existing circuit.*

It should be remembered that the theorems of switching algebra have general applicability to any type of switching circuit. In this article we have shown and discussed relay contact circuit equivalents of many of the theorems of the algebra. The contact network is a simple and convenient medium for use in illustrating algebraic methods, and for developing new methods. But the same theorems and procedures are likewise applicable to circuits built with other types of components, such as electronic or solid-state devices, as we shall see in later chapters.

Summary of Postulates and Theorems

The postulates and theorems of switching algebra which were introduced in this chapter are here grouped for convenient references.

* Theorems 21 and 22 also have an interesting application in the design of non-series-parallel and non-planar networks. This will be discussed in Chapter 8.

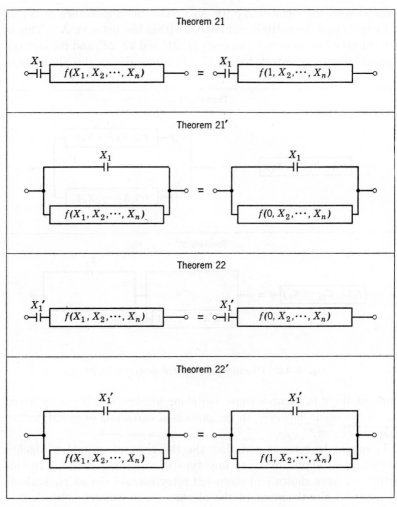

Fig. 3–17. Circuit equivalents of theorems 21, 21′ and 22, 22′.

POSTULATES

(1) $X = 0$ if $X \neq 1$ (2) $0 \cdot 0 = 0$

(1′) $X = 1$ if $X \neq 0$ (2′) $1 + 1 = 1$

(3) $1 \cdot 1 = 1$ (4) $1 \cdot 0 = 0 \cdot 1 = 0$

(3′) $0 + 0 = 0$ (4′) $0 + 1 = 1 + 0 = 1$

$$(5) \quad 0' = 1$$
$$(5') \quad 1' = 0$$

THEOREMS

(6) $X + 0 = X$ (7) $1 + X = 1$

(6') $X \cdot 1 = X$ (7') $0 \cdot X = 0$

(8) $X + X = X$ (9) $(X)' = X'$

(8') $X \cdot X = X$ (9') $(X')' = X$

(10) $X + X' = 1$ (11) $X + Y = Y + X$

(10') $X \cdot X' = 0$ (11') $X \cdot Y = Y \cdot X$

(12) $X + XY = X$ (13) $(X + Y')Y = XY$

(12') $X(X + Y) = X$ (13') $XY' + Y = X + Y$

(14) $X + Y + Z = (X + Y) + Z$ (15) $XY + XZ = X(Y + Z)$

$= X + (Y + Z)$ (15') $(X + Y)(X + Z) = X + YZ$

(14') $XYZ = (XY)Z = X(YZ)$

(16) $(X + Y)(Y + Z)(Z + X') = (X + Y)(Z + X')$

(16') $XY + YZ + ZX' = XY + ZX'$

(17) $(X + Y)(X' + Z) = XZ + X'Y$

(18) $(X + Y + Z + \ldots)' = X'Y'Z' \cdot \ldots$

(18') $(XYZ \cdot \ldots)' = X' + Y' + Z' + \ldots$

(19) $f(X_1, X_2, \ldots, X_n, +, \cdot)' = f(X_1', X_2', \ldots, X_n', \cdot, +)$

(20) $f(X_1, X_2, \ldots, X_n) = X_1 f(1, X_2, \ldots, X_n) + X_1' f(0, X_2, \ldots, X_n)$

(20') $f(X_1, X_2, \ldots, X_n) = [X_1 + f(0, X_2, \ldots, X_n)][X_1' + f(1, X_2, \ldots, X_n)]$

(21) $X_1 \cdot f(X_1, X_2, \ldots, X_n) = X_1 \cdot f(1, X_2, \ldots, X_n)$

(21') $X_1 + f(X_1, X_2, \ldots, X_n) = X_1 + f(0, X_2, \ldots, X_n)$

(22) $X_1' \cdot f(X_1, X_2, \ldots, X_n) = X_1' \cdot f(0, X_2, \ldots, X_n)$

(22') $X_1' + f(X_1, X_2, \ldots, X_n) = X_1' + f(1, X_2, \ldots, X_n)$

Bibliography

1. George Boole, *The Mathematical Analysis of Logic*, Cambridge, England, 1847 (reprinted in 1948, Oxford, Basil Blackwell).
2. George Boole, *An Investigation of the Laws of Thought*, London, 1854 (reprinted, Dover Publications, New York).
3. C. I. Lewis and C. H. Langford, *Symbolic Logic*, The Century Co., 1932 (reprinted, Dover Publications, New York).
4. G. Birkhoff and S. MacLane, *A Survey of Modern Algebra*, The Macmillan Co., New York, 1941 (Chapter XI).

5. C. E. Shannon, "A Symbolic Analysis of Relay and Switching Circuits," *Trans. AIEE,* Vol. 57, 1938, pp. 713–723.
6. G. A. Montgomerie, "Sketch for an Algebra of Relay and Contactor Circuits," Journal of IEE, Vol. 95, Part III, No. 36, July 1948, pp. 302–312. (Same paper also in *Journal of IEE,* Vol. 95, Part II, No. 45, June 1948, pp. 355–364.)
7. C. E. Shannon, "The Synthesis of Two-Terminal Switching Circuits," *Bell System Technical Journal,* Vol. 28, No. 1, January 1949, pp. 59–98.
8. W. Keister, A. E. Ritchie, and S. H. Washburn, *The Design of Switching Circuits,* D. Van Nostrand Co., New York, 1951.
9. Staff of the Computation Laboratory, *Synthesis of Electronic Computing and Control Circuits,* Harvard University Press, Cambridge, Massachusetts, 1951.

PROBLEMS

3.1 Simplify the algebraic expressions:
1. $xy + xyz + yz$
2. $xy + xy'z + yz$
3. $xy + x'yz' + yz$
4. $(xy' + z)(x + y')z$
5. $xy' + z + (x + y')z$
6. $(xy' + z)(x' + y)z'$
7. $xy' + z + (x' + y)z'$
8. $(x + y')(y + z')(z + x')(xyz + x'y'z')$
9. $a + a'b + a'b'c + a'b'c'd + \ldots$
10. $a'd(b' + c) + a'd'(b + c') + (b' + c)(b + c')$
11. $wx + xy + x'z' + wy'z$
12. $w'x' + x'y' + yz + w'z'$

3.2 Write the complements of
1. $[a + b'c'd][a'd' + f(bc' + e)]$
2. $ab'c + (a' + b + d)(abd' + e')$

3.3 Demonstrate, without using the method of perfect induction, whether or not the following equations are valid. (At least one is not valid.)
1. $a'b + b'c + c'a = ab' + bc' + ca'$
2. $bc + abd + ac' = bc + ac'$
3. $ab + a'b' + bc = ab + a'b' + a'c$
4. $ab + a'b' + bcd = ab + a'b' + a'cd$
5. $abc + acd + b'c'd = abc + ab'd + b'c'd$
6. $abc + ab'c' + b'cd + bc'd + ad = abc + ab'c' + b'cd + bc'd$
7. $ab + c'd' + a'bcd' + ab'c'd = (a + d')(b + c')$
8. $(a + b')(b + c')(c + a') = (a' + b)(b' + c)(c' + a)$
9. $(a + b')(b + c')(c + d')(d + a') = (a' + b)(b' + c)(c' + d)(d' + a)$
10. $(a + b)(b + c)(c + a) = (a' + b')(b' + c')(c' + a')$
11. $abx + a'b'x' + b'xy + bx'y' = aby' + a'b'y + axy + a'x'y'$

3.4 Two contact networks, N_1 and N_2, are described by the transmission and hindrance expressions

$$T_1 = AB + BC + AC$$
$$H_2 = AB + BC + AC$$

Prove that the networks are either equivalent or not equivalent.

3.5 Express $ac + bc' + b'c'd$, first in the form $(a + x)(a' + y)$, and then in the form $(bp + b'q)$.

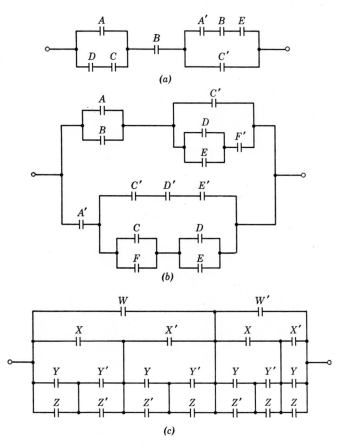

(a)

(b)

(c)

Problem 3.6.

3.6 Write both hindrance and transmission functions for the two-terminal contact networks shown.

3.7 Write hindrance and transmission functions which are the complements of those found in Problem 3.6. Draw schematic diagrams of the networks represented by these functions.

3.8   Simplify the transmission function

$$T = [A + BC][D'E'(C' + A'(B + C))] + (B + D)(B' + D') + B'C'DE$$

3.9   Write the hindrance function which describes the same circuit action as the transmission function of Problem 3.8.

3.10   Write the complement of the transmission function of Problem 3.8.

3.11   The transmission function for the circuit of Figure 3.8 can be realized by a contact network containing only 12 springs (4 transfer contacts). It is not a series-parallel network. Design the network.

Series-parallel
contact networks

We established in Arts. 3.6, 3.7, and 3.8 certain relations between algebraic expressions and contact-network configurations by showing that series and parallel arrangements of contacts could be represented by simple algebraic expressions. In this chapter we apply these ideas to a broader and more detailed study of series-parallel contact networks. This type of network is not only one of the most generally used of all switching circuits, but it is also the form which is frequently the starting point for developing more elaborate and more powerful types of networks.

Our first objective is to learn how to design a circuit which will satisfy a given set of requirements. Later we will want to know how to design circuits which are "optimum" circuits—usually in some economic sense—and, incidentally, how to do so with economic use of the designer's time. Before we can do any of these things, however, we must first be able to analyze existing circuits and to describe their performance characteristics clearly and compactly. This is best done by the application of switching algebra.

In the preceding chapter the hindrance concept was introduced in order to make the discussion complete, and as an aid to reading other literature, but there is no need to continue its use in the work which follows. The algebraic expressions and manipulations in the remainder of this book will hence be in accordance with the transmission concept.

4.1 Analysis of Series-Parallel Contact Networks

We may summarize the procedure for analyzing a series-parallel contact network in the form of a set of rules derived from the work of the preceding chapter. These rules are:

1. The transmission of a contact or of a group of contacts is 0 for an open circuit and 1 for a closed circuit.

2. Each contact in a network is identified by an algebraic symbol which will be called the *designator*.

3. The designator of a contact is unprimed if the contact is normally open, and is primed if the contact is normally closed. If X and X' are the designators of contacts on the same relay structure, they will always have complementary values of transmission. Note that the word "normal" in this rule means that the relay is not operated.

4. When two or more contacts are connected in series, the transmission of the series combination is given by the product of the designators of the contacts. Thus if the contacts X, Y', and Z' are connected in series, the transmission of the series combination is $XY'Z'$.

5. When two or more contacts are connected in parallel, the transmission of the parallel combination is given by the sum of the designators. The transmission of the contacts X', Y, and Z' connected in parallel is $X' + Y + Z'$.

6. When a contact network contains both series and parallel combinations, its transmission may be found by visualizing the network as broken down into elementary series and parallel combinations. The transmissions of these elementary combinations may then be treated as designators and may be combined in accordance with rules 4 and 5.

The procedure outlined in rule 6 will be illustrated by means of the network shown in Fig. 4–1. In addition to the algebraic designators which identify the contacts, reference numbers have been placed on the diagram to identify certain junction points. These are the points between which there are elementary series or parallel groups of contacts, or single contacts.

Between points 1 and 2 we find a series group of contacts having the transmission AB. Between points 2 and 5 there are three parallel paths, and by rule 6 the transmissions of these three paths are to be added. The upper path between 2 and 5 is composed of two parts in series. From 2 to 3 we have the transmission C', and from 3 to 5 the transmission is $(D + E')$. Hence the transmission of the upper path between 2 and 5 is $C'(D + E')$. To this term must be added the transmission G of the middle path and the transmission $D'E$ of the lower path. Thus the complete expression for the transmission between 2 and 5 is $G + D'E + C'(D + E')$.

Since the network from 1 to 2 is in series with the network from 2 to 5, we find the transmission of the upper path between 1 and 5 by taking the product of the two series groups. The resulting expression for the transmission of the upper path is $AB[G + D'E + C'(D + E')]$.

In a similar manner we find the transmission of the lower path between 1 and 5, which is $G'(B' + A'D)$.

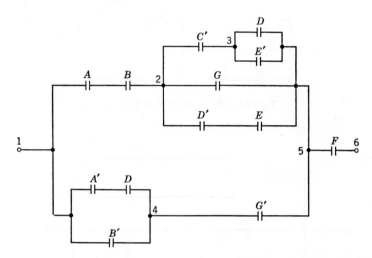

Fig. 4–1. A complex series-parallel contact network is composed of elementary series and parallel combinations.

Since the upper path from 1 to 5 is in parallel with the lower path between these points, the resultant transmission from 1 to 5 is given by the sum of the expressions just found. This sum must then be multiplied by F in order to account for the contact between 5 and 6 which is in series with everything else in the circuit. The final expression for the transmission of the entire network is

$$T = F\{AB[G + D'E + C'(D + E')] + G'(B' + A'D)\}$$

We observe that the systematic use of the process which was described formally by the six rules for series-parallel network analysis has enabled us to go from a circuit diagram, marked with contact designators, to an algebraic transmission function in which the designators have become the binary variables, and the series and parallel connections have been replaced by the operations of multiplication and addition. Figure 4–2 gives two additional examples of the application of this process. Each circuit diagram is accompanied by the corresponding transmission function written under the diagram.

The importance of this process lies beyond the fact that it enables us to replace a schematic description of a circuit by an algebraic description. Its greater importance is that the process of analysis is

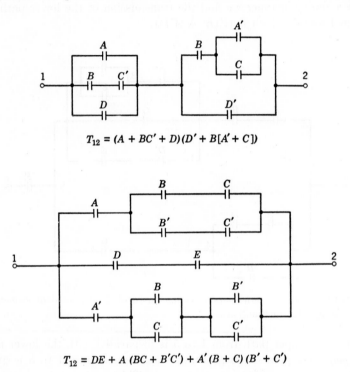

$$T_{12} = (A + BC' + D)(D' + B[A' + C])$$

$$T_{12} = DE + A\,(BC + B'C') + A'\,(B + C)\,(B' + C')$$

Fig. 4–2. Examples of the analysis of series-parallel contact networks.

reversible, and it can thus become a process of synthesis. This follows from the fact that any transmission function, in which the algebraic operations are limited to those of multiplication and addition, corresponds explicitly to a contact network in which there are only series and parallel connections. Hence, if we are given a transmission function, we can always draw a series-parallel type of contact network which behaves in accordance with that function. We shall see later that we can frequently find more advantageous realizations of transmission functions than those in the series-parallel form, but we always have the assurance that if no better way is found we can realize any switching function as a series-parallel circuit.

4.2   Verbal Description of Switching Functions

Let us for the moment assume that we had never heard of switching algebra, and then see how we would describe the operation of the circuits shown in Fig. 4–3.   Each part of Fig. 4–3—(a), (b), (c), and so on—shows the operating coil of a relay X with one side connected

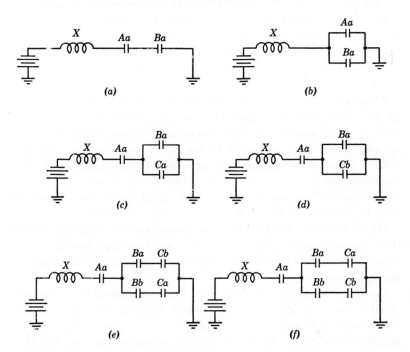

Fig. 4–3.   Series-parallel contact networks for the control of relay X.

through a battery to ground, and the other side connected through a contact network to ground.   Instead of using contact designators which have algebraic meaning, we will identify the types of contacts by means of the a-b-c system shown in Fig. 2–11, and use the capital letters A, B, and C to identify which relays carry these contacts.

The statements which describe the operation* of relay X might then be given as follows:

---

* Later we shall have to distinguish between a relay which is energized and one which is operated.   In the present discussion, factors such as operating time and sequence of operation have no important significance.   It is hence assumed that a relay which is energized is also operated, and that one which is not energized is released.

Fig. 4–3(a)   Relay X is operated when A and B are operated.

Fig. 4–3(b)   Relay X is operated when A or B, or both, are operated.

Fig. 4–3(c)   Relay X is operated when A and either B, or C, or both, are operated.

Fig. 4–3(d)   Relay X is operated when, with A operated, either B is operated, or C is not operated, or both.

Fig. 4–3(e)   Relay X is operated when A is operated and either B or C, but not both, are operated.

Fig. 4–3(f)   Relay X is operated when, with A operated, B and C are either both operated or both not operated.

There are several points we can observe with respect to these statements. First, there are quite a number of ways in which we can use even a small number of relay contacts. Second, when we try to describe a switching situation in words, we are likely to encounter either confusion of meaning or profusion of language, even when the situations are relatively simple. Third, one or both of the words "and" and "or" appear in each of the verbal descriptions associated with the circuits of Fig. 4–3.

We shall digress briefly to discuss these "and-or" relations because they appear frequently in the literature of switching circuits. Unfortunately, in some instances the terms have acquired rather rigid and unsatisfactory meanings.

From an inspection of Fig. 4–3 and the descriptive statements given above, it is apparent that broadly speaking the "and" is associated with a series connection and the "or" is associated with a parallel connection. In detail this is not quite true because there are two kinds of "or" statements. Fig. 4–3(b), for example, illustrates the "inclusive or" situation, where the meaning is "A or B or both." On the other hand, Fig. 4–3(e) illustrates the "exclusive or" situation—also known as the "or else" situation—in which we mean "B or C but not both."

Many workers have found it convenient to use the term "and circuit" to designate a circuit which performs a switching duty analogous to that of a series connection of relay contacts, and the term "or circuit" to designate one which has a function analogous to that of a parallel connection of relay contacts. There is no difficulty with such designations when they are used as purely descriptive devices.

But it is also true that the "and-or" concept has in some instances been associated with particular symbols of switching algebra, and at this point real confusion can arise. If two contacts, A and B, are connected in series, we write for the transmission $T = AB$. To describe this situation in words we can say either "The transmission is 1 when A *and* B are 1," or "The transmission is 0 when A *or* B is 0." A simple parallel connection can likewise be described using either of the "and-or" connectives, depending on whether we describe the conditions for 1 transmission or for 0 transmission. Taking into consideration the relative inadequacy of verbal descriptions of switching functions, and the difficulty of dealing with another set of dual relationships, there seems to be no real justification for the continued use of the "and-or" idea in the study of switching circuits. It has been discussed here for the sake of completeness but no important use will be made of it.

Now consider again the circuits of Fig. 4–3. In each of these the relay X will operate whenever the circuit through the contacts on relays A, B, and C is closed. Hence the transmission function of the contact network also describes the state of operation of the relay X, provided we allow the digit 1 to represent X operated, and the digit 0 to represent X unoperated. If T_X symbolizes the operation of relay X, we can write for the circuits of Fig. 4–3 (after substituting primed and unprimed contact designators for the symbols of the *a-b-c* system):

(a) $T_X = AB$ (d) $T_X = A(B + C')$

(b) $T_X = A + B$ (e) $T_X = A(BC' + B'C)$

(c) $T_X = A(B + C)$ (f) $T_X = A(BC + B'C')$

4.3 The Table of Combinations

The switching situations illustrated in the examples of Fig. 4–3 are quite simple, and yet the verbal descriptions of some of them require rather careful wording in order to be complete and precise. As the number of variables in a switching function increases, the language of verbal description becomes completely unwieldy, and it is essential to find simpler and more compact methods for specifying circuit performance. The methods which are now in common use all have their origin in the table of combinations.

At present we are considering only the type of switching circuit which is known as a combinational circuit. For this type of circuit the output state is completely specified whenever the input state is given. But what do we mean exactly by the terms "output state" and "input state"?

We have been discussing relay contact networks, and it might naturally be supposed that the contact network is the switching circuit. In Fig. 4–4, however, we see that the relay contact network is merely a part of the general relay switching circuit. The inputs to a relay switching circuit of the combinational type control the operating windings of the relays. In Fig. 4–4 there are n input terminals indicated, and the internal connections are such that if any input terminal is grounded the relay to which that terminal is connected will operate. The contacts within the contact network are

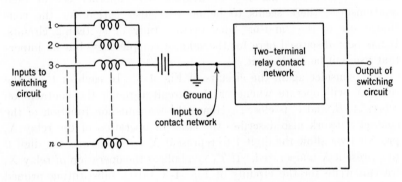

Fig. 4–4. Generalized combinational relay switching circuit containing a two-terminal contact network.

mounted on the relays, which are themselves within the broken line that marks the boundary of the switching circuit. While the output terminal of the contact network is also the output terminal of the switching circuit, the input terminal of the contact network is connected to ground within the switching circuit.

The true inputs of the switching circuit are those which control the windings of the relays, and the term "input state" therefore refers to the combined state of operation or non-operation of the n relays, as determined by the presence or absence of ground potential at the n input terminals.

The term "output state" refers to the presence or absence of ground potential at the output terminal or terminals of the switching circuit. Since the state of operation of the relays determines the positions of the contacts within the contact network, it becomes clear that for this type of circuit—the combinational type—the output state is completely determined whenever the input state is given.

It should also be noted by reference to Fig. 4–4 that although we specify the performance of a switching circuit by means of a transmission function, the switching circuit as a whole is not a "transmitting" device. However, the contact network does conduct current, and the transmission function of a contact network represents its ability to conduct or to prevent conduction. The transmission of a contact network is hence a binary variable, and it can be combined algebraically with the transmission functions of other contact networks in accordance with the rules given in Art. 4.1.

Suppose we consider a relay switching circuit which has two input terminals, controlling relays which we shall designate as X and Y. If we use an unprimed letter to represent the presence of an input ground (relay operated), and a primed letter to represent the absence of an input ground (relay not operated), we can readily see that there are only four possible input states, namely, (X, Y), (X, Y'), (X', Y), and (X', Y'). These are the four possible combinations of values which two binary variables can take.

If we were to perform the same process with three input variables, we would find that there are eight possible combinations of the three binary variables. Four variables can have sixteen combinations, five variables can have thirty-two, and so on. It can be seen in general that since each of the n input variables can take two values, the number of possible combinations of the n variables is 2^n.

Table 4–1

X	Y	Z
0	0	0
0	0	1
0	1	0
0	1	1
1	0	0
1	0	1
1	1	0
1	1	1

Instead of writing out all the combinations of the input variables in terms of primed and unprimed letters, it is convenient to tabulate the combinations by using a digit 1 to represent the presence of an input ground (unprimed letter) and a digit 0 to represent the absence of an input ground (primed letter). It is also convenient to arrange the table so that when the digits of each row are viewed as a group, these groups form an ascending or descending series of consecutive binary numbers. Table 4–1 shows the possible combinations of the three variables X, Y, and Z in terms of the digits 0 and 1, with the digit groups ordered so as to form a series of increasing binary numbers.

Since the tabulation given includes *all* the possible combinations of the three input variables, it is necessary only to provide an additional column which shows for which rows the transmission is to be 0 and for which rows it is to be 1, in order to have a complete specification of the performance required from the switching circuit.* This final tabulation which includes the listing of the transmission values is known as the table of combinations for the circuit.

4.4   Formation of the Table of Combinations

Consider the two-terminal contact network shown in Fig. 4–3(f) for which the transmission was found to be $T = A(BC + B'C')$. We understand that this expression refers only to the transmission of the contact network. But the elements of the contact network are physically operated by the armatures of three relays which we can also designate by the letters A, B, C. In our previous discussion of contact networks we adopted the convention that an unprimed contact designator would represent a normally open contact. Such a contact has the transmission 1 only when it is closed, that is, when the relay which carries it is operated. But in the preceding section we also adopted the convention that in the table of combinations a digit 1 represents an operated relay. Because these two conventions have been so chosen, it becomes possible to assign to the digits in the columns of a table of combinations either of two meanings. A digit 1 can represent either the operated condition of the relay, or it can represent the transmission of a normally open contact on that relay when the relay is operated. Similarly a digit 0 represents either the unoperated state of a relay, or it represents the transmission of a normally open contact on that relay when the relay is not operated. The point is that the table of combinations can be interpreted either in terms of the states of operation of the relays, or in terms of the transmission of the associated contact network.

Now let us write the table of combinations for the transmission of the contact network of Fig. 4–3(f), $T = A(BC + B'C')$. Referring to Table 4–2 we see that in the first four rows the digit in the A column is 0. The A relay is not operated, so the transmission of the contact A in the transmission function is 0.

---

* Only one output column is needed for a switching circuit which contains a two-terminal contact network because such a circuit has only a single output. In circuits to be studied later the contact network will have more than one output and it will then be necessary to provide more than one output column in the table.

Table 4–2

A	B	C	T
0	0	0	0
0	0	1	0
0	1	0	0
0	1	1	0
1	0	0	1
1	0	1	0
1	1	0	0
1	1	1	1

Since A is a multiplying factor, the transmission must be 0 for all the input states of the first four rows. In the remaining four rows A is 1, so we need examine only the conditions of B and C. In row 5 both B and C are 0, so these two relays are not operated. The transmission represented by the BC term is hence 0, but that due to the $B'C'$ term is 1. The network transmission is therefore $T = 1(0 + 1) = 1$.

In row 8 both the B and C relays are operated, so the BC term has the value 1 and the $B'C'$ term is 0, which again gives a network transmission of 1. In rows 6 and 7 although relay A is still operated, relays B and C have opposite states. Both terms within the parentheses have 0 values, so the network transmission is 0.

4.5 Synthesis of the Series-Parallel Network from the Table of Combinations

In Art. 4.4 we have seen that the table of combinations is a device which enables us to analyze an existing network by systematically recording the output states of the network for all possible input states. The usefulness of the table of combinations in synthesis arises from the fact that it requires us to specify completely what we want the terminal action of the network to be.

For simplicity, let us consider a switching circuit which has two inputs and a single output. We will designate the inputs A and B, and the corresponding relays are to operate whenever a ground is applied to one of the input terminals. An output from the circuit corresponds to a ground appearing at the output terminal.

From a study of the requirements which the circuit must satisfy we find that a ground must appear on the output terminal if input A is grounded and input B is not grounded, or if input B is grounded and A is not grounded, but for all other input conditions there is to be no output. This information can be expressed by the table of combinations shown in Table 4–3. Note that the input columns of the table list all the possible combinations of the input variables, and since for each of these the output is specified, we know that nothing in the specifications has been overlooked.

Table 4–3

A	B	Output
0	0	0
0	1	1
1	0	1
1	1	0

There are two ways in which we can develop a contact network which has the transmission described in Table 4–3. For each input condition corresponding to a 1 in the output we can set up a series circuit and then connect all the series circuits in parallel to form the required series-parallel network. The other way is to establish a parallel-connected set of contacts which has a transmission of 0 for each input state corresponding to a 0 in the output column, and then connect all these parallel groups in series. We shall show that the final result is the same by either method.

Table 4–3 has been drawn in the conventional form as a table of combinations, but at this point it will be helpful if we supplement it. In Table 4–4 the information presented is the same as that in

Table 4–4

Row No.	A	A'	B	B'	Output
1	0	1	0	1	0
2	0	1	1	0	1
3	1	0	0	1	1
4	1	0	1	0	0

Table 4–3. A column has been added to identify the row numbers, but the principal change is the addition of the two columns which show the values of the complementary variables A' and B'.

We now wish to design a network which satisfies the conditions for transmission 1 at the output. This is to be done by arranging a series connection of contacts for each 1 which appears in the output column, namely for rows 2 and 3. Since for a series connection of contacts the transmission is given by the product of the contact designators, we must select contact designators which have the value 1 under the conditions for which the output is to be 1.

Looking at row 2 in Table 4–4, we see that the designators A' and B have 1 values, and a series combination of contacts which has the transmission $A'B$ will produce the required output. In similar manner we find that for row 3 the term AB' produces the required 1 transmission. Hence a contact network which satisfies the table of combinations is one having these two series circuits connected in parallel. The transmission function for the network is $T = A'B + AB'$.

The other approach to the synthesis is by setting up contact combinations which satisfy each of the 0's in the output. This is to be done by arranging a parallel connection of contacts for each 0 in the output column, namely for rows 1 and 4. The transmission of parallel contacts is given by the sum of the contact designators, so we must select designators which have the value 0 for those input states which correspond to 0 output. In row 1, the designators A and B have 0 values, so a parallel connection which has the transmission $(A + B)$ will produce 0 transmission. In row 4 the required parallel connection is described by the transmission function $(A' + B')$ since the designators A' and B' are both 0 in that row. If the two parallel sets of contacts are connected in series, the resultant network is described by the transmission $T = (A + B)(A' + B') = A'B + AB'$. Thus we see that by both methods we arrive at the same algebraic result.

Usually, of course, we have more than two variables, but the synthesis procedure is the same. When the number of variables is larger, however, it is neither convenient nor necessary to write the table of combinations in the expanded form shown in Table 4–4. This method was used merely to emphasize the fact that when the value of a binary variable is given, the value of its complement is implied, even though it is not explicitly stated. The required contact designators are found by noting that if we are writing the transmission of a series combination (to produce an output of 1), we use the unprimed designator when there is a 1 in its column, and we use the primed designator if the entry in that column is 0. If we are writing the transmission of a parallel combination (to produce an output of 0), we use the unprimed designator if the column entry is 0 and we use the primed designator if the entry is 1.

For example, suppose we have a row taken from a table of combinations in five variables, and for this particular input state the output is to be 1.

A	B	C	D	E
0	1	1	0	1

If we wish a series circuit with these five variables to have a transmission of 1, we must write the transmission term $A'BCD'E$. Since relays A and D are not operated, we must use the normally closed contacts A' and D' in the series group in order to have the transmission 1. It is not necessary to write separate columns for A' and D', because we need only note that the presence of the 0 entries under A and D means that we must use their complements as contact designators.

If we consider another row from the same table, but one for which the transmission is to be 0, we will want to write the transmission of

A	B	C	D	E
1	0	1	0	0

a parallel group of contacts, and in order that the transmission of the entire group be 0, we must write $(A' + B + C' + D + E)$. Here relays A and C are operated, and we must use normally closed contacts on them to obtain 0 transmission. If we are trying to establish the 0 transmission of a parallel group, we use the unprimed variable as contact designator when the column entry is a 0, but we use the complementary variable when the column entry is a 1.

4.6 Standard Forms of Transmission Functions

Consider a switching circuit with n inputs, and a series connection of contacts, as in Fig. 4–5, in which a contact from each of the input relays appears. It is to be understood here that the contact labels are generic and can represent either normally open or normally closed contacts.

Fig. 4–5. Series circuit in n variables.

There are 2^n series circuits of this type which we can form by applying all the possible combinations of primes on the contact designators. For each of the 2^n series circuits there is just one way in which we can obtain 1 transmission. The relays which carry normally open contacts must operate, and those which carry normally closed contacts must remain unoperated. Hence in writing the product term for the transmission, we use an unprimed designator when the entry in the table of combinations is 1, and a primed designator when the entry is 0.

For any other input state this particular series circuit will be open and the transmission will be 0. Since there is only one input state which gives 1 transmission and $2^n - 1$ input states which give 0 transmission, we see that the general series circuit uniquely represents a row in a table of combinations for which 1 transmission is specified.

If there are j rows in the table, each of which requires 1 transmission, we need only establish a separate series circuit for each of the j rows and connect all the series combinations in parallel, as

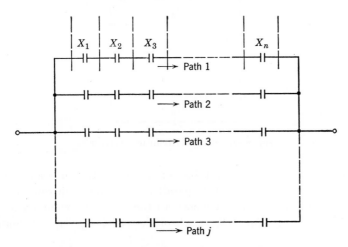

Fig. 4–6. Series-parallel circuit derived from 1 values of transmission.

shown in Fig. 4–6. Each of the series groups of contacts constitutes a path through the network for which there will be 1 transmission for a particular input state, and for that input state only. When similiar paths are established for all the j input states which require 1 transmission at the output, the network is complete.

If we turn now to the parallel circuit in n variables, as shown in Fig. 4–7, we see that there are again 2^n ways in which we can apply primes to the contact designators. We thus have 2^n possible parallel circuits. For each of these circuits there is just one way in which there can be 0 transmission. The relays which carry normally open contacts must be unoperated, and those which carry normally closed contacts must be operated. Hence in writing the sum which represents the transmission, we use the unprimed designator when the entry in the table of combinations is 0, and the primed designator when the entry is 1. The procedure is, of course, exactly the opposite of that followed for the series circuit.

For any other input state, one or more of the contacts in the parallel circuit will be closed and the transmission will be 1. Since there is only one input state which gives 0 transmission and $2^n - 1$ input states which give 1 transmission, the parallel circuit uniquely represents a row in a table of combinations for which 0 transmission is required.

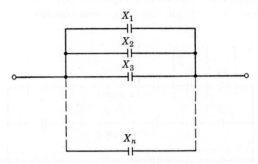

Fig. 4–7. Parallel circuit in n variables.

If there are k rows in the table for which the transmission is to be 0, we must establish a separate parallel circuit for each row in which the transmission is 0, and connect all these parallel combinations in series as shown in Fig. 4–8. Each of the parallel groups of contacts

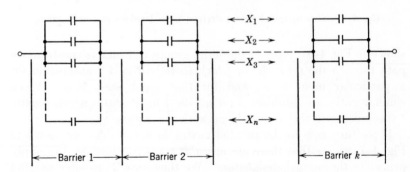

Fig. 4–8. Series-parallel circuit derived from 0 values of transmission.

constitutes a barrier which prevents transmission through the network for a particular input state, but not for any other input state. When a series of such barriers is established for all the k input states which require 0 transmission at the output, the network is complete.

Thus we see that there are two forms of the transmission function which can be written from the table of combinations. If we satisfy the 1 values of output transmission, we will write a *sum of products* in which each product term represents a series group of contacts, and in which the summation represents the parallel connection of all the series groups. When a sum of products is thus written, each product term contains all the input variables, either primed or unprimed, and no two product terms are identical. This form of the switching function will be called the **standard sum.**

If, however, we satisfy the 0 values of output transmission, we will write a *product of sums* in which each sum term represents a parallel group of contacts, and in which the product represents the series connection of all the parallel groups. When a product of sums is thus written, each sum term contains all the input variables, either primed or unprimed, and no two sum terms are identical. We call this form of the switching function the **standard product.**

It should be noted that any switching function may be expanded into either its standard-sum form or its standard-product form by the repeated application of theorems 20 and 20′, respectively. To obtain these results the expansions must be performed with respect to every variable in the function.

Example 4–1

For the given table of combinations find the transmission function in the two standard forms. Show that these reduce to the same transmission function.

A	B	C	Output
0	0	0	0
0	0	1	1
0	1	0	0
0	1	1	0
1	0	0	1
1	0	1	1
1	1	0	0
1	1	1	0

By satisfying the 1 values of output transmission, we obtain the transmission function in the sum of products form, that is, the standard sum.

$$T = A'B'C + AB'C' + AB'C$$

By satisfying the 0 values of output transmission, we obtain the transmission function as the product of sums, that is, the standard product.

$$T = (A+B+C)(A+B'+C)(A+B'+C')(A'+B'+C)(A'+B'+C')$$

These functions can both be simplified algebraically. The sum of products reduces to $T = B'C + AB' = B'(A + C)$. The product of sums likewise reduces to

$$T = (A+C)(A+B')(A'+B') = B'(A+C)$$

It remains to be shown that the transmission function obtained from a table of combinations is always the same whether it is derived from the 1 values or the 0 values of output transmission. This has been shown to be true in two instances, but not for the general case.

If we make a list of product terms which represent all the possible combinations of n variables, there will be 2^n products thus formed. We can select any of these terms and specify that for all the input states thus selected the transmission is to be 1 but that for all the terms not selected the transmission is to be 0. If the number of states for which there is to be 1 transmission is j, and the number of 0 transmission states is k, we must have $j + k = 2^n$. Designate each product term in the 1 transmission group by U, and each product term in the 0 transmission group by Z.

The transmission function represented is given by the sum of the products for which the transmission is 1, or

$$T = U_1 + U_2 + \ldots + U_j$$

The sum of the remaining k product terms must be a function which is the complement of the transmission function T, or

$$T' = Z_1 + Z_2 + Z_3 + \ldots + Z_k$$

This can be written as the transmission function T by the application of theorem 18, which gives

$$T = Z_1'Z_2'Z_3' \cdot \ldots \cdot Z_k'$$

Each of the Z_k' terms is a sum of variables which are the complements of the variables in the Z_k terms, and therefore the contact designators are correctly given for 0 transmission. The last expression found shows that the product of the k sum terms produces the same transmission function as the sum of the j product terms. Hence the transmission function obtained from a table of combinations is the same whether it is derived from the rows representing 0 transmission or from the rows representing 1 transmission.

We can frequently take advantage of this property to save time in deriving transmission expressions. If the rows of the table of combinations are evenly divided between 0 and 1 transmission, it is immaterial which route is followed in writing the transmission function, and the designer can follow his personal preferences. But if there is a preponderance of 1 values in the output column, it will often save time to derive the transmission from the 0 transmission rows, since there are fewer algebraic terms involved. The opposite is, of course, true if there are relatively few 1 transmission rows in the table.

4.7   The Incomplete Table of Combinations

One of the most important features of the table of combinations is that it provides an automatic verification of the completeness of a designer's specification of circuit performance. This is true whether the table is written out in full, or is written in part. A table of combinations which lists states for which the transmission is 1, together with the statement that for all other conditions the transmission is 0, constitutes a complete table of combinations, even though it is only partly written. Since the input states are mutually exclusive, when any group of them is specified the remainder are determined.

The incomplete table of combinations differs from the partly written table in that the former contains one or more input states for which no output state is specified. There can be two valid reasons for the deliberate omission of a row in the table of combinations:

1. The combination of input variables cannot occur.

2. The designer does not care what happens if the combination does occur. For example, an omitted combination may be one which can occur only after some other event which renders the resulting transmission meaningless.

In either case there is a relaxation of the specifications which frequently, but not always, can be used advantageously. We will call an input state for which no transmission is specified an optional state. The significance of the term is that in forming the transmission function represented by an incomplete table of combinations we are free to use an optional state as either a state of 1 transmission or of 0 transmission.

Example 4–2

In the given table of combinations the required transmission values are shown in the column marked T. The last three input states in the table cannot occur and the transmission values corresponding to them are optional. Derive the transmission function described by the table using the optional states to simplify the function.

A	B	C	T
0	0	0	0
0	0	1	1
0	1	0	0
0	1	1	1
1	0	0	0
1	0	1	–
1	1	0	–
1	1	1	–

Since there are only two input states (rows 2 and 4) which lead to 1 transmission we write the transmission as a sum of products, $T = A'B'C + A'BC$. This immediately reduces to the expression $T = A'C$. We now observe that among the optional input states, those in rows 6 and 8 have the same input variables except that A appears instead of A'. If we elect to make the transmission 1 for both these rows we can then add to the transmission function $T = AB'C + ABC = AC$. Combining this contribution from the optional states with the required transmission previously found, we obtain for the final network transmission function $T = A'C + AC = C$.

The effect of using the two optional states in this example was to eliminate the A' contact required by the original transmission function. Looking at the table of combinations, we see that this contact would have prevented 1 transmission under the input conditions described by the two selected optional rows. By electing to have 1 transmission for these rows, we have effectively said that since the input states involved cannot occur anyway, it is not necessary to have the A' contact as a guard against 1 transmission for these states. The transmissions elected will never occur because the input conditions never occur.

There is no assurance that the availability of optional states in an incomplete table of combinations will lead to simplification of the transmission function, and it is even less likely that all the available optional states can be used to advantage. In more complex and difficult combinational problems, however, optional states occur quite frequently. This is particularly true in the combinational problems which arise as the result of synthesizing sequential circuits. It is important, therefore, that we understand at this time the algebraic and physical basis for achieving simplification by the effective use of optional states.

4.8 Algebraic Simplification of Switching Functions

A general transmission function, as written directly from a table of combinations, is rarely in the form that is best suited for circuit realization. It may be regarded as simply the raw material which the designer has at his disposal for manipulation into acceptable form. In most circumstances the purpose of manipulation is to reduce the quantity of switching equipment which is needed to realize the required physical result. The quantity of equipment is measured roughly by counting the number of switching elements in a circuit, and we seek to minimize this number.

We shall discuss the problem of minimization more completely in the next chapter. At this point we wish to introduce the basic algebraic properties and processes which the designer uses most commonly, and to establish more of an understanding of the relations between mathematical and physical forms. It will become apparent that in many instances mathematical steps can be replaced by processes of physical reasoning, and that much network reduction can be accomplished by working directly with circuit diagrams. The development of this sort of skill is desirable, and it is one of our primary aims. We approach it by a study of algebraic methods because they tend to systematize our efforts, and to impart a certain degree of sure-footedness to the designer. Indeed, at times it becomes difficult to tell whether one is using algebra or a more highly developed form of circuit sense.

The objective in the algebraic reduction of a general transmission function is to get it into a form in which the number of occurrences of the letters which represent switching variables is as small as possible. Because each appearance of a designator in the function *may* correspond to the appearance of a contact in the network, the maximum number of physical elements needed is determinable directly from the function.

Consider the switching function described by the standard sum

$$T = A'B'C + A'BC' + A'BC + AB'C$$

To reduce this expression we group the first and fourth terms, and the second and third terms, and obtain

$$T = (A + A')B'C + A'B(C + C')$$
$$= B'C + A'B$$

The original expression contained 12 occurrences of contact variables and this was reduced to 4 occurrences by the algebraic process. Figure

4–9 shows the contact networks corresponding to both the original function and its reduced form.

It is instructive now to study the table of combinations represented by this function. The table shows only the rows for which the trans-

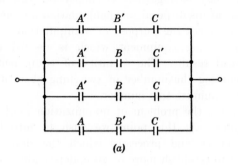

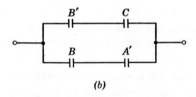

(a)

(b)

Fig. 4–9. Contact networks derived from (a) the transmission function written as a standard sum, and (b) its algebraically reduced form.

mission is 1; it is to be understood that the transmission is 0 for all other rows. Note in both rows 1 and 4 that the digits under B and C

A	B	C
0	0	1
0	1	0
0	1	1
1	0	1

are 0 and 1, respectively, while A has both 0 and 1 values. This signifies that the transmission for these two rows is independent of the variation of A and depends only upon B and C. We can thus immediately write the term $B'C$ to represent the transmission of the first and fourth rows. Likewise in both rows 2 and 3, the digits under A and B are 0 and 1, respectively, and C has both 0 and 1 values. Hence we can write the transmission term $A'B$ for these two rows. The sum of these two terms accounts for all the rows in the table of combinations and gives us the transmission expression previously found.

By a similar process of reasoning the contact network in Fig. 4–9(a) can be reduced without resorting to the relevant algebra. If we examine the top and bottom paths of the network we see that the contacts B' and C are in series with A' in the top path, and with A in the bottom path. If B' and C are closed, the circuit will be closed through one or the other of these paths, regardless of the position of the A relay. Hence the A' and A contacts in these paths are redundant, and when they are removed, the two sets of $B'C$ contacts can be reduced to a single set. For exactly the same reasons, the C' and C contacts in the two middle paths are redundant, and these two paths can be replaced by a single $A'B$ path.

Whenever a general transmission function contains within it a term which includes all the possible combinations of a smaller group of variables, that term becomes 1. For example, the function

$$T = W'X'YZ + W'XY'Z' + W'XY'Z + W'XYZ' + W'XYZ + WXY'Z'$$

may be factored to give

$$T = W'X'YZ + W'X\,(Y'Z' + Y'Z + YZ' + YZ) + WXY'Z'$$

The term within the parentheses contains all the possible combinations of the variables Y and Z, and is equal to 1. Hence the original transmission reduces to

$$T = W'X'YZ + W'X + WXY'Z'$$

We can now combine the $W'X$ term with each of the other terms to obtain the further reduction

$$
\begin{aligned}
T &= W'(X + X'YZ) + X(W' + WY'Z') \\
&= W'(X + YZ) + X(W' + Y'Z') \\
&= W'X + W'YZ + XY'Z'
\end{aligned}
$$

This example illustrates the kind of major simplification that can be achieved by observing particular groupings of terms within an algebraic expression, or of digit patterns in a table of combinations, or of contact configurations within a network diagram. The ability to discern such opportunities increases greatly with experience. We need not, however, rely entirely on the development of keen observation and personal skill. At this point we shall examine a general algebraic procedure for reducing the complexity of switching functions.* This

* W. V. Quine, "The Problem of Simplifying Truth Functions," *American Mathematical Monthly*, Vol. 59, October 1952, pp. 521–531; W. V. Quine, "A Way to Simplify Truth Functions," *American Mathematical Monthly*, Vol. 62, November 1955, pp. 627–631.

leads, in the next chapter, to more powerful methods for minimizing networks.

In this method we start with the function expressed as a standard sum. The first step is to compare each term in the function with all other terms and apply the theorem $XY + XY' = X$ wherever possible. All terms which have thus combined to form shorter terms should be checked off, so that in writing the final transmission function we can be certain that every term in the standard sum is included.

The process is repeated, comparing every pair of shorter terms, until no more combinations can be made. At the conclusion of this process there will be a group of terms which have not been checked off. These are known as the *prime implicants* of the function and we seek to write the final transmission function as a sum of terms taken from the prime implicants, but to reject those that are redundant.

Example 4–3

In organizing the work of obtaining the prime implicants of a function it is convenient to arrange the terms of the standard sum in a column and then form additional columns containing terms with one or more variables eliminated. The process is shown for the function

$$T = W'X'YZ' + W'XY'Z' + W'XY'Z + W'XYZ'$$
$$+ W'XYZ + WX'Y'Z + WXY'Z$$

Terms of Standard Sum	First Reduction	Second Reduction
$W'X'YZ'$ ✓	$W'YZ'$	$W'X$
$W'XY'Z'$ ✓	$W'XY'$ ✓	
$W'XY'Z$ ✓	$W'XZ'$ ✓	
$W'XYZ'$ ✓	$W'XZ$ ✓	
$W'XYZ$ ✓	$XY'Z$	
$WX'Y'Z$ ✓	$W'XY$ ✓	
$WXY'Z$ ✓	$WY'Z$	

There are three terms in the second column which are not checked because they could not be reduced further. These terms and the term $W'X$ in the third column are the prime implicants of the function.

A transmission function written as the sum of all its prime implicants would not be incorrect but it would not, in general, be the simplest equivalent function. In the preceding example the sum of the prime implicants is

$$T = W'X + W'YZ' + XY'Z + WY'Z$$

At this point we apply theorem 16', $XY + YZ + X'Z = XY + X'Z$. Since $W'X + XY'Z + WY'Z = W'X + WY'Z$, the term $XY'Z$ is redundant and we have for the final transmission

$$T = W'X + W'YZ' + WY'Z$$

We call this the *minimum sum* form of the function, since it contains no redundant terms or redundant variables. Although the function reduced in this example had only one minimum sum, many functions will have two or more sums which are minimum in this sense.

The reduction procedure described is also applicable to functions which are specified by standard products rather than by standard sums, and the final result is a *minimum product*. First we apply the theorem $(X + Y)(X + Y') = X$ to all pairs of terms in the standard product, and then to the reduced terms, until no further elimination of variables is possible. Those terms which have not entered into combination to form a reduced term (and are hence not checked off) are the prime implicants. By applying the theorem $(X + Y)(Y + Z)(X' + Z) = (X + Y)(X' + Z)$, we can eliminate redundant prime implicants and write a minimum product. Again, the result of this process may or may not be unique.

4.9 Tie and Cut Sets

The function which was simplified in Example 4–3 leads to the contact network of Fig. 4–10 when written in the factored form

$$T = W'(X + YZ') + WY'Z$$

If the inputs are such that $W = 0$ and $X = 1$, we will find that a conducting path has been established between the network terminals

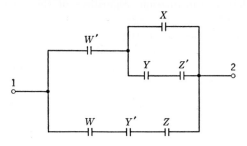

Fig. 4–10. Contact network described by the function given in Example 4–3.

1 and 2, and that this path is maintained regardless of the behavior of the Y and Z variables. In other words, although the network transmission is a function of the set of variables (W, X, Y, Z), there is

nevertheless a subset, namely (W, X), which when assigned the values $(0, 1)$ ensures that the network transmission will be 1. This subset corresponds in the network to the path through the contacts W' and X in series, which when closed literally ties the terminals 1 and 2 together.

There are two other paths in the contact network which when closed ensure that the transmission will be 1. These correspond to the terms $W'YZ'$ and $WY'Z$ in the transmission function, and both are independent of the X variable.

We observe, of course, that the three subsets which can ensure 1 transmission for the network correspond exactly to the three terms

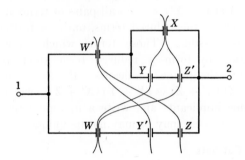

Fig. 4–11.   Graphical representation of cut sets.

of the transmission function written as a minimum sum. These subsets, or the contacts which they describe, are the *tie sets* of the network, and each term of a minimum sum is a tie set. Physically, a tie set is a minimum set of contacts which when closed ensure that the network has 1 transmission, regardless of the state of the other contacts in the network.

If a switching function is written in the form of a minimum product rather than a minimum sum, the individual terms of the product correspond to sets of contacts which when open ensure that the network transmission is 0, even though all other contacts be closed. The sets of contacts thus defined are the *cut sets* of a network.

It is not necessary to derive the minimum product by algebraic methods if the minimum sum is known. In Fig. 4–11 a graphical approach shows how the cut sets of a network, and hence the minimum-product form of its transmission function, may be derived from a network which was originally realized from its minimum-sum description. This is the same network as that shown in Fig. 4–10 and is derived from the function studied in Example 4–3. The light lines passing through various groups of contacts may be visualized as the paths taken by a knife cutting across the circuit diagram. Each cut starts through a contact in the top path and ends by passing through a contact in the bottom path, and the route chosen must pass through one and only one member of each tie set in the network. If all the contacts crossed by any one of these routes are open, the network is literally cut apart and the transmission between terminals 1 and 2 is 0. All such sets of contacts are cut sets. Physically, each cut set is a minimum set of contacts which when open ensure that the network transmission is 0, even though all other contacts be closed.

It was pointed out that each term of a minimum product corresponded to the contacts of a cut set. It is not true, however, that each cut set corresponds to a term in the minimum product. Some cut sets may be physically present even though they are algebraically redundant. If we identify the cut sets in Fig. 4–11, each of them can be used to form a term in a transmission function which is written as a product of sums. The function thus found is

$$T = (W' + Y')(W' + Z)(W + X + Y)(W + X + Z') \cdot$$
$$(X + Y + Z)(X + Y' + Z')$$

But, according to theorem 16,

$$(W' + Y')(W + X + Z')(X + Y' + Z') = (W' + Y')(W + X + Z')$$

and

$$(W' + Z)(W + X + Y)(X + Y + Z) = (W' + Z)(W + X + Y)$$

Hence the transmission expressed as a minimum product is

$$T = (W' + Y')(W' + Z)(W + X + Y)(W + X + Z')$$

Although the cut sets (X, Y', Z') and (X, Y, Z) are present in the physical circuit, they do not appear in the minimum-product form of the transmission function.

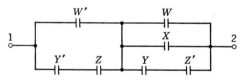

Fig. 4–12. Contact network derived from the cut sets of Fig. 4–11.

By using theorem 15' we may further simplify the minimum product and obtain $T = (W' + Y'Z)(W + X + YZ')$. The contact network represented by this function is shown in Fig. 4–12. We may now identify the tie sets in this network and write a transmission function which is a sum of products, with each term corresponding to one of the tie sets. The function thus found is

$$T = W'X + W'YZ' + WY'Z + XY'Z$$

But according to theorem 16′

$$W'X + WY'Z + XY'Z = W'X + WY'Z$$

and the transmission function thus reduces to the minimum sum

$$T = W'X + W'YZ' + WY'Z$$

It is evident, therefore, that although the terms of a minimum sum all correspond to tie sets in a network, a physical network may contain tie sets which are algebraically redundant and hence do not appear in the minimum sum.

It should be noted that in forming the cut sets of Fig. 4–11 we did not include those sets which contained a variable and its complement. These would introduce terms such as $(W + W')$ and $(X + Y + Y')$ in the product of sums expression for the transmission.

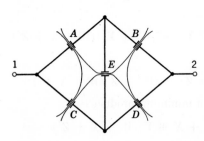

Fig. 4–13. Cut sets in a non-series-parallel contact network.

Since all terms of this type become 1, according to theorem 10, they vanish from the transmission function. Similarly, in forming the tie sets of Fig. 4–12, we did not include the path which would have introduced the term $Y'ZYZ'$ in the sum of products expression for the transmission. A term of this type becomes 0 in accordance with theorem 10′ and hence vanishes from the minimum sum.

The tie-set and the cut-set concepts contribute substantially to our understanding of contact networks of all types. However, when we undertake to analyze circuits which are not of the series-parallel form, it becomes essential to identify either the tie sets or the cut sets in order to write a transmission function. In the "bridge" circuit of Fig. 4–13, for example, the series-parallel approach fails completely. But we can determine the circuit transmission either by listing all the tie paths between terminals 1 and 2 as a sum of products, or by writing a product of sums in which each of the cut sets indicated in the drawing is contained as a sum. If we follow the first method we obtain $T = AB + AED + CEB + CD$. The second method yields the result $T = (A + C)(A + E + D)(C + E + B)$ $(B + D)$. The student may verify that these two expressions are identical by carrying out the indicated multiplications in the second function.

This brief digression from series-parallel networks has been designed to emphasize the broad applicability of the tie-set, cut-set concept, as a general method of circuit analysis. When we examine non-series-parallel circuits more fully we will find this same concept a valuable aid to synthesis.

4.10 Complementary Networks

For every two-terminal network which can be represented by a switching function there exists at least one complementary network. The complement of a network is a network which has opposite values of transmission for the same input states. The existence of at least one complementary network follows from the fact that if we can write a transmission function for the original network, by theorems 18, 18′ we can always write a complementary function. The complementary function is merely another switching function, and we have demonstrated that we can always obtain a series-parallel network which represents a given function.

We should distinguish carefully between complementary switching functions and the two forms of a switching function which can be derived from a table of combinations. A standard sum contains a term for each 1 value of transmission, and a standard product contains a term for each 0 value of transmission. It has already been demonstrated that these two expressions represent exactly the same network behavior. A complementary function, on the other hand, describes switching action which is exactly the opposite of the original. If we wish to obtain a complementary function directly from a table of combinations, we must change all the output 1's to 0's, and vice versa, and then write the function in the usual manner.

There are two reasons for our interest in complementary networks. For some problems, it is a remarkable fact that a simpler result is found if we specify operation which is exactly the opposite of what we really want, design a network to meet those opposite specifications, and then take the complement of it. The series-parallel type of circuit does not offer acceptable examples of this situation, but we will see examples of it in our later study of certain types of non-series-parallel networks.

A second reason for our interest is that through an understanding of complementary relations we gain increased facility in network manipulation. There are numerous situations in which the recognition of complementary forms provides the means for achieving substantial economy. Frequently these situations lead to networks which are non-series-parallel. Other important situations which require facility in handling complementary forms arise in the synthesis of multi-terminal networks.

While we can always obtain a complementary network by the algebraic approach, the method has a severe disadvantage when it is applied to non-series-parallel networks. The non-series-parallel form of network is usually a difficult one to design, but it is often highly economical in its use of switching elements. If we obtain a complementary network by the algebraic method, we first obtain a complementary switching function, and then we are faced with the task of finding the elusive but economical non-series-parallel network. Fortunately, we can go directly from a two-terminal network to its complementary network by a graphical process in which the number of switching elements is not changed. The one restriction is that the method works only for planar networks—no method has yet been described for taking the complement of a nonplanar network, other than by the algebraic process.

If we write a transmission function in the form of a minimum sum, as for example, $T = AB + CD$, the algebraic complement of that function is in the form of a minimum product, $T' = (A' + B')(C' + D')$. Each tie set of the original function has been replaced by a complementary cut set in the complementary function. More generally speaking, we can define complementary functions by noting that the tie sets of one are always replaced by complementary cut sets in the other, or vice versa. A complementary cut set is, of course, one in which the variables are the complements of the variables in the corresponding tie set, and a complementary tie set contains variables which are the complements of those in the corresponding cut set.

With these ideas in mind, let us examine the geometric construction shown in Fig. 4–14. The circuit drawn with solid lines, between terminals 1 and 2, has the transmission $T = AB + CD$. We visualize the external connections to these terminals as extending to infinity in both directions. Two external nodes, 3 and 5, are located in the upper and lower half planes, and node 4 is located in the one interior mesh of the original circuit. In a more complex circuit we would add additional nodes in each additional internal mesh, but no additional external nodes. This placement of nodes ensures that each branch of the original circuit will pass between one pair of nodes. If we now connect between each pair of nodes separated by a single branch a contact which is the complement of each contact in the branch thus crossed, the transmission, between the external nodes, of the network thus built up will be the complement of the original network transmission.

It can readily be seen in Fig. 4–14 that when we cross the tie set AB of the upper path we place between nodes 3 and 4 the cut set $(A' + B')$. Likewise, the cut set $(C' + D')$ appears between nodes 4 and 5 because these connections crossed the lower branch containing the tie set CD. The effect of placing node 4 in the internal mesh was to ensure that

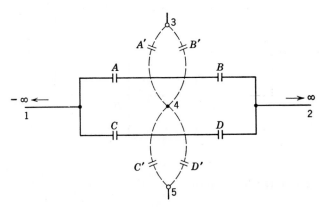

Fig. 4–14. The complement of the circuit between terminals 1 and 2 is the circuit between terminals 3 and 5.

these two cut sets would be connected in series, whereas the complementary tie sets were in parallel. Thus the geometric process in this example has replaced tie sets connected in parallel with complementary cut sets connected in series.

In Fig. 4–15 the complementary circuit found in Fig. 4–14 is drawn with solid lines, and the dotted construction shows that by taking the geometric complement the original circuit is obtained again. Note that the circuit between terminals 3 and 5 has two internal meshes, in which are placed the nodes 6 and 7.

The circuit of Fig. 4–10 is shown with its geometric complement in Fig. 4–16. For convenience in drawing the complementary circuit, the external nodes 3 and 6, and the internal nodes 4 and 5, are stretched out into solid lines.

Figure 4–17 shows a rather complex, non-series-parallel contact network for which we would like to obtain the complementary network. The advantage of the geometric method becomes quite clear in this example. Since we introduce only one contact in the complementary network for each contact present in the original network, we are able to preserve the economy of the original network. Rather than super-pose the complementary network on the original network, we can indi-cate, as in Fig. 4–17, the external and internal nodes which are to be

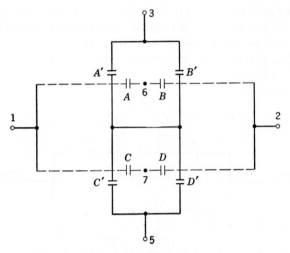

Fig. 4–15. The original circuit derived from its complement.

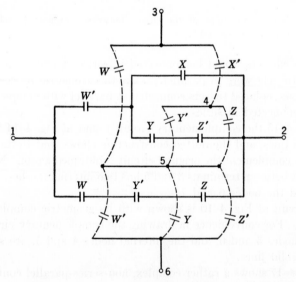

Fig. 4–16. Geometric complement of the circuit of Fig. 4–10.

interconnected with contacts. These nodes are then transferred to a new drawing, as in Fig. 4–18, and the required internode contacts are added.

The validity of the geometric method of complementation is quite evident on an intuitive basis when the method is applied to series-parallel configurations. It is perhaps not quite so apparent when we

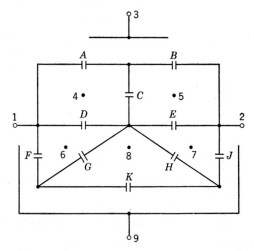

Fig. 4–17. A non-series-parallel contact network.

apply it to networks like that of Fig. 4–17. However, suppose we think of these two networks existing simultaneously, with their con-

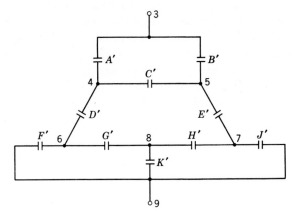

Fig. 4–18. A non-series-parallel network which is the complement of the network of Fig. 4–17.

tacts mounted on one set of relays $A, B, C, \ldots, K$. Then we want to know whether it is possible to prescribe input conditions such that when the transmission is 1 between terminals 1 and 2 in Fig. 4–17, there is also 1 transmission between terminals 3 and 9 in Fig. 4–18 (or we might ask whether it is possible for both transmissions to be 0 simultaneously). If the transmission is 1 between terminals 1 and 2 of the original network, then there must be at least one path between the terminals in which every contact is closed. However, corresponding to every closed contact in this path, there is in the complementary network a contact which is open. Moreover, these contacts in the complementary network are the only contacts which cross the conducting path in the original network. Hence, if a tie set is closed in one network, a cut set must be open in the complementary network. Since this is true of any tie set in the original network, it is true of all tie sets in the network. A similar argument shows that when any cut set is open in the original network, a tie set is closed in the complementary network. The replacement of tie and cut sets in the original network by cut and tie sets, respectively, in the complementary network are the necessary and sufficient conditions that the network transmission functions be complementary.

4.11   Modification of Contact Networks—Transfer Contacts

Switching algebra and the minimizing methods derived from it constitute powerful tools available to the designer of combinational switching circuits. Nevertheless, there are important circuit manipulations which must be sought out—they are not made evident in a routine way. However hopeful we may be that switching theory may eventually provide complete answers to all the problems of synthesis, the designer must be aware of at least those elementary manipulations which are indicated by common sense rather than by elegant theory. We cannot hope to discuss the subject completely in this one article. It will become abundantly clear throughout this book that as we increase our knowledge of synthesis based on scientific principles, we also increase our opportunity to seek and find more subtle designs.

The designer of a two-terminal network does not always have complete freedom of action in the realization of a network. A common problem is that of adding new switching duties to an already existing circuit. If the relays in the circuit have spare contacts, they can be combined with contacts on new relays to form a new network. But if the number of spare contacts is limited, it may not always be possible to realize the new network from the minimized algebraic form. Modification is then necessary, in order to redistribute the contacts so as to reduce the contact load on one or more selected relays. A similar problem arises when a new design leads to an excessively large number of contacts on a particular relay. The contact load may be considered too large either because it exceeds the mechanical limits of relay manufacture, or because the relay would have an undesirably long operating time.

A basic procedure for the reduction of the contact load on a particular relay is to expand the switching function by the use of theorem 20. If the function is expanded about the variable which designates a contact on a selected relay, the contact load on that relay will be reduced to a single transfer contact. If we apply the expansion theorem a second time, the contact load on a second relay can be reduced to two transfer contacts.

Example 4–4

Modify the switching function

$$T = AB(X'Y + XY') + A'B'(XY + X'Y')$$

so that it can be realized with a series-parallel contact network in which there is only a single transfer contact on the X relay.

By application of theorem 20, the function is immediately written in the form

$$T = X(ABY' + A'B'Y) + X'(ABY + A'B'Y')$$

It should be noted that the modified form could have been obtained by multiplying out the factors in the original expression, and then factoring out X and X'. This process is equivalent to the use of the expansion theorem only if the sum of products expression contains either the selected variable or its complement in every term. For most functions, in their simplified forms, the quickest way to obtain an expansion about a selected variable is to use theorem 20.

One of the challenging problems in the design of relay contact networks is that of modifying circuits so that contact springs are saved by the use of transfer contacts. If a single relay carries a normally open and a normally closed contact which, within the contact network are both connected to a common point, the two separate contacts may be merged into a single transfer-contact combination. Thus, three springs do the work which otherwise would require four springs—a saving of 25 per cent.

Algebraically, the possibility of using a transfer contact may be indicated by the presence of a variable and its complement in the same switching function.* A further physical requirement is that the contacts represented by a pair of complementary variables must connect to a common point. The algebra does not disclose in general whether this requirement is satisfied, but there are a number of particular alge-

* This is not a necessary condition. For an exception, see Fig. 4–31.

braic forms which can always be realized by means of transfer contacts. Other situations, which arise in the design of multiple-output networks, will be discussed in Chapter 6.

The disjuncts of two variables form the starting point for many types of network modifications, and it is important to be able to recog-

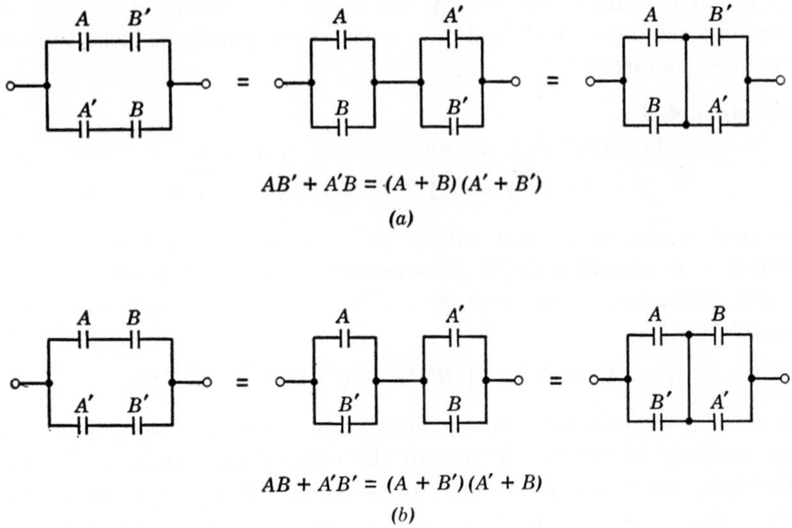

$$AB' + A'B = (A + B)(A' + B')$$

(a)

$$AB + A'B' = (A + B')(A' + B)$$

(b)

Fig. 4–19. Alternative contact networks and algebraic expressions for the disjuncts of two variables.

nize them in all their algebraic and circuit forms. Fig. 4–19 shows the circuit diagrams and the algebraic expressions for both disjuncts, and it should be noted that in each of these circuit forms the disjuncts have been realized entirely with the use of transfer contacts.

The network arrangement at the extreme right of parts (a) and (b) in Fig. 4–19 is interesting because of the way in which it can be combined with other networks. Figure 4–20 illustrates an algebraic form which occurs frequently. Here the disjunct $AB' + A'B$ has been separated, and its two terms have become factors which multiply two different functions of n variables, designated by $f_1(X_n)$ and $f_2(X_n)$. Although the terms of the disjunct have been separated, the pairs of complementary contacts still connect to a common point and thus both terms are produced with transfer contacts. By this arrangement it becomes possible to use the common connection at terminal 2 for combining contacts from the X_n networks into transfer contacts.

By an extension of the idea illustrated in Fig. 4–20, we can combine disjuncts with other disjuncts to form chains of transfer contacts, as shown in Fig. 4–21. In part (a) the term AB' has combined with $C'D$, and $A'B$ has combined with CD' to form the transmission $T = AB'C'D + A'BCD'$, and all the pairs of complementary variables

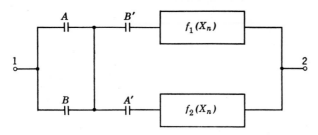

Fig. 4–20. A disjunct with its terms separated as factors.

are represented by transfer contacts because of the common connections which have been established. Part (b) of Fig. 4–21 shows the general transfer chain of this type. It will be noted that these transfer chains

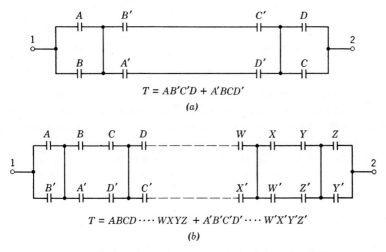

$$T = AB'C'D + A'BCD'$$

(a)

$$T = ABCD \cdots WXYZ + A'B'C'D' \cdots W'X'Y'Z'$$

(b)

Fig. 4–21. Chains of transfer contacts derived from the disjuncts.

can always be recognized from the algebraic form. The transmission function consists of the sum of two products in which all the variables appear as complementary pairs.

If a transmission function consists of two product terms, but the variables do not all appear in complementary pairs, it can be factored so that the complementary pairs of variables are realized by a transfer chain, the two branches of which are connected to networks that represent the remainder of the function. This situation was illustrated in Fig. 4–20 for a two-variable chain. Fig. 4–22 shows the same type of network for a larger number of variables in the chain. Part (a) of Fig. 4–22 shows the arrangement when there is an even number of

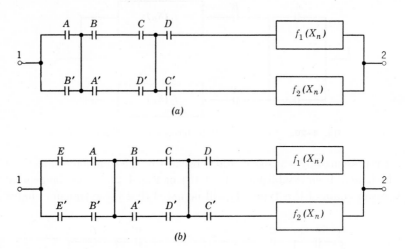

Fig. 4–22. Transfer contact chains with even and odd numbers of transfer contacts.

complementary pairs of variables in the chain. When there is an odd number of pairs, as in part (b), the chain should be started by means of a transfer contact at one terminal of the network. This leaves the second network terminal available as a common point for the formation of transfer contacts in the two terminating networks, $f_1(X_n)$ and $f_2(X_n)$. The transmission functions represented by the networks of Fig. 4–22 are:

(a) $T = ABCD\,f_1(X_n) + A'B'C'D'\,f_2(X_n)$

(b) $T = ABCDE\,f_1(X_n) + A'B'C'D'E'\,f_2(X_n)$

We may now note that the function discussed in Example 4–4 is of the type which can be realized by using transfer contacts only. Figure 4–23 shows in part (a) a circuit representing the function as first written, and in part (b) a circuit for the function obtained after expanding about the X variable. These circuits represent simple series-parallel realizations of the functions, in which we have done nothing more than to take advantage of all opportunities to form transfer contacts.

At the end of this article we shall return to Example 4–4 and show a still more economical realization of the function.

It was noted above that by purely algebraic methods we cannot determine whether, in a given function, common connections are possible which permit the merger of a pair of complementary contacts into a transfer contact. Guided by a circuit diagram we can, however, make

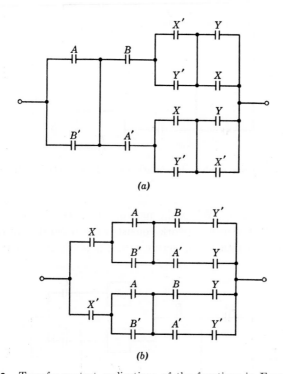

(a)

(b)

Fig. 4–23. Transfer-contact realizations of the functions in Example 4–4.

algebraic modifications which do establish common connections, and thus permit contact merger. This process will be illustrated by means of the circuit shown in Fig. 4–24, for which the transmission function is $T = AB(C + DE) + A'B'C'(D' + E')$.

We see in this function that all the variables appear as pairs of complementary variables. In the circuit diagram, by making use of the separated disjunct circuit for the contacts on relays A and B, we can merge them into transfer contacts. We can also merge the C and C' contacts because each of them has a connection in common to terminal 2. The pairs of contacts on the D and E relays, however, have no common connections and cannot be merged.

To improve this situation, we can make use of theorem 20 and expand the parallel network in the upper branch about the variable C. Figure 4–25 shows the effect of an expansion performed on a part of the network (see Fig. 3–16 for a representation of the general circuit equiva-

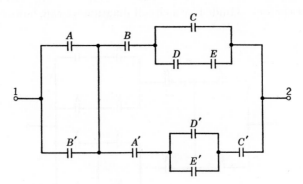

Fig. 4–24. The pairs of complementary contacts on relays D and E do not combine to form transfer contacts.

lent of theorem 20). When the network $C + DE$ is expanded about the variable C, the new network consists of two parallel branches. In one branch a C contact is in series with a network X, and in the other

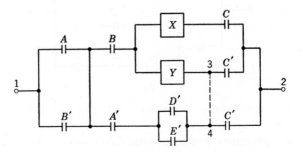

Fig. 4–25. Application of the expansion theorem makes possible a new common connection.

branch a C' contact is in series with a network Y. Because there is now a branch having a C' series contact, we can establish a new common connection by joining points 3 and 4, as shown by the dotted line in Fig. 4–25. The extra C' contact becomes redundant and is eliminated.

Whether we gain anything by this procedure is largely determined by the nature of the derived networks X and Y, and hence must be investigated by actual trial. In this example, the expansion gives us $C + DE = C(1 + DE) + C'(0 + DE)$, which reduces to $C + C'DE$.* The two derived networks thus become $X = 1$ (a closed circuit), and $Y = DE$. In the circuit of Fig. 4–26 the X and Y networks have been substituted, and the common connection between points 3 and 4 has been established as the point 3, 4. We see that the result of the expan-

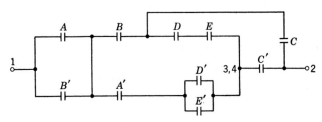

Fig. 4–26. Network of Fig. 4–24 after expansion of parallel circuit. Common connection to point 3, 4 now permits formation of a transfer contact on relay E.

sion process is that we have retained the previously established transfer contacts, and have added a common connection which enables us to merge the E and E' contacts into a transfer contact.

The next question is: can we do anything which will enable us to merge the D and D' contacts? Before we try to answer that question,

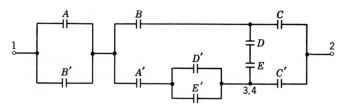

Fig. 4–27. Network of Fig. 4–26 redrawn to emphasize that it is not a series-parallel network.

it will be instructive to examine a little more closely the effect that the merger of the E and E' contacts has had on our original series-parallel circuit. In Fig. 4–27 the connections are identical with those of Fig. 4–26, but the shape of the network has been altered so that we can clearly observe that the network is no longer of the series-parallel type. The D and E contacts in series now form a shunt or "bridging" connection between the upper and lower branches of the original cir-

* Note that this result could have been obtained by the application of theorem 13′, in the reverse direction. The expansion theorem has the advantage of providing a sharper visualization of the circuit modification involved.

cuit. There is now the possibility that our circuit manipulation might have introduced a "sneak" path into the circuit, that is, a path which introduces an unwanted term in the transmission function. This condition would exist, for example, if the circuit could be closed by way of a path through the contact C, then down through the DE shunt combination, and through the lower branch of the network to terminal 1. But we observe that whenever the series combination DE is closed, the parallel combination $D' + E'$ is open, so there never can be a "sneak" connection through the additional path that was created by the circuit transformation. It is more fundamental to observe, however, that our circuit changes have been based on the substitution, in a part of the circuit, of an algebraically equivalent part, and this step in the procedure must always leave the performance unchanged. The

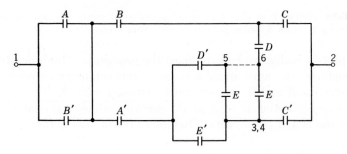

Fig. 4–28. Expansion theorem applied to parallel circuit in lower branch. Another common connection is made possible.

danger of establishing "sneak" paths lies in the subsequent steps in which common points are established and redundant contacts are removed. Each new path created by this process must either contain a complementary set of series contacts so that the transmission of the path thus created always contains a factor of the form $XX' = 0$, or it must be a permissible path.

The network of Fig. 4–27 can be further modified by repeating the expansion process on the $D' + E'$ contacts which are in the lower branch. This time we expand about the variable E because we want to get an E contact outside of the parallel network so that it can be combined with the E contact already present in the DE combination.

Performing the expansion, we obtain

$$D' + E' = E(D' + 0) + E'(D' + 1) = ED' + E'$$

In Fig. 4–28 the expanded network has replaced the original one, and we see that the points 5 and 6 can be connected, with the elimination of a redundant E contact. This connection supplies a common terminal for the D and D' contacts which can now be merged into a transfer contact. After points 5 and 6 are connected, a new shunt path is established, but conduction through this path is blocked by the DD' contacts in series. Figure 4–29 shows the same circuit drawn in a form which emphasizes its non-series-parallel character.

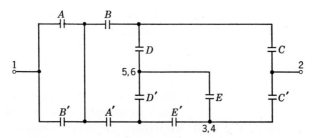

Fig. 4–29. Final reduction of network of Fig. 4–24 to non-series-parallel network in which all pairs of complementary variables are represented by transfer contacts.

The original circuit of Fig. 4–24 contained 10 elements, but because 3 pairs of contacts were merged into transfer contacts, there was a total requirement of 17 contact springs. In the final version of Fig. 4–29, all the switching operation is performed by transfer contacts, and a total of 15 springs is used.

We are not yet ready to consider non-series-parallel networks in a general way, but the procedures which led to the circuit shown in Fig. 4–29 are relatively simple. In the original function, and in the circuit of Fig. 4–24, we could observe that the contacts D, D', E and E' were all present, so we at least had a reason for seeking to establish common connections which would enable these complementary pairs to be combined into transfer contacts.

Consider now a transmission function in its minimum-sum form, $T = ab + cd + bc$, or in its minimum-product form,

$$T = (a + c)(b + c)(b + d)$$

By factoring, we can reduce these to

$$T = b(a + c) + cd = ab + c(b + d), \text{ or}$$
$$T = (ab + c)(b + d) = (a + c)(b + cd)$$

There are no pairs of complementary variables in any of these expressions, and the best we can do by factoring is to realize the function with 5 contacts and 10 springs.

Referring to Fig. 4–30, we see one of the factored forms of the minimum sum transmission represented by a series-parallel network. The dotted connection between nodes 3 and 4 suggests that if we can actually make this connection it becomes possible to eliminate one of the b contacts. However, if we do make this connection, we will have in addition to the specified terms of the transmission the tie set

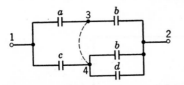

ad. This, of course, is not an allowed term.

The unwanted tie set can be avoided if instead of making a solid connection between nodes 3 and 4, we connect between these nodes either a' or d'. Either of these contacts in series with the ad contacts will cause the "sneak" path to be open. But now if, in the

Fig. 4–30. If nodes 3 and 4 are connected there is a "sneak" path.

left-hand circuit of Fig. 4–31, we remove the lower b contact, the tie set bc becomes either $a'bc$ or bcd'. In terms of the original minimum sum, this means that instead of $T = ab + cd + bc$, we have either

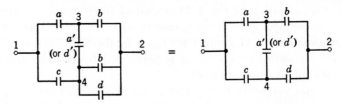

Fig. 4–31. The transmission is not changed if a' or d' is connected between nodes 3 and 4, and a b-contact is eliminated.

$T = ab + cd + a'bc$, or $T = ab + cd + bcd'$. Both derived forms are equivalent to the original transmission since, by theorem 13′, $ab + a'bc = ab + bc$, and $cd + bcd' = cd + bc$. The final network of Fig. 4–31 uses 5 contacts and 9 springs.

Figure 4–23 showed series-parallel realizations of the functions introduced in Example 4–4, with all complementary variables realized with transfer contacts. Another type of non-series-parallel circuit makes possible a further substantial reduction in the number of contacts, and still keeps all complementary variables on transfer contacts. In Fig. 4–32 there are shown two equivalent forms of a three-terminal circuit which produces both the disjuncts of two variables. This is no longer a network with a single output, but it will be used as a part of a two-terminal network. It is important to note that the transmission between terminals 2 and 3 is always 0 in this network because of the series combinations of either XX' or YY' which block conduction.

In Fig. 4–33 the network of Fig. 4–32(a) is connected to the terminals of a separated disjunct network of A,B contacts. Because there can

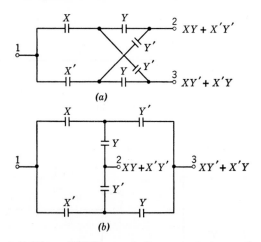

Fig. 4–32. Alternative arrangements of the network for producing both disjuncts of two variables.

be no transmission between points 2 and 3 through the X,Y network, the term AB is multiplied only by $XY' + X'Y$, and the term $A'B'$ is multiplied only by $XY + X'Y'$. The sum of these two products is the

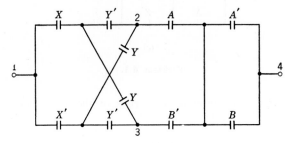

Fig. 4–33. The requirements of Example 4–4 are satisfied more economically by a combination of disjunctive networks.

output of the combined network, and this is exactly the transmission required in Example 4–4. Furthermore, all switching duties are performed by transfer contacts, and the requirement that the X relay carry only one transfer contact is satisfied.

   The network of Fig. 4–33 is an example of one which is non-series-parallel, and is also non-planar. By this we mean that the connections of the network, including the connections to the load, cannot be drawn without crossover, in a single plane.

PROBLEMS

4.1 For each of the contact networks shown, find an equivalent series-parallel network which uses as few contacts as possible. The method to be used for this simplification consists of the following steps:

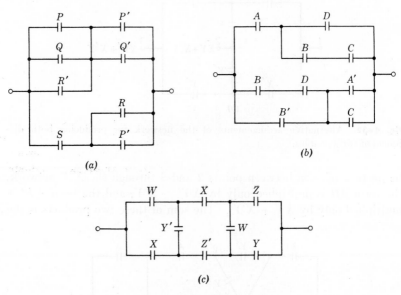

(a)

(b)

(c)

Problem 4.1.

1. Express the terminal properties of the given network in the switching algebra.
2. Simplify this algebraic expression as much as you can.
3. Draw the series-parallel network corresponding to the simplified expression.

4.2 A network, N_1, has the transmission function, $T = AB + C'$. A network, N_2, has the hindrance function, $H = (A' + B')C$.

1. Derive a contact network, N_3, which is equivalent to the parallel combination of N_1 and N_2 and which uses as few contact springs as possible.
2. Derive a contact network, N_4, which is equivalent to the series combination of N_1 and N_2 and which uses as few contact springs as possible.

4.3 The terminal action of a contact network, N_1, is described by the

transmission function
$$T_1 = A'(B + C') + AD$$

Another network, N_2, is described by the hindrance function
$$H_2 = A'D + ABC'$$

Determine whether the two networks are equivalent and prove your conclusion.

4.4 In the following word descriptions compare the algebraic meanings of "and" and "or" as you write the functions described.

1. The function, f, is 1 if X and Y have the value 1, or if X and Z have the values 0 and 1, respectively.
2. The function, f, is 0 if X or Y has the value 0, and if X or Z has the value 1 or 0, respectively.
3. The function, f, is 1 if X or Z has the value 1, and if X or Y has the value 0 or 1, respectively.
4. The function, f, is 0 if X and Z have the value 0, or if X and Y have the values 1 and 0, respectively.

4.5 For each of the networks shown
1. Describe the transmission properties by a table of combinations.
2. Write each transmission function as a standard sum and as a standard product.
3. Simplify each transmission function algebraically as much as possible.
4. Draw schematic diagrams of the corresponding networks if they are simpler than the given networks.

4.6 Replace the given network by an equivalent, minimum, series-parallel network. It is known that at least one relay is always operated (10 springs are sufficient).

4.7 Use the algebraic reduction procedure to derive the simplest possible contact networks for each of the five tables of combinations given. If more than one such network exists draw all of the simple forms possible.

X	Y	Z	T_1	T_2	T_3	T_4	T_5
0	0	0	0	–	0	–	1
0	0	1	0	1	–	1	–
0	1	0	0	–	–	0	–
0	1	1	1	1	0	–	1
1	0	0	1	0	–	1	–
1	0	1	1	–	1	1	0
1	1	0	0	0	0	–	1
1	1	1	1	–	0	1	1

4.8 A two-terminal contact network contains contacts from relays A, B, and C. When written as functions of these variables, the transmission, T, and the hindrance, H, can be written in algebraic forms such that $T = H$.

If the network contains a single contact (normally open or normally closed) from any one of the three relays, the relation $T = H$ is obviously true. However, there are ten non-trivial functions of three variables which, when realized by series-parallel contact networks, exhibit the $T = H$ relation.

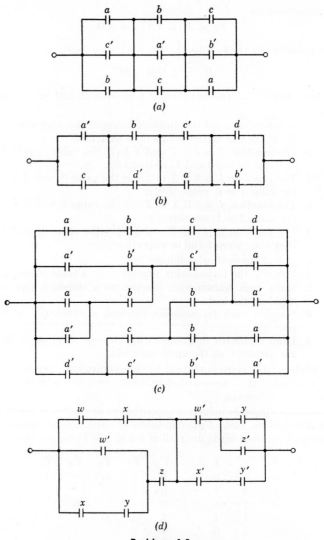

(a)

(b)

(c)

(d)

Problem 4.5.

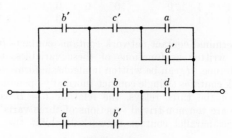

Problem 4.6.

Find a minimum network that contains at least one contact from each relay (there are eight functions which lead to such networks).

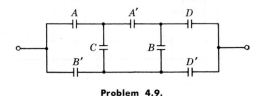

Problem 4.9.

4.9 Write the transmission function of the contact network shown, (a) as a standard sum, (b) as a standard product.

Show algebraically that one of the contacts is not needed, and modify the circuit accordingly.

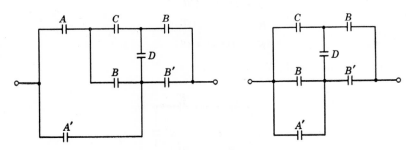

Problem 4.10.

4.10 Are the two contact networks shown equivalent? Justify your answer algebraically.

4.11 For the transmission function

$$T = B'(AD' + CD) + A'[C'(B' + D) + BCD'] + AB(C' + D)$$

    1. Express the transmission in standard-sum form.
    2. Express the transmission in standard-product form.
    3. Design a contact network which has the given transmission and in which there are as few contacts as possible.

4.12 In the network shown, the transmission functions T_1 and T_2, and the hindrance function H_1 are

$$T_1 = \sum (0, 2, 4, 8, 10, 14)$$

$$T_2 = \Pi (1, 2, 6, 7, 8, 11, 13)$$

$$H_1 = A'C' + AB'D + ABCD'$$

Find the simplest hindrance function, H_2, such that the terminal action of the network between

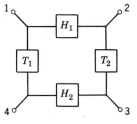

Problem 4.12.

terminals 1 and 3 is identical with the terminal action between terminals 2 and 4. Express the function H_2 algebraically.

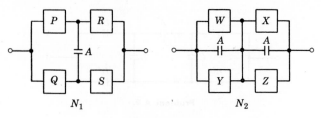

Problem 4.13.

4.13 Network N_1 is to be resynthesized in the form of network N_2. If

$$P = (A + B' + C')D$$
$$Q = D' + A'BC$$
$$R = A'C + AC'$$
$$S = AC + A'C'$$

find the functions for W, X, Y, and Z.

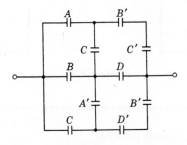

Problem 4.14.

4.14 Reduce the given contact network (5 contacts are sufficient).

4.15 For each of the networks given derive (two) corresponding transmission expressions which will describe
1. The tie sets of the given network.
2. The cut sets of the given network.

4.16 Derive, for each network given in Problem 4.15, a network having the complementary transmission and in which there are cut sets corresponding to the tie sets in Part 1, Problem 4.15, and tie sets corresponding to the cut sets in Part 2.

4.17 For the transmission function

$$T = A'B' + AD(B + C) + BC'D$$

1. Design a contact network, using as few contacts as possible, to realize the function.

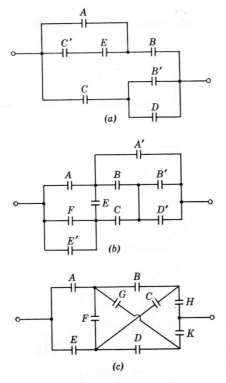

Problem 4.15.

2. Write the function as a standard sum.
3. Write the function as a standard product.
4. Write the complementary function and design a contact network to realize it.
5. Take the geometric complement of the network designed in Part 1 and compare it with the network designed in Part 4.

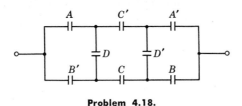

Problem 4.18.

4.18 The network shown contains no transfer contacts. How many transfer contacts are there in the complementary network?

4.19 Simplify the contact network shown. The equivalent network should have as few contacts as possible. Minimize the number of contact springs by forming transfer contacts wherever possible.

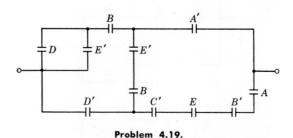

Problem 4.19.

4.20 Design a minimized contact network which has the transmission function

$$T = ABCD + A'BC'D + AB'CD' + A'B'C'D'$$

(8 contacts, 12 springs are sufficient).

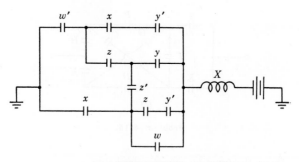

Problem 4.21.

4.21 A relay X is controlled by the contact network shown. The x contacts in the network belong to relay X.

1. What must be the states of the W, Y, and Z relays before relay X can operate?
2. Once operated, under what conditions can relay X be de-energized? Explain your answer.

CHAPTER 5

Minimization methods

In the preceding chapter we encountered situations where algebraic methods were used for improving the design of contact networks. There will be many more examples in the chapters that follow, for we will continually want to achieve the "best" possible switching circuit, regardless of its purpose or the type of components used in it.

Sometimes the statement of a combinational switching problem will lead to a unique, minimum design, in the sense that all alternative circuits will require more switching equipment. The more common problem however, has two or more alternative solutions, all of which may be of about equal merit. In this chapter we will study some of the procedures, graphical aids, and algorithms that have been found to facilitate the reduction of algebraic statements to optimum forms, and that also disclose the existence of alternative solutions. These methods do not represent a departure from the algebraic approach, because all are based on algebraic principles.

Besides saving time and effort, these methods have other advantages. They tend to improve our visualization of the nature of the problem and enable us to see more clearly the consequences of any steps we take. When we apply them later to more difficult problems we are able to put more emphasis on the total requirements of a problem rather than on the mechanics of turning out a result. For problems of still greater complexity we can expect that the routines developed can ultimately be handled by computing machinery.

5.1   Enumeration of Switching Functions

In this discussion we will consider switching functions written in the form of a standard sum only, since any minimized function may be written originally in either the standard-sum or the standard-product form.

If we want to count the number of all the switching functions of the two variables X and Y which we can possibly write, we find that any of the standard-sum forms of these functions are limited to a selection drawn from the terms XY, XY', $X'Y$, and $X'Y'$. How many ways can we select groups of these terms to form functions? This question is perhaps best answered by making a table similar to a table of combinations, as shown in Table 5–1. In Table 5–1 four columns are headed

Table 5–1

XY	XY'	$X'Y$	$X'Y'$	Function
0	0	0	0	0
0	0	0	1	$X'Y'$
0	0	1	0	$X'Y$
0	0	1	1	X'
0	1	0	0	XY'
0	1	0	1	Y'
0	1	1	0	$XY' + X'Y$
0	1	1	1	$X' + Y'$
1	0	0	0	XY
1	0	0	1	$XY + X'Y'$
1	0	1	0	Y
1	0	1	1	$X' + Y$
1	1	0	0	X
1	1	0	1	$X + Y'$
1	1	1	0	$X + Y$
1	1	1	1	1

by the four possible terms which may be included in a standard sum. For each row of the table a 0 or a 1 is entered in each column. If a 0 is entered in a particular column it means that the term at the head of that column is not included in the standard sum. If a 1 is entered in a column it means that the term at the head of that column is included in the standard sum. Since there are four terms, each of which may or may not be included in a standard sum, there are $2^4 = 16$ different ways in which the 0's and 1's may be entered, and hence there are 16 rows in the table. In each row the combined 0's and 1's are treated as a binary number, and the rows are listed in the ascending order of the decimal equivalents of the binary numbers.

The fifth column of the table shows the function of two variables which is obtained when the selected terms of the standard sum are combined and reduced algebraically. Of the 16 functions listed, the functions corresponding to $T = 0$ and $T = 1$ are, of course, trivial but they are included as part of the total count.

In Table 5–2 the functions found in Table 5–1 have been regrouped

Table 5–2

Number of Terms in Standard Sum	Standard Sum	Simplified Function
0	0	0
1	XY	XY
1	XY'	XY'
1	$X'Y$	$X'Y$
1	$X'Y'$	$X'Y'$
2	$XY + XY'$	X
2	$X'Y + X'Y'$	X'
2	$XY + X'Y$	Y
2	$XY' + X'Y'$	Y'
2	$XY + X'Y'$	$XY + X'Y'$
2	$XY' + X'Y$	$XY' + X'Y$
3	$XY + XY' + X'Y$	$X + Y$
3	$XY + XY' + X'Y'$	$X + Y'$
3	$XY + X'Y + X'Y'$	$X' + Y$
3	$XY' + X'Y + X'Y'$	$X' + Y'$
4	$XY + XY' + X'Y + X'Y'$	1

for more systematic examination. The first column of Table 5–2 shows the number of terms which are present in the standard sum, and it will be noted that the table is divided into sections corresponding to increasing numbers of terms in the standard sum. The second column shows the standard sums which are formed, and the third column shows the reduced switching function obtained from each standard sum.

We now see from Table 5–2 that the 14 non-trivial functions of two variables form four distinct classes of functions. There are four functions which reduce to single variables; these functions as a class may be represented by the generic variable X. Four functions are products and these may be represented by the class XY. Likewise the four sums may be represented by the class $X + Y$. There remain the two functions $(XY' + X'Y)$ and $(XY + X'Y')$ which are the disjuncts of two variables. Since each of these functions is the complement of the other, in terms of generic variables they represent a single class of functions.*

From the foregoing exhaustive listing of the functions of two variables we can readily see how to determine the number of functions of n variables. For n variables there are $j = 2^n$ possible terms in a standard sum (or in a standard product). If we make a table similar to Table 5–1 and indicate by a listing of 0's and 1's all the possible ways in which we can select these terms to form standard sums, we find that there are $J = 2^j$ possible ways in which the terms can be thus selected. Hence the number of standard sums which we can form in n variables is 2^{2^n}.

The behavior of the number $J = 2^{2^n}$ is rather startling. We see from Table 5–1 that there are 16 functions of two variables. As n increases we have: $n = 3$, $J = 256$; $n = 4$, $J = 65,536$; $n = 5$, $J = 4,294,967,296$. The series can be extended indefinitely by noting that each value of J is the square of the preceding value. In astronomical numbers of this sort we see both the opportunities and the problems in the synthesis of combinational circuits.

While it is comparatively easy to determine the total number of functions of a given number of variables it is quite a difficult problem to determine how many different classes of functions are represented. Indeed, the problem of counting the classes of functions becomes a major enterprise when the number of variables is as few as four or five.† The 256 functions of three variables are contained in 22 classes, there are 402 classes for the 65,536 functions of four variables, and there are 1,228,158 classes for the 4,294,967,296 functions of five variables. Beyond this point no count of the number of classes has been made. Although it is feasible to prepare reference lists‡ of the classes of functions up to $n = 4$, and even to work out "standard" switching circuits for each class of functions, this process becomes prohibitively expensive for $n > 4$. Since many problems of practical importance involve five or more variables, it is apparent that there is imperative need for effective methods of synthesis.

5.2 Numerical Descriptions of Functions

We have been writing switching functions as algebraic expressions in which letters that represent the variables are combined in accordance

---

* A convenient way to distinguish this class is to designate it the class $X \oplus Y$. This is known as the "sum modulo two," or the disjunctive sum, or the ring sum, of X and Y. By definition, $X \oplus Y = XY' + X'Y$. Consequently, $X \oplus Y' = X' \oplus Y = XY + X'Y'$, and $X' \oplus Y' = X \oplus Y$. See Appendix 2.

† Theodore Singer, "The Theory of Counting Techniques," *Proceedings of the Association for Computing Machinery*, May 1952, pp. 287–291; R. L. Ashenhurst, "The Application of Counting Techniques," *ibid.*, pp. 293–305.

‡ See Appendix 4 for a list of the classes of functions of 3 variables.

with the operations of logical addition and logical multiplication. Such expressions are subject to direct manipulation by the application of the postulates and theorems of switching algebra. In Art. 4.8 we studied a general method for the algebraic simplification of functions in which the first step, that of finding the prime implicants, depended on the repeated application of a single theorem, $XY + XY' = X$. For simple functions there is no particular disadvantage in working with algebraic terms, but as functions become more complex, the required term-by-term comparisons become more difficult and errors tend to increase. At best, the simplification of a complex function is tedious, but the numerical descriptions discussed below do facilitate the work.

A convenient arrangement of a table of combinations is one in which the digits which represent the input states are arranged in a binary-number sequence. When this is done, the digits within each row can be combined into a binary number, and this number can be used to identify the input state. Thus in a table of combinations for three variables, the row

X	Y	Z
0	1	0

can be identified by describing it as the 010 row. A further simplification results if we identify the row by using the decimal equivalent of the binary number. Thus, the binary number 010 is equal to the decimal number 2, and we can therefore call this the "2" row.

Now let us examine some algebraic forms in relation to these numerical conventions. Consider a row from a table of combinations in four variables, and let the transmission for this row be 1.

W	X	Y	Z	T
1	1	0	0	1

In binary form this is the 1100 row, and in its decimal equivalent it is the 12 row. When we write a transmission function from the table, the term which represents this row is $WXY'Z'$. If we substitute the digit 1 for an unprimed contact designator, and the digit 0 for a primed designator, we recover the binary number 1100 which described the row, and, of course the decimal number 12 is likewise recovered.

It follows, therefore, that if we have a transmission function written in the form of a standard sum, we can replace it by a group of binary numbers, or by a group of decimal numbers which are the equivalents of the binary numbers. This may be illustrated by

$$T = W'X'Y'Z' + W'X'YZ + W'XYZ + WX'Y'Z' + WX'YZ + WXYZ'$$
$$= 0000 \quad +0011 \quad +0111 \quad +1000 \quad +1011 \quad +1110$$
$$= 0 \quad\quad +3 \quad\quad +7 \quad\quad +8 \quad\quad +11 \quad\quad +14$$

For convenience we now abbreviate this to

$$T = \sum (0, 3, 7, 8, 11, 14)$$

In its final form the original transmission function has been reduced to a set of decimal numbers. The plus signs of the algebraic expressions have been replaced by commas, to emphasize the fact that this set of numbers identifies the members of a standard sum, and that the actual arithmetic sum of the numbers has no meaning.

It should be noted that this method of representation is valid only if the transmission function is in its standard form. Each term in the standard sum must contain all the switching variables. Thus, if a function contains the term $W'XZ'$, and the circuit includes the input Y, the term must be expanded to the standard form by means of the relation $W'XZ' = W'X(Y + Y')Z' = W'XYZ' + W'XY'Z'$, before it can be represented by the numerical method.

A similar process is applicable to the representation of functions which are in the form of the standard product. However, for these terms it is necessary to use the digit 1 to represent a primed variable, and the digit 0 to represent an unprimed variable. Otherwise, the conversion from algebraic terms to decimal equivalents is identical, and the function is described in the abbreviated form, $T = \prod(d_1, \ldots, d_n)$.

Example 5–1

Write the algebraic function of four variables which is described by $T = \sum (1, 4, 6, 9, 10, 15)$.

The decimal group is equivalent to the binary number group 0001, 0100, 0110, 1001, 1010, 1111. The corresponding algebraic transmission function is

$$T = W'X'Y'Z + W'XY'Z' + W'XYZ' + WX'Y'Z + WX'YZ' + WXYZ$$

Example 5–2

A function which represents the 0's of transmission is described by $T = \prod(2, 3, 6, 7)$. Write the transmission as an algebraic function of three variables.

The decimal group is equivalent to the binary group 010, 011, 110, 111. Interpreting these in the form of a standard product, we write the transmission function

$$T = (X + Y' + Z)(X + Y' + Z')(X' + Y' + Z)(X' + Y' + Z')$$

5.3 Graphical Representations of Switching Functions

One of the first methods used to visualize relationships between binary variables is that illustrated in Fig. 5–1. This is known as a Venn diagram. In Fig. 5–1 everything within the left-hand circle is represented by the variable X and everything outside of that circle is X'. The area within the right-hand circle represents the variable Y and outside of that circle is Y'. Where the two circles overlap we have a section of area which is inside both circles and this is designated as XY. Also the area which is completely outside both circles is $X'Y'$. The area which is in X but not in Y is XY' and the area that is in Y but not in X is $X'Y$.

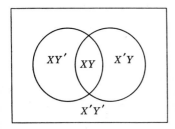

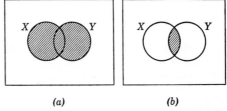

Fig. 5–1. Venn diagram representation of the terms of two-variable switching functions.

Fig. 5–2. Cross-hatched area represents in (a) the sum $X + Y$, and in (b) the product XY.

If we cross hatch the three areas XY', XY, and $X'Y$, the result appears as in part (a) of Fig. 5–2. This corresponds exactly to the addition of the three areas using the rules of Boolean algebra. But the sum $XY' + XY + X'Y = X + Y$. Thus part (a) of Fig. 5–2 is a graphical representation of logical addition. In part (b) of Fig. 5–2 the cross-hatched area represents the area which is common to both X and Y and is the area which is labeled XY in Fig. 5–1. This figure is hence a graphical representation of logical multiplication.*

We shall return to the Venn diagram after examining another geometric method for representing switching functions. This method represents the terms of a standard sum by nodes which are then interconnected by lines, squares, cubes, and hypercubes of successively higher orders. In Fig. 5–3 there are just two nodes connected by a single line. This is a representation of a single variable X, and each node represents one of the values it can take. In Fig. 5–4 there are four nodes at the corners of a square and each node represents one of the set of values which can be taken by the combined variables X and Y. If X and Y appear in the terms of a standard sum the four nodes as marked correspond to $X'Y'$, $X'Y$, XY, and XY'. We note also in this figure

---

* In formal logic the operation we call addition is called *union*. The symbol for union is ∪ (called "cup"). The operation we call logical multiplication is called *intersection* and the symbol for intersection is ∩ (called "cap").

that in going from any node along a line to an adjacent node, only one variable changes in passing between such nodes. If we add the algebraic terms corresponding to the two nodes at the end of any line we always find that one of the variables is eliminated and the line can therefore

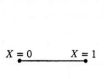

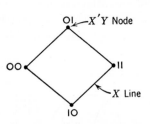

Fig. 5–3. A single variable represented by a one-dimensional figure.

Fig. 5–4. Each node of the two-dimensional figure is marked to show the states of $f(X, Y)$ represented.

be identified as representing the remaining variable. Thus, if we consider the line connecting the nodes 10 and 11, the sum of the algebraic terms represented is $XY' + XY$ and this, of course, reduces to X. The line joining these two nodes may hence be called the X line. Directly opposite the X line is the X' line and the remaining two lines are the Y and Y' lines.

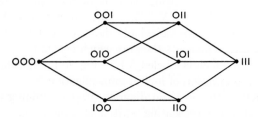

Fig. 5–5. The corners of a cube represent the states of $f(X, Y, Z)$.

The next step in the evolution of geometrical representations is shown in Fig. 5–5 where there are now eight nodes corresponding to the eight possible states of the variables X, Y, Z. We see again that for all lines shown in the figure the nodes at the ends of any given line represent states which differ in the value of just one variable. Hence if we add the terms corresponding to the nodes at the two ends of a given line, the addition will always result in the elimination of one variable. A line, therefore, in this figure corresponds to a term containing the two remaining variables. But we now can go one step further and add the terms corresponding to the nodes which are at the four corners of any face of the cube, and this will always result in the elimination of two variables. For example, consider the face which has the nodes 101, 111, 110, and 100, at its corners. The sum of the terms represented by these nodes is $XY'Z + XYZ + XYZ' + XY'Z' = X(Y'Z + YZ + YZ' + Y'Z') = X$. This face may then be designated as the X face of the cube.

Figure 5–6 shows how the cube can be used not only to represent a switching function, but also to carry out algebraic processes on the function. The function represented is given by the standard sum $\sum(1, 5, 6, 7)$. The four nodes corresponding to these terms are marked heavily and all other nodes are lightly indicated. The lines between the marked nodes are drawn solid and the remaining lines of the cube are

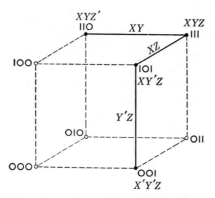

Fig. 5–6. The function $T = \Sigma(1, 5, 6, 7)$ represented on a cube. The lines joining the nodes represent two-variable terms.

dotted. Each of the heavy lines represents a prime implicant of the function, and using all of them we would write $T = XY + XZ + Y'Z$. Algebraically, of course, this reduces to $T = XY + Y'Z$. Examining Fig. 5–6 more closely, we see that the XY line includes the terms 6 and 7 of the standard sum and the $Y'Z$ line includes the terms 1 and 5 of the standard sum. These two lines account for all the terms specified by the standard sum, and any further accounting for them is redundant. Thus the line XZ accounts in redundant manner for terms 5 and 7. It is possible, therefore, from this type of representation to write a switching function in which redundant variables and redundant terms have been removed.

The next step in the evolution of geometrical representations of switching functions is shown in Fig. 5–7. This is the four-variable hypercube which has sixteen nodes, corresponding to the sixteen possible states of four variables. Although the construction appears to be quite complex, it is based on a rather simple procedure which can be extended to enable us to draw hypercubes representing any number of variables. At the bottom of Fig. 5–7 a set of dotted lines leads to the group of digits 0, 1, 2, 3, 4. The significance of these is as follows: Above the line marked 0 there is the node 0000. This number has no 1's in it. Above the dotted line marked 1 there is a group of four nodes each of which is designated by a binary number that contains exactly one 1.

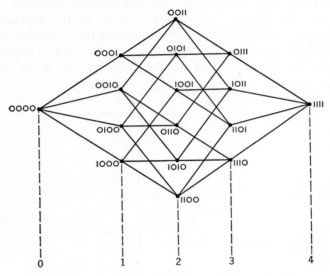

Fig. 5–7. Construction of a four-variable hypercube.

Above the line labeled 2 there are the six nodes whose designators each contain two 1's.* In the next column are contained the four nodes each of which have three 1's in their designators, and finally the last column is the node 1111. Having classified and located the nodes in this manner we must then draw lines connecting the nodes in adjacent columns, according to the rule that a line is drawn between every pair of nodes

---

* In constructing a hypercube the number of nodes present in each category can be computed easily. In the present example there are four variables, and we want to know in how many ways we can make two out of four variables unity. This is computed from the general formula for the number of combinations of n things taken m at a time. The formula is written $_nC_m = \dfrac{n!}{m!(n-m)!}$. To find how many nodes are required to represent all the ways in which four variables can have two of their values unity, $n = 4$, $m = 2$, and $\dfrac{4!}{2!(4-2)!} = 6$. The series of numbers thus computed, starting from the left and proceeding toward the right, will be recognized as the coefficients of the binomial expansion theorem, where m is the power of the expansion. See Appendix 3.

which differs in exactly one variable, and no other lines are drawn. Thus we find a line drawn between the node 0100 and the node 0101, but there is no line between 0100 and 1001 because although the two nodes are in adjacent columns they differ in the values of three of the variables. As a final check on the drawing it is merely necessary to count the total number of lines meeting at each node. In the construction of Fig. 5–7

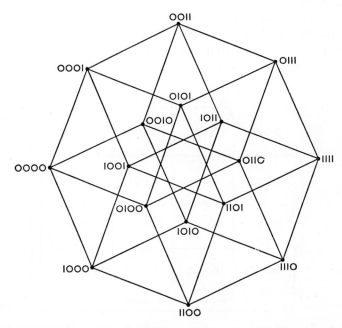

Fig. 5–8. The four-dimension hypercube in symmetrical form. The eight component cubes can be readily identified.

there are four lines coming to each node, because there are four variables each of which leads to another node when it changes. For an n-dimension hypercube it is evident that there should be n lines leading to each node.

In the four-variable hypercube each node represents a term containing four variables, each line connecting nodes represents a term with three variables, each group of four nodes connected by lines to form a square represents a term in two variables, and each group of eight nodes connected by lines to form a cube represents a term in one variable. These ideas are perhaps more evident in Fig. 5–8 in which the four-dimension hypercube is drawn in a more symmetrical pattern. If we count both primed and unprimed variables and if each of these variables is represented by a cube, we should find that the four-dimensional hypercube contains eight three-dimensional cubes. These may be found quite readily in Fig. 5–8.

These graphic interpretations of switching functions portray the interrelations among the terms of a function more vividly than the algebraic descriptions. It becomes desirable now to define a few terms which are used in discussing switching functions, in the light of the geometric representations.

By the *distance* between nodes we mean the number of variables which must be changed in passing between the nodes. Thus, the distance between node 0100 and 1001 is 3, because three of the four variables must be changed in going from one to the other.

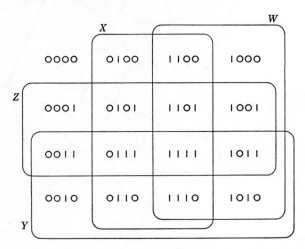

Fig. 5–9. The intersections within a modified four-variable Venn diagram correspond to the nodes of a four-variable hypercube.

An important concept developed from geometrical considerations is that of *adjacent states*. Two states are adjacent when they differ in the value of only one variable. The concept is important because the algebraic combination of two adjacent states always results in the elimination of one variable. One of the objectives of the graphical representations of functions is to display all the adjacencies which are present in a standard sum. When this is done it no longer becomes necessary to compare all possible pairs of terms in the standard sum in order to eliminate redundant variables. A graphical representation shows all the adjacencies which exist, and our attention is thus concentrated on those groupings of terms which lead immediately to simplification.

Although in this chapter we have begun to rely more and more upon the use of binary numbers, and their decimal equivalents, to represent the individual terms in a standard sum, we will still have occasion to refer to variables represented by letters and their complements. However, it becomes more and more awkward to refer repeatedly to "a variable and its complement" or "variables and their complements." For this reason, we shall adopt the term *literal*, as used by Quine (reference given in Art. 4.8) to mean any variable or its complement which appears in a transmission function. Thus a function in three variables may be written in terms of the literals X, X', Y, Y', Z, Z'.

The Venn diagrams of Figs. 5–1 and 5–2 were drawn with the use of overlapping circles. This method can be used for as many as three variables, but beyond that the circles must be distorted in order to produce all possible intersections, corresponding to all the possible states of the combined variables. In Fig. 5–9 the circles of the Venn diagram have been distorted into rectangular forms in order to get the results shown. The interesting thing about this diagram is that the areas corresponding to the sixteen possible states of four variables are now arranged in the form of a matrix.

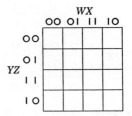

Fig. 5–10. The Karnaugh map for four variables is a simplification of the Venn diagram in Fig. 5–9.

In the form shown in Fig. 5–9 the Venn diagram is not particularly convenient for use, but the form shown in Fig. 5–10 is an excellent tool for working with four-variable functions. This is known as the Karnaugh map.*

It will be noted in the map that the values of WX are obtained from the headings of the columns and the values of YZ are obtained from the labels on the rows. Hence the area corresponding to $WXYZ = 0111$ is found at the intersection of the second column from the left and the third row from the top. By combining the column and row designators in this manner we describe cells within the map which correspond to every possible state of the four variables.

An important feature of the map is that if we start in any cell and move either horizontally or vertically the adjacent cell we reach always represents an adjacent state of the variables. The states represented by adjacent cells differ in the value of only one variable. These adjacencies exist not only within the interior of the map, but also from end to end

* M. Karnaugh, "The Map Method for Synthesis of Combinational Logic Circuits," *A.I.E.E. Trans., Part I: Communications and Electronics*, Vol. 72, November 1953, pp. 593–599.

of each column and each row. That is, the bottom cell in any column is adjacent to the top cell in the same column and the right-hand cell in any row is adjacent to the left-hand cell in that row. It is this property of displaying all possible adjacencies that makes the Karnaugh map of importance in simplifying four-variable functions.*

As a simple illustration of the application of the Karnaugh map, Fig. 5–11 shows the map used as a "plot" of the function $T = \sum (6, 7, 13, 15)$. In the squares of the map corresponding to the numbers in the standard sum, 1's have been entered to indicate that for those states the transmission is to be 1, and in all remaining squares of the map 0's have been entered. The lines placed around the pairs of 1's in the 01 and in the 11 columns indicate how the transmission points can be grouped in two terms which account for all four of the required 1 transmission points. We also see that it would be possible to group the pair of points in the 11 row into a third term, but since the other terms account for all the required 1's the last grouping would be redundant. Using the groupings indicated we can see that the transmission represented by this map is $T = W'XY + WXZ$. The grouping which was not used corresponds to the term XYZ, and we know from theorem 16' that if this term had been included in the transmission function it would have been redundant.

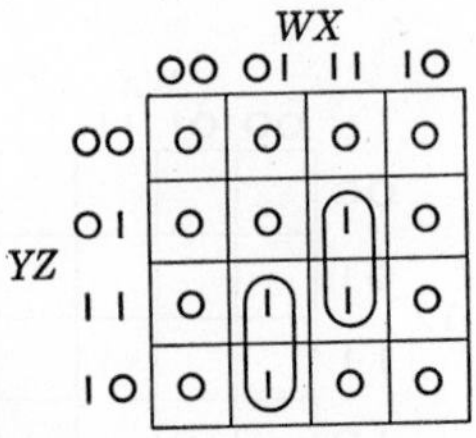

Fig. 5–11. A map of the function $T = \Sigma(6, 7, 13, 15)$.

5.4   Application of the Karnaugh Map

This article will discuss in some detail the use of the Karnaugh map in minimizing switching functions containing up to four variables. In Art. 5.3 we saw how states could be represented by nodes interconnected by lines or by the intersections of areas in the Venn type of diagram. The Karnaugh map is a simple construction which reproduces the inter-

---

* E. W. Veitch, "A Chart Method for Simplifying Truth Functions," *Proceedings of Association for Computing Machinery*, Pittsburgh, Pennsylvania, Meeting May 2 and 3, 1952, pp. 127–133.

The Veitch chart differs from the Karnaugh map in the ordering of the columns and rows. Whereas Karnaugh uses a cyclic ordering of the designators, namely 00, 01, 11, 10, Veitch has the designators arranged in the order of consecutive binary numbers, namely 00, 01, 10, 11. Consequently, although the 00 and 01 columns or rows are adjacent, as are the 10 and 11 columns or rows, the 01 and 10 columns and rows are not adjacent, nor are the end-to-end pairs. Although the Veitch chart is of advantage in contrast with strictly algebraic procedures, the Karnaugh map is much more convenient and rapid in use.

section areas of the Venn diagram quickly and conveniently. In the four-variable map, the individual squares or cells of the map correspond to the nodes of a four-variable hypercube, while the vertical and horizontal lines between cells correspond to the lines joining the nodes of the hypercube.

Suppose we wish to make a map of the function $T = X'Y + XY'$. A two-variable map can be drawn, as shown in Fig. 5–12, with separate

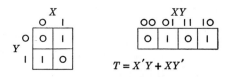

Fig. 5–12. Two-variable map forms.

axes for the X and Y variables, or with both variables along one axis. Entries of 1's and 0's have been made in these maps to designate the states for which transmission is 1 and 0, respectively. For the transmission of 1 corresponding to the input state $X'Y$, X must be 0 and Y must be 1. In the left-hand map a 1 is entered at the intersection of the 0 column of X and the 1 row of Y. In the right-hand map this corresponds to the entry of 1 in the 01 column of XY. Similarly the transmission of 1 corresponding to XY' is entered at the intersection of the 1 column of X and the 0 row of Y in the left-hand map, and in the 10 column of XY in the right-hand map. Since these are the only conditions for which the transmission is 1 the other cells in the map are filled with 0's.

For three input variables the map must contain either two columns and four rows or four columns and two rows, as shown in the left-hand and right-hand maps, respectively, of Fig. 5–13. The entries in these maps correspond to the transmission $T = XY + YZ$. Referring only to the right-hand map, we note that the transmission is to be 1 for the term XY. This particular term is independent of the value of Z and the entries should be the same for both the 0 and the 1 row of Z. Hence in the map 1's are entered in both rows of the column corresponding to $XY = 11$. The next term of the transmission, YZ, is independent of the value of X. In the row corresponding to $Z = 1$, we enter 1's in both the columns for which $Y = 1$ regardless of the value of X. The verification of the entries in the left-hand map is left as an exercise for the student.

The map of Fig. 5–14 represents the transmission function $T = W'X + X'Z' + X'Y' + XYZ$. We note that the term $W'X$ is independent of Y and Z and hence we enter 1's in the entire 01 column since the rows of that column represent all possible combinations of Y and Z. The $X'Z'$ term corresponds to the 1's entered in the four corners of the map. Note that $X = Z = 0$ in all four of these squares, and W and Y take all four possible combinations of values. The $X'Y'$ term requires that 1's be entered in all the squares for which X and Y are both 0, regardless of the values of W and Z. Y is 0 in the first and second rows while X is 0 in the first and fourth columns. Hence the 1's

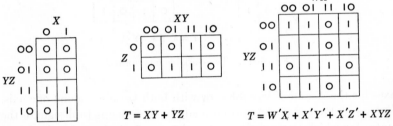

Fig. 5–13. A function of three variables and two forms of its map.

$T = XY + YZ$

Fig. 5–14. Map of a function of four variables.

$T = W'X + X'Y' + X'Z' + XYZ$

are entered in the squares corresponding to these four intersections. Finally, the term XYZ requires that 1's be entered wherever $X = Y = Z = 1$, regardless of the value of W. This places 1's in the third row and in the second and third columns.

It may have been noted in both Fig. 5–13 and 5–14 that there was some overlapping of the terms, so that a given 1 entry in the map might be included in more than one term of the transmission function. This will be true, for example, whenever the transmission function is factorable. The function mapped in Fig. 5–13 could have been written $T = Y(X + Z)$, and the function mapped in Fig. 5–14 could have been written $T = X(W' + YZ) + X'(Z' + Y')$.

Thus, it is a relatively simple matter to take a transmission function given in algebraic form and determine the appearance of its map. If the map, however, is to be a useful aid in synthesis we must have some procedure for reversing the process, so that we can derive from a map a minimized switching function.

Much of the convenience and time saving in the use of the map depends upon our ability to recognize certain patterns of entries. The basic patterns have been called "subcubes" and "patches"; we will use the name subcubes. A subcube may be defined as a set of cells of the map within which one or more of the variables have constant values. In a four-variable map a subcube consisting of two cells adjacent either horizontally or vertically is one in which three of the variables are constant and the fourth takes both its values. A subcube consisting of four cells, each of which is adjacent to two others in the same set, will have two variables that are constant while the other two variables take on all four possible combinations of values. Finally, a subcube consisting of eight cells, such that each cell is adjacent to three others in the same set, will have one variable that is constant and the other three will have all eight possible combinations of values. Thus, a two-cell subcube eliminates one variable, a four-cell subcube eliminates two variables, and an eight-cell subcube eliminates three variables.

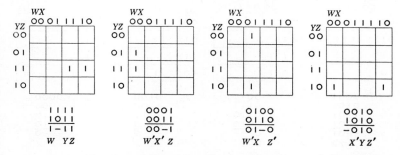

Fig. 5–15. Functions produced by adjacent pairs of transmission points.

In most of the remaining maps which are presented to illustrate the discussion in this article, the entries will designate only the states for which the transmission is 1, and unless otherwise indicated it is to be assumed that the cells without entries represent states of 0 transmission.

Figure 5–15 shows a group of maps each of which has the entries of a two-cell subcube. Beneath each map are shown the binary numbers which represent the two states of 1 transmission. Beneath each pair of binary numbers are listed the numbers which are constant throughout the subcube, with a dash to indicate which variable changes value. The digits in this last number by their location and value indicate the variables in the algebraic term represented. Since we are dealing with states of 1 transmission, each term is a product of literals, with 1 representing an unprimed variable and 0 a primed variable. A useful rule to follow in identifying a subcube of two cells is to note first whether the configuration is horizontal or vertical. If horizontal the variables of the row are constant and if vertical the variables of the column are constant. It is a simple matter then to determine which remaining variable is constant, and at what value, as we pass between columns or between rows. The product of the three variables thus found is the term represented. Particular attention should be paid to the situations shown in the third and fourth maps of Fig. 5–15 in each of which two cells that appear separated in space represent states which are actually adjacent.

Typical patterns of subcubes of four cells are illustrated in the maps of Fig. 5–16. The left-hand map contains four cells in a single row and there is a similar configuration of four cells in a column which is not illustrated. The second map shows four cells in a "square" pattern and this pattern may be located anywhere within the map. In the third map the pattern is still of the square form, but two of the adjacencies are of the end-around type. This same pattern may occur in any of the

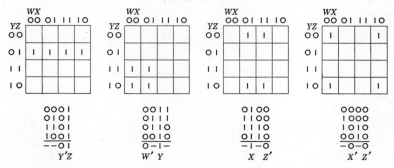

Fig. 5–16. Typical groups of four cells which correspond to two-variable terms.

adjacent columns or in any of the adjacent rows. The right-hand map is in a class by itself where the subcube occupies the four corner cells and the adjacencies are all of the end-around type.

Beneath each of these maps is listed the binary number designation of each of the four transmission points shown. Once these are listed it is a simple matter to determine which two of the variables are constant throughout the subcube and to write the algebraic description corresponding to the product of the two constant variables. Again it is useful to have simple rules so that these algebraic terms can be written by inspection. For a subcube having all four points in line, either horizontally or vertically, the designator of the row or column, respectively, indicates the algebraic result directly. Thus in the first map the rows represent the values of the Y and Z variables, and since all four points are in the row 01, the transmission represented is $Y'Z$. For the square patterns it becomes necessary to observe which variable is constant as we pass between the two columns and which variable is constant as we pass between the two rows of the square. Doing this in the second map, we see that $W = 0$ in both columns and $Y = 1$ in both rows. Hence the algebraic term is $W'Y$. The verification of the algebraic descriptions given in the remaining two maps is left as an exercise for the student.

Probably the easiest pattern to recognize is that of the eight-cell subcubes shown in the maps of Fig. 5–17. The eight cells will always be in either adjacent columns or in adjacent rows, as in the maps for X and Y', or in columns or rows with end-around adjacency, as in the maps of X' and Z'.

Many switching functions are specified in either standard sum or standard product form, and decimal numbers corresponding to the terms in the sum or product are given in accordance with the conventions discussed in Art. 5.2. In Fig. 5–18 the cells of a four-variable map are filled in with the decimal numbers which are the equivalents of the binary numbers that represent the variables W, X, Y, Z, taken in that

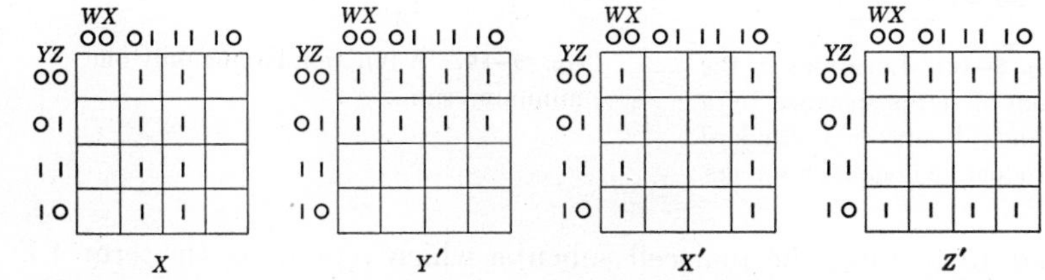

WX	00	01	11	10
YZ 00			1	1
01			1	1
11			1	1
10			1	1

X

WX	00	01	11	10
YZ 00	1	1	1	1
01	1	1	1	1
11				
10				

Y'

WX	00	01	11	10
YZ 00	1			1
01	1			1
11	1			1
10	1			1

X'

WX	00	01	11	10
YZ 00	1	1	1	1
01				
11				
10	1	1	1	1

Z'

Fig. 5–17. Patterns of eight cells and the single variables to which they correspond.

order. It should be particularly noted that since the binary-number designators of the columns and rows are not in consecutive order, the equivalent decimal numbers cannot be in consecutive order. Thus, in the first column starting at the top, we enter decimal 0, and 1 in the first two cells, but then jump to the bottom to enter 2, and move upward to enter 3. This "skipping" of the third row is repeated in all the columns. After numbering the second column, we see that we must skip the third column and put 8, 9, 10, and 11 in the fourth column, and then return to the third column to enter 12, 13, 14, and 15. This non-consecutive ordering of the decimal equivalents is about the most awkward feature of the Karnaugh map, but the advantages of the cyclic ordering of the binary numbers are such that the awkwardness is a small price to pay for its use.

It will be useful at this time to examine a few functions which have been specified by their standard sums and entered on Karnaugh maps. We are required to write a minimum sum for each of them. First, in Fig. 5–19, we have mapped the function $T = \sum (3, 4, 5, 7, 11, 13, 15)$. A guiding principle to be followed in selecting the subcubes that are chosen as terms in the minimum sum is first to account for those entries in the map which can be included in only one subcube. In this map, the entry of cell 4 can be coupled only with the entry of cell 5, to form the term $W'XY'$. The entry of cell 13 can be combined either with 5 or with 15, but 13 can also be combined with 5, 7, and 15 to form a four-cell subcube corresponding to the term XZ. Where this choice exists we always use the largest subcube which will cover the entry in question. The remaining entries are in cells 3 and 11. These will combine with 7

YZ \ WX	00	01	11	10
00	0	4	12	8
01	1	5	13	9
11	3	7	15	11
10	2	6	14	10

Fig. 5–18. Locations in the map of terms specified by a standard sum or a standard product, in decimal numbers.

$$T = \Sigma(3,4,5,7,11,13,15) = W'XY' + XZ + YZ$$

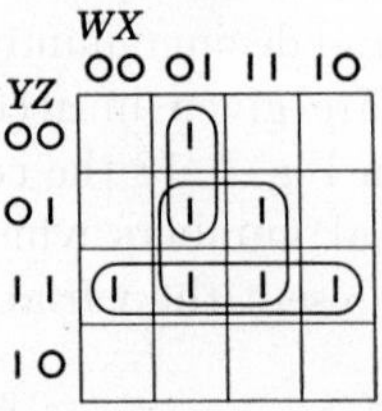

Fig. 5–19. A function having only one minimum sum.

and 15 to form the four-cell subcube which represents the term YZ. Thus we derive for the specified transmission the algebraic minimum sum $T = W'XY' + XZ + YZ$. We can see from the map that each term of the minimum sum (a *subcube* on the map) contains at least one term from the standard sum (an *entry* in the map) which is contained in

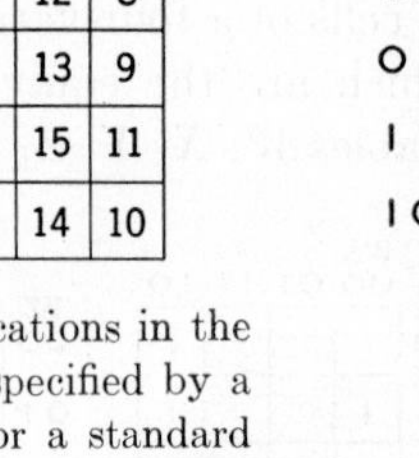

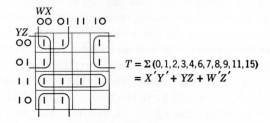

$$T = \Sigma(0,1,2,3,4,6,7,8,9,11,15) = X'Y' + YZ + W'Z'$$

Fig. 5–20. An example which requires careful selection of subcubes.

no other term (in no other subcube), and since each of these terms is combined with as many others as possible (each entry is contained in the largest possible subcube), the minimum sum written for this function is unique. No other sum can be written with as few literals.

The choice of subcubes to be included in the algebraic statement of a minimum sum is not always as evident as it was in Fig. 5–19. In Fig. 5–20 the map shows the function $T = \sum(0, 1, 2, 3, 4, 6, 7, 8, 9, 11, 15)$. Inspection shows that this map contains a total of six four-cell subcubes. Since there are only eleven terms in the standard sum it is evident that there is much overlapping of subcubes. Again, we look for entries which can be combined with other entries into one and only one subcube of maximum size. Inspection shows that every entry in the map can be in a four-cell subcube, but some of the entries can be in only one such subcube. The first of these is the entry 4 which can combine only with 0, 2, and 6 to form a subcube representing the term $W'Z'$. Next there is the entry 8 which can combine only with 9, 0, and 1 to form a subcube which represents the term $X'Y'$. Finally, entry 15 can combine only with terms 3, 7, and 11 to form a subcube which represents the term YZ. Encircling lines indicate the selected subcubes in Fig. 5–20 and also in Fig. 5–19. For the function represented by Fig. 5–20 the three subcubes required to cover points which could be included in no other subcubes of maximum size have accounted for all the entries in the map. Hence the transmission $T = YZ + X'Y' + W'Z'$ is a unique minimum sum since no other sum can be written for this function with as few literals.

Figure 5–21 is the map of a function which is an extreme example chosen to illustrate the need for care in the selection of subcubes. At the left this function is shown on a map without any encircling of the entries to indicate those which are combined to form subcubes. At first glance,

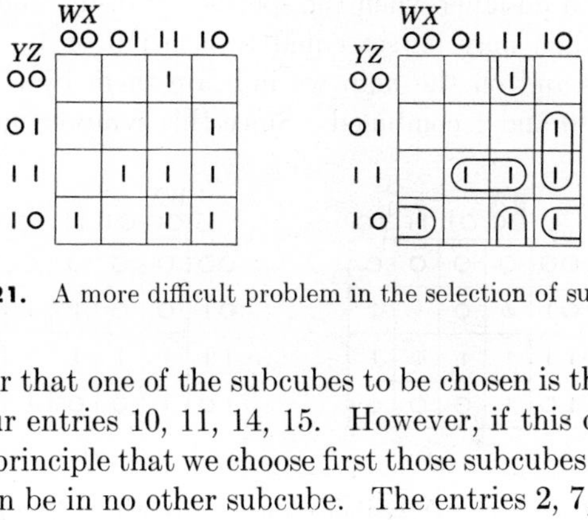

Fig. 5–21.   A more difficult problem in the selection of subcubes.

it might appear that one of the subcubes to be chosen is that which consists of the four entries 10, 11, 14, 15. However, if this choice is made it violates the principle that we choose first those subcubes which contain entries that can be in no other subcube. The entries 2, 7, 9, and 12 are so located that each of them is part of one and only one two-cell subcube. When these subcubes are chosen, as shown in the right-hand part of Fig. 5–21, we find that every entry in the four-cell subcube is included, so the term which we might have written for this subcube would have been redundant. The final transmission function is hence written $T = X'YZ' + XYZ + WXZ' + WX'Z$. If the rather obvious four-cell subcube is included, the transmission function must contain the term WY. It is left as an interesting exercise for the student to prove algebraically (not by a map) that the term WY is redundant.

Many transmission functions can be written in more than one minimum-sum form. The map of Fig. 5–22 represents an example of this type. The entries are such that all subcubes contain two cells, but it is possible for every entry in the map to be contained in two such subcubes.

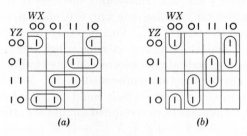

Fig. 5–22. A function which may be written in two forms, both of which are minimum sums.

There are just two ways in which every entry in the map can be contained in one two-cell subcube, as shown in parts (*a*) and (*b*) of the figure.

A particularly important feature of the Karnaugh map is the ease of choice it offers a designer when the specified transmission function contains terms which may be set equal to either 0 or 1. We call these optional terms and on the map we indicate them by a symbol which consists of the 0 and 1 combined. Since this symbol turns out to look

(a)

YZ \ WX	00	01	11	10
00	0	0	0	0
01	φ	0	1	1
11	1	1	φ	1
10	1	0	0	φ

(b)

YZ \ WX	00	01	11	10
00	0	0	0	0
01	0	0	1	1
11	1	1	1	1
10	1	0	0	1

Fig. 5–23. Map in part (*a*) contains three cells where transmission value is optional. Part (*b*) shows the choices made.

like the Greek letter ϕ, it is convenient to call the terms ϕ terms. The left-hand map of Fig. 5–23 is marked to show the transmission $T = \sum(2, 3, 7, 9, 11, 13)$ and the terms 1, 10, 15 as optional terms. By choosing to make the decimal 1 term equal to 0 and the 10 and 15 terms equal to 1, we obtain the map at the right of Fig. 5–23 in which all transmission terms are contained within four-cell subcubes. The minimum sum specifying this transmission is $T = WZ + X'Y + YZ$.

Up to this point we have elected to interpret all maps by writing the transmission as a minimum sum. This is not a necessary restriction; the transmission may be read directly from any map in the form of a minimum product by selecting subcubes of 0's instead of subcubes of 1's. If the minimum-product form is to be written, however, it must be re-

WX

YZ	00	01	11	10
00	0	1	1	1
01	0	1	1	1
11	1	0	0	1
10	1	1	1	1

$T = (W + X + Y)(X' + Y' + Z')$

Fig. 5–24. Minimum product form of transmission obtained directly from the map.

membered that in the column and row designators of the variables a 0 represents an unprimed variable and a 1 represents a primed variable. Thus for the map at the right of Fig. 5–23, for which the minimum sum transmission is given in the preceding paragraph, the minimum product transmission would be written $T = (W + Y)(Y + Z)(X' + Z)$. For this particular function we note that the minimum-sum form contains exactly the same number of literals as the minimum-product form. Each transmission function is obtained from three four-cell subcubes. Consider on the other hand the transmission mapped in Fig. 5–24. The 1's of transmission all lie within four-cell subcubes and the 0's of transmission are within two-cell subcubes. But the minimum-sum function, $T = X'Y + XY' + WX' + YZ'$, contains eight literals while the minimum-product transmission, $T = (W + X + Y)(X' + Y' + Z')$, contains only six literals. Whenever we note, as in this example, that the standard sum contains many more terms than the standard product it pays to examine both the minimum sum and the minimum product to see whether there is a choice of a simpler form.

We shall have occasion, particularly in the design of multi-terminal contact networks, to deal with functions which are represented by the sum or the product of other functions which in turn are represented on Karnaugh maps. Figure 5–25 illustrates the addition of two functions by working directly with their mapped representations, and Fig. 5–26 shows the multiplication of the same two functions by use of the maps. The rule for the addition of maps can be visualized by thinking of the two functions as being represented by their standard sums. When two standard sums are added, the result must contain every term which is present in either of the original functions. Hence when we add functions represented by maps, the map which represents the sum must contain a 1 in a cell if either or both of the functions being added contains a 1 in that cell. The rule for multiplying two maps can be visualized by considering the two functions as being written in terms of their standard

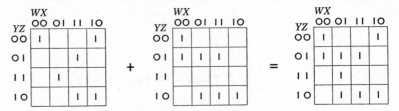

Fig. 5–25. The sum of two functions represented by the sum of their maps.

products. Then every term which appears in either or both of the original functions must appear in the product of the two. This means that if either or both of the maps being multiplied contains a 0 in a cell, the corresponding cell in the product map must contain a 0.

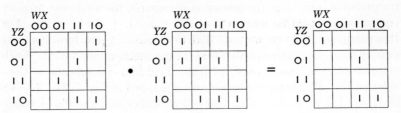

Fig. 5–26. The product of two functions represented by the product of their maps.

These rules for the addition and multiplication of maps may be summarized by saying that on a cell-by-cell basis the entries in the map representing the sum or the product are obtained by applying the rules for Boolean addition and multiplication to the corresponding entries in the maps of the original functions.

An example showing one application of the concept of map multiplication is shown in Fig. 5–27. The map at the left is visualized as the product of the two maps at the right and the transmission function is written in the factored form $T = (Y'Z + YZ')(W'X + WX')$. In this instance, the result offers no new economy, for the transmission function could have been written directly from the map at the left in the form of the minimum product $T = (W + X)(W' + X')(Y + Z)$ $(Y' + Z')$. Both forms of the transmission function contain the same number of literals.

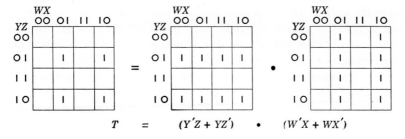

$$T \quad = \quad (Y'Z + YZ') \quad \bullet \quad (W'X + WX')$$

Fig. 5–27. A transmission function written as the product of two mapped functions.

5.5 Functions of Five or More Variables

By its very nature, the map method which was discussed in the preceding article is most effective in the minimization of functions of four variables. It is less effective in treating functions of three variables because so many of them respond readily to simple algebraic steps. And there is no need for a map in working with functions of two variables.

Several methods have been suggested for extending the map method to the treatment of functions of more than four variables. In general, these methods attempt to go only as far as functions of five and six variables. One procedure, which is not discussed here, is to divide each square of a four-variable Karnaugh map into two or four parts to accommodate either five or six variables, respectively. These ideas are attractive on the surface but when actually tried it is found difficult to achieve any decisive advantage.

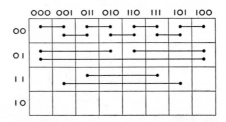

Fig. 5–28. A five-variable map with columns designated in cyclic ordering. All column adjacencies are indicated by lines connecting nodes.

Other suggestions involve the expansion of the four-variable map so that each cell of the map still represents a single term of a standard sum or standard product. One version of this expansion is illustrated in Fig. 5–28. This is a five-variable map which consists of eight columns and four rows. The variables represented by the columns are designated by three binary digits and the three-digit binary numbers are ordered in a cyclic order so that each column is adjacent to its neighbor and there is end-around adjacency between the first and the eighth columns. The rows are given the normal cyclic ordering of the four-variable map.

Since the purpose of a map is to display more or less simultaneously all the adjacencies among the individual terms of a switching function represented by a standard sum or a standard product, it is important to examine the adjacencies displayed by the five-variable map. The adjacencies among rows are now well understood and are therefore not shown in Fig. 5–28. The adjacencies between pairs of columns are indicated by placing nodes in two columns which are adjacent and then connecting them by lines. Thus, the connections shown in the 00 row indicate that each column is adjacent to its neighbor. In the 01 row the

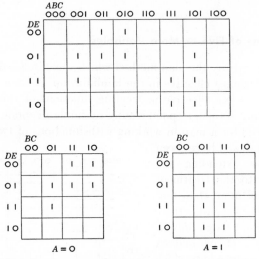

Fig. 5–29. A five-variable function mapped in a single map and (below) in separate four-variable maps.

first and fourth columns and the fifth and eighth columns are shown to be adjacent and we also see that the end-around adjacency of the first and eighth columns is indicated. In the 11 row, the third and sixth and the second and seventh columns are shown as adjacent. Although this pattern contains many symmetries which are helpful in remembering it, it is a complex one to use.

Another method for mapping functions of five variables is indicated in Fig. 5–29. At the top of the figure the function is entered on a map of the type shown in Fig. 5–28 while at the bottom of Fig. 5–29 the function is mapped as two four-variable functions. The left-hand map contains terms for which the variable A is 0, and the right-hand map contains terms for which the variable A is 1. Effectively, we expand the five-variable function about the variable A and map separately the two resulting four-variable functions of which A' and A are coefficients.

For the particular function mapped in Fig. 5–29, it is easy to see that one subcube appears in both the left- and right-hand maps and the variable A therefore vanishes in the term represented by that subcube. The transmission function shown is $T = A'BD' + ACD + B'CE$. If we had not observed that the same subcube was present in both maps we might have written in the transmission the two terms $A'B'CE + AB'CE$, and the A variable would have vanished from these two by ordinary algebraic elimination. However, we cannot always depend on this process to operate satisfactorily. It is possible in some functions to have a subcube present in both the A' and the A maps but to have those cells included in different subcubes when the functions are written.

The difficulties are even more severe when we attempt to handle functions of six variables by means of mapping methods. Karnaugh has suggested a three-dimensional map consisting of four four-variable maps, marked on transparent plastic, and spaced vertically one above the other. Markers, such as poker chips, are placed on each of the planes to indicate entries. An alternative is to expand a six-variable function about two of its variables and to map each of the residuals of the expansion in a separate four-variable map. This simply compounds the difficulties that we have observed in mapping a function of five variables.

Before the introduction of the map method, a chart method had been developed at the Harvard Computation Laboratory.* Essentially this chart provided a tabulation of all possible prime implicants for a given number of variables and then by a systematic procedure of ruling out rows and columns, or portions of columns, the actual prime implicants of a given function were left unruled. In a second operation a systematic selection of the prime implicants could be made so as to write a minimized function. In the procedure to be discussed in this article the method of selecting the prime implicants to be entered into the minimum sum is very similar to that used with the Harvard chart, but it differs in that the final selection chart contains only those prime implicants which are pertinent to the function under examination and is hence much more compact, even for a relatively large number of variables.

The method to be described here for minimizing functions of five or more variables is a modification of the Quine method which is the work of McCluskey.† While the method is immediately applicable to

---

* See Reference 9, Bibliography at the end of Chapter 3.

† E. J. McCluskey, Jr., "Algebraic Minimization and the Design of Two-Terminal Contact Networks," Doctoral thesis, Department of Electrical Engineering, Massachusetts Institute of Technology, June 1956. The first part of this thesis, dealing with algebraic minimization, is published in the *Bell System Technical Journal*, Vol. 35, November 1956, pp. 1417–1444.

functions of more than four variables, most of the examples presented in this article will be functions of four variables, primarily to permit direct comparison with the results obtained on the same functions by the map method. The discussion will be in terms of functions described by standard sums, but it should be understood that the method is applicable also to functions described by standard products; the only requirement is that the binary-number representations of terms be interpreted appropriately.

A preliminary comparison of the Quine method and the McCluskey modification shows that Quine's description of individual terms was entirely algebraic whereas McCluskey uses binary numbers to replace the algebraic symbols. This change in itself is not new, for a number of workers have found that it is much easier and less conducive to error to compare variables represented by binary numbers than it is to compare them in their algebraic form. However, McCluskey, using the binary-number representation, observed another important fact that results in a considerable saving of time over the original Quine method. Quine indicated that the first step in simplifying a function expressed as a standard sum was to make an exhaustive comparison of all pairs of terms for the purpose of eliminating variables according to the rule $XY + XY' = X$. McCluskey uses the same comparison process, but he so directs the procedure as to materially cut down the number of comparisons which must be made. This will be best observed by summarizing the steps in the Quine-McCluskey method for obtaining the prime implicants and then illustrating them in examples. The procedure for obtaining the prime implicants of a function is as follows:

1. Whether the function is described by an algebraic standard sum or by a set of decimal numbers, the individual terms are to be described by their equivalent binary numbers.

2. The individual terms are to be divided into groups such that all members of a group have the same number of 1's in their binary designators. For convenience, we may call the number of 1's in a binary number its *index*, so all members of a given group have the same index.

3. The groups of binary numbers are arranged in a column beginning with the group of lowest index and continuing with groups of increasing index. Draw a line between each pair of groups to indicate where the index changes.

4. McCluskey now observes that if we have a group of terms of index i, we need compare these terms, for elimination of variables, only with those in the group of index $(i + 1)$. Terms which differ in index num-

ber by more than 1 will of course differ in more than one variable and no algebraic elimination of a variable is possible. Hence, instead of the exhaustive comparison of the Quine method, we start with the terms in the set of lowest index and compare them with those, if any, in the set of an index which is 1 greater. The comparison between the terms of two such adjacent groups must be exhaustive.

5. In a second tabulation we record all terms which combine to form a reduced term and in the first column we check off those terms which entered into the combination. When a variable is eliminated by such combination we indicate this fact in the binary number form by inserting a dash in the position occupied by that variable. For example, 0100 and 0101 combine to form the term 010–. The original terms 0100 and 0101 are checked off because they are accounted for by the combined term and need not appear explicitly in the final result.

6. The terms in the tabulation found as a result of the first comparison are again partitioned into groups. The first group consists of the results of comparing the first two groups of the original tabulation. Although the original index identification has been lost, the groups in the second tabulation will also be characterized by having an increasing number of 1's in their representations.

7. After the first comparison is completed and all possible terms have been checked off in the first column, the entire process is repeated on the second column and the results entered in a third tabulation. We note that in comparing terms from the second tabulation we again observe the rule of comparing terms in one group only with those terms in the group containing a single additional 1 in their binary representations. There is another requirement, however, and that is that in view of the fact that all members of the second tabulation will have one dash in the representation, the only terms that can be combined are those which have their dashes in the same location. For example, 010– and 110– combine to give –10–, but 010– and 11–0 cannot be combined.

8. After every set of comparisons is made for a given column, the process is repeated until no new columns can be formed. Every term, regardless of column, which is used in combination to form a new term must be checked off.

9. When no further combinations are possible the terms which have not been checked are the prime implicants from which a minimum sum is to be selected.

Our first example is a very simple one, and indeed a trivial one, but its very lack of detail is advantageous in showing the steps.

Example 5-3

$$T = \sum(5, 7, 12, 13)$$

5	0 1 0 1 ✓	5, 7	0 1 - 1
12	1 1 0 0 ╱	5, 13	- 1 0 1
7	0 1 1 1 ✓	12, 13	1 1 0 -
13	1 1 0 1 ✓		

In the first column there are only two groups, corresponding to terms which have two 1's in their binary numbers and terms which have three 1's in their binary numbers. Since there are only two groups in the first column, there can be only one group in the next column. In the first column each binary number is preceded by the decimal number that it represents. In the second column each term with a single dash in it is preceded by the pair of decimal numbers which combined to form the new term. Although this identification of terms by the decimal numbers is not a necessary step it is carried out throughout these examples. Later in this chapter we will show that the decimal numbers themselves are sufficient to guide the entire process.

Since all the numbers in the first column entered into combination in one or more of the terms of the second column we have checked off the entire first column. Because no further combinations are possible, the three terms described in the second column are all prime implicants. We may determine the minimum sum in this example by a process of inspection, for we notice that the first prime implicant is derived from the decimal terms 5 and 7 and the third prime implicant comes from the decimal terms 12 and 13. These four terms constitute the entire standard sum, so the middle term in the second column which came from decimal terms 5 and 13 is redundant. Consequently, if we interpret the first and last binary numbers of the second column in terms of the variables W, X, Y, Z, we write the transmission function $T = W'XZ + WXY'$. We also note that the redundant term is $XY'Z$, and if we had included this in the transmission function it would have been discarded because of theorem 16'.

In Fig. 5-20 we mapped a function which required some care in the determination of the minimum sum by the map method. In the next example the same function will be minimized by the Quine-McCluskey method.

Example 5-4

$$T = \sum(0, 1, 2, 3, 4, 6, 7, 8, 9, 11, 15)$$

0	0 0 0 0 ✓	0, 1	0 0 0 − ✓	0, 1, 2, 3	0 0 − −	A
1	0 0 0 1 ✓	0, 2	0 0 − 0 ✓	0, 1, 8, 9	− 0 0 −	B
2	0 0 1 0 ✓	0, 4	0 − 0 0 ✓	0, 2, 4, 6	0 − − 0	C
4	0 1 0 0 ✓	0, 8	− 0 0 0 ✓	1, 3, 9, 11	− 0 − 1	D
8	1 0 0 0 ✓	1, 3	0 0 − 1 ✓	2, 3, 6, 7	0 − 1 −	E
3	0 0 1 1 ✓	1, 9	− 0 0 1 ✓	3, 7, 11, 15	− − 1 1	F
6	0 1 1 0 ✓	2, 3	0 0 1 − ✓			
9	1 0 0 1 ✓	2, 6	0 − 1 0 ✓			
7	0 1 1 1 /	4, 6	0 1 − 0 ✓			
11	1 0 1 1 ✓	8, 9	1 0 0 − ✓			
15	1 1 1 1 ✓	3, 7	0 − 1 1 ✓			
		3, 11	− 0 1 1 ✓			
		6, 7	0 1 1 − ✓			
		9, 11	1 0 − 1 ✓			
		7, 15	− 1 1 1 ✓			
		11, 15	1 − 1 1 ✓			

The standard sum contains terms in five different groups, from the 0 term, which contains no 1's, up to the 15 term which contains four 1's. An exhaustive comparison of the terms in each group with the terms of the group of the next higher index produces the entries in the second column which are identified at the left of the column by the decimal numbers of the terms which contribute to each entry. All terms in the first column enter into one or more combinations and hence all are checked off. The student should verify step-by-step each entry made in this example to make sure that the details of the process are understood.

A third column is formed and in this example every member of the second column enters in one or more combinations to form an entry in the third column, and hence each member of the second column is checked off. The third column has three groups of terms but it is not possible to combine any members from adjacent groups, so the six terms remaining are all prime implicants.

The groupings of the original terms of the standard sum into prime implicants in Example 5–4 are both more numerous and more complex than in Example 5–3. While a method of inspection would ultimately succeed, it would be time consuming to say the least and would be quite unsatisfactory in still more complex problems. In order to select a suitable minimum sum from the group of prime implicants we shall construct a prime implicant chart* which for this problem is shown in Fig. 5–30.

* A chart similar to this was first proposed by Quine but McCluskey has simplified its construction and systematized its use. It essentially carries out the same operations as the Harvard minimizing chart but with a much simpler structure.

In the prime implicant chart shown in Fig. 5–30, we establish a number of columns each of which carries a number at the top corresponding to one of the decimal numbers in the standard sum of the function. Each row corresponds to one of the prime implicants, as identified by the letters **A, B** . . . **F** at the right (note these same letters placed beside the prime implicants found in Example 5–4). In each row we mark a cross under each decimal number of a term contained

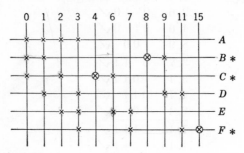

Fig. 5–30. Prime implicant chart for Example 5–4.

in the prime implicant represented by that row. Thus in Example 5–4 the first prime implicant, A, was the result of combining terms 0, 1, 2 and 3, so in Fig. 5–30 the crosses in the A row are in the 0, 1, 2, and 3 columns. The remainder of the chart is completed in the same manner.

The first step in using the prime implicant chart is to scan the columns to see whether any column has exactly one cross in it. We find this is true of columns 4, 8, and 15. We place circles around each of the crosses which stand alone in a column and then rule a line through all the crosses in each row that contains a circled cross. The significance of this is that the particular prime implicant which has thus been marked is the *only* one which can supply the transmission required for the term encircled. But since it also supplies the transmission corresponding to all other crosses in the same row we rule out those crosses to indicate that no other prime implicant need be chosen to supply these terms of transmission. A single asterisk is placed at the end of each row corresponding to a prime implicant which is thus required. McCluskey calls such rows basis rows, and in view of other methods of choice to be discussed later we will here call them primary basis rows if they have been chosen to satisfy a column which has only one cross in it. In addition to satisfying the columns under which the crosses are circled, each primary basis row satisfies columns where other crosses lie in that row. Thus row B in Fig. 5–30 satisfies not only the circled cross in column 8 but also the uncircled crosses in columns 0, 1, and 9. Consequently having indicated that row B is a primary basis row we then go along it and rule out all columns in which that row contains crosses. In other words, prime implicant B is required to furnish term 8 but in the process of doing so it also furnishes terms 0, 1, and 9.

We continue this process for the columns containing crosses which are in the other two primary basis rows, and at the end find that we have ruled out all the crosses in all the columns. Hence we have determined that the minimum sum is formed from prime implicants B, C, and F with no other terms needed. Since B, C, and F are all primary basis rows and no other terms are needed, this represents a unique minimum sum.

Returning now to the tabulations in Example 5–4, we find that the representations of prime implicants B, C, and F are $-0\,0\,-$, $0\,-\,-\,0$, and $-\,-\,1\,1$, respectively. Interpreted as algebraic expressions in the variables W, X, Y, Z, this transmission is written $X'Y' + W'Z' + YZ$. This is, of course, the result that was obtained originally by the map method. Example 5–4 illustrated a situation in which it was convenient to have a chart for the selection of prime implicants, but the situation was a very simple one indeed. In the next example we will study a function of five variables for which the selection of a minimum sum is not quite so self-evident even with the use of a chart.

Example 5–5

$T(A, B, C, D, E) = \sum(0, 1, 3, 8, 9, 13, 14, 15, 16, 17, 19, 24, 25, 27, 31)$

0	0 0 0 0 0 ✓	0,1	0 0 0 0 – ✓	0,1,8,9	0 – 0 0 – ✓		
1	0 0 0 0 1 ✓	0,8	0 – 0 0 0 ✓	0,1,16,17	– 0 0 0 – ✓		
8	0 1 0 0 0 ✓	0,16	– 0 0 0 0 ✓	0,8,16,24	– – 0 0 0 ✓		
16	1 0 0 0 0 ✓	1,3	0 0 0 – 1 ✓	1,3,17,19	– 0 0 – 1 **C**		
3	0 0 0 1 1 ✓	1,9	0 – 0 0 1 ✓	1,9,17,25	– – 0 0 1 ✓		
9	0 1 0 0 1 ✓	1,17	– 0 0 0 1 ✓	8,9,24,25	– 1 0 0 – ✓		
17	1 0 0 0 1 ✓	8,9	0 1 0 0 – ✓	16,17,24,25	1 – 0 0 – ✓		
24	1 1 0 0 0 ✓	8,24	– 1 0 0 0 ✓	17,19,25,27	1 – 0 – 1 **B**		
13	0 1 1 0 1 ✓	16,17	1 0 0 0 – ✓	0,1,8,9,16,17,24,25	– – 0 0 – **A**		
14	0 1 1 1 0 ✓	16,24	1 – 0 0 0 ✓				
19	1 0 0 1 1 ✓	3,19	– 0 0 1 1 ✓				
25	1 1 0 0 1 ✓	9,13	0 1 – 0 1 **D**				
15	0 1 1 1 1 ✓	9,25	– 1 0 0 1 ✓				
27	1 1 0 1 1 ✓	17,19	1 0 0 – 1 ✓				
31	1 1 1 1 1 ✓	17,25	1 – 0 0 1 ✓				
		24,25	1 1 0 0 – ✓				
		13,15	0 1 1 – 1 **E**				
		14,15	0 1 1 1 – **F**				
		19,27	1 – 0 1 1 ✓				
		25,27	1 1 0 – 1 ✓				
		15,31	– 1 1 1 1 **G**				
		27,31	1 1 – 1 1 **H**				

There are eight prime implicants identified by the letters **A, B, . . . , H**. The prime implicant chart is shown in Fig. 5–31.

In this prime implicant chart the circled crosses indicate that rows A, C, and F are primary basis rows. When the columns they cover are ruled out we find that only columns 13, 27, and 31 remain unruled. However, all three of these columns have two crosses in them and we have hence exhausted all possibility of setting up primary basis rows.

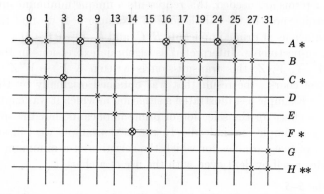

Fig. 5–31. Prime implicant chart for Example 5–5. There is a choice between two minimum sums.

We observe however that row B has a cross remaining in column 27 and row G has one cross remaining in column 31. Row H has crosses in both these columns, so by selecting row H we can satisfy the requirements of rows B and G. We mark row H with two asterisks, as shown, to indicate that it is a secondary basis row.

After ruling out columns 27 and 31 the only column left unsatisfied is 13. This transmission can be supplied either by prime implicant D or by E. If one of these rows contained more crosses than the other it would mean that the corresponding prime implicant contained fewer literals than the other, and that would be a basis for choosing one rather than the other. Here, however, D and E contain the same number of literals and there is absolutely no basis for guiding the choice at this point. There are, therefore, two possible minimum sums which are composed of prime implicants A, C, F, H, and either D or E. When the prime implicants are written algebraically in the variables A, B, C, D, and E, the transmission function becomes $T = C'D' + B'C'E + A'BCD + ABDE + A'BD'E$, or the same expression with the last term replaced by $A'BCE$.

Our next example by this method is taken from the map shown in Fig. 5–22.

Example 5–6

$$T = \sum(0, 2, 6, 7, 8, 9, 13, 15)$$

0	0 0 0 0 ✓		0, 2	0 0 – 0	**A**
2	0 0 1 0 ✓		0, 8	– 0 0 0	**B**
8	1 0 0 0 ✓		2, 6	0 – 1 0	**C**
6	0 1 1 0 ✓		8, 9	1 0 0 –	**D**
9	1 0 0 1 ✓		6, 7	0 1 1 –	**E**
7	0 1 1 1 ✓		9, 13	1 – 0 1	**F**
13	1 1 0 1 ✓		7, 15	– 1 1 1	**G**
15	1 1 1 1 ✓		13, 15	1 1 – 1	**H**

There are no further combinations possible so all terms in the second column are prime implicants. The prime implicant chart for this example is shown in Fig. 5–32.

Examination of the prime implicant chart shows that there are two crosses in each column and hence there are no primary basis rows. Moreover, the student should redraw this prime implicant table without

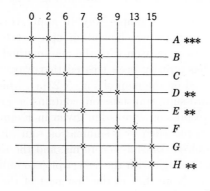

Fig. 5–32. The prime implicant chart for Example 5–6 is cyclic in form.

any rows or columns crossed out, and verify for himself that there are no secondary basis rows in the original chart. That is, there are no rows which can be chosen so that they will account for the transmissions required in two other rows.

McCluskey calls this a cyclic type of chart, in view of the fact that there is no way to break into the structure for some clearly indicated reason. The problem chosen for this example is such that its entire prime implicant chart is cyclic, but the more frequent situation is that after some initial selections of primary and secondary basis rows the remainder of the chart is cyclic in form.

To handle this problem we start with the 0 column which contains crosses in rows A and B. We can choose either of these as a starting point and here we choose to accept row A as a basis row, or rather as a trial basis row, which is indicated by marking it with three asterisks. After ruling out row A we must rule out columns 0 and 2, and in doing so we leave rows B and C with only one cross each in them. Now we note that if we select rows D and E as secondary basis rows that this selection satisfies the remaining requirements of rows B and C and at the same time reduces rows F and G to one cross each. Finally, the remaining requirements of F and G are satisfied by the selection of row H as a secondary basis row. Thus, starting with row A as a trial basis row we have found that a selection of prime implicants A, D, E, and H satisfies all the requirements of the transmission. This selection leads to the transmission $T = W'X'Z' + WX'Y' + W'XY + WXZ$, which is the same transmission that is represented by the choice of subcubes made in Fig. 5–22(b).

If we had started with row B as a trial basis row we would have been led to the use of rows B, C, F, and G in forming a minimum sum, which would correspond to the subcubes shown in Fig. 5–22(a).

McCluskey has shown a simple way to apply this method to the simplification of functions which contain optional terms. Again, in order to get a direct comparison with the map method we will examine a problem which has already been treated that way. Hence the next example will be based on the map of Fig. 5–23(a), which in addition to a specified standard-sum transmission contains a group of optional terms. In the transmission expression given in Example 5–7 the first group of numbers is preceded by a summation sign without a subscript to indicate the required transmission terms, and the next group is preceded by a summation sign with the subscript ϕ to indicate three terms which are optional. Note that in the first part of the process, that of obtaining the prime implicants, the optional terms are combined with the required terms. Thus, the prime implicants found are those which satisfy all terms whether required or optional.

Example 5–7

$$T = \sum(2, 3, 7, 9, 11, 13) + \sum_\phi(1, 10, 15)$$

1	0 0 0 1 ✓	1, 3	0 0 – 1 ✓	1, 3, 9, 11	– 0 – 1	**A**
2	0 0 1 0 ✓	1, 9	– 0 0 1 ✓	2, 3, 10, 11	– 0 1 –	**B**
3	0 0 1 1 ✓	2, 3	0 0 1 – ✓	3, 7, 11, 15	– – 1 1	**C**
9	1 0 0 1 ✓	2, 10	– 0 1 0 ✓	9, 11, 13, 15	1 – – 1	**D**
10	1 0 1 0 ✓	3, 7	0 – 1 1 ✓			
7	0 1 1 1 ✓	3, 11	– 0 1 1 ✓			
11	1 0 1 1 ✓	9, 11	1 0 – 1 ✓			
13	1 1 0 1 ✓	9, 13	1 – 0 1 ✓			
15	1 1 1 1 ✓	10, 11	1 0 1 – ✓			
		7, 15	– 1 1 1 ✓			
		11, 15	1 – 1 1 ✓			
		13, 15	1 1 – 1 ✓			

In the tabulations we combine the optional terms with the required terms in order to find a set of prime implicants which satisfies all the terms, but when we draw the prime implicant chart in Fig. 5–33 we want to select prime implicants which satisfy only the required terms in the standard sum. Hence the columns in Fig. 5–33 do not include those corresponding to terms 1, 10, and 15. The fact that the prime implicants finally chosen may include optional terms is of no consequence. Effectively, what the optional terms do is to give us a larger group of prime implicants from which to make a choice, without increasing the number of columns to be satisfied. We note also in Fig. 5–33 that the number of crosses in a given row is no

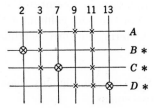

Fig. 5–33. Prime implicant chart in which optional terms are included in forming the prime implicants. The optional terms, $\Sigma_\phi(1, 10, 15)$ are not included in the column headings.

longer an integral power of 2, as it is when the prime implicants are derived from required terms only. The missing crosses in the various rows of the prime implicant chart are those which would appear in columns corresponding to optional terms.

The chart of Fig. 5–33 is a rather simple one to complete. Circled entries in columns 2, 7, and 13 establish B, C, and D as primary basis rows and these three among them account for all the remaining columns in the chart. Accordingly the transmission function is found to be

$T = X'Y + YZ + WZ$.   This is the same function that was found by the map method through the choices made in Fig. 5–23(b).

5.6   Algebraic Determination of Minimum Sums

The method for selecting the terms of a minimum sum described in Art. 5.5 has the disadvantage that it depends to some extent upon skill in determining basis rows, after the primary basis rows have been marked.   In simple problems this is not particularly apparent, but as the complexity of the prime implicant table increases it becomes more and more difficult to evaluate, without considerable trial and error, the relative merits of various alternatives.   This article will describe an algebraic process that determines all the minimum sums which satisfy a prime implicant table.*

Consider the prime implicant chart shown in Fig. 5–30.   For the "0" term of the function there are crosses in rows A, B, and C.   Let us express this by saying that we can write a Boolean sum

$$P_0 = A + B + C$$

By this we mean that the transmission required to produce the "0" term will be present if any one or more of the sub-set A, B, C of the prime implicants is present in the minimum sum selected.

For the next column of the chart in Fig. 5–30, which represents the "1" term, the corresponding sum is

$$P_1 = A + B + D$$

Now, considering only these two columns, let us form the product of the two sums

$$F_m = P_0 P_1 = (A + B + C)(A + B + D)$$

If we now carry out the indicated multiplication we will obtain a sum of products, and each product will contain one variable from each of the original sums.   For the product above the indicated multiplication yields

$$F_m = AA + AB + AD + AB + BB + BD + AC + BC + CD$$

When this expression is reduced by the application of the theorems of Boolean algebra there remains

$$F_m = A + B + CD$$

a result which could, of course, have been written by inspection of the original product of sums.   This final expression says that the require-

---

* S. R. Petrick, "A Direct Determination of the Irredundant Forms of a Boolean Function from the Set of Prime Implicants," AFCRC–TR–56–110, April, 1956, Air Force Cambridge Research Center.

ments of columns "0" and "1" of the chart are satisfied by the selection of row A, or row B, or both rows C and D, and this will be found true by inspection of the chart.   More important, though, is the fact that this algebraic process discloses two alternatives which require only a single prime implicant, A or B.   The third alternative of selecting rows C and D is not minimum in any sense.   It appears in the F_m, or *minimizing function*, because it is a combination which is not algebraically redundant. We normally would choose, if alternatives exist, a combination which contains a minimum number of prime implicants, taking into account, of course, the number of literals in the various prime implicants.

In the preceding discussion we have included only two of the columns of the prime implicant chart.   The process may now be extended to include all the columns, and the F_m found by carrying out the complete multiplication is a sum of terms each of which represents a selection of prime implicants which satisfies all the columns, and which is not redundant algebraically.   From these terms we may readily choose one or more terms which contain a minimum number of prime implicants, and which therefore represent minimum sums.

For the function treated in Example 5–4 we write

$$F_m = (A + B + C)(A + B + D)(A + C + E)(A + D + E + F)$$
$$(C)(C + E)(E + F)(B)(B + D)(D + F)(F) = BCF$$

The reduction in this example is quite simple because three of the "sums" consist of one of the variables B, C, and F, and each of the remaining sums contains at least one of these variables.   We find that this selection is the same as that shown in Fig. 5–30, and we also observe that the algebraic reduction was swift because B, C, and F were all primary basis rows.

A simple illustration of alternative minimum sums is given by Example 5–5, for which the prime implicant chart is drawn in Fig. 5–31.   For this we may write the minimizing function

$$F_m = (A)(A + C)(C)(A)(A + D)(D + E)(F)(E + F + G)(A)$$
$$(A + B + C)(B + C)(A)(A + B)(B + H)(G + H)$$
$$= ACF(D + E)(B + H)(G + H)$$
$$= ACF(DH + EH + BDG + BEG)$$

From this expression the choice of either rows A, C, D, F, H, or rows A, C, E, F, H to form a minimum sum is indicated, and this is the result previously found.

It is not necessary in writing F_m above to write a term for each column, because there are many obvious redundancies.   The expression is written in full only to show the method more clearly.   No redundancies occur, however, when we write the minimizing function for the prime implicant table of Example 5–6, Fig. 5–32,

$$
\begin{aligned}
F_m &= (A + B)(A + C)(C + E)(E + G)(B + D)(D + F)(F + H) \\
&\quad (G + H) \\
&= (A + BC)(E + CG)(D + BF)(H + FG) \\
&= (AE + ACG + BCE + BCG)(DH + DFG + BFH + BFG) \\
&= ADEH + ADEFG + ABEFH + ABEFG + ACDGH \\
&\quad + ACDFG \,(+ ABCFGH) + ABCFG + BCDEH \\
&\quad + BCEFH + BCEFG + BCDGH + BCDFG + BCFGH \\
&\quad + BCFG
\end{aligned}
$$

The term in parentheses in the final sum of products is algebraically redundant, but no other terms are redundant. However, we observe that two terms contain only four prime implicants in each, while all others contain five. We hence would expect to choose either rows A, D, E, H, or rows B, C, F, G, in forming a minimum sum. The former of these was chosen by the selection of basis rows in Fig. 5–32.

It is unlikely that the algebraic method is of advantage in treating problems of the general complexity of those discussed above. Perhaps the best indication for using it is that a selection made by the use of the prime implicant chart is difficult enough to be questionable. For the treatment of extremely complex problems, there is no question that the algebraic method is attractive, particularly since it can be adapted to machine computation processes.

5.7   The Residue Test

When a function is expanded about one of its variables, say X, theorem 20 shows that the resulting expression can be written in the form $T = XR_1 + X'R_2$. Theorem $20'$ gives the expansion as a product of terms and either form of the expansion may be used as the basis for a residue test. The test developed here is based on the form given by theorem 20.

In the expansion R_1 is the original expression for T after X has been placed equal to 1 and X' equal to 0, while R_2 is the expression for T after X has been placed equal to 0 and X' equal to 1. These two expressions we call the residues of the expansion about X, or simply the X residues.

The residue test is a process which enables us to determine, by examining the residues, whether the variable about which the function is expanded, or its complement, need actually be represented in a switching circuit which realizes that function. The test has become somewhat academic, for if the transmission is a minimum sum, derived say by the Quine-McCluskey method, a redundant literal cannot be present in its algebraic expression. Nevertheless, the test is worth examining for a variety of reasons, of which the most important is that it throws further light on the nature of switching functions and the mechanics of the minimizing process. In designing contact networks it assures the designer that if he has reached the lower bound established by the residue test he need not try any further to reduce his network. It is a convenient check against gross error. If, for example, we have reason

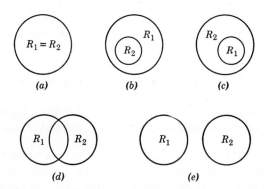

Fig. 5–34. Possible relations between residues in residue test.

to believe that a particular contact in a network is not needed, we can resolve the question by use of the residue test without considering any other of the contacts and regardless of whether the transmission function of the network as built represents a minimum sum or not.

In theory, the residue test depends upon a comparison of the two residues of the expansion to determine which of the five possible situations illustrated by the Venn diagrams in Fig. 5–34 are applicable. The algebraic relations between the residues are listed here for each of these situations.

(a) $R_1 = R_2$
   $R_1 R_2 = R_1 = R_2$
   $R_1 + R_2 = R_1 = R_2$

(b) $R_1 > R_2$ (R_1 *contains* R_2)
   $R_1 R_2 = R_2$
   $R_1 + R_2 = R_1$

(c) $R_1 < R_2$ (R_2 *contains* R_1)
   $R_1 R_2 = R_1$
   $R_1 + R_2 = R_2$

(d) Some parts of each residue are the same
   $R_1 R_2 \neq R_1 \neq R_2$
   $R_1 + R_2 \neq R_1 \neq R_2$

(e)   Residues have no parts in common

$R_1 R_2 = 0$

$R_1 + R_2 \neq R_1 \neq R_2$

We determine the meanings of the five situations illustrated as follows:

(a)   Let $R_1 = R_2 = R$. Then, $T = XR + X'R = R$. Hence, both the X and X' literals are redundant.

(b)   If R_1 contains R_2, and if R_0 is the part of R_1 which is not common to R_2, we can write $R_1 = R_0 + R_2$. Then $T = XR_0 + XR_2 + X'R_2 = XR_0 + R_2$. The conclusion is that the X literal is required but that the X' literal vanishes.

(c)   If R_2 contains R_1, an argument similar to that for situation (b) demonstrates that the X' literal is required but that the X literal vanishes.

(d) (e)   In these situations both X and X' will be required. None of the relations found in situations (a), (b), and (c) are applicable.

It is clear, from the examination of the five ways in which residues can be related, that the situations represented by (a), (b), and (c) mean that a redundant literal can appear in the algebraic expression of a transmission function. This cannot be true of a minimum sum expression derived by the Quine-McCluskey method. That procedure exhaustively eliminates all redundant literals in forming the prime implicants, and then selects a minimum set of prime implicants to express the function. Hence we never need apply a residue test to a function expressed as a minimum sum (or a minimum product).

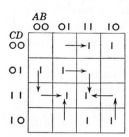

Fig. 5–35. Residue test applied to a mapped function.

It is interesting to observe that there is a version of the residue test which can be applied directly to a function represented on a map. In Fig. 5–35 a function is represented on a map by entries indicating the states for which the transmission is 1. For all other states the transmission is 0. Now consider the map location where the states of the variables change from 0100 to 1100, as shown by one of the arrows in Fig. 5–35. That change of state means that the variable A changes from 0 to 1 while all other variables remain unchanged. But this change of one variable causes a change of transmission from 0 to 1 also. Since the states of all other variables remain unchanged, the change of transmission must have been due to the physical presence of an A contact in the network, which in closing caused the network transmission to change from 0 to 1. However, in the second row of Fig. 5–35 we see an arrow corresponding to the change of state from 0101 to 1101, and again the A relay alone has gone from the 0 (unoperated) state to the 1 (operated) state. In doing so, however, the network transmission has gone from 1 to 0. Since the other three variables remained unchanged while the A relay was operating, the change of network transmission could only be caused by the physical presence of an A' contact which opened when the A relay operated. Thus, by a physical argument, we see that this network will require at least one A and at least one A' contact in order to have the transmission mapped in Fig. 5–35.

Similarly, we may examine the requirements for contacts on the B relay. The B relay changes its state of operation only when there is a change, in either direction, between column 1 and column 2 on the map or between column 3 and column 4. Changes between column 1 and column 4 or between column 2 and column 3 do not involve the B relay. For the function shown there are only two places where the transmission changes value when B changes. In going from state 0011 to state 0111 the B relay operates and the transmission changes from 0 to 1. Also in going from states 1011 to 1111 the B relay operates and the transmission changes from 0 to 1. These transitions both indicate that a B contact is needed, but there are no transitions in which the operation of the B relay alone causes the transmission to change from 1 to 0. Hence no B' contact is needed to realize this function. The remainder of the arrows shown in Fig. 5–35 point out transitions which require the presence of C, C', D, and D' contacts in the network.

Finally, we may observe that when the residue test is applied to a transmission function expressed as a standard sum it is merely necessary to carry out a process of factoring in order to write the residues. Consider the function $T = \sum(5, 7, 11, 15)$. When this is written algebraically we have $T = A'BC'D + A'BCD + AB'CD + ABCD$. Suppose we want to apply the residue test to the B variable. We may perform the expansion by factoring out B and B' to obtain $T = B(A'C'D + A'CD + ACD) + B'(ACD)$. The residue of B' is the single term ACD and we see that this is also one of the terms of the residue of B. Hence R_B contains $R_{B'}$ and the B' literal is not needed. In general, when we treat the standard-sum form it is merely necessary to compare the residues term by term and apply the rules derived, or to note as in the above example

$$T = B(A'C'D + A'CD) + (B + B')(ACD)$$
$$= B(A'C'D + A'CD) + ACD$$

We also note that when this transmission is reduced to a minimum sum it becomes $T = A'BD + ACD$. The literals contained in this expression are exactly those which the residue test shows to be required, that is, the literals B', C', and D' are unnecessary.

5.8 Operations Using Decimal Symbols

It is convenient and compact to specify a standard sum or a standard product as a set of decimal numbers, which are the equivalents of a set of binary numbers, which in turn represent algebraic terms. It would be still more convenient if we could work directly with the decimal numbers and not have to convert to binary or literal forms to perform algebraic operations. Fortunately, some of the more important operations involving groups of terms can be performed without converting the decimal numbers. An interesting example is in the application of the residue test to a function which is specified in its standard sum form by a set of decimal numbers.* We can apply the test to any desired complementary pair of literals or we can use it to test all literals exhaustively.

In Art. 5.7 we saw that by expanding a standard sum its residues could be compared term by term. We will repeat this process on a function that was treated in the preceding article, but for the moment we will use binary numbers instead of the algebraic terms that we previously wrote. The function was $T = \sum(5, 7, 11, 15)$ and if we express it with binary number equivalents, $T = \sum(0101, 0111, 1011, 1111)$. To test the variable B we will "expand" the function about the second digit of the binary number and merely indicate the "expansion" by writing

$$T = (1) \cdot \sum (0\text{--}01, \quad 0\text{--}11, \quad 1\text{--}11) + (0) \cdot \sum (1\text{--}11)$$

We note that the 0 residue is the single term $(1\text{--}11)$ and that this is one of the terms contained in the 1 residue. Hence we know that the B' literal must vanish.

It is apparent that in order to find the residues of a given expansion by numerical methods, our problem is to determine for a given binary digit position whether that digit is a 1 or a 0, and then to group the terms to form the 1 residue and the 0 residue. Moreover, we want to be able to do this without actually writing any binary numbers.

The method we use depends upon the relations shown in Fig. 5–36, where we see that the familiar decimal point has its counterpart, when we deal with binary numbers, that we call the binary point. If in a given decimal number we shift the decimal point one digit position to

---

* A. A. Mullin and W. G. Kellner, "A Residue Test for Boolean Functions," Unpublished teaching memorandum, Department of Electrical Engineering, Massachusetts Institute of Technology, November 1955.

the left, we divide the number by ten. If in a binary number we shift the binary point one digit position to the left we divide the number by two.

With this in mind consider a binary number, such as 101101, which may represent one of the terms in a standard sum. It is equivalent to the decimal number 45. We would like to know whether, say, the third

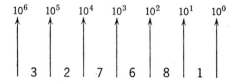

When a decimal point is placed in one of the indicated positions its effect is to divide the decimal number by the power of 10 shown.

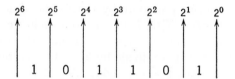

When a binary point is placed in one of the indicated positions its effect is to divide the binary number by the power of 2 shown.

Fig. 5–36. Comparison of decimal and binary points.

digit from the left in this binary number is a 1 or a 0, without actually writing the binary number. Suppose we put a binary point after the third digit from the left and write 101.101. This number means

$$2^2 + 2^0 + 2^{-1} + 2^{-3} = 4 + 1 + \tfrac{1}{2} + \tfrac{1}{8} = 5\tfrac{5}{8}$$

By locating the binary point at the position shown we have actually divided the original number by 2^3 or 8. If we divide the equivalent decimal number 45 by 8 we obtain exactly the same result, $5\tfrac{5}{8}$. Now discard all the binary digits to the right of the binary point. The result is the binary number 101, equivalent to the decimal number 5 which we get by discarding the decimal fraction $\tfrac{5}{8}$. The whole-number part of the quotient $\tfrac{45}{8}$, or 5, is an odd number, and this indicates that the right-hand digit of its binary equivalent is a 1. If the whole number part of the decimal quotient is even, the right-hand binary digit is a 0.

Our general procedure for determining whether a given variable in a term of a standard sum is primed or unprimed is to determine whether the digit which represents it in binary form is a 0 or a 1, respectively.

This we do, in effect, by dividing the binary number by the power of 2 that places the binary point to the right of the digit in question, but actually we do it by dividing the decimal equivalent of the binary number by that power of 2, and then observe whether the whole number part of the quotient is an even or an odd number.

A formal and compact statement of the principle involved* is:

The decimal integer d will be said to contain 2^k in its binary number representation if in the following equation expressing d in the base 2, $b_k = 1$.

$$d = b_n 2^n + b_{n-1} 2^{n-1} + \cdots + b_k 2^k + \cdots b_1 2^1 + b_0$$
$$(0 \leqslant k \leqslant n)$$

If we denote by [a] the greatest integer not exceeding a, where a is a real number, then it is possible to state the following theorem:

THEOREM 1   The decimal number d contains the number 2^k in its binary number representation if and only if $\left[\dfrac{d}{2^k}\right]$ is odd. $k = 0, 1, 2, 3 \ldots$

We will illustrate this procedure by testing the same function that we used previously, $T = \sum(5, 7, 11, 15)$, and again we will apply the test to the B variable. This requires that we move the binary point two places to the left, or that we divide by $2^2 = 4$. The results, term by term, are: $\frac{5}{4} = 1 +$, odd; $\frac{7}{4} = 1 +$, odd; $\frac{11}{4} = 2 +$, even; $\frac{15}{4} = 3 +$, odd. Hence we may group the decimal numbers as residues in the form $T = B \cdot \sum(5, 7, 15) + B' \cdot \sum(11)$.

Now examine the binary equivalents of decimal 15 and decimal 11, for which we find $15 \rightarrow 1111$ and $11 \rightarrow 1011$. We can indicate that we have factored out the B digit by writing $15 \rightarrow B(1\text{–}11)$ and $11 \rightarrow B'(1\text{–}11)$. In this form, the residues are shown to be identical. We can also detect the fact that the residues of 1111 and 1011 are equal when expanded about the B digit by replacing the 0 in 1011 by a 1. This requires that we add 2^2 to the binary number, or 4 to the decimal number. Hence in the expansion represented by $T = B \cdot \sum(5, 7, 15) + B' \cdot \sum(11)$ we add 4 to the 11 to get $B' \cdot \sum(15)$. Since this numerical residue is contained in the B residue, B' is not needed.

To summarize, we note that in the general expansion $T = XR_1 + X'R_2$, when R_1 and R_2 are written as groups of decimal numbers found by first dividing by some 2^k, and then observing which quotients are odd and which are even, those numbers in the X' group all have 0 and those in the X group all have 1 in the X digit position. We therefore modify the X' group by adding the decimal equivalent of 2^k to all numbers in that group. The residue groups thus found may be compared term for term for equality or inclusion.

---

* Mullin and Kellner, *ibid*. The reference contains a proof of theorem 1 which is here omitted.

Example 5–8

$$T(A, B, C, D) = \sum(2, 3, 4, 5, 6, 10, 11, 12, 13, 14)$$

Apply the residue test to all variables.
Expand about D and add 2^0 to the D' residue group.

$$T = D(3, 5, 11, 13) + D'(2, 4, 6, 10, 12, 14)$$
$$D'(3, 5, 7, 11, 13, 15)$$

The D' residue contains the D residue; D is not essential.
Expand about C and add 2^1 to the C' residue group.

$$T = C(2, 3, 6, 10, 11, 14) + C'(4, 5, 12, 13)$$
$$C'(6, 7, 14, 15)$$

Both C and C' are essential.
Expand about B and add 2^2 to the B' residue group.

$$T = B(4, 5, 6, 12, 13, 14) + B'(2, 3, 10, 11)$$
$$B'(6, 7, 14, 15)$$

Both B and B' are essential.
Expand about A and add 2^3 to the A' residue group.

$$T = A(10, 11, 12, 13, 14) + A'(2, 3, 4, 5, 6)$$
$$A'(10, 11, 12, 13, 14)$$

The A and A' residues are equal. Hence both A and A' are nonessential.

One further example indicates the manner in which this procedure using decimal numbers produces a desired result with a minimum of detail.

Example 5–9

Determine whether C or C' are required in the function

$$T(A, B, C, D, E, F, G) = \sum(8, 9, 10, 14, 26, 45, 67, 79, 83, 95)$$

Group the decimal numbers after division by 2^4, and add 2^4 to all members of the C' residual group.

$$T = C(26, 83, 95) + C'(8, 9, 10, 14, 45, 67, 79)$$
$$C'(24, 25, 26, 30, 61, 83, 95)$$

The C' residue contains the C residue; hence C is not essential.

An even more important process which can be performed with decimal-number representations is the Quine-McCluskey method for finding prime implicants.* Referring to Example 5–4 we see that each binary number is identified by its decimal-number source or sources. Now consider the following entry found in the second column:

$$2, 6 \qquad 0 - 1\ 0$$

This entry was derived from the terms

$$2 \qquad 0\ 0\ 1\ 0$$
$$6 \qquad 0\ 1\ 1\ 0$$

by eliminating the second digit. All other entries in that column resulted from the application of the same rule. But note that since every pair of binary terms that so combine must differ by a single digit, their decimal equivalents must differ by a power of 2. In this instance $6 - 2 = 4 = 2^2$. This is a necessary condition but not a sufficient one.

In the first column of Example 5–4, the decimal numbers are grouped in the ascending order of the index numbers, and we compare numbers in one group only with those in the group having the next higher index number. But although we can combine the terms 2 and 6, because they differ by 2^2 and have index numbers of 1, 2, respectively, we cannot combine the terms 8 and 6, even though they differ by 2^1 and have the index numbers 1, 2. The reason is, that, in order to combine, the number of higher index must have all the 1's of the number of lower index in the same digit positions, and also must contain one additional 1 in a position occupied by a 0 in the lower-index number. Hence the higher-index number must be numerically *larger* than the lower-index number, a condition which is not true of the 8, 6 pair.

The rule for combining two decimal numbers is then stated: If P_i is a number of index i and Q_{i+1} is a number of index $(i + 1)$, they may be combined to denote a new term P, Q provided the difference $(Q - P)$ is positive and equal to 2^k, $(k = 0, 1, 2, 3, \ldots)$. The Boolean variable eliminated by this combination is that represented by the 2^k digit in a binary number representation.

The combinations found in the first column are entered in the second column by recording each pair of decimal numbers with the lower number written first. We must also be certain to maintain the partitions established in the first column; that is, a group in the second column

---

* It is a pleasure to record that this treatment is based on the work of two students during the period they were studying Switching Circuits at the Massachusetts Institute of Technology. They discovered the method independently and then collaborated in preparing a class memorandum: P. W. Abraham and J. G. Nordahl, "Modified McCluskey-Quine Reduction Procedure," November, 1955.

must contain only numbers derived from two adjacent groups in the first column.

It is convenient, although not necessary, to associate with each combined pair of decimal designators, the numerical difference between them, which must always be a number from the series $1, 2, 4, 8, \ldots 2^k$. When the difference is thus written it expedites the next set of comparisons, for then we seek to combine only those terms which have had the same variable eliminated in the first set of comparisons. Hence we need compare only those terms having the same first difference.

In the second set of comparisons, the same rules apply, with the modification that we examine the differences between the leading numbers of terms in adjacent groups, and this difference again must be a power of 2 to make a valid combination. For example, two of the terms in the second column of Example 5–4 are

$$0, 1 \qquad (1)$$
$$\overline{}$$
$$2, 3 \qquad (1)$$
$$\overline{}$$

These first-column combinations both have a difference of 1, as indicated by the number in parentheses. There is the required difference of 1 in the index for numbers in these two groups, and the leading numbers 0 and 2 differ by 2^1 (as, of course, do the 1 and 3). These terms hence combine to form $0, 1, 2, 3(1, 2)$. We note at this step that both difference numbers are recorded.*

We should observe now that instead of the term $0, 1, 2, 3(1, 2)$, formed as shown, we might have combined the terms $0, 2(2)$ and $1, 3(2)$ to form $0, 2, 1, 3(2, 1)$. The two forms are identical and we certainly need not write both of them. The simple rule suggested is that we retain only the form in which the decimal number group forms a nondecreasing series. Hence when we form the group $0, 1, 2, 3(1, 2)$ we check off in the preceding column not only the $0, 1(1)$ and $2, 3(1)$ but also $0, 2(2)$ and $1, 3(2)$.

A complete reduction is shown in Example 5–10, working with the same function as in Example 5–5 so that the two methods may be compared.

---

* It has been pointed out that some of these descriptive numbers are redundant, for they are implied by other numbers. For example, 0–$3(1, 2)$ is quite as descriptive as $0, 1, 2, 3(1, 2)$. Some prefer the more compact description, but others find it easier to retain all the details.

Example 5–10

$$T(A, B, C, D, E) = \sum (0, 1, 3, 8, 9, 13, 14, 15, 16, 17, 19, 24, 25, 27, 31)$$

0 ✓	0, 1	(1) ✓	0, 1, 8, 9		(1, 8) ✓	
1 ✓	0, 8	(8) ✓	0, 1, 16, 17		(1, 16) ✓	
8 ✓	0, 16	(16) ✓	0, 8, 16, 24		(8, 16) ✓	
16 ✓	1, 3	(2) ✓	1, 3, 17, 19		(2, 16) **C**	
3 ✓	1, 9	(8) ✓	1, 9, 17, 25		(8, 16) ✓	
9 ✓	1, 17	(16) ✓	8, 9, 24, 25		(1, 16) ✓	
17 ✓	8, 9	(1) ✓	16, 17, 24, 25		(1, 8) ✓	
24 ✓	8, 24	(16) ✓	17, 19, 25, 27		(2, 8) **B**	
13 ✓	16, 17	(1) ✓	0, 1, 8, 9, 16, 17, 24, 25		(1, 8, 16) **A**	
14 ✓	16, 24	(8) ✓				
19 ✓	3, 19	(16) ✓				
25 ✓	9, 13	(4) **D**				
15 ✓	9, 25	(16) ✓				
27 ✓	17, 19	(2) ✓				
31 ✓	17, 25	(8) ✓				
	24, 25	(1) ✓				
	13, 15	(2) **E**				
	14, 15	(1) **F**				
	19, 27	(8) ✓				
	25, 27	(2) ✓				
	15, 31	(16) **G**				
	27, 31	(4) **H**				

Note that the prime implicant A in Example 5–10 was derived from the terms 0, 1, 8, 9 (1, 8) and 16, 17, 24, 25 (1, 8), but it also accounted, in the checking-off process, for the terms 0, 1, 16, 17 (1, 16), 0, 8, 16, 24 (8, 16), 1, 9, 17, 25 (8, 16), and 8, 9, 24, 25 (1, 16).

Finally, we must be able to write an algebraic equivalent of a prime implicant when it is described only by its decimal-number components and their differences. Consider the algebraic interpretation of prime implicant B in Example 5–10, which is described by the group 17, 19, 25, 27 (2, 8). In the tabulation given below we have written immediately under the variables A, B, C, D, E, the decimal equivalent of a binary 1 contained in each digit position in a binary representation. We note now that the smallest decimal number in the combined descriptive group must account for all the 1's in the final binary representation. Hence the number 17 requires the 1's under A and E. Next, the differences shown in the parentheses indicate which variables were

A	B	C	D	E	
16	8	4	2	1	
1				1	Required by 17
	–		–		Blanks indicated by (2, 8)
		0			Must be 0 in 17
1	–	0	–	1	Compare with Example 5–5

eliminated, and hence account for the blanks under B and D. Finally, the digits in any remaining positions must be 0's in order that the smallest decimal number be preserved, so we enter a 0 in the C position. If we combine all these entries we obtain the designation 1–0–1.

5.9   Problems in Factoring

Strictly speaking, the factoring problem belongs in the realm of circuit design rather than in that of minimization, algebraic or otherwise. The minimum sum or the minimum product form the starting point of many designs.*

It has been observed that a function map may serve somewhat as a guide in indicating various ways in which a function can be factored.†
The map in Fig. 5–37 shows a function having three prime implicants, all of which are present in the minimum sum $T = ABC' + ABD + BC'D$. The term $ABC'D$ is included in each prime implicant and the variable B is in all four of the entries in the map. It hence is not surprising that B is a factor in all the prime implicants. When B is factored out, we have $T = B(AC' + AD + C'D)$. Further than this, the map is of little help. However, since all possible pairs of the variables A, C', and D appear within the parentheses above, it is evident

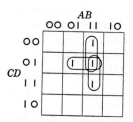

Fig. 5–37.   Map indication of a factorable function.

that additional factoring can be performed by starting with any one of the variables within the parenthesis. We thus obtain the following alternative factored forms:

$$T = B[A(C' + D) + C'D]$$
$$= B[C'(A + D) + AD]$$
$$= B[D(A + C') + AC']$$

---

* In designing switching circuits with rectifiers as the basic components we are frequently limited to so-called two-stage circuits. Such circuits realize minimum sums or minimum products with no factoring. See Art. 9.3.

† M. Karnaugh, "The Map Method for Synthesis of Combinational Logic Circuits," *Trans. A.I.E.E.*, Part I, Communications and Electronics, Vol. 72, November 1953, pp. 593–599.

It thus appears that whatever guidance a map might give will probably depend on how well map patterns are known and recognized as indicating a variety of factors.

We are reasonably sure that by the methods presented in this chapter we can carry minimization to the point of getting a minimum sum or minimum product, and we can even display the alternatives among these if such exist. In factoring, however, we have little to offer aside from exhausting all possibilities for grouping the variables. Even then, we are not sure that we cannot do better by being a little more clever. One writer shows some particularly frustrating examples.*

Exhaustive study of the function $T = AB + BD + DE' + CD + ACE$, which is a minimum sum, indicates that the grouping $T = A(B + CE) + D(B + C + E')$ has only eight literals and all others contain nine literals. But, if we observe that in the second term $C + E' = CE + E'$, and write the transmission in the form

$$T = A(B + CE) + D(B + CE + E')$$
$$= A(B + CE) + D(B + CE) + DE'$$
$$= (A + D)(B + CE) + DE'$$

we finally have an expression which contains only seven literals.

In another example, Burkhart emphasizes the point that the elimination of variables and redundant terms does not necessarily lead to true minimization. Consider the minimum sum, $T = ABE + ABF + ACDE + BCDF$. Straightforward factoring of this yields the expression

$$T = AB(E + F) + CD(AE + BF)$$

But now we can observe that

$$AB(E + F) = AB(AE + BF)$$

Algebraically we have introduced redundant literals within the parentheses, but note that

$$T = AB(AE + BF) + CD(AE + BF)$$
$$= (AB + CD)(AE + BF)$$

The number of literals contained in the transmission function has been reduced from ten to eight by not insisting on every possible elimination of a redundant literal.†

---

* W. H. Burkhart, "Theorem Minimization," *Proceedings of the Association for Computing Machinery*, Pittsburgh, Pennsylvania, May 2 and 3, 1952, pp. 259–263.

† Both of Burkhart's minimum factored functions may be found by simple factoring of the complementary function. The function in his first example is $T = AB + BD + DE' + CD + ACE$. Its complement is $T' = (A' + B')(B' + D')(D' + E)(C' + D')(A' + C' + E')$. When the indicated multiplications are per-

Later we shall see other instances where similar advantages arise from considering the use of deliberate and controlled redundancy. One of the most important of these is the "valid sneak"—a tie path which is eliminated by the minimizing process but which is found advantageous in final synthesis.

It does appear at times that there is such a thing as too much minimization.

PROBLEMS

5.1   Derive with the aid of four-variable maps minimal factored expressions for the functions of the variables A, B, C, D represented by the following standard sums:

1. $\sum (2, 3, 5, 7, 8, 12, 14)$
2. $\sum (0, 4, 6, 7, 10, 12, 13, 14)$
3. $\sum (0, 1, 2, 3, 4, 6, 8, 9, 10, 11)$
4. $\sum (1, 3, 7, 9, 12, 13, 14, 15)$

5.2   The following functions of the variables A, B, C, D are described as standard sums in which some of the members are optional, as indicated by the subscript ϕ. Use four-variable maps to determine minimum-sum expressions for each function, making optimum use of the optional terms.

Design a minimum contact network for the realization of each function.

1. $\sum (2, 5, 6, 9, 13, 14) + \sum_\phi (0, 7, 8, 10, 15)$
2. $\sum (0, 5, 9, 10, 12, 15) + \sum_\phi (2, 7, 8, 13)$
3. $\sum (4, 10, 11, 13) + \sum_\phi (0, 2, 5, 15)$
4. $\sum (2, 6, 7, 8, 10) + \sum_\phi (0, 12, 13, 15)$
5. $\sum (1, 4, 6, 8, 11, 12) + \sum_\phi (2, 5, 13, 15)$

5.3   Design contact networks which have the following transmission functions and use the specified number of contacts and springs.

	Number of Contacts	Number of Springs
1. $T = \sum (0, 1, 14)$	7	11
2. $T = \sum (0, 3. 12)$	9	14
3. $T = \sum (0, 1, 2, 5, 6)$	6	10
4. $T = \sum (0, 1, 2, 5, 6, 7)$	7	11
5. $T = \sum (0, 1, 2, 13, 14)$	8	12
6. $T = \sum (0, 1, 2, 3, 4, 11)$	6	11
7. $T = \sum (0, 1, 2, 5, 6, 13, 14)$	7	11
8. $T = \sum (4, 5, 7, 8, 9, 11, 12, 15)$	8	13
9. $T = \sum (5, 6, 9, 10, 11, 12, 13, 14, 15)$	8	14

5.4   Write the transmission

$$T(A, B, C, D) = \sum (1, 2, 4, 5, 6, 11, 12, 13, 14, 15)$$

formed, and redundant terms are eliminated, the result is $T' = A'D' + B'(D' + E)$ $(C' + E')$. Hence, $T = (A + D)(B + CE + DE') = (A + D)(B + CE) + DE'$, which is the form obtained by Burkhart.

as two different minimum sums. Design a minimal contact network having this transmission.

5.5 Determine the minimum sum, or the minimum sums for the given transmission functions:

1. $T = \Pi(3, 10, 12, 17, 22, 31)$
2. $T = \sum(1, 2, 3, 4, 5, 6, 8, 10, 12)$
3. $T = \sum(0, 1, 2, 5, 6, 7, 8, 10, 12, 13, 14, 15, 41, 57)$
4. $T = \sum(0, 1, 3, 8, 9, 13, 14, 15, 16, 17, 19, 25, 27, 31)$
5. $T = \sum(3, 5, 8, 9, 10, 12, 13, 14, 19, 23, 25, 26, 27, 28, 31)$
6. $T = \sum(0, 2, 4, 6, 9, 10, 13, 14, 15, 16, 17, 21, 26, 28, 30, 31)$
7. $T = \sum(0, 1, 4, 6, 12, 14, 15, 17, 19, 20, 21, 23, 26, 28, 30)$
8. $T = \sum(0, 2, 6, 14, 18, 21, 27, 32, 41, 49, 53, 62)$
9. $T = \sum(5, 10, 13, 14, 21, 22, 29, 30, 34, 37, 42, 45, 50, 53, 54, 61)$
10. $T = \sum(0, 2, 5, 8, 10, 12, 13, 16, 18, 21, 24, 26, 28, 29, 30, 32, 34,$
    $37, 39, 40, 42, 45, 46, 48, 50, 53, 55, 56, 58, 61)$

5.6 For the function

$$T(A, B, C, D, E, F) =$$
$$\sum(8, 9, 10, 11, 13, 15, 29, 33, 35, 41, 42, 43, 47, 49, 51, 57, 59)$$

1. Write the prime implicants.
2. Determine the minimum sum or sums.

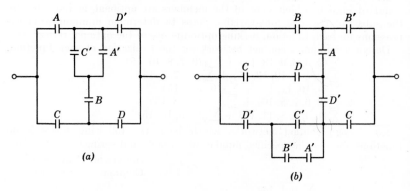

(a)

(b)

Problem 5.7.

5.7 For each of the two networks shown:
1. Write the transmission function in a simple form.
2. By use of the residue test determine a lower bound on the number of contacts required in any network having the same transmission.
3. Derive an equivalent contact network having as few contacts (and springs) as possible.

5.8 For each of the following transmission functions, (a) use the residue test to determine the essential variables; (b) design a minimum contact network, using the information found in part (a). Note: the residue test establishes a lower bound on the number of contacts required, but there is no assurance that a network can be designed using as few contacts as the test indicates.

1. $T = \sum (2, 3, 4, 5, 6, 10, 11, 12, 13, 14)$
2. $T = \Pi (0, 1, 2, 4, 7, 9, 10, 12, 15)$
3. $T = \Pi (1, 3, 5, 7, 8, 10, 11, 12, 14)$
4. $T = \sum (3, 6, 8, 10, 11, 13, 14, 15)$
5. $T = \sum (0, 2, 3, 4, 5, 8, 10, 11, 12, 13, 14, 15)$
6. $T = \sum (2, 3, 4, 5, 6, 7, 13, 22, 23, 30, 31)$

5.9 Design a minimum contact network to realize the transmission function described by

$$T = \sum (0, 4, 5, 7, 9, 11, 16, 20, 21, 23, 25, 27)$$

Show whether or not the network you design is *necessarily* the optimum contact network having the given transmission function.

CHAPTER 6

Multi-terminal contact networks

The two-terminal network is a basic structure in all switching circuits built with relay contacts. It yields a single switching function of any prescribed form.

Problems of more practical consequence, however, frequently call for the simultaneous execution of a number of switching duties. The designer has the opportunity to meet such requirements by means of multi-terminal networks, and he may be able to make them more economical than mere aggregates of two-terminal networks.

In this chapter we shall discuss some basic procedures for developing economic syntheses as they apply to multi-terminal problems in general. Also, we shall examine more specialized methods for use in particular kinds of problems.

6.1 Multiple-Output Contact Networks

We must again make a clear distinction between a relay switching circuit and its associated contact network. Figure 6–1 shows the most common form of multiple-output relay switching circuit, and the multi-terminal contact network contained in it. The circuit is arranged with an internal battery so that input conditions can be established by applying grounds to combinations of the input terminals $1 \ldots n$, thus operating the corresponding combinations of the relays

$X_1 \ldots X_n$. The associated contact network has a single "input" terminal, 0, from which ground potential is transmitted to the j output terminals. The output conditions are defined by a group of switching functions, all of which are functions of the input variables $X_1 \ldots X_n$.

Comparison of the multiple-output circuit with the circuit of Fig. 4–4 shows that the only change is in the contact network. It is evident that we could provide the j outputs of Fig. 6–1 by using j two-terminal contact networks within the switching circuit. In general, however,

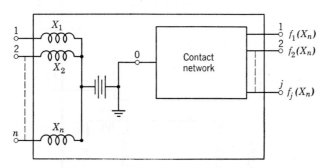

Fig. 6–1. A multiple-output relay switching circuit contains a multi-terminal contact network.

we can expect to achieve better economy by using switching elements so that they serve more than one of the outputs of a $(j + 1)$-terminal contact network. We also find in the design of multi-terminal contact networks enlarged opportunities for the use of powerful types of non-series-parallel configurations.

The generalized switching circuit of Fig. 6–2 is a type which we will encounter in the design of iterative networks. The input terminals $1 \ldots n$ are arrayed along the bottom of the diagram in order to emphasize the change which has been made in the contact network. The outputs of this circuit consist of the establishment of conducting paths between pairs of terminals, with each path beginning at a terminal in the left-hand set $1 \ldots j$, and ending at a terminal in the right-hand set $1' \ldots k'$. Each output is specified as a function of the input variables $X_1 \ldots X_n$, and the only new feature is that these functions now describe transmissions between terminals. The typical transmission function is written $T_{jk'} = f(X_n)$. It should be noted that the circuit of Fig. 4–4 can be modified to provide a single connecting path of this sort. Since the contact network still has only two terminals, no special procedure is needed for its design.

In the switching circuits shown in Figs. 6–1 and 6–2, we arranged the inputs so that the relay windings would be controlled through series networks. This is the method most commonly employed, but we can control the input relays in a variety of ways, as will be shown in Art. 6.6, without loss of generality. In fact, one of the most important reasons for designing multiple-output contact networks is to provide control networks for other groups of relays.

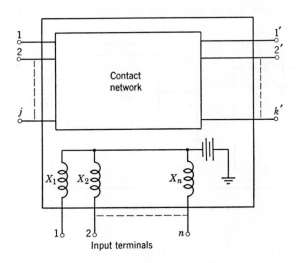

Fig. 6–2. Switching circuit which establishes connections between terminals of contact network.

6.2   Synthesis from Algebraic Descriptions

There are a number of simple circuit configurations which are encountered again and again in the manipulation of multiple-output networks. It is important that we learn the algebraic basis for recognizing these configurations, because it is then frequently possible to apply them in simplification procedures.

Figure 6–3 illustrates the construction of a three-terminal network from two networks which have identical series components. In part (a) the transmissions $T_{01} = XY$, and $T_{02} = XZ$, result from contacts of those designations, and the use of a single X contact for both paths is quite evident.

In part (b) the same letters are used to represent the transmissions of contact networks, and the transmissions to the terminals 1 and 2 are again XY and XZ, respectively. The variable X is a factor in both transmission functions, and this is the algebraic form that discloses the possibility of using a single X network for both paths. Sometimes a common factor is easily found, and sometimes there is not even evidence that a factor exists, as we shall see in later examples.

Before considering an example, we should note that the networks shown in Fig. 6–3 are not disjunctive with respect to the output terminals 1 and 2. A disjunctive multiple-output network is one for which the transmission between all possible pairs of output terminals

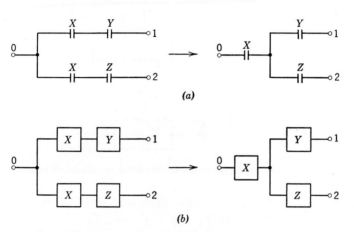

(a)

(b)

Fig. 6–3. When each path contains the same series contact, or network, they may combine to form a single contact, or network.

is always 0. The networks illustrated are not of this type because the transmission between terminals 1 and 2 is YZ. If for any reason this condition is not tolerable, the common series element cannot be used. If duplicate X networks are used the transmission from 1 to 2 becomes XYZ, and this must inherently be tolerable if the output transmissions are to be XY and XZ.

Example 6–1

The transmissions to the three output terminals of a four-terminal contact network are given by:

$$T_1 = ABCD' + ACD'E'F$$
$$T_2 = ABCD'E' + AB'CD'E$$
$$T_3 = AB'C'D' + AC'D'F'$$

To design this network we may look for the possibility of using common series elements by factoring the functions as follows:

$$T_1 = ACD'(B + E'F) \quad = AD'[C(B + E'F)]$$
$$T_2 = ACD'(BE' + B'E) = AD'[C(BE' + B'E)]$$
$$T_3 = AC'D'(B' + F') \quad = AD'[C'(B' + F')]$$

In the factored form we see that there are two kinds of common series terms. The term AD' is a factor in all three of the functions, and C is a factor in the functions for terminals 1 and 2. The circuit diagram of Fig. 6–4 shows the form of the four-terminal network thus derived.

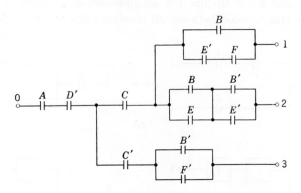

Fig. 6–4. A four-terminal network, simplified by algebraic factoring.

A situation which occurs quite often is that which requires two transmissions of the form $T_1 = X + Y$, and $T_2 = X' + Y$. These forms may be realized by the three-terminal network of Fig. 6–5. In contrast to the preceding example, this network contains a common element which forms a shunt path between the two output terminals. The two versions of the network in Fig. 6–5 merely remind us once

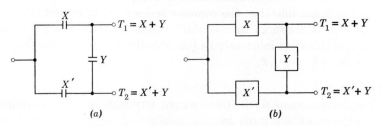

Fig. 6–5. Three-terminal network for producing two selected sums.

more that the elements of the network may be either individual contacts or groups of contacts.

An important property of this adding network is brought out in Fig. 6–6. If we examine the transmissions of the basic network in Fig. 6–5 we write $T_1 = X + X'Y = X + Y$, and $T_2 = X' + XY = X' + Y$. In Fig. 6–6(a), a network of transmission P is connected in parallel with X. For this circuit the transmissions are $T_1 = X + P + X'Y =$

$X + P + Y$, and $T_2 = X' + XY + PY = X' + Y + PY = X' + Y$. We have then the rather surprising discovery that we can add to one of the sums without restriction and the other sum remains unchanged. Actually, as is shown in Fig. 6–6(b), additive modifications

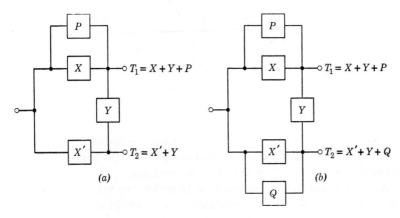

Fig. 6–6. The basic sums produced by the network of Fig. 6–5 may be modified independently.

can be made independently to each sum without introducing "coupling" to the other sum.

These additive networks are frequently used in the process of minimizing multi-terminal networks, as we shall see in Art. 6.4. Usually their use is suggested by the appearance of the two sums, written generically as $(X + Y)$ and $(X' + Y)$. If these two basic parts are present, either or both may be augmented in the manner illustrated in Fig. 6–6. There are other situations, however, where the indications for the use of this network are less evident. Consider the two functions $T_1 = Y(X + Z)$, and $T_2 = Z'(X' + Y')$. Six literals are present in these two functions and each literal appears just once. We cannot possibly realize the functions with fewer than six contacts, and this can be done with two series-parallel circuits. However, if we do it that way, only one pair of contacts can be combined into a transfer contact. Can we do any better?

In the expressions for the required transmissions, the presence of the X in one sum and the X' in the other suggests a possible double-sum network, provided we can augment the remainders of the sum to the required form. We note that the first sum is multiplied by Y, and the second sum is multiplied by Z'. If the complements of these two literals are added to their respective sums, neither transmission is changed, but the sums are now $(X + Y' + Z)$ and $(X' + Y' + Z)$, and the double-sum network can be used. As drawn in Fig. 6–7 all the elements are shown to be separate networks with pairs of networks having complementary transmissions. When we substitute contacts

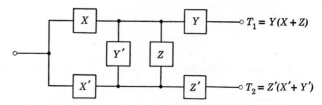

Fig. 6–7. A modification which converts all contacts to transfer contacts.

for the networks we find that all the contacts are contained in transfer contacts. In the next article we will examine complementary pairs of networks to see how they may best be realized.

Another common situation is that in which two transmission functions are expressed as sums containing one term in common, but not

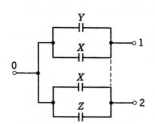

Fig. 6–8. Direct merging of parallel contacts causes the introduction of spurious transmission terms.

in the form which permits the use of the double-sum circuit. A simple example is given by $T_1 = X + Y$, and $T_2 = X + Z$. These functions are realized by the network of Fig. 6–8. If we attempt to eliminate one of the X contacts by a direct connection, such as the one shown by a dotted line, we introduce terms which are not permitted by the specifications. In this example the result of adding the dotted connection is to make the transmission to both terminals $X + Y + Z$.

The difficulty is that we do not have an isolated X contact in either part of the network. In the upper branch, a Y contact is connected solidly in parallel with the X contact, and there is no process of mere rearrangement which will enable us to isolate the transmission function X—we always get the function $X + Y$. The same situation is present in the lower branch because of the contact Z which is in parallel with the X contact.

We shall use the term "interfering variable" to designate a variable, such as Y or Z in the above instances, which is in parallel with a variable we wish to isolate for the purpose of making a circuit consolidation.

Isolation of a variable within a parallel circuit is accomplished by expansion of the transmission function about the interfering variable in accordance with theorem 20. In Fig. 6–9 this process is illustrated for the parallel combination of transmission $T = X + Y$. The variable Y is the interfering variable, if we wish to isolate X, and expansion about Y yields the transmission $T = Y + Y'X$. In the circuit shown at the right of Fig. 6–9 the transmission between terminals 1 and 2 is that of the expanded function, and hence is identical with the transmission of the original parallel circuit at the left of the figure. But the

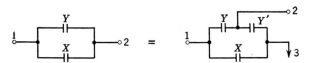

Fig. 6–9. Isolation of the X variable by expansion about the interfering variable Y.

right-hand figure is drawn to emphasize the fact that the X contact now has in parallel with it the series combination of $YY' = 0$, and that between terminals 1 and 3 the X transmission is isolated.

Figure 6–10 shows how this expansion procedure is applied to the circuit of Fig. 6–8. When the two parallel networks are expanded with respect to the interfering variables Y and Z, the X contacts become

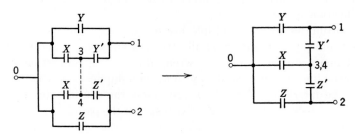

Fig. 6–10. Expansion about the interfering variables permits the use of a common X contact.

isolated in both branches and the points 3 and 4 may be connected as shown by the dotted line. The consolidated circuit is shown at the right of Fig. 6–10.

A comparison of Fig. 6–8 and Fig. 6–10 shows that in order to save one pair of springs, by eliminating an X contact, we had to add two springs through the conversion of the Y and Z contacts to transfer contacts. There seems to be no advantage in the process unless we remember that although the discussion has been entirely in terms of contact designators X, Y, and Z, these symbols can also represent the transmissions of networks of contacts. The economic advantage, if any, is readily determined. If X represents a relatively complex network, and Y and Z represent relatively simple networks, it will pay to add springs to the interfering networks in order to avoid duplicating the more complex network. If the relative complexity is not obvious,

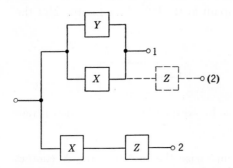

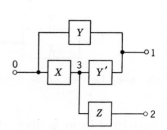

Fig. 6–11. The connection shown by dotted lines does not give the correct transmission to terminal 2.

Fig. 6–12. The expansion method modifies the parallel circuit so that the X network can be used in two paths.

a trial may be necessary in order to determine whether the circuit modification is advantageous.

Opportunities for the multiple use of parallel elements arise in a variety of ways. Figure 6–11 illustrates a situation which seems to tempt many students to do the wrong thing. The connection shown by dotted lines is not a valid way to avoid a duplicate X network, because the interfering variable Y introduces the spurious term YZ in the transimission to terminal 2. Expansion of the parallel transmission XY about the interfering variable leads to the modification shown in Fig. 6–12, where the use of a common X network is successful because the path through Y to terminal 2 is blocked by the series combination of YY'.

The procedure for making common use of parallel elements has been discussed here on an algebraic basis. In difficult situations the method offers firm guidance in making valid circuit transformations of this type. It must be recognized, however, that with increased experience we learn to solve many of these problems without going through the steps of a formal expansion procedure. Essentially we have learned that if we want to make additional use of a switching element or network which is part of a parallel connection, we must isolate the desired element. The element becomes isolated when the transmission function of the circuit in parallel with it reduces to 0. The expansion method is a general means for assuring isolation, but we need not always apply it to an entire interfering network. In fact, we have examples, as in Fig. 6–13, of networks in which some functions are isolated without modification. The network of Fig. 6–13 is designed for transmission between terminals 0 and 1, and it is to be understood

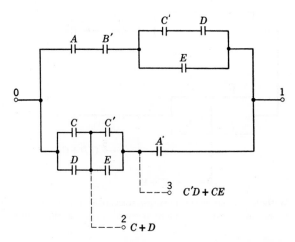

Fig. 6–13. Examples of isolated functions in an unmodified parallel network.

that the terminal 0 is the common input of a multiple-output network. The dotted lines to terminals 2 and 3 indicate points at which isolated functions may be obtained.

Between terminals 0 and 2 we have a network of transmission $(C + D)$, and the remainder of the main network, proceeding counterclockwise from terminal 2 back to terminal 0, may be visualized as a shunt across the $(C + D)$ network. We observe, however, that this shunt network contains the series combination of A and A' contacts. Regardless of the detailed structure of the shunt network, the presence of the AA' factor reduces the shunt transmission to 0. Hence the $(C + D)$ network is isolated.

By a similar argument we can see that the network of transmission $(C'D + CE)$, between terminals 0 and 3, also is isolated.

Figure 6–14 illustrates the way in which other isolated functions can be obtained by rearrangement of the circuit. The change in the lower branch is minor, but in the upper branch we are able to isolate two new functions. This is brought about by moving the A contact to the location adjacent to terminal 1. In this position, it acts in combination with the A' terminal in the lower branch to reduce the shunt transmission to 0 for any of the functions between terminal 0 and terminals 2, 3, 4, and 5.

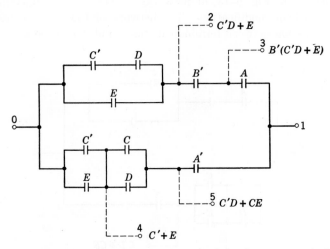

Fig. 6–14. Without changing the network transmission between terminals 0 and 1, other functions are isolated by mere rearrangement of the contacts.

6.3   Three-Terminal Networks with Complementary Outputs

It can be seen from the preceding article that we must frequently design a three-terminal network which has for its output transmission functions a specified function and the complement of that function. The typical situation may be seen in Fig. 6–12. The main three-terminal network starts at terminal 0 and has its outputs at terminals 1 and 2. It contains within it, however, an auxiliary three-terminal network which, starting at terminal 1, produces the functions Y and Y' at terminals 0 and 3, respectively. Some of the importance of this type of network comes from the fact that it is a disjunctive network. Regardless of its complexity the transmission between its output terminals is always 0.

A three-terminal network for the production of a function and its complement can always be built using transfer contacts throughout. If a series-parallel network of minimum form has been designed for one of the functions, the complementary function may be realized by the addition of one spring to each of the contact elements present in the original network. Any transfer contacts present in the original network are considered to be two contacts.

To demonstrate the validity of these statements, let us assume that we have expanded a function to the standard-product form. We can now divide the terms of the product into two groups, and we will call these the P-group and the Q-group. If P and Q also represent the

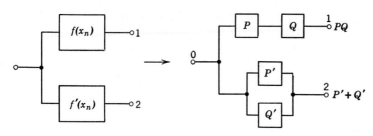

Fig. 6–15. A network and its complement may be resolved into complementary series and parallel component networks.

transmissions of the terms within their respective groups, the transmission of all the terms is PQ.

The complement of the same function is in the form of a standard sum, and the terms may again be divided into two groups. The terms of the original P and Q groups become complementary terms in P' and Q' groups, and the transmission due to all the terms in the complementary function becomes $P' + Q'$.

Figure 6–15 shows schematically the resolution of a pair of complementary functions into series and parallel connections of complementary groups. We note that the function $P' + Q'$ appears at terminal 2, and PQ at terminal 1. But we can write the transmission to terminal 1

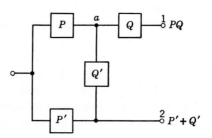

Fig. 6–16. The three-terminal network of Fig. 6–15 is reconnected to form two smaller three-terminal networks.

as $(P + Q')Q = PQ$. Thus we have the sums $(P' + Q')$ and $(P + Q')$ for which we can use the double-sum circuit of Fig. 6–5. The result is shown in Fig. 6–16.

There are several things to observe about Fig. 6–16. First, it produces the required results without adding any switching equipment beyond that shown in Fig. 6–15. Second, both of the complementary pairs of networks, P, P' and Q, Q', are connected to common points, at terminal 0 and point a, respectively. If P and Q happen to designate contacts instead of networks, the circuit is in form to use transfer contacts immediately. Third, the original three-terminal network has been broken down into two simpler three-terminal networks. One of these is the network for producing P and P', which starts at point 0 and terminates at points a and 2. The other network produces Q and Q', starting at point a and terminating at points 1 and 2.

We can now take both of the three-terminal networks of Fig. 6-16 and decompose them into more elementary networks by repeating the procedure just described as often as necessary. Eventually, we arrive at the point where we must deal with simple contacts instead of networks. It should then be clear that if we treat the contact designators just as we have been treating the network variables, the result must be that we provide a common connection for every pair of complementary contacts, and all contact elements will hence combine into transfer contacts.

In order to make the discussion general, the above demonstration was based on a resolution of the function and its complement into P and Q groups derived from the standard-sum and the standard-product forms. This is not a restriction on the method, for it can be applied directly to functions which have been reduced to minimal forms. This will be illustrated by Example 6–2.

Example 6–2

Design a network for producing the complementary functions, $T = A(B' + C)(D + E')$ and $T' = A' + BC' + D'E$, using transfer contacts only.

Both functions are expressed in a minimum form, and we wish to avoid an expansion process which would lead to a less economic circuit.

The steps in the design are shown schematically in Fig. 6–17, and the step numbers used in the discussion below refer to the similarly numbered parts of the figure.

STEP 1. The transmission functions are broken down into the transmission of the A and A' contacts, and functions describing the remainders of the original functions. Thus we have $T = AP$ at terminal 1, and $T' = A' + P'$ at terminal 2. We draw a circuit for this step, and find that point x (Fig. 6–17) provides a common connection for a three-terminal network to produce P and P'.

STEP 2. By examining the original functions, we can define the functions P and P', and decompose them into simpler functions, as follows:

$$P = (B' + C)(D + E') = QR$$
$$P' = BC' + D'E = Q' + R'$$

The diagram illustrating this step shows that the point x is now the common point for the Q, Q' network, and there is a new point y which is the common point for the R, R' network.

STEP 3. From the previous step we can identify $Q = B' + C$, and $Q' = BC'$. No further resolution into component networks is needed, and we can immediately draw the circuit shown for these functions.

STEP 4. In similar manner, we draw a diagram for the functions $R = D + E'$, and $R' = D'E$.

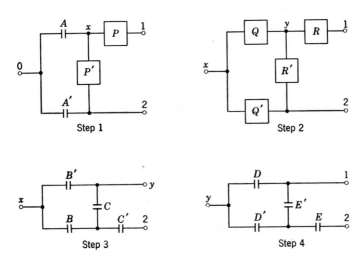

Fig. 6–17. Steps in the formation of a network and its complement.

It should be noted that in the diagrams illustrating each of these steps, the terminals of the various component three-terminal networks have been identified. This makes it a simple matter to combine the separate diagrams to form the complete circuit. If we connect points y and 2, in the diagram of Step 4, to the corresponding points in the diagram of Step 3, we obtain the detailed network represented by the functions shown in the diagram of Step 2. It is also the contact network represented by the P, P' functions of Step 1. When we replace the P, P' network by the contact network found by combining Steps 3 and 4, we obtain the complete circuit diagram shown in Fig. 6–18. It may readily be verified that this network contains only transfer contacts.

The generality of this method for producing a function and its complement is useful in making economic decisions. We saw in Art. 6.2 that in order to make multiple use of parallel networks, it was sometimes necessary to insert the complement of another network which

was acting as an interfering variable. We now see that if we know
the number of contact springs used in the interfering network, we can
obtain the complementary network by adding 50 per cent more springs.
If we add fewer springs than the number saved by not duplicating a
parallel network, it is frequently a step worth taking.

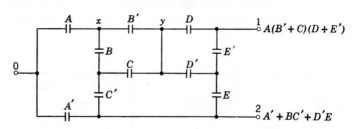

Fig. 6–18. Final combination of elementary networks from Fig. 6–17. The
required function and its complement are produced, and only transfer contacts
are used.

We may also observe in Figs. 4–24 to 4–29 that the series of
steps taken to minimize that network could have been reduced to
the single step of synthesizing a network with the complementary
transmission functions $T = C + DE$, and $T' = C'(D' + E')$.

6.4 Multi-Terminal Network Synthesis by the Method of Assumed Form

In this article we develop a method for synthesizing a multi-terminal
network by first assuming that a set of component networks are to be
interconnected in a prescribed way and then determining what rules
must be followed in synthesizing the component networks. We shall
treat the type of circuit shown in Fig. 6–19, in which a three-terminal
network has two output transmission functions specified. The function T_1 between terminal 0 and terminal 1 and the function T_2 between terminal 0 and terminal 2 are given, but the function T_{12} between
terminals 1 and 2 is usually not given. The discussion will be concentrated on the problem of satisfying the specified output transmission
functions by using networks which have one of the two assumed forms
shown in Fig. 6–19. In the so-called wye (Y) form a common series
network X feeds through a Y network to provide T_1, and through a
Z network to provide T_2. In the delta (Δ) form, networks P and
Q feed directly to T_1 and T_2, respectively, and network R is shunted
across the two output terminals. In many problems the assumption
of either form will lead to the same final result, and usually it is
preferable to try both. There is, of course, no assurance that some

entirely different form than those shown in Fig. 6–19 would not lead
to a still better result. In other words, the method of assumed form
does not necessarily minimize the final network, but it is an effective
design procedure in many situations.

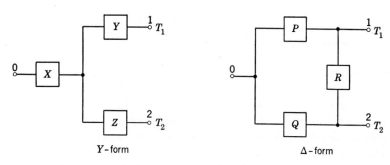

Y-form   Δ-form

Fig. 6–19. A three-terminal contact network and two of the forms in which it
is synthesized.

In order to understand more fully the problem of designing multi-
terminal networks it will be instructive to carry through an example in
which the desired synthesis is already known, and to see some of the
ways in which that result might be obtained.

Example 6–3

A three-terminal contact network is in the Y-form shown in Fig.
6–19. Its component networks have the transmissions: $X = A + CD'$,
$Y = BC' + D$, and $Z = A'B + B'D$. From these, the three interterminal transmission functions are found to be:

$$T_{01} = XY = A(BC' + D)$$

$$T_{02} = XZ = AB'D + A'BCD'$$

$$T_{12} = YZ = A'BC' + A'D + B'D$$

The problem is, given only the three interterminal functions, to find at
least one set of functions X, Y, Z which satisfies these relations.

An inspection of the three interterminal transmission functions for factors is unrewarding, even though we know the factors exist. The maps of the functions, Fig. 6–20, do not help. We hence resort to a process of equation solving in which we treat the three functions as simultaneous equations. By setting up a table of combinations, we

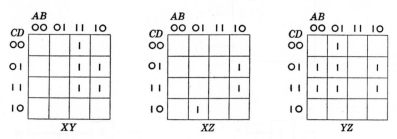

Fig. 6–20. Maps of the three interterminal functions of Example 6–3.

will compute the values of XY, XZ, and YZ for each combination of A, B, C, and D.

Because the three products contain all pairs of the variables X, Y, and Z, we interpret the various combinations of product values in terms of variable values. The typical sets of values and their interpretations are:

XY	XZ	YZ	
0	0	0	$X = Y = Z = 0$, or any one of them $= 1$
0	0	1	$Y = Z = 1; X = 0$
0	1	1	X, Y, Z have no consistent values
1	1	1	$X = Y = Z = 1$

Table 6–1 is a complete table of combinations in A, B, C, D, with the corresponding values of XY, XZ, and YZ, and the separate values of X, Y, and Z. Where $XY = XZ = YZ = 0$ the entries under X, Y, Z are left blank because we may find it advantageous to enter a 1 for one of the three variables. It should be noted that no combination of A, B, C, D leads to a combination of XY, XZ, YZ in which two of the three products are 1. There is no possible assignment of X, Y, Z which would satisfy that combination of product values.

It is now convenient to transfer the values of X, Y, Z from Table 6–1 to a set of Karnaugh maps as shown in Fig. 6–21. Examination of these maps shows that the 1's of the Y and Z maps already represent the functions $Y = BC' + D$ and $Z = A'B + B'D$. When some of the optional entries are used to place 1's in the cells checked off in the X map, we obtain $X = A + CD'$. Thus we have been able to solve the

Table 6–1

A	B	C	D	XY	XZ	YZ	X	Y	Z
0	0	0	0	0	0	0	–	–	–
0	0	0	1	0	0	1	0	1	1
0	0	1	0	0	0	0	–	–	–
0	0	1	1	0	0	1	0	1	1
0	1	0	0	0	0	1	0	1	1
0	1	0	1	0	0	1	0	1	1
0	1	1	0	0	1	0	1	0	1
0	1	1	1	0	0	1	0	1	1
1	0	0	0	0	0	0	–	–	–
1	0	0	1	1	1	1	1	1	1
1	0	1	0	0	0	0	–	–	–
1	0	1	1	1	1	1	1	1	1
1	1	0	0	1	0	0	1	1	0
1	1	0	1	1	0	0	1	1	0
1	1	1	0	0	0	0	–	–	–
1	1	1	1	1	0	0	1	1	0

equations and recover all the original component functions. It is evident, however, that there are many ways to distribute the optional 1's in these maps. Figure 6–22 shows a distribution for which

$$X = AB + CD' + AD$$

$$Y = C' + D$$

$$Z = A'B + B'D$$

In the preceding example, one reason we were successful in finding the transmission functions of the component networks was that we had available the transmission $T_{12} = YZ$. Generally, we will have $T_{01} = XY$ and $T_{02} = XZ$, but these functions tell us nothing about the function T_{12}. We certainly cannot assume that $T_{12} = T_{01}T_{02}$.

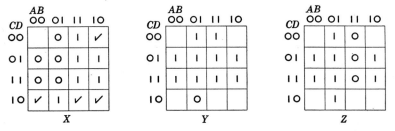

Fig. 6–21. Maps of X, Y, Z in Example 6–3 with optional entries chosen to recover original component networks.

If, in the preceding example, we carried out this indicated multiplication we would find $T_{01}T_{02} = AB'D$, and this is certainly not equal to YZ.

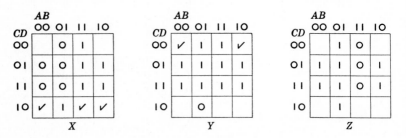

Fig. 6–22. One of the alternative ways to use optional entries in Example 6–3.

When T_{01} and T_{02} are realized by separate series-parallel networks, then it is true that $T_{12} = T_{01}T_{02}$. This is shown in Fig. 6–23, where the only tie path between terminals 1 and 2 is the series connection $AB'D$ which is given by the product $T_{01}T_{02}$. In the more economic network of Fig. 6–24, the X network can be distinguished as a separate

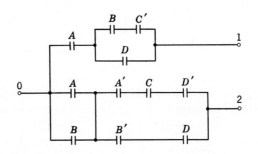

Fig. 6–23. Series-parallel networks for T_{01} and T_{02}.

network but the Y and Z networks have now been partially consolidated by sharing a common D contact. (It was not necessary to add contacts which would isolate the D contact in this merger because the possible sneak paths in Fig. 6–24 are both blocked by BB' contacts in series.) Although the output transmissions are realized correctly by the multi-terminal network, we cannot clearly identify separate Y and Z networks. The transmission $T_{12} = B' + A'BD + A'BC' = B' + A'(D + C')$, which is not the transmission given by the product YZ.

In general the situations from which the specifications of multi-terminal networks arise are such that the specifications of the output transmissions are available but there is no way to specify the transmissions between output terminals. A method which depends upon

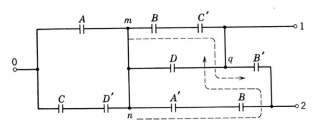

Fig. 6–24. Circuit from Example 6–3, using a common series element. Possible sneak paths are indicated by dotted lines.

the solution of simultaneous equations requires that we specify all interterminal transmission functions, or that we at least have enough independent equations to solve for all the variables. If any restriction must be placed upon the transmission between output terminals the method used in the preceding example is the most direct one. It has the additional advantage that if the output transmission and the transmission between terminals are inconsistent, this will become known because it will be impossible to solve the equations. If, however, there are no restrictions placed on the transmission between output terminals the method of assumed form can be used in another way to find the component network transmissions.

The method to be described next will make liberal use of Karnaugh maps. This is emphasized in Fig. 6–25 where an assumed Y form of three-terminal network has its component networks replaced by maps. Each output transmission is represented by another map which must be derived as the product of two component maps. Our problem is to determine how to specify the three component maps when only the two maps corresponding to T_1 and T_2 are known.

The component maps are filled in by a series of operations based on the following rules:

1. Since the X network is in series with both the Y network and the Z network, it follows that if any input condition requires a 1 at either output, a 1 must be entered in the X map for that input condition. Therefore, the X map will contain entries of 1 wherever either the T_1 or the T_2 map contains a 1. Furthermore, since any undesired transmissions in the X map can always be blocked by 0 entries in the

Y and Z maps, we need not limit the entries in the X map to the 1's contained in the combined T_1 and T_2 map. Hence, the map of the X component network must contain all the 1's in the T_1 and T_2 maps, but it may also contain additional 1 entries chosen for the purpose of simplifying the X network.

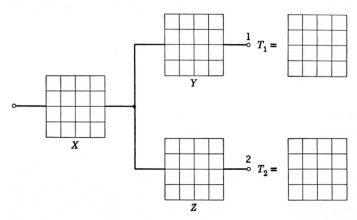

Fig. 6–25. The component circuits in a three-terminal, two-output network are represented by maps.

2. The Y map must contain at least the 1 entries corresponding to those in the T_1 map. In addition, wherever the X map has a 0 entry, the entry in the Y map is optional.

3. The Z map must contain at least the 1 entries corresponding to those in the T_2 map. In addition, wherever the X map has a 0 entry, the entry in the Z map is optional.

In the next example we will use these rules to determine the transmission functions of X, Y, and Z networks which satisfy the functions T_1 and T_2 of Example 6–3.

Example 6–4

A three-terminal contact network is to produce the two outputs

$$T_1 = A(BC' + D)$$

$$T_2 = AB'D + A'BCD'$$

Assume that the network is to have the Y-form of Fig. 6–19. Find the transmission functions of the component networks X, Y, and Z.

In Fig. 6–26 are shown the maps of T_1 and T_2, together with a preliminary map of X. According to the first rule X must contain 1 entries in all the cells for which the transmissions of T_1 and T_2 are 1. However, at this stage all the remaining entries in the X map may be considered optional, since transmission to the output terminals for undesired input states can still be prevented by 0 entries in the maps

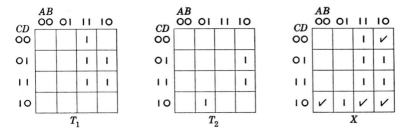

Fig. 6–26. Maps of the specified transmissions T_1 and T_2 of Example 6–4, and a map showing the points at which $X = 1$ must be entered.

of the Y and Z functions. Inspection shows that the cells checked off in the X map of Fig. 6–26 might well be entered with 1's in order to get a simple series network. The resulting map then represents $X = A + CD'$.

CD \ AB	00	01	11	10
00			I	O
01			I	I
11			I	I
10	O	O	O	O

Y

CD \ AB	00	01	11	10
00			O	O
01			O	I
11			O	I
10	O	I	O	O

Z

Fig. 6–27. Maps showing the required entries for the Y and Z functions—all blank cells have optional entries.

In Fig. 6–27, the Y and Z maps are partially plotted. Each of these maps contains all the 1's in T_1 and T_2, respectively, and in addition they contain 0's wherever the X map contains 1's which are not specified in the respective output functions. Since all the remaining cells of Y and Z correspond to 0's of transmission in X, they may all be considered optional. One selection of optional values is shown in Fig. 6–28. The corresponding transmission functions are:

$$Y = BC' + D$$
$$Z = A'B + B'D$$

In this example we have, of course, found expressions for X, Y, and Z which are exactly those stated at the beginning of Example 6–3. The procedure, however, has not been dependent upon a knowledge of the transmission T_{12}. Instead, from the assumed form of the network we were able to establish logical rules for making entries in the component

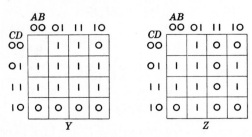

Fig. 6–28. The completed maps of Y and Z with options chosen to minimize both component networks.

maps, and with the optional entries fully revealed, any alternative mapping can be chosen.

A summary of the rules for mapping the component networks of an assumed Y form is: when $T_1 = XY$ and $T_2 = XZ$, we must determine X, Y, and Z maps such that for *any* position in the maps (say the ith position), $T_{1i} = X_iY_i$, and $T_{2i} = X_iZ_i$, for all i. Also:

(1) X *must* contain all the 1's in T_1 and T_2.

(2) Y *must* contain all the 1's in T_1.

(3) Z *must* contain all the 1's in T_2.

(4) Wherever $T_1 = 0$, *either* X or Y must be 0.

(5) Wherever $T_2 = 0$, *either* X or Z must be 0.

If a Δ form of network is assumed, we see from Fig. 6–19 that $T_1 = P + QR$ and $T_2 = Q + PR$. When T_1, T_2, P, Q, and R are represented by maps, these relations must hold for all positions in the maps. That is, for the ith position, $T_{1i} = P_i + Q_iR_i$, and $T_{2i} = Q_i + P_iR_i$. These algebraic requirements are satisfied when map entries are made according to the following rules:

(1) P_i *must* be 0 if $T_{1i} = 0$.

(2) Q_i *must* be 0 if $T_{2i} = 0$.

(3) R_i *must* be 0 if $T_{1i} \neq T_{2i}$.

(4) R_i is optional (ϕ) if $T_{1i} = T_{2i}$.

(5) $P_i = 0$ and $Q_i = 1$ if $T_{1i} = 0$ and $T_{2i} = 1$.

(6) $P_i = 1$ and $Q_i = 0$ if $T_{1i} = 1$ and $T_{2i} = 0$.

(7) In all remaining positions, $T_1 = T_2 = 1$. At least two of the three maps P, Q, R must contain 1's in each of these positions.

The formal listing of these rules may make them appear complex, but they are easily visualized and applied. This will become clearer by their use in an example. Note the implication of rule (4) above. This says that if the two output transmissions are the same in any map positions, the R map has optional entries in those positions. This is true if we do not care to specify the transmission T_{12}, but if any restrictions are placed upon this transmission, such restrictions would be reflected in the allowable mapping of the R network.

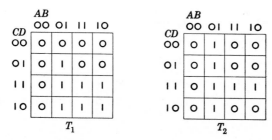

Fig. 6–29. Maps of the output functions specified in Example 6-5.

Example 6–5

The output transmission functions

and

$$T_1 = A'BD + AC + BC$$

$$T_2 = A'B + ACD$$

are to be realized by a multi-terminal contact network for which the Δ form of Fig. 6–19 is to be assumed.

AB				
CD \\	OO	OI	II	IO
OO	O	O	O	O
OI	O		O	O
II	O			
IO	O		I	I

P

AB				
CD \\	OO	OI	II	IO
OO	O	I	O	O
OI	O		O	O
II	O			
IO	O		O	O

Q

AB				
CD \\	OO	OI	II	IO
OO	φ	O	φ	φ
OI	φ	φ	φ	φ
II	φ	φ	φ	φ
IO	φ	φ	O	O

R

Fig. 6–30. Partially completed maps of the component networks in Example 6-5.

In Fig. 6–29 the output functions T_1 and T_2 are mapped. In Fig. 6–30 we have carried out the following steps:

1. From rule (1), all the 0's of T_1 have been entered in P.
2. From rule (2), all the 0's of T_2 have been entered in Q.

3. From rule (3), 0's have been entered in R wherever the entries in P and Q are complementary.

4. From rule (4), optional values, ϕ, have been entered in R wherever the entries in P and Q are alike.

5. From rule (5), 0's have been entered in P and 1's have been entered in Q wherever $T_1 = 0$ and $T_2 = 1$.

6. From rule (6), 1's have been entered in P and 0's have been entered in Q wherever $T_1 = 1$ and $T_2 = 0$.

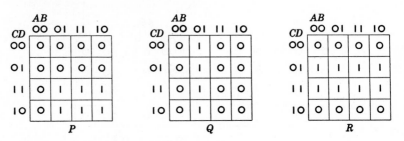

Fig. 6–31. Completed maps of component networks in Example 6–5.

All remaining entries in the three maps must be in accordance with rule (7). This rule allows an extremely large range of choice. The range of minimizing choices is, however, more limited. The entries made in Fig. 6–31 are probably an optimum set for this particular problem. They lead to the component transmission functions

$$P = (A + B)C$$

$$Q = A'B$$

$$R = D$$

In Fig. 6–32 the left-hand network shows the component networks in series-parallel realizations. The two B contacts can be merged, as

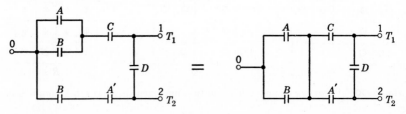

Fig. 6–32. Network derived from the synthesis of Example 6–5.

shown at the right of Fig. 6–32, because the series AA' contacts do not permit a "sneak" path.

The network of Fig. 6–32 can also be derived by assuming the Y form. This derivation is left as an exercise for the student.

The method of assumed form is not limited to Y and Δ forms. These happen to be useful forms for which the rules of mapping are readily stated and applied, and they have been found to be effective in a wide variety of problems. There are many other forms of two-output networks which can be assumed and still more forms for networks designed to supply more than two outputs. There are, however, no simpler forms than the Y and Δ types, and these are sufficient to illustrate the method.

6.5 Wye-Delta Relations in Three-Terminal Networks

In the preceding article we developed a procedure for synthesizing three-terminal networks for which only two of the interterminal transmission functions are specified. The result of the synthesis is either a

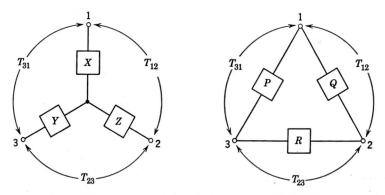

Fig. 6–33. Y-Δ transformation rules use symbols shown.

Y or a Δ network, depending upon the form assumed. It is convenient to be able to obtain other three-terminal networks which display the same terminal action. One such set of equivalents may be found by using wye-delta transforms.

In Example 6–3 we developed a Y network to realize three specified interterminal transmission functions. In doing so we found that the table of combinations for the component networks contained combinations which permitted the assignment of optional transmission values. We will study this point further in developing the rules for transforming between the Y and Δ forms and vice versa. The following treatment of this problem uses the symbols defined in Fig. 6–33.

In transforming a Y network to the Δ form, we are given the component network transmission functions X, Y, and Z. The interterminal transmission functions are then

$$T_{12} = XZ; \qquad T_{23} = YZ; \qquad T_{31} = XY$$

The component networks of the Δ form, P, Q, and R, are to have their transmissions specified as functions of X, Y, and Z. We will treat this problem by forming a table of combinations in which X, Y, and Z have all possible combinations of values, and for each of these T_{12}, T_{23}, and T_{31} are computed. We then determine what the corresponding values of P, Q, and R must be. From the tabulation thus prepared the P, Q, and R functions are written directly.

We note in the last row of Table 6–2, where all three interterminal

Table 6–2

X	Y	Z	T_{12}	T_{23}	T_{31}	P	Q	R
0	0	0	0	0	0	0	0	0
0	0	1	0	0	0	0	0	0
0	1	0	0	0	0	0	0	0
0	1	1	0	1	0	0	0	1
1	0	0	0	0	0	0	0	0
1	0	1	1	0	0	0	1	0
1	1	0	0	0	1	1	0	0
1	1	1	1	1	1	1	1	1
						0	1	1
						1	0	1
						1	1	0

transmissions are 1, that this condition can be realized in the Δ network by assigning 1 transmission to all three component networks, or to any two of the three. Thus there are four ways to make the entries in this row, and there will be four Δ networks which are equivalent in terminal action to the Y network.

If we use the first assignment in the last row, we write

$$P = XY; \qquad Q = XZ; \qquad R = YZ$$

This is the set of relations commonly given for the Y to Δ transformation. There are, however, three other sets of rules which can be written directly from the alternative entries in Table 6–2.

$$P = XYZ' \qquad Q = XZ \qquad R = YZ$$

$$P = XY \qquad Q = XY'Z \qquad R = YZ$$

$$P = XY \qquad Q = XZ \qquad R = X'YZ$$

A corresponding set of relations for Δ to Y transformation is derived by writing another table of combinations, this time starting with the functions P, Q, and R as the independent variables.

In Table 6–3 the top row requires the three interterminal trans-

Table 6–3

P	Q	R	T_{12}	T_{23}	T_{31}	X	Y	Z
0	0	0	0	0	0	0	0	0
						1	0	0
						0	1	0
						0	0	1
0	0	1	0	1	0	0	1	1
0	1	0	1	0	0	1	0	1
0	1	1	1	1	1	1	1	1
1	0	0	0	0	1	1	1	0
1	0	1	1	1	1	1	1	1
1	1	0	1	1	1	1	1	1
1	1	1	1	1	1	1	1	1

missions to be 0. This condition is satisfied by the X, Y, and Z functions if all three are 0, or if any two of the three are 0. There are hence four ways to make the entries in the row and there will be four sets of Δ to Y transform relations. If we use the first assignment shown in the table, we write

$$X = P + Q; \qquad Y = P + R; \qquad Z = Q + R$$

The other row entries give sets of relations in which one member of the set is changed by adding the term shown in parentheses:

$$X = P + Q\ (+R'); \qquad T = P + R\ (+Q'); \qquad Z = Q + R\ (+P')$$

6.6 Networks for the Control of Relay Operation

In Art. 4.3 we discussed a generalized relay switching circuit in which the relays were actuated by grounding one or more input terminals, as illustrated in Fig. 4–4. This is an exceedingly useful form of circuit because it enables us to use the output of one switching circuit as an input to another switching circuit. A transmission of 1 at an output is an indication of a ground at that terminal, and is exactly the condition required in order to have an input of 1 to another circuit of this same type.

The two-terminal contact network is the basic structure used for controlling the current in a relay winding. In our discussion up to this point we have used only the arrangement shown in Fig. 6–34. In this circuit X is a two-terminal contact network. The designation of this method as "series" control is obvious (it is also known as "direct" control).

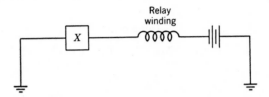

Fig. 6–34. Series control of a relay.

In contrast with the control method of Fig. 6–34 is that shown in Fig. 6–35 and known as "shunt" control. Again the control is established by means of a two-terminal contact network X, but the network is now connected in parallel with the relay winding. A current-limiting resistor R must be placed in series with the relay winding so

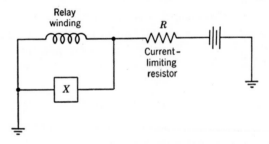

Fig. 6–35. Shunt control of a relay.

that when the transmission of X is 1, and the relay winding is short circuited, there will not be a short circuit of the battery. The resistance R must have a low enough value that when the contact network X is open circuited there will be a current in the winding sufficient to operate the relay.

It is apparent from these diagrams that if the digit 1 represents in each case the condition that the relay is operated, and X represents the transmission of the two-terminal network; the following statements apply:

Series Control	Shunt Control
Relay operation $= X$	Relay operation $= X'$

Thus the state of operation of the relay is described by the transmission of the controlling network, or the complement of the transmission, for the series and shunt circuits, respectively.

These relations immediately suggest that there may be a useful duality between the two circuits. Let the transmission of the two-terminal network X in Fig. 6–34 be a function T. This function also describes the state of operation of the relay in the series circuit. Now suppose that we want the state of operation of the relay in the shunt-control circuit of Fig. 6–35 to be described by the same switching function T. We must then use a two-terminal network which is the

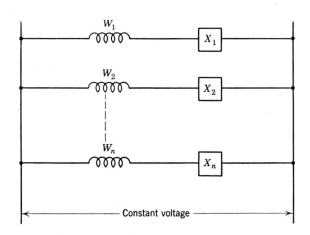

Fig. 6–36.   Relay control in a constant-voltage system.

complement of the network in Fig. 6–34. By definition (Art. 3.8), therefore, the contact networks of these two circuits are duals. There is, however, no clearly dual relation between the two complete circuits, if we take into account electrical properties and not merely switching properties.

We can understand this situation better if we examine circuits which do exhibit duality. In Fig. 6–36 there are n relays, each of which has a winding W controlled by a series control network X; the individual windings and control networks are distinguished by subscripts from 1 to n. The power for operating the relays is derived from a constant-voltage source, and we have a series-parallel electrical system in which each relay and its series control network is connected across the supply voltage.

Figure 6–37 shows the system which is the dual of that in Fig. 6–36. The power for operating the relays is now derived from a constant-current source, and we have a series-parallel system in which each relay winding is connected in parallel with its control network, and the parallel pairs are connected in series with each other and with the current source. We note also that the control networks in the constant-current system are the complements of those in the constant-voltage system.

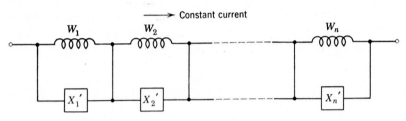

Fig. 6–37. Relay control in a constant-current system.

The important point we have thus established is that a series-control network is a characteristic of the constant-voltage system of relay operation, and a shunt-control network is a characteristic of the constant-current system. Referring to Fig. 6–35, we see that the current-limiting resistance R is effectively a means for producing an approximation to the constant-current mode of operation. When we wish to operate a group of relays in this manner, we use the system illustrated in Fig. 6–38, rather than the true constant-current system. In the system of Fig. 6–38 each relay is provided with a separate current-limiting resistor, and we thus have a group of approximately constant-current circuits which are actually supplied from a constant-voltage source.

The practical advantage of the approximation described is that it enables us to use both modes of operation within the same system and to obtain all the electrical power required from a common source. And it is even more important that it enables us to use both methods of control on the same relay.

In Fig. 6–39 there are two versions of a circuit in which a relay winding is controlled through both series and shunt networks. A current-limiting resistor R is required in both circuits to avoid a short circuit of the constant-voltage supply through the shunt control network Y. The difference between the two networks is that in part (a) the shunt network Y is placed across the series combination of winding W and control network X, while in part (b) the shunt network is across the relay winding only. The switching characteristics of the two networks are the same.

Designating the transmissions of networks X and Y in the usual

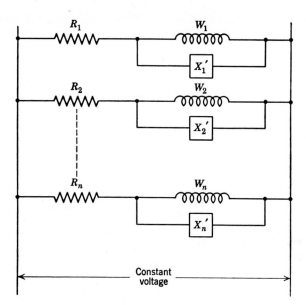

Fig. 6–38. Practical approximation to the constant-current system.

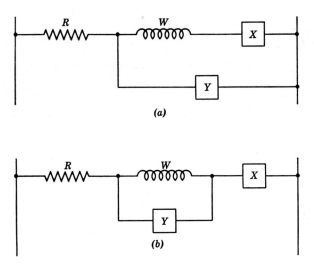

Fig. 6–39. Relay controlled by both series and shunt networks.

manner, and letting W represent the state of operation of the relay, we can write a table of combinations for W as a function of X and Y.

Table 6–4

X	Y	W
0	0	0
0	1	0
1	0	1
1	1	0

There is only one combination for which the relay operates, and from this we write for the state of operation of the relay, $W = XY'$. A simple example will illustrate the application of this expression.

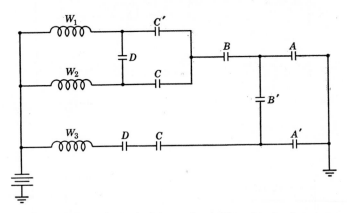

Fig. 6–40. Control of three relays with series circuits.

Example 6–6

The operation of three relays is to be controlled in accordance with the functions:

$$W_1 = AB(C' + D)$$
$$W_2 = AB(C + D)$$
$$W_3 = (A' + B')CD$$

Using series control of the relays, we can achieve all three of these operating functions by means of the circuit shown in Fig. 6–40.

Now we can rewrite the three control functions in the form

$$W_1 = AB(C' + D) = AB(CD')'$$
$$W_2 = AB(C + D) = AB(C'D')'$$
$$W_3 = (A' + B')CD = CD(AB)'$$

Each control function is now in the form XY', and can be interpreted as a direct-control network X and a shunt-control network Y. Thus the function W_1, for instance, can be realized by using a network AB in series with the relay coil, and the network CD' shunting the coil. Figure 6–41 shows a circuit in which all three relays are controlled by combinations of series and shunt networks, and in which the objective of design is to reduce the number of contacts required. The circuit of Fig. 6–40 contains 9 elements and uses 15 springs, while that of Fig. 6–41 contains 7 elements and uses 13 springs.

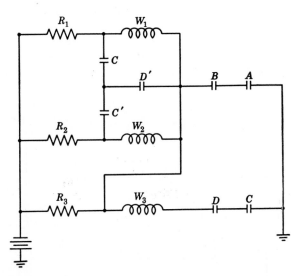

Fig. 6–41. Fewer contacts are required than in Fig. 6–40, because of the use of combined series and shunt control.

Shunt control of relays has certain disadvantages which must be considered in circuit engineering. Equipment cost is increased by the cost of the series resistance, and the cost of installing it. The circuit may draw current from the power source whether the relay is operated or not, and this increases the cost of power supply. Since the relay is released by a short circuit across its winding, there is an approximately exponential decay of current in the winding, and the release time is in general longer than it is with series control. This is usually considered a disadvantage, but under some conditions it may actually be a good reason for choosing shunt control.

Control circuits containing both series and shunt components are effectively synthesized by the use of maps. The optional entries are powerful aids in obtaining minimum networks. When a group of relays is to be controlled it will be necessary to assume a network form and then develop the rules for making entries in the maps. This process is best shown by an example.

Example 6–7

The two transmission functions synthesized in Examples 6–3 and 6–4 are to be treated as the control functions of two relays. Design control networks for the relays using both series and shunt components.

The relay control functions are

$$T_1 = A(BC' + D)$$

$$T_2 = AB'D + A'BCD'$$

For this synthesis we will assume a network of the form indicated in Fig. 6–42. Network X is in series with the coils of both relays. Network Y supplies shunt transmission to relay W_1 and network Z

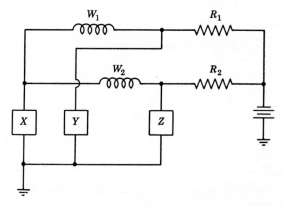

Fig. 6–42. Assumed form of a network controlling relays W_1 and W_2.

supplies shunt transmission to relay W_2. These networks are to be designed so that in combination they cause relays W_1 and W_2 to operate as they would if they were controlled directly by T_1 and T_2, respectively.

From an examination of the assumed form in Fig. 6–42, we can see that for all map positions occupied by 1's in either T_1 or T_2, there must be 1's in the map of X. The map of Y must contain 0's wherever the map of T_1 contains 1's, and the map of Z must contain 0's wherever the map of T_2 contains 1's. Furthermore, wherever the map of T_1 contains 1's that are not present in the map of T_2, the map of Z must contain 1's; and wherever the map of T_2 contains 1's that are not present in T_1, the map of Y must contain 1's.

These map entries ensure that: (a) each relay receives a series ground for all input conditions which require that the relay operate; (b) no shunt ground is applied when the input conditions require operation; and (c) each relay receives a shunt ground for those input conditions which require that it should not operate, although the other relay does operate.

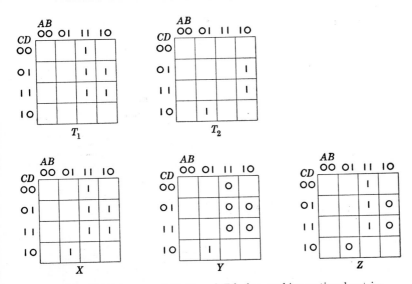

Fig. 6–43. Partial maps of X, Y, and Z before making optional entries.

Figure 6–43 shows the maps of T_1 and T_2, and the partial maps of X, Y, and Z. These partial maps contain only those entries which are fixed by the analysis given. They are the mandatory entries; all other entries in the X, Y, and Z maps are mutually optional. By this we mean the following:

1. A 0 can be entered in any remaining position in the X map. For such positions, the entries in the Y and Z maps are completely optional.

2. A 1 can be entered in any remaining position in the X map, but for such positions 1's must also be entered in both the Y and Z maps. (This makes it possible to apply a series ground to both relays, which would cause false operation, but to prevent that operation by also applying shunt ground to both relays.)

3. A 1 can be entered in any remaining positions in either or both of the Y and Z maps without influencing the X map. (All remaining positions correspond to 0's in the T_1 and T_2 maps. The shunt ground can only prevent operation.)

Maps completed in accordance with these rules are shown in Fig. 6–44. They represent the functions

$$X = AD + ABC' + A'BCD'$$

$$Y = A'B$$

$$Z = AB$$

There are many ways to complete the maps, and the particular choices made in Fig. 6–44 are not necessarily those which lead to the

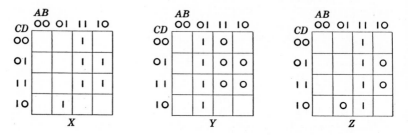

Fig. 6–44. Completed maps of Example 6–7.

minimum network. They do reduce the number of contacts and springs more than other, apparently better, choices. For instance, in the Y map the function represented is $A'B$. The rules permit addi-

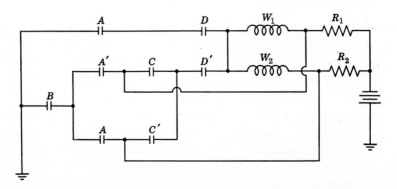

Fig. 6–45. Circuit synthesized in the form assumed in Fig. 6–42.

tional entries anywhere in the Y map, so we could just as well obtain simply $Y = A'$. However, we see in the network of Fig. 6–45 that $A'B$ is available as an isolated function in the X network. Of course, the B contact might have been moved to a position to the left of the D'

contact, leaving A' available instead of $A'B$, but with the B contact in the position shown, the function $Z = AB$ is also available as an isolated function. Note that no additional map entries were made to simplify the X function. Any useful, additional 1 entries in the X map are such that they must be compensated by 1 entries in either the Y map, or the Z map, or both. The circuit as actually drawn does not contain the term ABC' in the X function, but $ABC'D'$ instead. Examination of the X map, however, shows that the term $ABC'D'$ is sufficient to satisfy the requirements. In Fig. 6–45 we were able to achieve the required control with the duplication of only one contact. This circuit contains 8 contacts, 13 springs. The series control circuit shown in Fig. 6–24 contains 9 contacts, 15 springs.

6.7 Switching Properties of Tree Networks

The tree networks comprise a class of multi-terminal circuits which may be used either alone or in combination with other circuits. They are also known as transfer trees because in their complete forms most

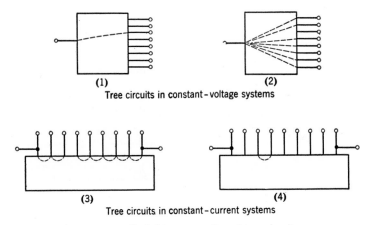

(1)   (2)

Tree circuits in constant–voltage systems

(3)   (4)

Tree circuits in constant–current systems

Fig. 6–46. Switching properties of tree circuits.

of the switching is done by transfer contacts. Incomplete trees will frequently contain elements which are not parts of transfer contacts, and in one type of complete tree network it is not possible to place all the elements in transfer combinations.

When it is used alone, and as a multiple-output circuit, the tree circuit is essentially a selecting circuit. A particular switching function is associated with transmission to each of its outputs, or to a group of outputs. Figure 6–46 illustrates schematically the switching properties of four basic types of tree circuits, and the numbers under the individual diagrams correspond to the type numbers used in the outline below.

For purposes of classification it is convenient to distinguish between tree circuits for use in constant-voltage and in constant-current systems. This serves to emphasize certain dualities in the modes of operation of the various types, but the circuits are not necessarily restricted to use in one system.

CONSTANT-VOLTAGE TYPES:

    1. Transmission is established between a common input terminal and any selected output terminal.

    2. Transmission is established between a common input terminal and all output terminals except a selected one.

CONSTANT-CURRENT TYPES:

    3. A short circuit is applied to all except one selected pair of adjacent terminals.

    4. A short circuit is applied to one selected pair of adjacent terminals.

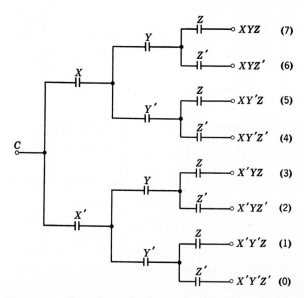

Fig. 6–47. Type 1 tree circuit completed for three variables.

Type 1 is by far the most common form of tree circuit. In Fig. 6–47 it is shown in its complete form for the three variables X, Y, and Z. It is a systematic structure which can readily be extended to include any number of variables. In its fully developed form a type 1 tree in n variables produces 2^n output functions, each of which is a single term of the 2^n possible terms in a standard sum. These terms are marked in algebraic form in Fig. 6–47, and the numbers in parentheses are the decimal identification numbers of the terms.[*]

As a switching device the type 1 tree merely serves to establish a connection between the common terminal C, and an output terminal which is determined by the combination of operated and unoperated relays X, Y, and Z. A most useful property of the tree is that its outputs are disjunctive with respect to each other—there can be no transmission between any pair of output terminals.

The type 1 tree circuit can readily be converted to a two-terminal network, and when thus used it enjoys the distinction of being the most general of all switching networks. There are 2^{2^n} standard sums in n

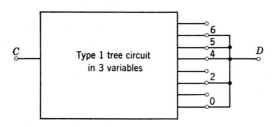

Fig. 6–48.   A tree circuit converted to a two-terminal network.

variables, and any of these may be realized by simply connecting together those outputs of a type 1 tree which represent the terms in the desired standard sum. Figure 6–48 illustrates this process for the transmission function $T = \sum(0, 2, 4, 5, 6)$. Between the terminals C and D we have a two-terminal network of the required transmission.

When groups of output terminals are tied together as in Fig. 6–48, many elements in the original tree circuit may be discarded. Figure 6–49 shows how the tree is thus simplified for this particular example. None of the elements forming paths to the unused terminals are needed. Terminals 4 and 5 are tied together so the Z transfer contact is not needed, and a Y transfer contact is eliminated because terminals 0 and 2 are connected. The Y contact shown encircled can be eliminated because it is part of a transmission $Y' + YZ'$.

The process illustrated in Fig. 6–49 is one of the ways in which we obtain incomplete tree circuits. More generally, however, the incomplete tree is a multiple-output circuit in which not all the possible

[*] S. H. Washburn, "Relay Trees and Symmetric Circuits," A.I.E.E. Trans., Vol. 68, 1949, pp. 582–586.

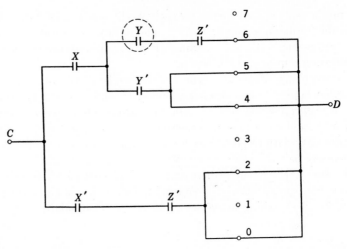

Fig. 6–49. Simplification of tree circuit after conversion to a two-terminal network.

output terminals are needed. This is illustrated in Fig. 6–50 where the incomplete tree provides transmission between terminal C and any

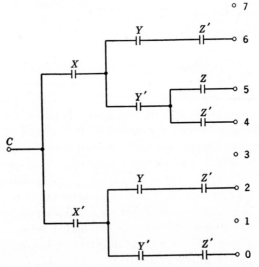

Fig. 6–50. An incomplete tree circuit provides a more limited selection of output terminals.

one of the outputs 0, 2, 4, 5, or 6. Note, however, that we cannot simplify this circuit except to discard elements which are connected to unused terminals. There is a general rule which applies to the type 1 tree, whether it is complete or incomplete, when it is used in a multi-terminal circuit: every path between the common terminal and an output terminal must include a contact element on each relay. It should also be noted that the incomplete tree is disjunctive with respect to the output terminals, just as the complete tree.

The remaining three types of tree circuits are of somewhat less practical interest, but they offer further insight to the problems of multi-terminal circuit design.

By definition, the type 2 tree circuit is required to isolate a selected output terminal and to connect all the remaining outputs to the common input terminal. For two variables, this requires that we establish a group of parallel-circuit transmissions as shown at the left of Fig. 6–51. There is for each output terminal only one cut set; for all

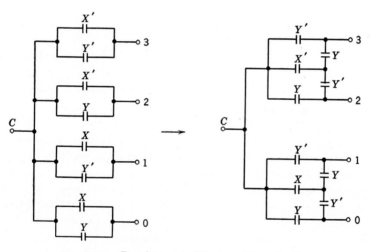

Fig. 6–51. Development of the type 2 tree circuit.

other input conditions the terminal is connected to C. By the methods discussed in Art. 6.2 (see Fig. 6–10), the circuit is consolidated into the form shown at the right of Fig. 6–51.

In Fig. 6–52 the type 2 tree circuit has been redrawn as in Fig. 6–51 and has its common terminal marked C. It is now interesting to note the effect of adding the X and X' contacts which attach to the terminal B. If we operate the relay X only, we find that terminal B is connected to terminal 2 by the path of transmission XY', while terminal C is connected to terminals 0, 1, and 3. The transmission of terminal C to terminal 2 is $X' + Y$, which is the complement of the transmission between B and 2. Note that the decimal number, 2, assigned to the terminal represents both the standard-sum term, XY', and the standard-product term, $X' + Y$, of the complementary function.

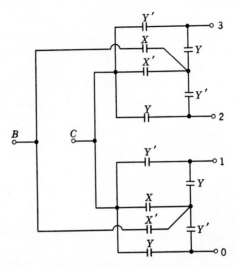

Fig. 6–52.   Superposition of types 1 and 2 tree circuits.

In the circuit of Fig. 6–53, the part of the circuit shown solid represents a type 1 tree in three variables, with B as its common terminal. The circuit connected by dotted lines shows the contacts which are added to the type 1 tree to obtain a type 2 tree superposed. The transmission between B and any output terminal is the complement of the transmission between C and the same output terminal. Stated in another way, we can by means of this combined tree circuit establish a path between terminal B and any selected output terminal, and at the same time establish a connection from C to all the remaining output terminals. This feature can be of use, for example, in situations which require that all but one selected path be grounded.

In Fig. 6–51 the type 2 tree was developed from a group of parallel-connected circuits. Each of these circuits produced the sum of two variables. A more economical arrangement is that shown in Fig. 6–54, in which the sums are grouped so as to use the basic circuit of Fig. 6–5. We may well ask whether the type 2 tree is an economical way to realize its particular output functions, for both of the non-tree circuits shown use fewer contacts. In the three-variable circuit of Fig. 6–54 there are 16 contacts and 28 springs, while the part of Fig. 6–53 which is required in the type 2 tree uses 26 contacts and 39 springs.

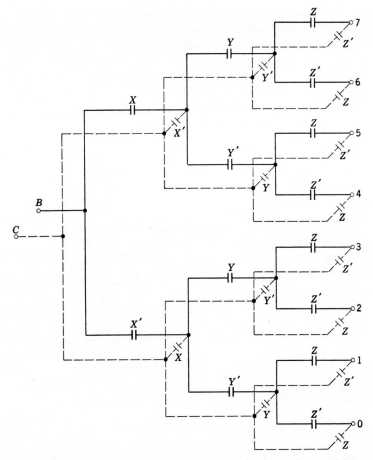

Fig. 6–53. Superposed type 1 and type 2 tree circuits in three variables.

It is only when the type 2 tree circuit is extended to a larger number of variables that it becomes more economical. The number of springs required by the type 2 tree when built for n variables is given by

Table 6–5

Number of Variables	Springs in Circuit of Fig. 6–54	Springs in Type 2 Tree
2	10	15
3	28	39
4	72	87
5	176	183
6	416	375

$3(2^{n+1}) - 9$ and for the non-tree circuit of Fig. 6–54 by $(2n + 1)$ (2^{n-1}). These numbers are compared in Table 6–5, where we see that for $n > 5$ the tree uses fewer springs.

In its switching action the type 3 tree circuit can perform the same duty in a constant-current system that the type 1 tree circuit performs in a constant-voltage system. In the constant-current mode of operation, if we wish to operate a relay we remove a short circuit from across its winding, and if we want to release it we short circuit the

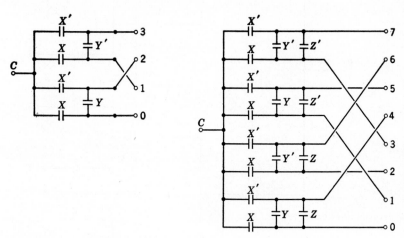

Fig. 6–54. Circuits equivalent to the type 2 tree circuit in two and three variables.

winding. In Fig. 6–55 a type 3 tree is arranged to operate selectively any one of four relays, the windings of which are connected in series

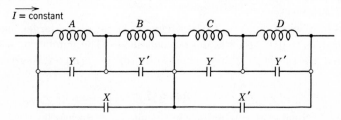

Fig. 6–55. A type 3 tree circuit in two variables controlling relay windings connected in series.

in a constant-current system. Consider the condition in which X is not operated and Y is operated. Starting at the left-hand side, we see that winding A is short circuited by the Y contact across it. The current I passes through winding B and operates that relay. Windings C and D are both short circuited by the X' contact. Hence B is the only winding energized by the tree. Note that the control conditions are not expressed in terms of transmission to a particular output terminal, but in terms of the absence of a short circuit across a selected pair of adjacent terminals. We can quite properly think of this in terms of the transmission concept by writing a table of combinations which shows which relay in the load circuit is controlled by each combination of variables, and then designating the operated condition of a load relay by the digit 1. This may then be taken as the equivalent transmission of the tree between each pair of terminals.

X	Y	Load Relay Operated	Equivalent Transmission
0	0	A	$X'Y'$
0	1	B	$X'Y$
1	0	C	XY'
1	1	D	XY

Figure 6–56 shows the type 3 tree circuit extended to include three variables. We may visualize the switching properties of this network,

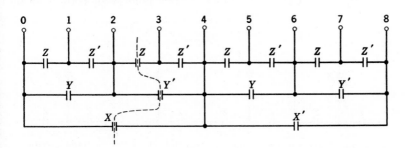

Fig. 6–56. Extension of the type 3 tree circuit to three variables.

quite aside from the control of relays in a constant-current system, by observing that for any cut set we choose, such as the set $(X + Y' + Z)$ indicated by the dotted line, all the terminals to the left of the cut set become connected, and all the terminals to the right of the cut set become connected. The type 3 tree circuit can also be built in the incomplete form. The procedure is to short circuit any pair of adjacent terminals which are not to be used, and then remove any elements of the tree network which thereby become superfluous.

The type 4 tree circuit is the constant-current equivalent of the type 2 tree, when the latter is used to control a load relay at each of its output terminals. There are 2^n pairs of adjacent terminals in the constant-current tree circuits, and the type 4 tree can selectively short circuit any pair. Figure 6–57 shows this type of tree developed for

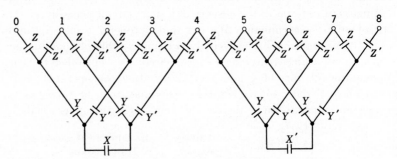

Fig. 6–57. The type 4 tree circuit in three variables.

three variables. It should be noted that for the type 4 tree there is no common connection between the X and X' contacts, and they therefore cannot be combined into a transfer contact.

There is a non-tree circuit, shown in Fig. 6–58, which is the equivalent of the type 4 tree. It uses the same number of springs as the

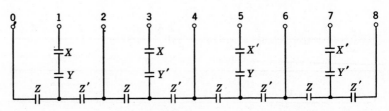

Fig. 6–58. Circuit which is equivalent to the type 4 tree in three variables.

type 2 tree equivalent of Fig. 6–54. From the tabulation of spring requirements in Table 6–6, it may readily be verified that the type 4 tree uses fewer springs for $n > 5$.

The number of contact springs required for each of the types of tree circuits, in its complete form, is given as a function of the number of variables by the following expressions:

Type 1	$3(2^n - 1)$
Type 2	$3(2^{n+1}) - 9$
Type 3	$3(2^n - 1)$
Type 4	$3(2^{n+1}) - 8$

Table 6–6 shows an evaluation of these expressions for all types of trees, and up to six variables.

Table 6–6

Number of Variables	Type 1	Type 2	Type 3	Type 4	Type 2 and Type 4 Equivalents
2	9	15	9	16	10
3	21	39	21	40	28
4	45	87	45	88	72
5	93	183	93	184	176
6	189	375	189	376	416

6.8   Distribution of Contact Springs in Tree Networks

It is evident from an inspection of the tree circuits discussed in Art. 6.7 that all four types contain a non-uniform distribution of contacts. In Fig. 6–47 we see that a type 1 tree circuit for three variables requires four transfer contacts on the relay nearest the output terminals. If the number of variables n in the tree is increased, and the contacts are not redistributed, the number of transfer contacts required on the most heavily loaded relay increases as 2^{n-1}. By rearrangement of the contacts to secure more uniform distribution of the contact load among most of the relays in the tree, it becomes possible to construct larger trees without exceeding the maximum allowable number of springs on a single relay. The general principles of contact redistribution apply to all types of tree circuits. We shall consider their application in terms of the type 1 tree only.*

It would be ideal if the contacts of a type 1 tree circuit could be uniformly distributed among all the variables. This result cannot be achieved for two reasons: first, one of the variables will always be represented by a single transfer contact connected to the common input terminal of the tree; second, the number of transfer contacts in the remainder of the tree is not in general exactly divisible by the remaining number of variables $(n - 1)$. As an example of the second point, a four-variable tree requires $1 + 2 + 4 + 8 = 15$ transfer contacts. Since 1 transfer contact is used on 1 variable, the remaining 3 variables must share 14 transfer contacts, and there is no way to

* C. E. Shannon, "The Synthesis of Two-Terminal Switching Circuits, Part II," *Bell System Technical Journal*, Vol. 28, 1949, pp. 59–98; A. W. Burks, R. Mc-Naughton, C. H. Pollmar, D. W. Warren, and J. B. Wright, "The Folded Tree," *Journal of the Franklin Institute*, Vol. 260, Nos. 1 and 2, July and August 1955, pp. 9–24, and 115–126.

assign the contacts so that the distribution is absolutely uniform. We shall see, however, that aside from the single transfer contact on the initial variable, the distribution of contacts among the remaining $(n-1)$ variables can always be made, as Shannon expresses it, "almost uniform."

For the three-variable tree circuit of Fig. 6–47, the distribution of transfer contacts among the variables X, Y, and Z, is 1, 2, and 4, respectively. In Fig. 6–59, the same tree circuit appears with the variables Y and Z interchanged in the upper and lower halves of the

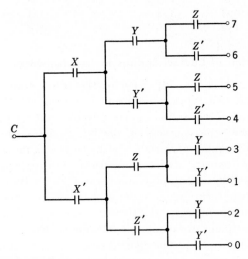

Fig. 6–59. Redistribution of spring load in a three-variable tree of type 1.

tree, and the distribution of transfer contacts is now $1, 3, 3$. We have been able to divide the contacts equally between two of the variables, but we can do nothing about the single transfer contact on one of the variables. It should be remembered, however, that the variables themselves may be interchanged completely within the tree. For example, in Fig. 6–59, instead of assigning the variables in the order X, Y, Z, we could use the order Z, X, Y, and for that sequence of variables the contact distribution 1, 3, 3 can still be used. It should be understood throughout this discussion that complete interchange of variables is always a valid step.

For a three-variable tree the only possible distributions of transfer contacts are $1, 2, 4$, and $1, 3, 3$. If we now add a fourth variable, the resulting tree consists of an initial transfer contact on one of the variables, with its terminals connected to the initial points of two three-variable trees on the remaining three variables. The upper and lower three-variable trees must each contain either the distribution $1, 2, 4$, or the distribution $1, 3, 3$, but these numbers may now be permuted among the three variables. Table 6–7 shows all the possible distributions of transfer contacts within complete four-variable trees, together with the required distributions within the upper and lower three-variable trees.

Figure 6–60 shows a complete four-variable tree circuit in which the

Table 6–7

Distribution within Four-Variable Tree				Distributions within Three-Variable Trees					
				Upper			Lower		
W	X	Y	Z	X	Y	Z	X	Y	Z
1	2	4	8	1	2	4	1	2	4
1	2	5	7	1	2	4	1	3	3
1	2	6	6	1	2	4	1	4	2
1	3	3	8	1	2	4	2	1	4
1	3	4	7	1	3	3	2	1	4
1	3	5	6	1	4	2	2	1	4
1	4	4	6	1	3	3	3	1	3
1	4	5	5	1	4	2	3	1	3

"almost uniform" distribution $1, 4, 5, 5$ is obtained, using the upper and lower distributions which are given in the last line of Table 6–7.

Shannon establishes the following rule for the redistribution of contacts within a type 1 tree for any number of variables. The initial distribution of transfer contacts is always $1, 2, 4, 8, \ldots, 2^{n-1}$. A new distribution is obtained by moving one or more units from a larger number to a smaller number, without moving any units to the number 1. A succession of such moves may be made, but units can be shifted only from higher numbers to lower numbers. Thus, if we have the initial distribution $1, 2, 4, 8, 16$, we can modify it by the following steps under the Shannon rule:

V	W	X	Y	Z	
1	2	4	8	16	
					Shift 1 from X to W; shift 4 from Z to Y
1	3	3	12	12	
					Shift 4 from Y to X
1	3	7	8	12	
					Shift 4 from Z to W
1	7	7	8	8	Final "almost uniform" distribution

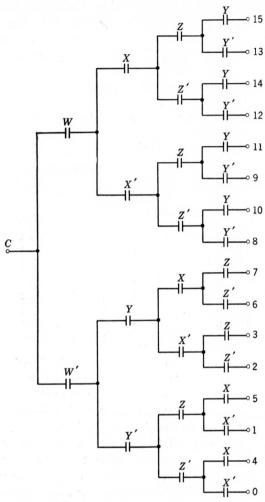

Fig. 6–60. Rearrangement of type 1 tree in four variables to equalize spring loads.

Example 6–8

This "almost uniform" sequence of numbers tells how many transfer contacts are on each relay, but it tells nothing about where the contacts are located in the tree, except for the single transfer contact on the V relay. Determine a detailed distribution.

We do know that the sub-sequence $7, 7, 8, 8$ must be found by adding the number of transfer contacts on W, X, Y, and Z, respectively, in an upper tree and a lower tree. Moreover, the distributions within these two four-variable trees must be taken from the list of possible distributions in Table 6–7.

Each sub-sequence must contain a 1 in it, and these 1's must refer to different variables, since each relay except V must carry at least seven transfer contacts. Assume that the W and X relays carry single transfer contacts in the upper and lower tree, respectively. We can arrange a tabulation as follows:

W	X	Y	Z	
7	7	8	8	Total number required
1	6	4	4	Number in upper tree
6	1	4	4	Number in lower tree

If W carries one transfer in the upper tree, it must carry 6 in the lower tree, and the opposite applies to X. Relays Y and Z carry a total of 8 transfers each, and an equal division between the upper and lower trees produces in both trees the valid distributions $1, 4, 4, 6$, but these are carried on the relays as follows:

Upper tree $1, 4, 4, 6$ on W, Y, Z, X, respectively

Lower tree $1, 4, 4, 6$ on X, Y, Z, W, respectively

The steps above are repeated on the sub-sequence $4, 4, 6$, with the following results:

	Y	Z	X	
Upper$_1$	4	4	6	
	1	3	3	Upper$_2$ on $Y X Z$
	3	1	3	Lower$_2$ on $Z X Y$
Lower$_1$	Y	Z	W	
	4	4	6	
	1	3	3	Upper$_2$ on $Y W Z$
	3	1	3	Lower$_2$ on $Z W Y$

These distributions are shown schematically in Fig. 6–61.

The redistribution of contacts within an incomplete tree is not readily subject to general treatment because of the fact that the 2^n outputs of the complete tree may be used in $(2^{2^n} - 1)$ ways to form incomplete trees. It is true, however, that any valid redistribution of the complete tree may be used as the starting point for forming an incomplete tree. Consequently, the variables in the upper and lower halves of an incomplete tree may be permuted in the manner shown for complete tree circuits.

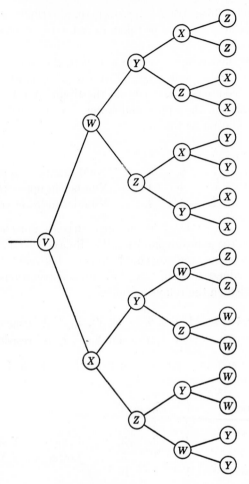

Fig. 6-61. Transfer contact distribution computed in Example 6–8.

PROBLEMS

6.1 The following pairs of transmission functions are to be realized by contact networks which require as few springs as possible. A *sufficient* number of springs is given with each pair of functions.

1. $T_1 = B(A + C)$
   $T_2 = C(A + B)$ 10 springs
2. $T_1 = B(A + C)$
   $T_2 = C(A' + B')$ 10 springs

3. $T_1 = B(A + C)$
   $T_2 = C'(A + B')$ 8 springs

4. $T_1 = B(A + C)$
   $T_2 = C'(A' + B')$ 9 springs

5. $T_1 = B + AC$
   $T_2 = B' + C$ 8 springs

6. $T_1 = ABC + A'B'C$
   $T_2 = A'D + ABC'D$ 11 springs

6.2 Design a three-terminal contact network which realizes the transmission of the network given, and the complement of that transmission, using transfer contacts only.

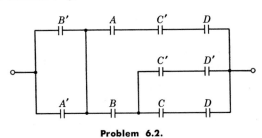

Problem 6.2.

6.3 The following pairs of transmission functions are to be realized by contact networks which require as few springs as possible.

1. $T_1 = \sum (0, 1, 4, 5, 11, 15)$
   $T_2 = \sum (5, 8, 10, 11, 14, 15)$

2. $T_1 = A[BC + D(E + F)]$
   $T_2 = A' + (B' + C')(D' + E'F')$

3. $T_1 = \Pi(0, 1, 3, 7, 11, 15)$
   $T_2 = \Pi(3, 7, 8, 10, 11, 15)$

4. $T_1 = \sum (1, 5, 6, 8, 10, 12, 13, 15)$
   $T_2 = \sum (2, 3, 4, 5, 8, 13, 14, 15)$

5. $T_1 = \sum (2, 3, 10, 11, 12, 13, 14, 15)$
   $T_2 = \sum (1, 3, 9, 11, 15)$

6. $T_1 = \sum (1, 3, 5, 7, 10, 11, 12, 13, 14, 15)$
   $T_2 = \sum (1, 5, 7, 8, 9, 10, 12, 13, 14, 15)$

7. $T_1 = \sum (1, 5, 6, 12, 13, 14)$
   $T_2 = \sum (1, 2, 3, 9, 11, 12, 15)$

8. $T_1 = \sum (3, 7, 12, 13, 14, 15)$
   $T_2 = \sum (2, 3, 6, 7, 13, 15)$

9. $T_1 = \Pi(0, 1, 4, 6, 8, 9)$
   $T_2 = \Pi(0, 1, 3, 7, 8, 9)$

10. $T_1 = \sum (1, 4, 5, 6, 8, 9, 10, 11, 13)$
    $T_2 = \sum (4, 5, 6, 7, 8, 10, 13, 15)$

11. $T_1 = \sum (1, 2, 8, 11, 13)$
    $T_2 = \sum (3, 9, 10, 12)$

12. $T_1 = \sum (0, 2, 3, 4, 6, 9, 13)$
    $T_2 = \sum (0, 2, 3, 8, 9, 12)$

13. $T_1 = \sum (0, 5, 9, 12)$
    $T_2 = \sum (2, 7, 11, 14)$

14. $T_1 = \sum (6, 7, 9, 10, 11, 14, 15)$
$T_2 = \sum (5, 7, 9, 10, 11, 13, 15)$

6.4 (a) Write transmission functions for the transmissions between terminals 1–2 and terminals 1–3 of the given circuit.

(b) Design a network which produces between like-numbered terminals the complements of the transmissions found in part (a).

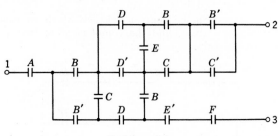

Problem 6.4.

6.5 Two three-terminal networks, N_1 and N_2, contain contacts on the relays A, B, C, and D. Network N_1 has the two outputs $T_1 = \sum (0, 1, 10)$ and $T_2 = \sum (0, 10, 11)$. Network N_2 has the outputs $T_1 = \sum (0, 1, 4, 5, 10)$ and $T_2 = \sum (0, 10, 11, 14, 15)$. These transmission functions are obtained by using exactly the same number and types of contacts in each network (10 springs are sufficient in each network). Find both networks.

6.6 A switching circuit has four input variables, W, X, Y, and Z, and four output variables, A, B, C, and D. When the input variables are given values in the sequence shown in the table, the output variables take successive values which are the binary equivalents of the first ten decimal digits of the constant π, as shown in the table. The input combinations which are not listed cannot occur. Design a multiple-output contact network to realize these functions.

W	X	Y	Z	A	B	C	D
0	0	0	0	0	0	1	1
0	0	0	1	0	0	0	1
0	0	1	1	0	1	0	0
0	1	1	1	0	0	0	1
0	1	1	0	0	1	0	1
0	0	1	0	1	0	0	1
1	0	1	0	0	0	1	0
1	1	1	0	0	1	1	0
1	1	0	0	0	1	0	1
1	0	0	0	0	1	0	0

6.7 The transmission functions at the three outputs of a four-terminal contact network are represented by the standard sums:

$$T_1 = \sum (2, 4, 5, 10, 11)$$
$$T_2 = \sum (4, 5, 10, 11, 13)$$
$$T_3 = \sum (2, 3, 4, 10, 11, 12)$$

Design a minimal four-terminal contact network to realize these functions.

6.8 Given the assumed form for a multi-terminal contact network shown:
1. Develop and state the rules for its use in the design of minimal contact networks.
2. Design in this form a contact network to realize the functions

$$T_1 = \sum (0, 1, 4, 5, 9, 15)$$
$$T_2 = \sum (1, 7, 8, 10, 12, 14)$$

(10 contacts, 16 springs are sufficient)

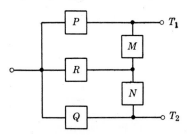

Problem 6.8.

6.9 Design and draw a minimum contact, three-terminal network which has the following interterminal transmission functions

$$T_{12} = AB + C; \qquad T_{23} = ABD' + C; \qquad T_{31} = D' + C$$

6.10 Given the contact network N_1 with its interterminal transmission functions designated as S_{12}, S_{23}, and S_{31}, another contact network N_2 is to be derived with its interterminal transmission functions defined by the relations

$$T_{12} = S_{23}S_{31}; \qquad T_{23} = S_{31}S_{12}; \qquad T_{31} = S_{12}S_{23}$$

(12 springs are sufficient)

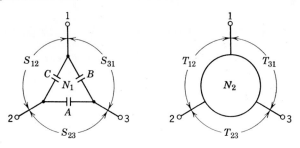

Problem 6.10.

6.11 The network shown is to be converted to a simpler network having the same interterminal transmission functions. The branches of the original network contain the functions:

$$X = C'D + C(A + B) + AB$$
$$Y = B'D' + BC + AC$$
$$Z = C'D + B'D' + A'C'$$

Draw the derived contact network (11 springs are sufficient).

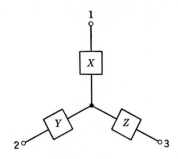

Problem 6.11.

6.12 In the diagrams shown, network N_1 is an arbitrary three-terminal contact network with the interterminal transmissions S_{12}, S_{23}, and S_{31}.

Provided that the network N_1 is physically realizable, but that otherwise it may have any set of interterminal transmission functions, determine

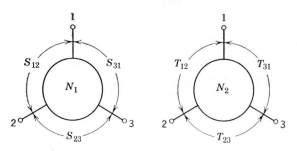

Problem 6.12.

whether or not another three-terminal network N_2 (at the right in the diagram) is *always* physically realizable, under each of the sets of conditions given below. For each part of this problem give a clear statement of the reasons for your answer.

    1. If $T_{12} = S_{12}'$; $T_{23} = S_{23}'$; $T_{31} = S_{31}'$
    2. If $T_{12} = S_{23} + S_{31}$; $T_{23} = S_{31} + S_{12}$; $T_{31} = S_{12} + S_{23}$

6.13 A three-terminal contact network contains only normally open contacts from the relays A, B, and C. The following relations hold between terminals

$$T_{12} = T_{23} = T_{31} = H_{12} = H_{23} = H_{31}$$

where T and H represent transmission and hindrance functions, respectively. Design a minimum network which exhibits these inter-terminal relations.

    6.14 For each of the circuits shown
        1. Write an algebraic expression that describes the operation of the X relay.
        2. Derive a two-terminal contact network for the series control of X.
        3. Derive a two-terminal contact network for the shunt control of X.

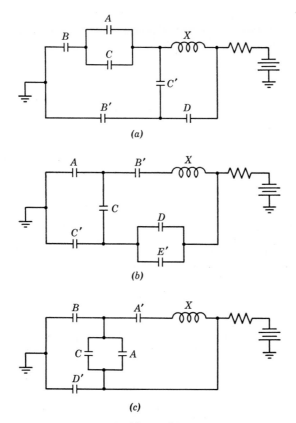

(a)

(b)

(c)

Problem 6.14.

6.15 Two relays, X and Y, are controlled by the network of resistors and relay contacts shown. This control network is to be replaced by a network using contacts only, as indicated. The required contact network should have

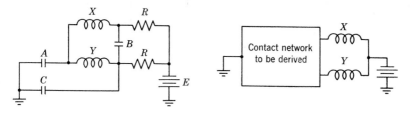

Problem 6.15.

as few springs as possible and must produce the same conditions of relay operation in terms of the variables A, B, and C.

The new contact network is to be derived for each of the following conditions of operation.

1. Either relay can operate when it is in series with a resistance R, but the supply voltage E is insufficient to operate the relays when they are connected in series with each other and with the resistance R.
2. The supply voltage E is sufficient to operate either relay in series with a resistance R, or to operate the two relays connected in series with each other and with the resistance R.

6.16   The operation of a relay X is described by the function

$$X(A, B, C, D) = \Sigma\ (12, 13, 14)$$

Design the control network under the restriction that only normally open contacts are available.

6.17   The operation of a relay X is described by the function

$$X(A, B, C, D) = \Sigma\ (2, 7, 8, 13)$$

Design a minimum contact network to provide the required control (12 springs are sufficient).

6.18   Each of the two circuits shown has a combination of series and shunt control. Each network contains 6 contacts and 10 springs. However, both circuits can be improved so that the same control functions are obtained with 5 contacts and 9 springs. Design the simplified circuits.

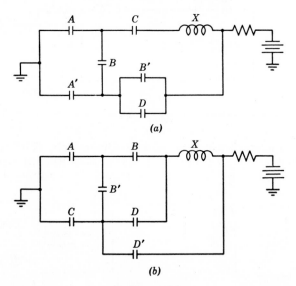

(a)

(b)

Problem 6.18.

6.19   A relay is to be controlled by a contact network with two outputs which provide transmission functions for combined series and shunt control. The state of operation of the relay is described by the function

$$R = ABC' + A'B'D + C'D$$

Design a contact network which realizes this function (4 contacts, 8 springs are sufficient).

6.20 The networks N_1, N_2, N_3, and N_4 contain contacts from relays A, B, C, and D. Derive minimum networks such that the operation of X is described by Σ (5, 10), using the assumed form shown.

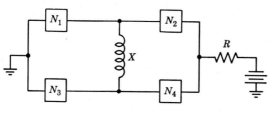

Problem 6.20.

6.21 Derive a network, N, for the control of the relay Y such that the operation of Y is complementary to the operation of the relay X. Use only one of each of the contacts B, C, and D, and use no contacts of the type B', C', and D'.

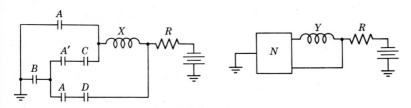

Problem 6.21.

6.22 A relay, X, is controlled by a three-terminal contact network, N, which contains no contacts from X. If T_{01}, T_{02}, and T_{12} are the inter-

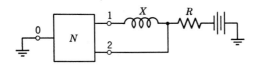

Problem 6.22.

terminal transmission functions of N, determine for each of the following expressions whether it correctly describes the state of operation of X.

1. $T_{01}T_{02}'$
2. $T_{01}T_{12}'$
3. $T_{01}T_{02}'T_{12}'$
4. $T_{01}(T_{02}T_{12})'$
5. $(T_{01} + T_{02}T_{12})(T_{01}' + T_{02}'T_{12}')$

6.23   Relays X and Y have identical electrical characteristics, and either one will operate if a voltage E is applied, with either polarity across its winding.

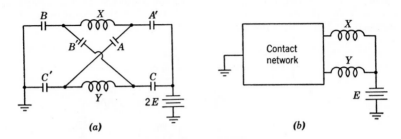

(a)   (b)

Problem 6.23.

The circuit in (a) is to be replaced by an equivalent one in which both X and Y are series controlled.

       1. For the contact network of (b) determine the required transmission functions to the terminals connected to X and Y, respectively.

       2. Design a contact network, as in (b) in which a minimum number of contacts is used, and in which transfer combinations of contacts are used whenever possible.

6.24   If the operation of the relays R_1, R_2, and R_3, is described, respectively, by

$$R_1 = \Sigma\ (2, 10, 11, 12)$$
$$R_2 = \Sigma\ (12)$$
$$R_3 = \Sigma\ (2, 6, 8, 9, 12)$$

find minimal contact networks for T_1, T_2, T_3, and T_4, in the relay control network shown.

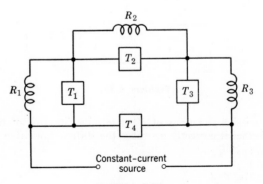

Problem 6.24.

6.25 Design type 1 tree networks in six variables having the indicated distributions of transfer contacts.

	A	B	C	D	E	F
1.	1	3	5	9	15	30
2.	1	6	6	10	16	24
3.	1	8	8	11	15	20
4.	1	9	10	11	14	18
5.	1	11	12	12	13	14

CHAPTER 7

Symmetric functions

Before beginning the study of general types of contact networks which are not of the series-parallel form, it will be instructive to examine a special type of non-series-parallel network described by a symmetric function. When a symmetric function is specified, its contact network realization can be drawn immediately, and with ease, despite the fact that for most symmetric functions the network is non-series-parallel, and for many symmetric functions it can be non-planar.

Symmetric networks can also be classified with the iterative networks which we will study in more detail in Chapter 11. However, once the iterative nature of the symmetric network has been observed, we no longer need the iterative approach in designing specified symmetric circuits. Moreover, symmetric functions have algebraic properties which make it desirable to treat them as a separate class.

7.1 Basic Contact Network for Symmetric Functions

The most elementary concept of a symmetric function is that which specifies a contact network built on m relays, and which provides 1 transmission if any n of the m relays are operated. We will start with this concept and generalize the treatment in Art. 7.4.

It is not difficult to write transmission functions which express algebraically the idea of n out of m relays operated. For example, if we have three relays, A, B, and C, and the transmission of the contact network built on them is to be 1 whenever two of the three relays are operated, we can express this by the function

$$T = ABC' + AB'C + A'BC$$

There are just three ways in which we can have two out of three relays operated and each term of the function represents one of those ways.

While it is relatively easy to write symmetric functions algebraically, it is quite another matter to design economical circuits merely from the algebraic expressions. In the very simple example given, we observe that there are no pairs of terms which permit the elimination of literals. All three terms in the expression are prime implicants and all three are required in the minimum sum. Although this is not always true of symmetric functions it tends to be inherently true. In the function written above, A, B, and C are called the *variables of symmetry*. Each term of the function has two of the three variables unprimed and the third primed. Hence the state of two variables must be changed in going from one term to another.

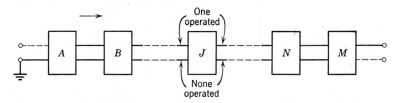

Fig. 7–1. A chain of contact networks forming a simple symmetric circuit.

This quite intractable algebraic situation is easily dealt with by the use of a basic circuit which we shall here develop by the iterative method. The schematic diagram in Fig. 7–1 indicates a chain of contact networks in which each network contains contacts from just one of the relays $A, B, \ldots, M$. Each network in the chain has two input terminals at its left and two output terminals at its right. These terminals are connected as shown in the diagram so that the input terminals of each network are connected to the output terminals of the network at its left. Exceptions are made for the two cells at the extreme ends of the chain. At the left, cell A has its lower terminal connected to ground and its upper input terminal is not used, while at the right cell M provides the final output of the network on its upper terminal and its lower terminal is not used. These terminal cells have their contact structures modified to remove any contacts which are redundant because of unused connections.

We now direct attention in Fig. 7–1 to the network J which we will select to represent a typical cell of the chain. If there is a ground on the lower input terminal of the J cell, it means that in the portion of the chain to the left of the J cell no relays are operated. A ground on the lower output terminal of the J cell signifies that no relays up to and including the J relay are operated. A ground on the upper input terminal of the J cell means that in the portion of the chain to the left of the J cell there is one and only one relay operated. A ground on the upper output terminal of the J cell means that in the part of the chain up to and including the J cell there is one and only one relay operated.

If there is no ground on either input terminal of the J cell it means that two or more relays to the left of the J cell are operated.

At the left-hand end of the chain, ground is applied to the lower input terminal of the A cell and the presence of ground at this point

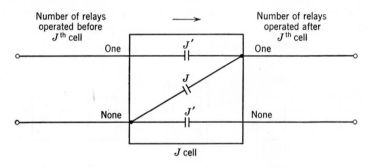

Fig. 7–2. Contacts within the typical cell of Fig. 7–1.

correctly signifies that no relays to the left of the A cell have operated. Since there are no relays to the left of the A cell, it is not necessary to provide an upper input terminal for that cell.

At the right-hand end of the chain we find that the M cell has only an upper output terminal. A ground will appear on that terminal, according to our specifications, if one and only one relay has operated in the entire chain. We are not interested in having an output if no relays operate, so the M network has no lower output terminal.

A contact network which meets the requirements imposed upon the typical cell is illustrated in Fig. 7–2. The arrow above the cell indicates that ground is being propagated along the chain from left to right as indicated. In a sense, the typical cell receives at its input terminals information about the state of the network to its left, and passes on to its output terminals information which its right-hand neighbor can interpret in a similar manner. In the contact network we see that if the J cell does not operate, it transmits any ground which is present on either of its input terminals to the output terminal at the same level by way of one of the J' contacts. If, however, the J cell is operated, and there is a ground on the lower input terminal, it switches that ground by means of a J contact to the upper output terminal. At the same time, of course, the lower J' contact prevents ground from appearing on the lower output terminal. If there is a ground on the upper input terminal at the time the J relay operates, the upper J' contact prevents the ground from advancing any further through the chain.

We would now like to build a contact network on six relays so that the transmission of the network will be 1 if one and only one of the relays is operated. To do this we arrange contacts on each relay in

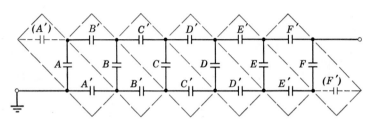

Fig. 7–3. Symmetric circuit formed by the interconnection of six typical cells.

accordance with the diagram of the typical cell of Fig. 7–2 and connect cells in a chain to form the network shown in Fig. 7–3. The dashed lines indicate the boundaries of the individual cells, and a redundant contact in each end cell is shown dotted. We can readily verify that the network transmission is correct but it is also important to note here that we have designed a somewhat complex non-series-parallel circuit. An attempt to design this circuit from the algebraic expression for its transmission would be found exceedingly troublesome, but the iterative method yields the result without difficulty.

The idea of a *chain* construction, as in Fig. 7–1, is extended to the general problem in the chain shown in Fig. 7–4. Again we have information passed along the chain by a ground which propagates from left to right. The number of operated relays among those to the left of a given point in the chain is indicated by the level of the intercell connection which is grounded at that point. In this chain we cannot define a typical cell, because the number of intercell connections increases linearly when going from left to right. Although no one of the cells can be called typical, there is no difficulty in determining the contact structure of any particular cell, such as the J cell in Fig. 7–5. The thing that is typical about this cell is that there is a j output terminal but there is no j input terminal. Obviously, we cannot have more relays operated than there are relays.

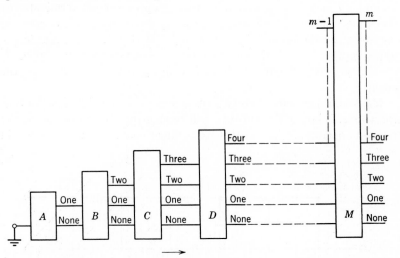

Fig. 7–4.   Structure of the basic symmetric circuit.

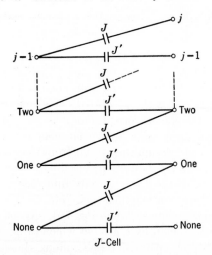

Fig. 7–5.   Contacts within a typical cell of Fig. 7–4.

The cell construction in this type of network is disjunctive at both the input and the output terminals. That is, the transmission between every pair of input terminals and between every pair of output terminals is 0. Because of this construction, a ground never appears on more than one cell terminal at a time, either at the inputs or at the outputs.

When we interconnect cells having the contact structure of Fig. 7–5 in accordance with the chain diagram of Fig. 7–4, the basic symmetric network shown in Fig. 7–6 is obtained. This network is drawn in full for a chain of five cells and its extension to any larger size is indicated. The structure of the basic symmetric network should be studied care-

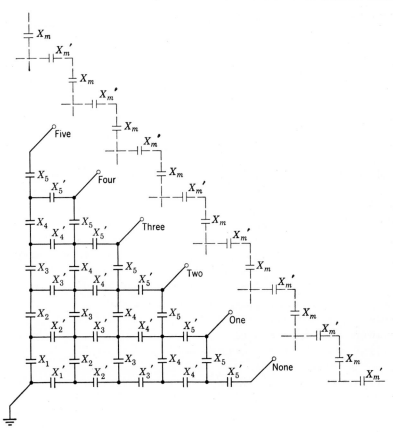

Fig. 7–6. The basic symmetric network.

fully because we will use it as the starting point for the design of all symmetric circuits, and it will no longer be necessary to go through an iterative process. It is a multi-terminal network with outputs which can indicate any number of relays in the group operated, from none to the total number.

Physically, it will be seen that the contacts are so arranged that the normally open contacts propagate ground upward in the diagram while the normally closed contacts propagate ground from left to right.

Thus, whenever a relay operates, its contacts shift the ground from one horizontal level to the next higher level. Whenever a relay does not operate, its contacts shift the ground from one vertical line to the next vertical line to the right. It is impossible in this network for ground to be propagated either downward or to the left. Select any node within the diagram and approach it from the left through a normally closed contact. Now if we try to leave that node going downward we will always encounter the complement of the contact through which we just passed, so the path is blocked. The same situation will prevail if we approach a node through a contact from below and try to leave that node by going to the left. These properties make it possible to perform rather radical modifications of the basic symmetric network without introducing "sneak" paths.

7.2 Modification of the Basic Symmetric Circuit

It will be convenient at this time to introduce a symbolic representation of a symmetric function. For a transmission function that is symmetric we will use the symbol S with one or more numerical subscripts which, for the present, indicate how many relays must be operated in order to make the transmission 1. The variables of symmetry will be indicated either specifically or merely by a generic variable with a subscript indicating how many relays are in the circuit. Thus, $S_{2,3}(A, B, C, D)$ symbolizes a symmetric circuit built with contacts on relays A, B, C, D, and which provides 1 transmission whenever either two or three of the relays are operated. If we have a contact network built on seven relays and want to have 1 transmission when no, one, or five relays are operated, we can designate this by the shorter form $S_{0,1,5}(X_7)$.

Consider a symmetric circuit built on five relays for which there is to be an output ground if any three are operated, that is $S_3(X_5)$. In Fig. 7–7 the required network is shown as derived from the basic symmetric circuit of Fig. 7–6. We may visualize the process of selecting the elements of the required network by starting with the basic circuit drawn so as to produce all its possible outputs. Then, starting at the input terminal we go vertically through three contacts, since that is the number of operated relays required to produce an output, and then go horizontally through two contacts, since that number of relays must be unoperated in order to get an output. The node that we then reach becomes the output terminal of the network. All contacts of the basic circuit above the output node and all contacts to the right of it can then be discarded. These discarded contacts cannot possibly influence the transmission of the remaining network. Any path between the input node and the output node which uses the discarded part of the basic network requires a reversal of direction, which is impossible. Figure 7–7 shows the network for $S_3(X_5)$ drawn with solid lines and the discarded part of the basic network drawn with dotted lines.

The basic symmetric circuit is in the form of a multiple-output tree. If we connect together two of its output nodes to form a single output terminal we obtain a network which has 1 transmisson when either of

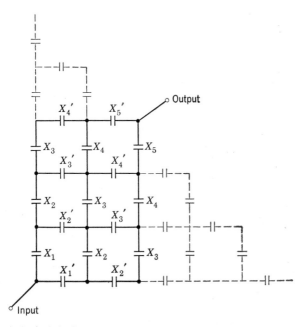

Fig. 7–7. A part of the basic symmetric circuit is used to provide a single output.

the indicated numbers of relays are operated. Thus in Fig. 7–8 the output is taken from the nodes which receive ground when two relays are operated or when four relays are operated. This network is symbolized by $S_{2,4}(X_5)$. The part of the basic symmetric circuit to be retained is shown with solid lines and the parts to be discarded are shown dotted. The discarded contacts can have no possible effect on the network transmission.

When adjacent output nodes of the basic symmetric circuit are connected, as they must be to realize the symmetric function $S_{1,2,4}(X_5)$, additional contacts can be removed. This function is realized in the circuit of Fig. 7–9. Examination shows that when two adjacent output nodes are connected, two complementary contacts on the same relay, in this example X_5 and $X_5{}'$, are connected in parallel between the

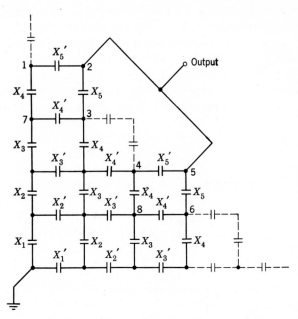

Fig. 7–8. Outputs of the basic symmetric circuit may be combined.

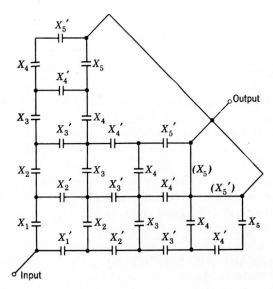

Fig. 7–9. Additional contacts are eliminated when adjacent outputs of the basic symmetric circuit are combined.

common output terminal and an interior node. These contacts may be replaced by a closed circuit, as is shown in Fig. 7–9. If additional adjacent output nodes of the basic symmetric circuit are connected to the common output terminal, it will be found that this elimination process continues and can penetrate even more deeply into the network.

Another type of redundancy is illustrated in Fig. 7–10 which is the network realizing the symmetric function $S_{0,1}(A, B, C, D)$. In part (a) of Fig. 7–10 the retained part of the basic symmetric circuit is shown with the two output nodes connected. Since these output nodes are

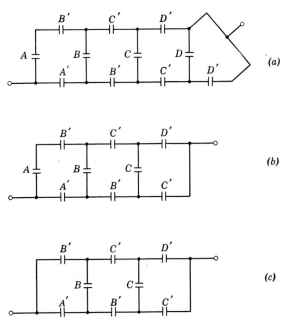

Fig. 7–10. Successive steps in the removal of redundant contacts from a symmetric network.

adjacent, a D contact and a D' contact are in parallel and can be removed, as is shown in part (b). Physically, we now see that if the A, B, and C relays are not operated there is a tie path from the input terminal at the left to the right-hand node to which the eliminated D and D' contacts were connected. If three of the relays are not operated, it makes no difference in the transmission whether the fourth operates or not because we require 1 transmission if either none or one operate. Now, we observe in part (b) of Fig. 7–10 that the top horizontal line includes the series connection of B', C', and D' contacts. This path can be reached only through the A contact at the left. But again, if the

B, C, and D relays are not operated, it makes no difference whether the A relay is operated or not. Hence, the A contact can be removed as is shown in part (c).

Let us return now to Fig. 7–8 and the circuit for $S_{2,4}(X_5)$. In this network the output nodes used are not adjacent in the basic circuit, so we do not get the savings in contacts which result when adjacent nodes connect to the output. We can, however, reduce the number of contacts in this network by the process known as "folding," which is possible because of the disjunctive properties of the basic circuit. In Fig. 7–8 a group of nodes have been numbered. Nodes 2 and 5 are connected to form the output of the circuit. Node 1 is immediately to the left of node 2, and node 4 is to the left of node 5. Node 3 is below node 2 and node 6 is below 5. Node 7 is to the left of node 3 and node 8 is to the left of node 6. Examine the transmission between node 1 and node 3. The two shortest paths between nodes 1 and 3 have contacts X_5 and X_5' in series or X_4 and X_4' in series. It will be found that no matter what paths are chosen between nodes 1 and 3 the transmission between nodes is 0. If we extend a line through nodes 1 and 3 and then downward from left to right the line will pass through nodes 4 and 6. It may be verified that no matter what path is chosen *between any pair of the nodes along this diagonal* the internode transmission is 0.

Now consider the transmission between nodes 1 and 2. The only path between these nodes which can conduct is that through the X_5' contact. The same is true of the transmission between nodes 4 and 5. Since nodes 2 and 5 are connected at the output terminal, we see that if there is a ground at the output which has passed through node 1, that ground is also transmitted back through the network to node 4. Also, if the output is grounded but node 1 is not grounded, there cannot possibly be a ground at node 4. These two nodes can therefore be thought of as being equipotential points in the network which we may hence connect solidly. But if we make this connection, the two X_5' contacts are then in parallel and one of them may be removed. Suppose, after connecting nodes 1 and 4, we remove the X_5' contact between nodes 1 and 2. Then, if the first four relays are operated and the fifth is not, the required tie path will pass through node 1, then to node 4, and finally to the output through the X_5' contact between nodes 4 and 5.

A simple way to determine whether pairs of nodes can be thus connected is to examine the transmission from the output terminal backward through the network to the nodes in question. When these transmissions are identical, the connection can be made. As we have seen above, the transmission between the output and node 1 is simply X_5' and that transmission is repeated at node 4. The transmission between the output and node 3 is X_5, and this is repeated at node 6. Consequently, nodes 3 and 6 can be connected. Finally, the transmission between the output and node 7 is $X_4X_5' + X_4'X_5$, and that transmission is duplicated between the output and node 8, so nodes 7

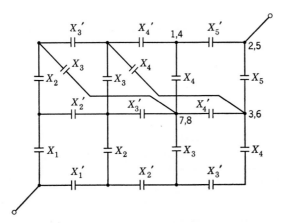

Fig. 7–11. Redundant contacts in Fig. 7–8 are here eliminated by folding.

and 8 can be connected. If we now think of the schematic circuit of Fig. 7–8 as being built of some rubber-like material, we can figuratively take the square at the top which contains nodes 1, 2, 3, and 7 and bring it down so that it is superposed on the square which contains

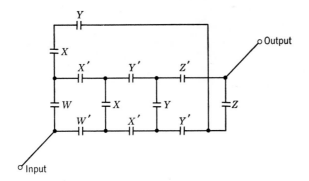

Fig. 7–12. Simplification of network for $S_{1,4}(W, X, Y, Z)$ by folding.

nodes 4, 5, 6, and 8. The four pairs of "equipotential" nodes are thus merged and we can discard four duplicate contacts. The final result of this process is shown in Fig. 7–11. Each merged node is numbered to show the original pair of nodes that were superposed. The X_3

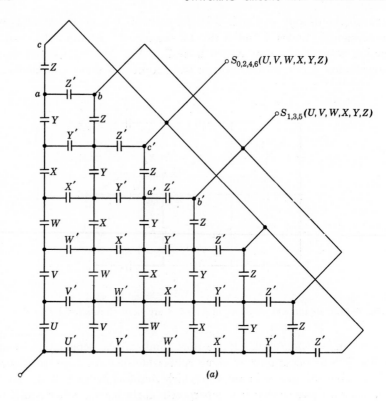

(a)

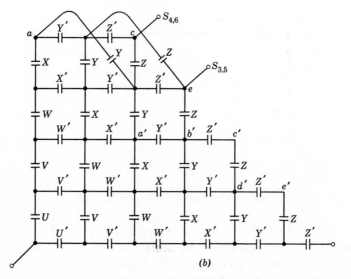

(b)

Fig 7–13. First step in folding the basic symmetric network.

and X_4 contacts that originally connected to nodes 7 and 3, respectively, must now connect to the equivalent merged nodes. These connections can be made only by crossing other connections, so the folded circuit must be non-planar.

The opportunity for saving contacts by the folding process occurs in many forms. Figure 7–12 shows a rather simple situation which can occur frequently.

Another type of folding operation is illustrated by steps, beginning with Fig. 7–13. Part (a) shows a basic symmetric network in six variables. We want to fold the basic network after its output nodes have been connected so as to yield the two transmission functions

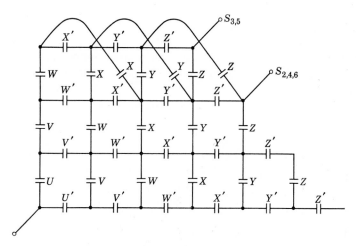

Fig. 7–14. Partially folded symmetric network.

$S_{0,2,4,6}(X_6)$ and $S_{1,3,5}(X_6)$. This means that in the basic symmetric the even-numbered output nodes are connected to a single output terminal and the odd-numbered nodes are connected to another output terminal. For clarity, the complete output connections are shown in Fig. 7–13(a), but are omitted elsewhere.

The first step in the folding places nodes a, b, c of Fig. 7–13(a), on nodes a', b', c' with the result shown in Fig. 7–13(b). Output terminals are indicated at which the functions $S_{4,6}(X_6)$ and $S_{3,5}(X_6)$ have been developed. In the next step, the nodes marked a, b, c in Fig. 7–13(b) are placed on nodes a', b', c', with the result shown in Fig. 7–14. After two more folds we reach the final network of Fig. 7–15. When redrawn as in Fig. 7–16 it becomes evident that this is an iterative structure. It can be designed directly by iterative methods.

It is possible to apply the folding process in the design of any network for which the symbolic symmetric function contains a set of subscripts which form an arithmetic series. There is one feature of these

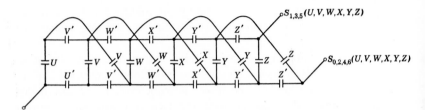

Fig. 7–15. Completely folded symmetric network. This is the "odd-even" circuit.

networks, however, that must not be overlooked. Suppose, for example, we wish to produce from a network built on ten relays, the functions $S_{0,3,6}(X_{10})$ and $S_{4,7,10}(X_{10})$. We can readily design a network to realize both these functions without folding. But, because the sub-

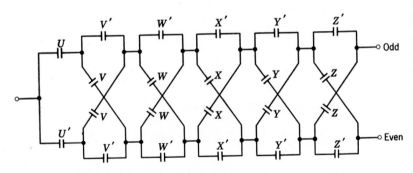

Fig. 7–16. Iterative structure of the odd-even circuit.

script numbers given in the specifications bracket the entire possible range of numbers, namely from 0 to 10, the actual symmetric functions we get from a completely folded network with two output terminals will include all the subscript numbers possible in the arithmetic series, and not just the selected numbers. That is, we will actually obtain $S_{0,3,6,9}(X_{10})$ and $S_{1,4,7,10}(X_{10})$. The additional numbers may be completely unwelcome. Another output terminal may be added to this particular folded network at which we can obtain the transmission $S_{2,5,8}(X_{10})$.

7.3   Complementary Symmetric Networks

Consider the symmetric function described by $S_{0,2,3}(W, X, Y, Z)$.
A circuit to realize this function, designed in the manner described in
the preceding article, is shown in Fig. 7–17.   Without modification
this circuit contains 15 contacts and requires 23 springs.   It can be
verified, however, that one of the Z' contacts is redundant and can be
removed by folding.   After that, the circuit contains 14 contacts and
21 springs.

According to the meaning of the symbols used, the transmission of
this circuit is 1 if none, two, or three of its relays are operated.   If one
or four of its relays operate the transmission must be 0.   Hence the

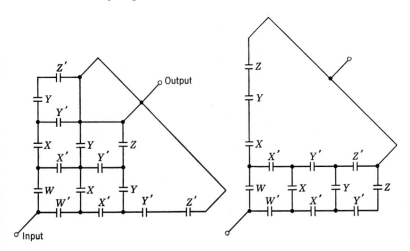

Fig. 7–17.   Network for the symmetric   **Fig. 7–18.**   Network for the sym-
function $S_{0,2,3}(W, X, Y, Z)$.   metric function $S_{1,4}(W, X, Y, Z)$.

symmetric function which is the complement of the original function is
$S_{1,4}(W, X, Y, Z)$.   A complementary network has 1 transmission when
the original network has 0 transmission, and vice versa.   The circuit
for the complementary function $S_{1,4}(W, X, Y, Z)$ is shown in Fig. 7–18.
As drawn, this circuit contains 13 contacts and 21 springs, but one of
the Z contacts can be eliminated by folding, and this makes it possible
to form another Y transfer contact, so the folded network contains
12 contacts and 18 springs.

We are interested in comparing the number of contacts and springs
in these two networks because the geometric complement of the network
of Fig. 7–18 must have the same transmission as the network of Fig. 7–17,

and we may thus be able to realize a symmetric function with fewer contacts and springs than we can by direct synthesis. It turns out that economies of this type are often possible. Unfortunately, the folded networks are non-planar and we cannot obtain geometric complements of them.

However, if we start with the network of Fig. 7–18, and do not fold it, we can take the geometric complement with the result shown in Fig. 7–19. This network must contain the same number of contacts,

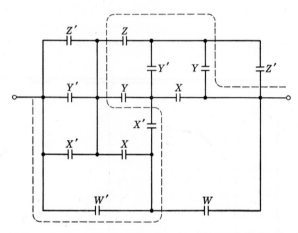

Fig. 7–19. Network for the symmetric function $S_{0,2,3}(W, X, Y, Z)$, obtained by taking the geometric complement of the network for $S_{1,4}(W, X, Y, Z)$.

namely 13, as the network of Fig. 7–18. However, there are only 20 springs in the complementary network, instead of the 21 in the original network, because in the geometric complement a Y and Y' pair of contacts became connected to a common point.

The geometric complements of networks designed by starting from the basic symmetric circuit form a highly interesting group, and the example in Fig. 7–19 is no exception. It must have the same cut and tie sets as the conventional network of Fig. 7–17, but sometimes the routes taken by these sets are indeed devious. For example, in Fig. 7–17 if, starting at the input we go to the right through the W' and X' contacts, and then go up through the Y and Z contacts, we trace through the $W'X'YZ$ tie set. From the input to the output we make only one change of direction. In Fig. 7–19 the same tie set is indicated by a dotted line. The path changes direction seven times going from input to output. It is still more interesting to observe that this tie path is not used in the circuit of Fig. 7–19. If any two relays are operated and a third is not operated, the transmission is 1, since it makes no difference whether the fourth operates or not. Thus the path $X'YZ$ is one of four paths of this type contained in the circuit of Fig. 7–19. There are three such paths in Fig. 7–17.

A number of special types of networks can be derived from the basic symmetric circuit. At the left of Fig. 7–20 is shown a schematic repre-

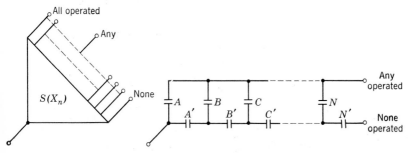

Fig. 7–20.   Specialized circuits derived from the basic symmetric network.

sentation of the basic symmetric circuit with all its possible outputs indicated. We can recognize the zero level as corresponding to the verbal statement "none operated." The nth output level corresponds to "all operated," and if we tie together all output terminals except the zero level this group forms an output which we can describe as "any operated." At the right of Fig. 7–20 is shown the reduced network which provides the two outputs corresponding to "any operated" and "none operated."

Suppose we want a network built on five relays which will have 1 transmission if some of the relays operate but 0 transmission if all of them operate. The complementary function has 1 transmission when

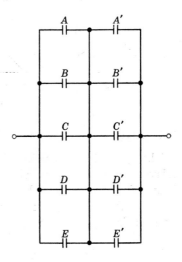

Fig. 7–21.   Circuit derived from the analysis of a complementary symmetric function.

none of the relays operate or when *all* operate, and is symbolized by $S_{0,5}(A, B, C, D, E)$. When this complementary function is realized and its geometric complement taken the result is the very interesting circuit of Fig. 7–21.

The basic symmetric circuit with all its outputs available is another type of tree network. In Fig. 7–22 node X is the input to such a tree. Between the input X and any output terminals, the transmission is that represented by the symmetric functions indicated at the output nodes. By adding the contacts which are connected to the Y input, we obtain transmission between Y and each output node which is the complement of the transmission from X to the same node.

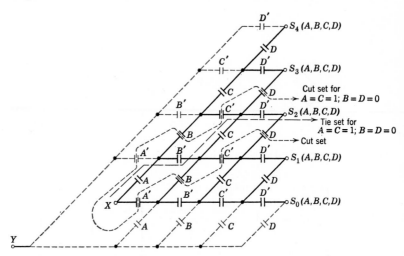

Fig. 7–22. Basic symmetric circuit with additional contacts required to realize all complementary functions.

7.4 Algebraic Properties of Symmetric Functions

The symmetric network which has 1 transmission when n out of m relays operate is readily visualized and may be described by simple language. This concept, however, covers only a small part of the full scope of the symmetric network. In this article we will introduce a broader definition of the symmetric function, and discuss some further properties of symmetric functions.

The algebraic treatment of symmetric functions is derived from a general definition of the symmetric function and a number of theorems, first stated by Shannon.*

By definition,

A function of the n variables $X_1, X_2 \ldots X_n$ is said to be symmetric in these variables if any interchange of the variables leaves the function identically

---

* See Reference 5 at the end of Chapter 3. In the discussion in this chapter the quoted statements have been modified, when necessary, so that they apply to functions written on the transmission basis, rather than as hindrance functions.

the same. . . . Since any permutation of variables may be obtained by successive interchanges of two variables, a necessary and sufficient condition that a function be symmetric is that any interchange of two variables leaves the function unaltered.

It should be noted that the n variables in which a function is symmetric are not necessarily unprimed variables; any selection of them may be primed. For example, the function $XYZ' + XY'Z + X'YZ$ is a function which is symmetric about the variables X, Y, Z, in accordance with the above definition. But the function $XYZ' + XY'Z + X'Y'Z'$ is also, by definition, a symmetric function. It is more difficult to determine this, because the variables of symmetry are X, Y', Z', and the function is not symmetric in X, Y, Z.

The symmetric networks described earlier in this chapter were all of the type for which the transmission was 1 when n out of m relays operated. This is a limited class of symmetric networks because they are all described by symmetric functions which are symmetric in a set of unprimed variables. The more general symmetric function which we have now defined can also be realized by means of the basic symmetric network, provided we know the variables about which the function is symmetric. The determination of these variables is a problem which will be discussed further in Art. 7.5.

The symbolic method we use for writing symmetric functions is derived from one of the theorems stated by Shannon:

A necessary and sufficient condition that a function be symmetric is that it may be specified by stating a set of numbers $a_1, a_2, \ldots a_k$, such that if exactly a_j $(j = 1, 2, 3, \ldots k)$ of the variables have the value 1, then the function has the value 1 and not otherwise.

The set of numbers, $a_1 \ldots a_k$, may be any set of numbers selected from the numbers zero to n inclusive, where n is the number of variables in the symmetric function. For convenience, they will be called the a-numbers of the function.

For the type of symmetric function considered earlier in this chapter, the a-numbers are simply the number or numbers of relays which must operate for the network to have 1 transmission.

Following the symbolic notation introduced in Art. 7.2, we use the letter S to represent a transmission function which is symmetric. It is written with all its a-numbers as subscripts, and the variables of symmetry are given as the arguments of the function. Thus we describe the transmission of the network of Fig. 7–7 as $S_3(X_1, X_2, X_3, X_4, X_5)$. If the variables of symmetry are all unprimed, or all primed, it is convenient to avoid writing the arguments of the function in detail. These functions can be abbreviated by writing, for example, $S_{2,3}(X_6)$ or $S_{2,3}(X_6')$, with the understanding that the arguments of the functions are a set of six unprimed variables, or a set of six primed variables respectively. If the arguments contain both unprimed and primed variables, it will be necessary to write them in full, as for example, $S_3(A, B', C, D')$. The complete function represented by this symbolic form is $AB'CD + AB'C'D' + ABCD' + A'B'CD'$.

Care must be used in writing symmetric functions to be sure that they are complete. For example, the function $S_2(X, Y, Z)$ is written $XYZ' + XY'Z + X'YZ$. We can test this by Shannon's a-number theorem, and we find that if we assign the value 1 to *any two* of the variables (the remaining variable must be 0), the function has the value 1. Suppose, however, that we fail to write the complete function, and write only $XYZ' + XY'Z$. This function satisfies the theorem for the selections X, Y, and X, Z, but if we place Y and Z equal to 1, the function becomes 0.

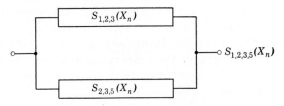

Fig. 7–23.   Parallel connection of symmetric networks.

When symmetric networks are connected in parallel, as in Fig. 7–23, the transmission of the parallel network is given by the sum of the symmetric functions. A simple rule can be used for writing the sum, provided both symmetric functions are *functions of the same variables*. Since the parallel transmission must be 1 if either of the branch transmissions is 1, the transmission represented by the sum of two given symmetric functions of the same variables is a symmetric function of those variables, which has for its a-numbers all the a-numbers appearing in either or both of the given functions. Thus in Fig. 7–23 symmetric functions with a-numbers 1, 2, 3 and 2, 3, 5, when added yield a symmetric function with a-numbers 1, 2, 3, 5.

If the symmetric networks of the same variables are connected in series, the resulting transmission is given by the product of the given functions. This product can be written quite simply by noting that in order to have a series transmission of 1, both the given functions must have transmissions of 1. Since the same variables are involved in each function, this can be true only for those a-numbers which are the same in each given function. Hence a product of symmetric functions is a symmetric function in the same variables, and it has as a-numbers those numbers which are common to both given functions. Thus, in Fig. 7–24, the two symmetric functions of X_n which are to be multiplied have the a-numbers 1, 2, 3, and 2, 3, 5. The series transmission is the symmetric function of X_n which has the a-numbers 2, 3, or $S_{2,3}(X_n)$.

A symmetric function may be expanded about any of its variables just as any other switching function can be expanded, by application of theorem 20. However, it would be convenient to be able to carry out an expansion in terms of the compact symbols we have used for sym-

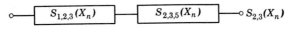

Fig. 7–24. Series connection of symmetric networks.

metric functions. We will now develop a modified version of the expansion theorem which can be applied directly to symmetric functions written in symbolic form.*

Apply theorem 20 to a symmetric function of n variables, where the a-number of the function is p. We can expand the function about any of its variables, but for simplicity let us expand about the variable X_n. We then write

$$S_p(X_1 \ldots X_n) = X_n \cdot S_p(X_1, \ldots X_{n-1}, 1) + X_n{}' \cdot S_p(X_1, \ldots X_{n-1}, 0)$$

The residual function, $S_p(X_1 \ldots X_{n-1}, 1)$, is a symmetric function, of a-number equal to p, in which the value of one variable has been set equal to 1; that is, $X_n = 1$. Since the a-number defines the number of variables which must equal 1 in order that the transmission be 1, if any one of the variables such as X_n has the fixed value of 1, the transmission will then become 1 if any $(p - 1)$ of the remaining $(n - 1)$ variables have the value 1. This residual function must therefore be a symmetric function of $(n - 1)$ variables, with the a-number $(p - 1)$. We can hence rewrite the first term of the expanded function in the form $X_n \cdot S_{p-1}(X_1 \ldots X_{n-1})$.

The other residual function, $S_p(X_1 \ldots X_{n-1}, 0)$, contains only $(n - 1)$ variables, because X_n has been made 0. Since none of the variables has been set equal to 1, the a-number of the residue remains unchanged. Hence this residual function is a symmetric function of $(n - 1)$ variables, with the a-number p, and it is written in the form $S_p(X_1 \ldots X_{n-1})$.

* The expansion theorem for symmetric functions was privately communicated to the author by Mr. R. Grea, of the Graphic Arts Research Foundation, Cambridge, Massachusetts.

These results combine to give us an expansion theorem for symmetric functions. It is stated as theorem 23 to follow consecutively in the list of theorems presented in Chapter 3.

$$(23) \quad S_p(X_1 \ldots X_n) = X_n \cdot S_{p-1}(X_1 \ldots X_{n-1}) + X_n' \cdot S_p(X_1 \ldots X_{n-1})$$

If a symmetric function has more than one a-number, the expansion theorem takes the form given as theorem 24.

$$(24) \quad S_{p,q}(X_1 \ldots X_n) = X_n \cdot S_{p-1,q-1}(X_1 \ldots X_{n-1}) \\ + X_n' \cdot S_{p,q}(X_1 \ldots X_{n-1})$$

The proof of theorem 24 follows directly from the relation

$$S_{p,q}(X_1 \ldots X_n) = S_p(X_1 \ldots X_n) + S_q(X_1 \ldots X_n)$$

One point in the application of theorems 23 and 24 is of special interest. The residue of X_n is a symmetric function in which all the original a-numbers are reduced by one. Suppose the original symmetric function contains the a-number zero. This question is most readily answered by considering a symmetric function in which all variables of symmetry are unprimed. Then we note that the a-number zero corresponds to the term $X_1'X_2'X_3' \ldots X_n'$. There cannot be a contribution from this term to the residue of X_n because X_n is not a factor of the term. Therefore, in expanding a symmetric function with an a-number equal to zero, the a-number zero vanishes in the X_n residue.

The X_n' residue contains terms representing all the original a-numbers without reduction. A similar problem occurs here if the a-number n occurs, in the function being expanded, because in the X_n' residue we are faced with the possibility of calling for n variables to be equal to 1 when there are only $n-1$ variables present. Here we find that X_n' is not a factor of the term which represents the a-number n and there can be no contribution in the X_n' residue from that term. Consequently, an a-number equal to n must vanish from the X_n' residue. (This algebra has the strange consequence that a number vanishes because it is too large.)

7.5 Identification of Symmetric Functions

In the preceding article it was shown that we could write symmetric functions of any set of variables, and that the "variables of symmetry" need not necessarily be unprimed. It is a relatively simple matter to detect the symmetric nature of a function of unprimed variables when the function is written as a standard sum or as a standard product. A count of the primed or unprimed variables in each term of the function will show whether or not the transmission depends only on the number of variables in one state or the other, and a count of the number of such terms will show whether all possible ways of producing that number have been used. This method will succeed if all the variables of symmetry are unprimed, or if all the variables are primed. It fails if some of the variables of symmetry are primed and some are not.

If the variables of symmetry are not mixed, it makes no difference whether they are chosen as primed variables or as unprimed variables. Thus the function

$$XY'Z' + X'YZ' + X'Y'Z$$

can be expressed as a symmetric function either of the variables X, Y, Z, or of the variables X', Y', Z'. We note, however, that the a-numbers are usually different in the two expressions. The two symbolic descriptions of the above function are $S_1(X, Y, Z)$ and $S_2(X', Y', Z')$. If the

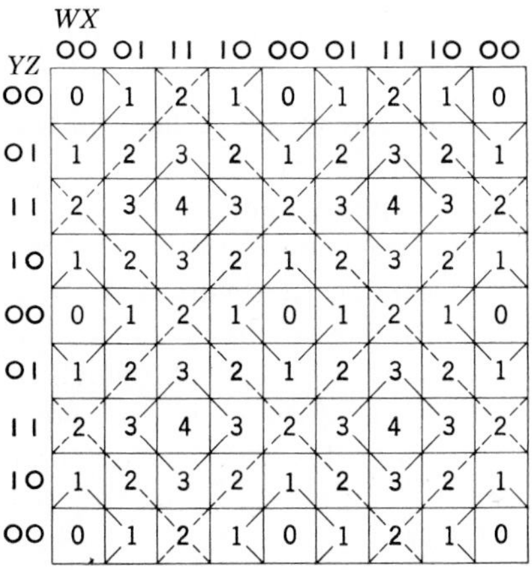

Fig. 7–25. Extended map to show patterns of symmetric functions.

number of variables of symmetry is an even number, and there is a single a-number which is equal to exactly one half the number of variables, then the function has the same a-number in both forms. Thus $S_2(W, X, Y, Z) = S_2(W', X', Y', Z')$. This is merely a special case of the general rule that if a function of n variables has a set of a-numbers, say p, q, r, the set of a-numbers of the function expressed with all variables complemented is $(n - p)$, $(n - q)$, $(n - r)$.

The recognition of a symmetric function of four variables is easily accomplished by observing its pattern when it is entered in a Karnaugh map.* The procedure will be discussed with reference to Fig. 7–25.

* S. H. Caldwell, "Recognition and Identification of Symmetric Switching Functions," *A.I.E.E. Trans.*, Part II, *Communications and Electronics*, Vol. 73, May, 1954, pp. 142–146.

In preparing the map of Fig. 7–25 the first step was to extend the usual Karnaugh map by adding rows and columns and continuing the cyclic ordering of the designators of the rows and columns as shown. The effect of this step is to bring out explicitly the adjacency of cells which, in the usual map, are at the ends of each row, and at the top and bottom of each column. Our next step is to enter a number in each cell equal to the total number of 1's contained in the combined column and row designators. For example, in the cell formed at the intersection of a column marked 11 and a row marked 01, the number 3 is entered, because there are three 1's in the combined designator 1101. Finally, we join by solid and dotted lines the diagonally adjacent cells which contain the same number. This serves to emphasize the patterns formed by these numbers. In the extended map there are many repetitions of the same state of the variables, but the repeated pattern thereby obtained enables us to see more vividly the map forms of the symmetric functions of four variables.

We now note that the number 4 is in map positions which represent the term $WXYZ$, which is also $S_4(W, X, Y, Z)$. The number 3 occurs in patterns of diagonal squares, and each group of 3's occupies the positions in the map which represent the terms of the function $S_3(W, X, Y, Z)$. The number 2 occurs in a larger diagonal square pattern, in which the positions occupied by the numbers represent the terms of the function $S_2(W, X, Y, Z)$. Although there are eight 2's in each of these arrays, only six of the positions represent different combinations of the variables, and this is the correct number of terms in the

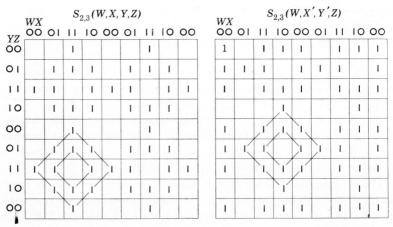

Fig. 7–26. Symmetric function chart showing shift in location of pattern when variables of symmetry are changed.

function. The number 1 positions are located in a diagonal square array surrounding the positions which represent 0000, and the pattern cannot be distinguished from that formed by the number 3. This is immaterial, however, because $S_3(W, X, Y, Z)$ is the same function algebraically as $S_1(W', X', Y', Z')$. If a small diagonal square pattern is identified by either rule, the result is the same.

Now let us see what happens when we use these patterns to detect the presence of a symmetric function. We will compare the transmission charts of two functions which differ only in the variables of symmetry. In the left-hand map of Fig. 7–26 the entries show the terms for which transmission is 1, for the function

$$S_{2,3}(W, X, Y, Z) = WXY'Z' + WX'YZ' + WX'Y'Z + W'XYZ'$$
$$+ W'XY'Z + W'X'YZ + WXYZ' + WXY'Z$$
$$+ WX'YZ + W'XYZ$$

In the right-hand map similar entries are made for the function

$$S_{2,3}(W, X', Y', Z) = WX'YZ' + WXY'Z' + WXYZ + W'X'Y'Z'$$
$$+ W'X'YZ + W'XY'Z + WX'Y'Z' + WX'YZ$$
$$+ WXY'Z + W'X'Y'Z$$

By comparison of the two maps we see that two diagonal square arrays, which indicate symmetric functions having a-numbers equal to either $(1, 2)$ or $(2, 3)$, are present in both maps. The effect of the change in the variables of symmetry is to shift the pattern in the map without distorting it. Since the cell about which the diagonal squares are centered represents one of the two possible arguments of the symmetric function, we are able by means of the map to determine not only that a function is symmetric, but also what its variables of symmetry are. The central point in the diagonal array of the right-hand map in Fig. 7–26 is the cell 1001. Since the map is constructed in W, X, Y, Z variables, this cell represents the variables of symmetry W, X', Y', Z. We know that the larger diagonal array surrounding the central cell corresponds to an a-number 2, but we do not know whether the smaller diagonal array corresponds to an a-number of 1 or 3.

We can determine the a-number of a small diagonal array by testing one of its cells against the variables of symmetry. Consider the cell 1000 in the small pattern. In map coordinates this represents $WX'Y'Z'$. When we compare this term with the variables of symmetry W, X', Y', Z, we see that the test term represents a transmission of 1 when the three variables W, X', and Y' have the value 1, and Z has the value 0. Hence by Shannon's a-number theorem, the a-number represented by the small diagonal array is 3, and the function is thus completely identified.

The symmetric functions of three variables are relatively simple and they can be identified by means of the patterns shown in the extended chart of Fig. 7–27.

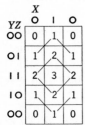

Fig. 7–27. Extended three-variable chart showing patterns of symmetric functions.

When the number of variables of symmetry exceeds four, the recognition of symmetric functions by map patterns becomes quite difficult. By application of the expansion theorem, however, we can reduce the number of variables to which the map test is applied.

Since the expansion theorem can be applied by expanding successively with respect to any number of variables, we can always obtain a set of residual functions of four variables. If these residual functions are symmetric, and have the a-number relations required by theorems 23 and 24, then the original function must be symmetric. Both the a-numbers and the variables of symmetry of the original function can be determined from the map patterns of the residual functions.

Example 7–1

Determine whether the given function is symmetric. If it is symmetric, identify its variables of symmetry and determine its a-numbers.

$$T = A'BCDE + ABCD'E + ABCDE' + AB'C'DE$$
$$+ A'B'CD'E + A'B'CDE' + A'BC'D'E + A'BC'DE'$$
$$+ AB'CD'E' + ABC'D'E' + A'B'C'D'E'$$

If the function is symmetric, the result given by the expansion process is independent of the variable about which the function is expanded. For convenience, we will expand about the variable E to obtain residual functions of the remaining variables. Since the function is given in the standard sum form, the "expanded" form can be obtained by simple factoring. Thus

$$T = E(A'BCD + ABCD' + AB'C'D$$
$$+ A'B'CD' + A'BC'D') + E'(ABCD + A'B'CD$$
$$+ A'BC'D + AB'CD' + ABC'D' + A'B'C'D')$$

The residual functions of A, B, C, D are mapped in Fig. 7–28. In the left-hand map, the terms containing E as a factor present a pattern of small diagonal squares and isolated points. This pattern identifies a symmetric function in which the diagonal arrays are associated with an a-number of either 1 or 3, and the single cells with an a-number of either 0 or 4. In the right-hand map, the terms containing E' as a factor present the large diagonal square pattern which indicates a symmetric function of a-number 2. The arrays in both maps are centered about the same cells, so the variables of symmetry are the same.

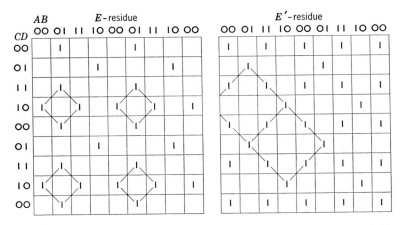

Fig. 7–28. Map patterns derived from expansion of a function of five variables.

Although the residual functions are now identified as symmetric functions, they do not necessarily satisfy theorems 23 and 24. One apparent contradiction is the fact that two a-numbers are indicated by one map, and only one a-number appears in the other. This combination can still satisfy theorem 24, however, if one of the original a-numbers is 0 or 4. Suppose $p = 0$. Then in one residue the a-number $(p - 1)$ must vanish. If we assume that the isolated points in the left-hand map indicate an a-number of zero, then the pattern indicates that the small diagonal squares must represent an a-number 3, and this is consistent with the single a-number 2 represented by the pattern in the other map. Moreover, the pattern of the left-hand chart now indicates that the variables of symmetry must be A', B, C, D', because the diagonal square pattern surrounds the cell 0110. The cell 0110 is one of the two central cells in the pattern of the right-hand map also, so both residual functions have the same variables of symmetry.

We can now write the function in the following form:

$$T = E \cdot S_{0,3}(A', B, C, D') + E' \cdot S_2(A', B, C, D')$$

Comparing this expression with the general form shown in theorem 24, we find that the theorem is satisfied if the fifth variable of symmetry is E'. Hence the complete function is identified as $S_{0,3}(A', B, C, D', E')$. If we express this with the variables complemented it becomes $S_{2,5}(A, B', C', D, E)$.

Networks for symmetric functions containing mixed variables of symmetry can readily be built from the basic symmetric network. The process is illustrated in Fig. 7–29, where part (a) shows the network for $S_2(A, B, C, D, E)$. Part (b) shows the network for the same

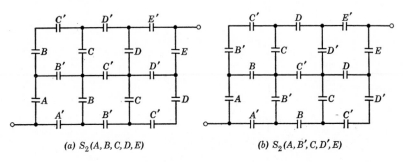

(a) $S_2(A, B, C, D, E)$ (b) $S_2(A, B', C, D', E)$

Fig. 7–29.   Effect on symmetric network of mixed variables of symmetry.

function, except that B' and D' are variables of symmetry instead of B and D. It will be noted that, as a practical matter, the network can be drawn by first assuming that all the variables of symmetry are unprimed, and after the network is designed for that set of variables, replacing all contact designators by their complements for those variables of symmetry which are primed.

This is a trivial problem of design, but it makes a profound change in the network. If we examine part (b) of Fig. 7–29, we see that because of the change in the B and D variables, we can no longer think of the network as being composed of a chain of typical cells. Hence, the real effect of mixing the variables of symmetry is to produce a non-iterative symmetric network.

McCluskey has proposed another method* for detecting and identifying symmetric functions of mixed variables, which requires no maps. Unlike the map method, it is not necessary to expand a function of more than four variables. The procedure will be shown by means of examples.

* See Reference given in Art. 5.5.

Example 7–2

Determine what symmetric function, if any, is represented by

$$T = \sum (3, 5, 6, 9, 10, 12, 17, 18, 20, 24)$$

When expressed as binary numbers and placed in a column these terms are:

0	0	0	1	1	(2)
0	0	1	0	1	(2)
0	0	1	1	0	(2)
0	1	0	0	1	(2)
0	1	0	1	0	(2)
0	1	1	0	0	(2)
1	0	0	0	1	(2)
1	0	0	1	0	(2)
1	0	1	0	0	(2)
1	1	0	0	0	(2)

4/6 4/6 4/6 4/6 4/6

$$_5C_2 = \frac{5!}{2!(5-2)!} = 10$$

Under each column is written the ratio of the number of 1's to the number of 0's in the column. If the function is symmetric and the variables are not mixed this ratio will be the same for all columns. If the variables of symmetry are mixed, the reciprocal ratio will be found under those columns which represent complementary variables.

At the right of each term is shown the number of 1's in the binary number representation. This number is two and indicates that two of the five variables have the value 1. The formula for the combinations of five things taken two at a time shows that there are 10 ways to assign values of 1 to two out of five variables. A count of the number of terms shows that all combinations are present. Hence this function is identified as $S_2(A, B, C, D, E)$.

Note the three conditions that must be satisfied:

1. The ratio of the number of 1's to the number of 0's must be the same for each column.

2. The number of 1's in each term must be the same for all terms representing a given a-number.

3. The number of terms of the same a-number must be that given by the formula for the number of combinations of n things taken m at a time.

Using the McCluskey method, we will again analyze the function treated in Example 7–1.

Example 7–3

The algebraic terms when converted to binary form give the tabulation at the left:

A	B	C	D	E		A	B'	C'	D	E	
0	1	1	1	1		0	0	0	1	1	(2)
1	1	1	0	1		1	0	0	0	1	(2)
1	1	1	1	0		1	0	0	1	0	(2)
1	0	0	1	1		1	1	1	1	1	(5)
0	0	1	0	1		0	1	0	0	1	(2)
0	0	1	1	0		0	1	0	1	0	(2)
0	1	0	0	1		0	0	1	0	1	(2)
0	1	0	1	0		0	0	1	1	0	(2)
1	0	1	0	0		1	1	0	0	0	(2)
1	1	0	0	0		1	0	1	0	0	(2)
0	0	0	0	0		0	1	1	0	0	(2)
5/6	6/5	6/5	5/6	5/6		5/6	5/6	5/6	5/6	5/6	

The column ratios show three columns with five 1's and six 0's and two columns with six 1's and five 0's. The ratio can be made the same for all columns by complementing the B and C variables. This has been done in the right-hand tabulation, where all entries under B' and C' are now the complements of those under B and C. We now find ten terms which contain two 1's each, and 2 is hence a valid a-number. There is one term with five 1's and 5 is a valid a-number. The function is identified as

$$S_{2,5}(A, B', C', D, E)$$

In Art. 5.8 we showed a method for determining from the decimal equivalent of a binary number whether a particular digit in it was odd or even. In the next example we will again examine the function treated in Example 7–1. Exactly the same procedure is followed as in Example 7–3, but decimal numbers are used to represent the terms of the function.

Example 7–4

The function of Example 7–1 is described by

$$T = \sum (0, 5, 6, 9, 10, 15, 19, 20, 24, 29, 30)$$

E	0	5	6	9	10	15	19	20	24	29	30	5/6
D	0	2	3	4	5	7	9	10	12	14	15	5/6
C	0	1	1	2	2	3	4	5	6	7	7	6/5
B	0	0	0	1	1	1	2	2	3	3	3	6/5
A	0	0	0	0	0	0	1	1	1	1	1	5/6
	2	2	2	2	2	2	5	2	2	2	2	

The first row in the tabulation contains the decimal numbers just as they appear in the standard sum. The odd numbers in this group correspond to 1's in the E digit of the binary number, and accordingly we identify the row by the variable E marked at the left. By counting the odd and even numbers in the row we can obtain the ratio of the number of 1's to the number of 0's in the E variable as shown at the right of the row. In the next row is shown the result of dividing all the original decimal numbers by 2 and discarding the fractional remainder. An odd number in this row indicates a 1 in the D digit position. By successive divisions by 2 we can enter the appropriate decimal numbers in the rows corresponding to the other three variables. The ratios shown at the right will be found to correspond to those computed in Example 7–3 for the same digit positions. We may again consider the B and C variables complemented and proceed to check for the a-numbers. To do this, we count the number of odd decimal numbers in each of the columns, remembering that when we complement the B and C variables we change a reading of odd to even and vice versa. Hence the number of odd numbers indicated by the count at the bottom of each of the columns above takes this reversal into account. It should be apparent that the rows and columns of Example 7–4 correspond to the columns and rows, respectively, of Example 7–3.

In analyzing a function for symmetry by the McCluskey method, using either binary or decimal numbers, we encounter one situation which is ambiguous and a further step is required to resolve it. This will be illustrated in the following example.

Example 7–5

Identify the symmetric function represented by the set of binary numbers tabulated.

A	B	C	D	
0	1	0	1	(2)
0	0	1	1	(2)
1	1	1	1	(4)
0	0	0	0	(0)
1	1	0	0	(2)
1	0	1	0	(2)
3/3	3/3	3/3	3/3	

We observe that every column contains three 1's and three 0's, but in checking the 1's in each term we find there are only four terms which contain two 1's, and there should be six terms. The column ratios offer no guide as to which variables, if any, should be complemented.

We can resolve this difficulty by expanding the function about any of its variables. This can be done in the numerical form as indicated. Here we have grouped the terms in which the A digit is 0 and also the terms in which the A digit is 1. Within each of these groups we have counted 1's and 0's in the B, C, and D columns only and in both tabulations we find that either B and C should be complemented or D should be complemented.

A	B	C	D
0	1	0	1
0	0	1	1
0	0	0	0
	1/2	1/2	2/1
1	1	1	1
1	1	0	0
1	0	1	0
	2/1	2/1	1/2

An inspection of the tabulation of the complete terms shows that if we complement B and C the requirements for an a-number equal to 2 are satisfied. The function is therefore identified as $S_2(A, B', C', D)$.

7.6　Symmetric Networks in Constant-Current Systems

The basic symmetric network of Fig. 7–6 is a multiple-output network essentially suited for use in constant-voltage systems. It may also be regarded as a form of tree circuit, and thus be added to the types of tree circuits discussed in Art. 6.7. We might then expect to find symmetric networks which are applicable in constant-current systems.

Figure 7–30 shows the constant-current equivalent of a multiple-output symmetric network in two variables. The load relay windings

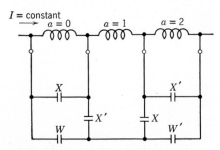

Fig. 7–30. Two-variable, constant-current, symmetric network.

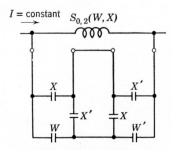

Fig. 7–31. Modification of constant-current symmetric network for a function with more than one a-number.

shown are energized when the number of operated relays in the W, X system equals the a-number placed above each load winding. This network can therefore produce, on a constant-current basis, any one of the functions $S_0(W, X)$, $S_1(W, X)$, $S_2(W, X)$. If any of the a-numbers are not needed, the corresponding terminals are short circuited, and any contacts thereby made redundant can be removed. If a single load winding is to be controlled in accordance with a function with more than one a-number, the load is placed across the outside terminals of the entire network, and short circuits are placed across those pairs of terminals which correspond to the unwanted a-numbers. This is illustrated in Fig. 7–31 for the function $S_{0,2}(W, X)$.

In Fig. 7–32 and 7–33 the basic symmetric networks for three and four variables, respectively, are presented on a constant-current basis. It should be noted that there is a slight variation in the network

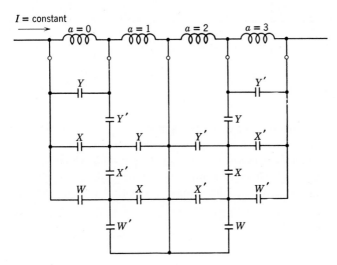

Fig. 7–32. Three-variable, constant-current, symmetric network.

structure, depending upon whether the number of variables is odd or even. Otherwise the extension of these networks to include larger numbers of variables is readily performed. The way in which the larger networks perform their switching tasks is sometimes quite complex. For example, note in Fig. 7–33 the path through the network indicated by the dotted line. This is the path taken by the current to energize the winding for $a = 3$ when the three relays W, X, Y are operated. It should also be noted that when this path is established, all other windings are short circuited.

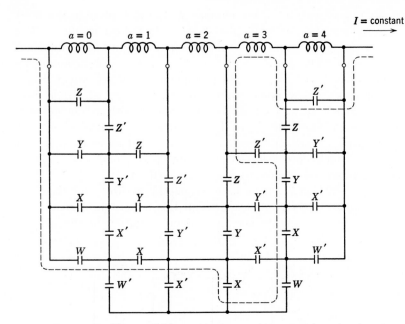

Fig. 7–33. Four-variable, constant-current, symmetric network.

Constant-current networks for symmetric functions of mixed variables can also be drawn by a method analogous to that discussed in Art. 7.5. It is merely necessary to design the network which would be used if none of the variables of symmetry are primed, and then replace the contacts associated with the primed variables by their complementary forms.

PROBLEMS

7.1 A two-terminal contact network built on four relays is to have transmission 1 if none, one, or three of the relays are operated. Use the iterative method to design the network. Show the structure of a typical cell.

7.2 A two-terminal contact network built on four relays is to have transmission 0 if none, one, or three of the relays are operated. Use the iterative method to design the network. Show the structure of a typical cell.

7.3 Take the geometric complement of the network found in Problem 7.2 and compare it with the network found in Problem 7.1. Do they have the same transmission functions? Is there any difference in the number of springs required?

7.4 Design a minimum multi-terminal contact network having the two output transmission functions described by

$$T_1 = S_{0,1}(A, B, C, D); \qquad T_2 = S_{3,4}(A', B, C, D)$$

7.5 Six relays are grouped into group 1, consisting of relays A, B, and C, and group 2, consisting of relays X, Y, and Z. A contact network on these relays is to transmit a ground to one of three output terminals, depending upon the relative numbers of relays operated in the two groups, as follows:

Terminal 1 is grounded when the number in group 1 is larger than the number in group 2.

Terminal 2 is grounded when the number in group 1 equals the number in group 2.

Terminal 3 is grounded when the number in group 1 is smaller than the number in group 2.

Design a contact network which satisfies these specifications.

7.6 A two-terminal network is to be built on contacts from two groups of relays. Group 1 consists of the relays A, B, and C; group 2 consists of the relays X, Y, and Z.

The network is to have transmission 1 for either of the following conditions:

(a) When the number of operated relays in group 1 equals the number of operated relays in group 2, or

(b) When any three of the six relays, regardless of group designation, are operated.

For all other conditions the transmission is to be 0.

Design and draw a minimal network that satisfies these conditions (20 contacts, 30 springs are sufficient).

7.7 The symmetric function $S_{2,3,5}(A, B, C, D, E)$ is to be realized by means of a relay contact network which contains a minimum number of springs.

1. Draw the network for the direct realization of this function and eliminate as many contacts as possible.

2. Draw the network for the realization of the complement of the original function and eliminate as many contacts as possible, retaining the planar form.

3. Draw the geometric complement of the network of part 2. Compare the contact and spring count with that for the network of part 1.

4. In the network of part 2, how many cut sets are there when relays A, C, and D are operated, and B and E are not operated? Sketch these cut sets on the circuit diagram.

7.8 Express the following as symmetric functions:

1. $A'S_{0,1,4}(B, C, D, E) + AS'_{0,3,4}(B, C, D, E)$

2. $A'S_{0,1,4}(B, C, D, E) + AS_{0,3,4}(B, C, D, E)$

3. $A'S_{0,1,4}(B, C, D, E) + AS_{0,3,4}(B', C', D', E')$

4. $A'B'S_{1,4}(C, D, E, F) + A'BS_{0,3}(C, D, E, F)$
   $+ AB'S_{0,2}(C, D, E, F) + ABS_{1,4}(C, D, E, F)$

5. $A'B'S_{1,4}(C, D, E, F) + A'BS_{0,3}((C, D, E, F)$
   $+ AB'S_{0,3}(C, D, E, F) + ABS_{2,4}(C, D, E, F)$

6. $S_{0,2}(A, B) + S_{0,2}(B, C)$

7.9 Identify the symmetric functions described by the following standard sums. Determine the a-numbers and the variables of symmetry for each function.

1. $T = \sum (18, 34, 48, 51, 54, 58, 114)$
2. $T = \sum (2, 13, 21, 25, 28, 31, 32, 34, 35, 38, 42, 50, 61)$
3. $T = \sum (0, 3, 5, 10, 12, 15, 17, 24, 27, 29)$
4. $T = \sum (0, 3, 5, 6, 10, 12, 15, 18, 20, 23, 25, 30)$
5. $T = \sum (0, 1, 3, 5, 6, 8, 10, 11, 12, 13, 15, 17, 18, 20, 23, 24, 25, 27, 29, 30)$
6. $T = \sum (1, 3, 8, 10, 13, 15, 16, 18, 21, 23, 28, 30)$

7.10 The function described by the standard sum

$$T = \sum (1, 2, 4, 7, 8, 11, 13, 14, 16, 19, 21, 22, 26, 28, 31)$$

is symmetric.

1. Determine the variables of symmetry and the a-numbers of the function.
2. Derive a circuit, using "folding," which has as few contacts as possible (29 springs are sufficient).

7.11 The three output functions of a multi-terminal contact network are represented by the standard sums marked on the terminals of the block diagram shown.

Design a minimal multi-terminal contact network which realizes these outputs.

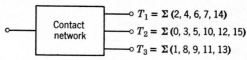

$T_1 = \Sigma\ (2, 4, 6, 7, 14)$
$T_2 = \Sigma\ (0, 3, 5, 10, 12, 15)$
$T_3 = \Sigma\ (1, 8, 9, 11, 13)$

Contact network

Problem 7.11.

7.12 In the network given determine N_5 so that the transmission T_{12} is a symmetric function of the variables (A, B', C, D', E).

Express N_5 as a standard sum. Identify the symmetric function T_{12}.

$$N_1 = S_{1,2,5}(A, B, C, D, E)$$
$$N_2 = S_{1,3,4}(A, B, C, D, E)$$
$$N_3 = \sum (7, 11, 13, 14, 19, 22, 25, 26, 28)$$
$$N_4 = \sum (7, 13, 18, 25, 26, 31)$$

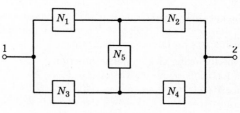

Problem 7.12.

7.13 An existing contact network has the symmetric transmission function

$$T = \sum (0, 1, 3, 4, 6, 7, 8, 10, 11, 14)$$

1. Determine the variables of symmetry and the a-numbers.
2. It becomes necessary to include in the transmission function the additional terms represented by $\sum(16, 19)$. What *other* terms must be added if the transmission function is to remain symmetric?
3. What are the new variables of symmetry and the a-numbers?

7.14 In the circuit shown the relay X will operate in series with either resistor R_1 or R_2, or with neither resistor in series.

Identify the symmetric function which represents the operation of X.

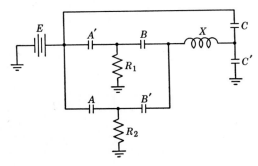

Problem 7.14.

CHAPTER 8

Synthesis of non-series-parallel contact networks

In Chapter **7** we studied one large group of switching functions which led, in their realizations, to non-series-parallel contact networks. A general method was developed for the synthesis of any member of this class of functions, and there were reasonably good methods for the elimination of redundant elements. In Chapter **11** we will study another class of switching functions which leads to non-series-parallel realizations. The symmetric functions studied in Chapter **7**, and the iterative problems which we will examine in Chapter **11**, are always realized by non-series-parallel networks, except for those members of each class which are extremely simple or even trivial. The non-series-parallel realization is inherent to the iterative concept.

We have also encountered a few scattered problems in which the manipulations we performed led to non-series-parallel networks. But at no time was there any intention to design a non-series-parallel structure; the results achieved, although welcome, were hardly more than accidental. In this discussion we are referring exclusively to two-terminal networks. In the synthesis of multi-terminal networks we frequently produce networks which appear to be of the non-series-parallel form. However, if we examine the networks more carefully between pairs of terminals, and particularly between the input terminal and each output terminal, we often find that each of these networks is series-parallel in form.

In this chapter we shall discuss synthesis procedures which usually lead to non-series-parallel realizations. This is important to us because, starting with a series-parallel network we can add one or more very simple bilateral bridging elements (elements which permit conduction in either direction) and by such addition modify the network transmission to an extent that could be accomplished only by the addition of a disproportionate number of series-parallel elements. If we happen to add exactly the right elements in the right places we can often achieve a specified transmission function with extraordinary economy. The non-series-parallel configuration offers the ultimate in contact network economy, but the problem of synthesizing it remains an outstanding challenge.

8.1 Disjunctive-Tree Synthesis

One of the first descriptions of a synthesis procedure which leads to non-series-parallel forms is that which we here call the disjunctive-tree method.* The method can also appropriately be called a method of assumed form. While there is never any uncertainty about getting a synthesis by this method, we are not necessarily sure that the result will be non-series-parallel. However, the networks found are so frequently non-series-parallel, and even non-planar, that the discussion belongs in this chapter.

The method is based on the interconnection of two networks as indicated schematically in Fig. 8–1. Boxes M and N both represent networks having $(n + 1)$ terminals. Network M has the transmission

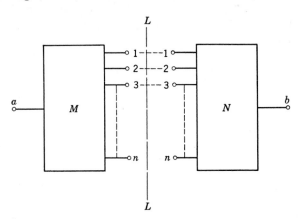

Fig. 8–1.   Assumed form of networks in disjunctive tree synthesis.

* C. E. Shannon, "The Synthesis of Two-Terminal Switching Circuits," *Bell System Technical Journal*, Vol. 28, January 1949, pp. 59–98.

functions $U_k (k = 1, 2, 3 \ldots n)$ between terminals a and k; network
N has the transmissions V_k between terminals b and k. Also, M is a
disjunctive network for which $U_{jk} = 0$, where $j, k = 1, 2, \ldots, n$, but
$j \neq k$.

In his description of the method, Shannon states the theorem, "If the
correspondingly numbered terminals $1, 2, 3, \ldots, n$ of M and N are
connected together then

$$T_{ab} = \sum_{k=1}^{k=n} U_k \cdot V_k$$

The proof of this theorem becomes fairly evident by reference to
Fig. 8–2. Any term of the type $U_k \cdot V_k$ represents a path between ter-

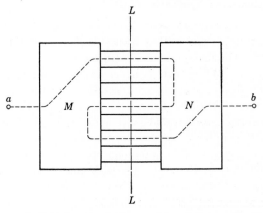

Fig. 8–2   Any path between terminals a and b must cross the line LL an odd
number of times.

minals a and b which crosses the line LL in Fig. 8–2 exactly once.
Since the N network is not necessarily disjunctive, a path which has
crossed LL once may cross it a second time. However, in that event,
in order to complete the path to the terminal b there must be a third
crossing of the line LL. Conceivably, this might go on to any number
of crossings but the final number must always be odd. However, the
network M is defined as a disjunctive network, so the transmission of
all such paths must be 0, and in the transmission expression only the
$U_k \cdot V_k$ terms remain.

We will apply this method first to a function of three variables.
From this process it will become evident that any function of three
variables $f(X, Y, Z)$ can be realized by not more than eight elements,
and with not more than four elements on any one relay.

By the expansion theorem, any function of three variables can be written

$$f(X, Y, Z) = XYf(1, 1, Z) + XY'f(1, 0, Z)$$
$$+ X'Yf(0, 1, Z) + X'Y'f(0, 0, Z)$$

In accordance with Shannon's theorem we can now define

$$U_1 = XY \qquad V_1 = f(1, 1, Z)$$
$$U_2 = XY' \qquad V_2 = f(1, 0, Z)$$
$$U_3 = X'Y \qquad V_3 = f(0, 1, Z)$$
$$U_4 = X'Y' \qquad V_4 = f(0, 0, Z)$$

Then

$$T_{ab} = f(X, Y, Z) = \sum_1^4 U_k V_k$$

We recognize the network required to produce the functions $U_1, \ldots,$ U_4 as the disjunctive tree of Fig. 8–3. The functions $V_1, \ldots, V_4$ must be selections from the set $(0, 1, Z, Z')$. It is evident then that the

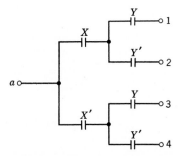

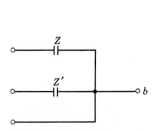

Fig. 8–3. The M network is a disjunctive tree.

Fig. 8–4. Maximum size of N network for functions of three variables.

largest N network ever needed for a function of three variables is that shown in Fig. 8–4. In the combined networks the most we ever need are the two contacts on X, four contacts on Y, and two contacts on Z.

We may summarize the steps taken thus far as follows:

(1) Write the given transmission function in the form of a sum of products such that the functions U_k are the same for a large class of transmission functions, with the V_k determining the particular transmission function under consideration.

(2) Form a basic disjunctive network M to realize the U_k functions.

(3) Form the N network to realize the V_k.

(4) With the U_k and V_k functions realized at appropriately numbered terminals, the connections 1–1, 2–2, and so forth, between the M and N networks are made. For $V_k = 0$, no connection is needed and a corresponding element in the M network can be eliminated.

Example 8–1

Synthesize, by the disjunctive-tree method, a contact network to realize the function

$$T = X(YZ' + Y'Z) + X'(YZ + Y'Z')$$

The component networks are indicated by expansion as:

$$U_1 = XY \qquad V_1 = Z'$$
$$U_2 = XY' \qquad V_2 = Z$$
$$U_3 = X'Y \qquad V_3 = Z$$
$$U_4 = X'Y' \qquad V_4 = Z'$$

When like-numbered terminals of the M and N networks are connected, we have the network of Fig. 8–5. It is non-series-parallel and

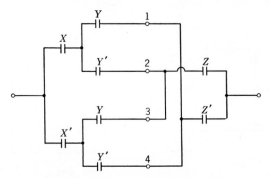

Fig. 8–5. Network of Example 8–1.

it is non-planar. Of course, it can also be realized quite easily by methods discussed in Chapter 4. Here, however, the non-series-parallel form of the network is an inevitable consequence of the method used.

A function of four variables can be treated in either of two ways. One method is to expand the function about three of the variables. Thus, the N network is again derived from the functions of a single variable and is the same as that shown in Fig. 8–4. The disjunctive tree for the M network contains 14 contact elements if all U_k are present. Thus the combined networks have a total of 16 contacts as an upper limit.

A second way is to expand the function about two of its variables and use the disjunctive tree of Fig. 8–3 for the M network. The upper limit for the N network is now more difficult to define. Shannon gives an upper bound of 8 contacts for the N network and hence 14 contacts for the combined networks. To determine this limit he first expands the function to get

$$f(W, X, Y, Z) = WXV_1(Y, Z) + WX'V_2(Y, Z)$$
$$+ W'XV_3(Y, Z) + W'X'V_4(Y, Z)$$

From this expansion the U_k and V_k are identified as

$$U_1 = WX \qquad V_1 = f(1, 1, Y, Z)$$
$$U_2 = WX' \qquad V_2 = f(1, 0, Y, Z)$$
$$U_3 = W'X \qquad V_3 = f(0, 1, Y, Z)$$
$$U_4 = W'X' \qquad V_4 = f(0, 0, Y, Z)$$

The V_k are now functions of two variables and, in general, may be any selection from the entire set of such functions. For convenience, all the functions of two variables are grouped as follows:

A	$0, 1$	Extremes
B	Y, Y', Z, Z'	Single Variables
C	$(Y + Z), (Y + Z'), (Y' + Z), (Y' + Z')$	Sums
D	$YZ, YZ', Y'Z, Y'Z'$	Products
E	$(YZ + Y'Z'), (YZ' + Y'Z)$	Disjuncts

Shannon's upper bound on the number of contact elements required to realize any function of four variables was based on an exhaustive study of all possible selections of these functions of two variables. For the most part, this required a study of selections which contained one or both of the disjuncts from group E. We can readily see that if all four of the V_k functions are derived from groups A, B, C, and D, the N network never requires more than eight contacts. This follows from the fact that any such selection of V_k functions contains a maximum of eight literals in the four functions.

It is quite a different situation when the selections include one or both of the functions in group E. Obviously, since the two disjuncts alone contain 8 contacts, or 6 contacts if they share 1 transfer contact, we must use many stratagems to realize additional V_k when the disjuncts are also required. In Fig. 8–6(a), for example, we see how the disjunct $YZ + Y'Z'$ is "tapped" so that by adding one Y' contact the product $Y'Z$ is obtained. In Fig. 8–6(b) the same disjunct is realized from a circuit which is "tapped" without an additional contact to yield the sum $Y' + Z$. It is instructive to observe, as in Fig. 8–7, that *all*

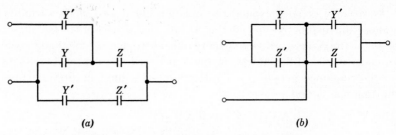

Fig. 8-6. Partial N networks containing disjuncts.

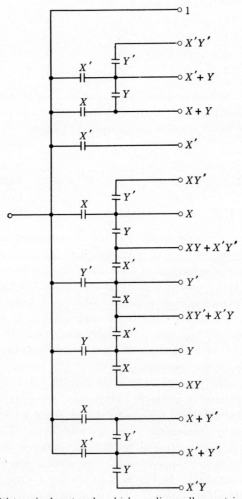

Fig. 8-7. Multi-terminal network which realizes all non-trivial functions of two variables.

the functions of two variables can be realized in a multi-terminal network which contains only 18 contacts and 27 springs.*

We shall not discuss all the possible selections of the V_k. In the examples which follow a few of the more difficult situations are shown.

Example 8–2

An N network is to realize one function from group E, two from group C, and one from group D. The functions from groups C and D are to be chosen so that they cannot be derived from the E network.

One selection of this type is $YZ + Y'Z'$ from the E group, $Y + Z$ and $Y' + Z'$ from the C group, and $Y'Z$ from the D group.

The network in Fig. 8–8 realizes these functions with 8 contacts. Actually it is possible to obtain an additional function, as shown by

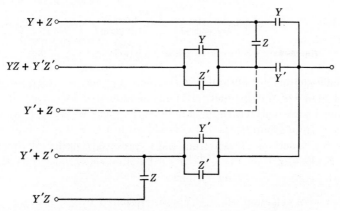

Fig. 8–8. N network to realize functions of Example 8–2.

dotted lines, without additional contacts. Seven contacts are required for the disjunct and the two sums. The remaining element can be used to produce any of the remaining functions, except the other disjunct.

Example 8–3

Construct an N network to realize both group E functions, any one function from group C, and any one function from group D.

In the network of Fig. 8–9, the group C function determines whether a Z or a Z' contact is used. If Z' is required in the sums, the contacts in the disjunct networks must also be changed as indicated. Finally,

---

*This network is based on a home-problem solution by K. H. Bhavnani, November, 1952. In an unpublished memorandum, C. E. Shannon has proven that the circuit shown is minimal, that the entire group of functions of two variables cannot be realized with 17 or fewer contacts.

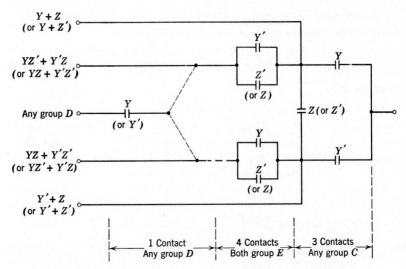

Fig. 8–9. N network to realize functions of Example 8–3.

the single contact for obtaining a D-group function is chosen and connected to one of the disjunct terminals as indicated by dotted lines.

If the V_k are selected to include both functions of group E and two functions from group C, the network shown in Fig. 8–9 is still adequate unless the functions chosen from the C group are either of the pairs $(Y + Z, Y' + Z')$ or $(Y + Z', Y' + Z)$. For these selections the N network requires 9 contact elements.

Consider a selection of this type, represented by

$$f(W, X, Y, Z) = WX(YZ + Y'Z') + WX'(YZ' + Y'Z) \\ + W'X(Y + Z') + W'X'(Y' + Z)$$

This situation is best treated by changing the variables of expansion. There are six different combinations of two variables out of the four, and it sometimes is advisable to try them all to find the pair which yields the best N network. For the function given above, we expand about the variables Y and Z to obtain the following U_k and V_k:

$$U_1 = YZ \qquad V_1 = f(W, X, 1, 1) = WX + W'X + W'X' = W' + X$$
$$U_2 = YZ' \qquad V_2 = f(W, X, 1, 0) = WX' + W'X$$
$$U_3 = Y'Z \qquad V_3 = f(W, X, 0, 1) = WX' + W'X' = X'$$
$$U_4 = Y'Z' \qquad V_4 = f(W, X, 0, 0) = WX + W'X + W'X' = W' + X$$

We note that since $V_1 = V_4$, terminals 1 and 4 of the M network will be connected to a single output of the N network. It is more conven-

ient to change the terminal order so that those to be connected together
are adjacent.   The subscripts of the U_k and V_k are hence changed to
the ordering

1.	YZ'	$WX' + W'X$
2.	YZ	$W' + X$
3.	$Y'Z'$	$W' + X$
4.	$Y'Z$	X'

The contact network shown in Fig. 8–10 realizes the required function with **12** contacts instead of the **15** contacts required when W and

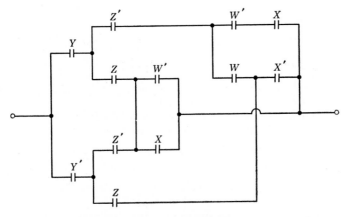

Fig. 8–10.   Expansion about Y and Z instead of W and X saves three contacts.

X are the variables of expansion.   When the network of Fig. 8–10 is
redrawn in the form shown in Fig. 8–11 we see that the effect of tying
together two of the terminals of the M network is to convert that
network to a symmetric tree, which is also a disjunctive form.   The
function realized is one of a class which Shannon calls a partially
symmetric function.   This function shows symmetry in the variables
YZ' and $Y'Z$.   Note that we can write the function in the form

$$f = X'S_0(Y, Z') + (W' + X)S_1(Y, Z') + (W'X + WX')S_2(Y, Z')$$

In the network of Fig. 8–10 the term $W' + X$ was generated in the
N network by a separate pair of contacts.   This term is obtained in
Fig. 8–11 by a method which does not decrease the number of contacts
in the N network but does decrease the number of springs.

In Example 8–2 the N network requires 8 elements.   Let us examine
this function somewhat further.

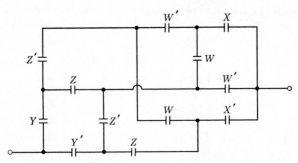

Fig. 8–11. The M network is a symmetric tree.

Example 8–4

$$f = WX(YZ+Y'Z')+WX'(Y+Z)+W'X(Y'+Z')+W'X'(Y'Z)$$

If we expand the function about the variables Y and Z, we obtain for the U_k and V_k

$$
\begin{array}{ll}
YZ & WX + WX' = W \\
YZ' & WX' + W'X = (W + X)(W' + X') \\
Y'Z & WX' + W'X + W'X' = W' + X' \\
Y'Z' & WX + W'X = X
\end{array}
$$

We see from Fig. 8–12 that the function which previously required 14 contacts is now realized using 12 contacts.

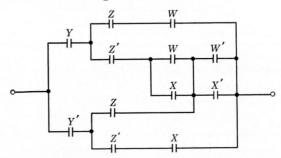

Fig. 8–12. Network found in Example 8–4.

The disjunctive tree method has not been too satisfactory from the standpoint of establishing the upper bound on the number of contact elements required in realizing a function of four variables. A bound based on an analysis of the configurations of N networks does not take into account the possibility of changing the variables in the M network and hence completely changing the structure of the N network. An exhaustive study of all types of functions of four variables has shown that no function requires more than 13 contacts for its realization and this number is required by only two types of functions. These are the complementary symmetric functions $S_{2,4}(W, X, Y, Z)$ and $S_{0,1,3}(W, X, Y, Z)$. Because the functions are symmetric, the V_k residues of these functions always contain both disjuncts of the E group and one term from either the C or the D group. This synthesis is left as an exercise for the student.

It is sometimes found that after the routine steps of a disjunctive tree synthesis are completed, further simplification can be made by other methods. The M network in particular should be inspected for contacts which are redundant, as illustrated in Example 8–5.

Example 8–5

The function $f = W'X'(Y' + Z') + XZ(W'Y + WY')$ when expanded about W, X and about X, Z, yields the following residues

WX	$Y'Z$	XZ	$W'Y + WY'$
WX'	0	XZ'	0
$W'X$	YZ	$X'Z$	$W'Y'$
$W'X'$	$Y' + Z'$	$X'Z'$	W'

The networks corresponding to these expansions are shown in Fig. 8–13. Part (a) of Fig. 8–13 shows two X contacts, indicated by a

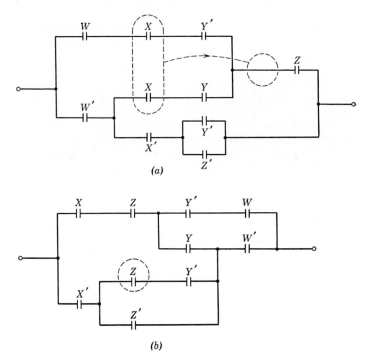

(a)

(b)

Fig. 8–13. After synthesis by the disjunctive tree method, networks must still be examined for possible redundant contacts.

dotted line, which can be moved to the right and merged into a single contact. In part (b) of Fig. 8–13, the encircled Z contact is present because the synthesis puts it there. Algebraically it is redundant, because $Z' + ZY' = Z' + Y'$, and hence it can be removed.

Occasionally we encounter algebraic forms which suggest the possibility of using a modified disjunctive tree approach. Although the "tree" may not actually be disjunctive the important point is to be sure that there is sufficient disjunctivity where it is needed to prevent unwanted tie paths.

Example 8–6

Consider the function

$$T = X'(WY + W'Y') + (X' + Y')(WZ + W'Z')$$

This function is certainly not in the form required for a disjunctive tree synthesis. However, the presence of the terms $(WY + W'Y')$ and $(WZ + W'Z')$ does suggest the possibility of writing the function in the form

$$T = U_1(W, Y)V_1(X) + U_2(W, Z)V_2(X, Y)$$

The network of Fig. 8–14 is in the form suggested by the preceding expression and the result is an interesting variation of the method.

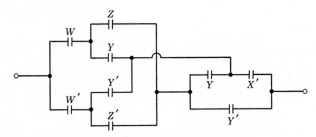

Fig. 8–14. Network suggested in Example 8–6.

Functions of more than four variables can be treated by the disjunctive tree method, usually in a variety of ways. The variables can be distributed between the M and N networks in accordance with the requirements of the problem. Little can be said which is sufficiently general to serve as a guide. Whether a function of five variables should be realized with two variables in the M network and three in the N network or vice versa is a question which probably can be answered only in terms of particular problems.

8.2 Absorption Method

Consider the network of Fig. 8–15, which is commonly called a bridge network. If the E contact were not connected between nodes 3 and 4 this would be a simple series-parallel circuit.

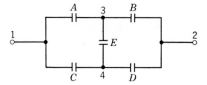

Fig. 8–15. Bridge-type contact network.

Let us write the transmission function for the network of Fig. 8–15 and then expand it about the variable E, as follows

$$
\begin{aligned}
T &= AB + CD + ADE + BCE \\
&= E(AB + CD + AD + BC) + E'(AB + CD) \\
&= E\left[A(B + D) + C(B + D)\right] + E'(AB + CD) \\
&= E(A + C)(B + D) + E'(AB + CD)
\end{aligned}
$$

In Fig. 8–16 the expanded transmission function has been realized as a series-parallel contact network. Because of the expansion about the

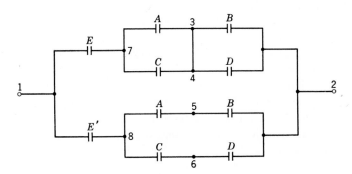

Fig. 8–16. Bridge network expanded about the bridging variable.

variable E, we see that it is composed of one network with E external to the network, and another with E' external to the network. These two residue networks contain identical contacts in the same locations. The only difference between them is that the E-residue has a connection between the nodes 3 and 4 but there is no connection between the corresponding nodes 5 and 6 of the E'-residue.

Suppose we had placed an E contact in series with the original network of Fig. 8–15 and then applied theorem 20, which is

$$
X \cdot f(X, Y, Z, \dots) = X \cdot f(1, Y, Z, \dots)
$$

The effect of using this theorem is to place a solid connection between nodes 3 and 4, exactly as it appears in the upper branch of the circuit of Fig. 8- 16.

If we had connected an E' contact in series with the original bridge circuit and then applied theorem 21, which is

$$X' \cdot f(X, Y, Z, \dots) = X' \cdot f(0, Y, Z, \dots)$$

we would obtain exactly the same circuit that is present in the lower branch of Fig. 8–16.

It has been pointed out that any of the theorems of switching algebra may be used backwards. Theorems 20 and 21 when used in the reverse direction signify that if a contact X is in series with a network the contact X may also be placed between any points i, j, within the network, for which $T_{ij} = 1$. Also, when a contact X is in series with a network the complementary contact X' may be placed between any points i, j, in that network which are not otherwise connected.

Let us apply these ideas to the network of Fig. 8–16. In the upper branch, E is in series with a network of contacts, A, B, C, and D. From the rules we have just derived, we see that the transmission of the upper branch is not changed in any way if we also insert an E contact in the connection between nodes 3 and 4. In the lower branch we have an E' contact in series with a network containing contacts A, B, C, D. Nodes 5 and 6 of this network are not directly connected. When an E' contact is in series with the network, there is no change in transmission in the lower branch if we place an E contact between nodes 5 and 6. After both these insertions are made we find that between node 7 and terminal 2 there is a network which is identical to that between node 8 and terminal 2. Therefore, we can connect node 7 and node 8 and discard either the upper or lower network. Then between terminal 1 and the common connection of nodes 7 and 8 there will be an E contact and an E' contact in parallel. These may be replaced by a solid connection.

The foregoing example did not illustrate all the changes which might have been made. In the upper residue network we can connect an E' contact between nodes 4 and 7 without changing the transmission of the upper branch. Similarly in the lower residue network we can insert an E' contact in series with the A contact between nodes 5 and 8 without changing the transmission of the lower branch. These manipulations, of course, are of no advantage. Our objective is to use the external contacts, E and E', to modify the residue networks until they become identical. Then the two residue networks can be superposed and the external contacts discarded. Effectively, we have "absorbed" the external contacts into the residue networks. The process will become clearer by going through some examples step by step.

Example 8-7

Design a minimal contact network to realize the transmission function

$$T = W(X + Y + Z) + XYZ$$

The first difficulty is to determine about what variable or variables an expansion should be made. There is no fixed rule to answer this question. Usually a few trial expansions are advisable so that various residues may be examined for favorable structure. We are trying to find residues which are nearly enough alike that they can be made identical by the expenditure of relatively few insertions of the external variables. In this example, we expand about W and obtain

$$T = W(X + Y + Z)$$
$$+ W'(XYZ)$$

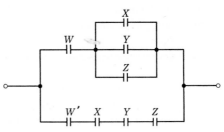

Fig. 8-17. Expanded network of Example 8-7.

Figure 8-17 shows the variables of expansion with their associated residual networks. The residues in Fig. 8-17 do not look much alike, but at this point a certain amount of imagination is needed to see the kind of distortion of the network forms that lead to a profitable synthesis.

In Fig. 8-18(a) the W and W' residual networks are identical with those in Fig. 8-17, but the modifications in shape are sufficient to bring out sharply the similarities which we can use with profit.

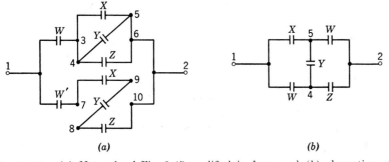

(a)   (b)

Fig. 8-18. (a) Network of Fig. 8-17 modified in form, and (b) absorption of external variable completed.

Applying the rules for insertion of external contacts, we can insert a W contact in the connection between nodes 3 and 4 and another W contact in the connection between nodes 5 and 6. We can place a W contact across the gap between nodes 7 and 8 and another W contact across the gap between nodes 9 and 10. When this is done the modified residue networks are identical and may be superposed, and the external contacts may then be replaced by a solid connection from terminal 1. In Fig. 8–18(b) the final network is shown.

We may better understand the procedure by examining its physical significance. When we have a contact which is completely external to a residue network, if that contact is open the transmission of the entire path in which it is located is 0. Hence it makes no difference what other contact may be closed in the residue network, and we may accordingly place the complement of the external contact *between* any pair of points in the residue network. When the external contact is open, its complement is closed within the residue network, but this has no effect on the transmission.

We may also insert a duplicate of an external contact within any solid connection of the residue network. If the external contact is closed, its internal duplicate is also closed and the required solid connection is maintained.

Functions of larger numbers of variables may be treated by the absorption method in various ways. We are free to expand the function about as many variables as we wish. This will be illustrated by synthesizing a function of five variables.

Example 8–8

Synthesize by the absorption method a network which has the transmission function

$$T = \sum(1, 7, 9, 14, 15, 16, 21, 24, 29)$$

A reduction by the Quine-McCluskey method yields the minimum sum

$$T = V'X'Y'Z + VX'Y'Z' + V'XYZ + V'WXY + VXY'Z$$

We expand about two variables and choose to select V and Y as the variables of expansion. (This choice was made by trying a few expansions and examining the residues for similarities of structure. The final result does not seem to be critically dependent on the choice made.)

The residues of the expansion are:

$$
\begin{array}{ll}
VY & 0 \\
VY' & XZ + X'Z' \\
V'Y & XZ + WX \\
V'Y' & X'Z
\end{array}
$$

Figure 8–19 shows the first step in the absorption of two variables. The four residue networks are shown with heavy lines and their con-

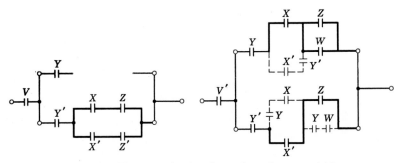

Fig. 8–19. First step in the absorption of two variables.

nections to the external variables are shown with light lines. We note first that the residue of VY is 0 so there seems to be little point in absorbing the Y' variable into the residue of VY'. The residues of V' have been drawn so that similarities of structure are emphasized. In Fig. 8–19 the connection shown by dotted lines indicate the additions which must be made to the two residues of V' in order to make them identical. Also, two Y contacts must be inserted in the heavy lines of the Y residue and one Y' contact must be inserted in the heavy line of the Y' residue. When these insertions are made, the networks superposed, and the redundant external variables removed, the V' residue appears as in Fig. 8–20.

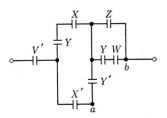

Fig. 8–20. Absorption of the Y variable in the V' residue.

The next step is to combine the residue just found with the V residue. This consists of the entire lower branch of the left-hand network of Fig. 8–19. We first note in Fig. 8–20 that between points a and b there is a network containing Y', Y, and W in series, which does not appear in the V residue. However, this network always has 0 transmission so it may be added to the V residue without any use of corrective contacts. The

Z' contact in the V residue is placed in the V' residue with a V contact in series. A Y contact in the V' residue must be put into the V residue with a V contact in parallel with it. A solid connection in the V' residue must have a V' contact placed in it in order to put it in the V residue. Finally, the Y' contact in the V residue has a V' contact placed in parallel with it. The final result, after redrawing is shown in Fig. 8–21. It is suggested that the student repeat this synthesis step by step to confirm the modifications made.*

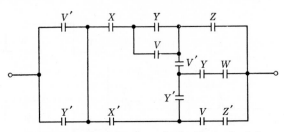

Fig. 8–21.   Completed synthesis, Example 8–8.

The absorption process is merely another of the possible methods we have for obtaining more advantageous syntheses of combinational contact networks. In particular problems it may not be of any advantage.

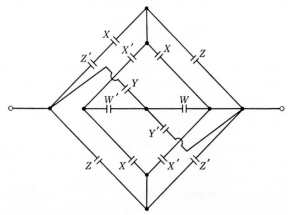

Fig. 8–22.   A realization of the symmetric function $S_{2,4}(W,X,Y,Z)$ obtained by the absorption method.

Its possibilities are indicated by the network shown in Fig. 8–22. The symmetric function $S_{2,4}(W,X,Y,Z)$ is one of the two functions of four

* It is not known whether this function can be realized with fewer contacts than appear in Fig. 8–21. The function is actually one chosen at random by drawing from a group of poker chips numbered from 0 to 31.

variables that have never been realized in fewer than 13 contacts. The absorption method does not do any better but it does provide a different version of the symmetric network.

8.3 Synthesis by Boolean Matrix

The Boolean matrix is the one device we have that enables us to describe both the algebraic transmission of a network and its detailed structure, compactly and without ambiguity. If a primitive connection matrix* of a network is known, then the identity and location of every contact element in the network is specified.

Why, then, have we not used the matrix almost exclusively in the synthesis of contact networks? The difficulty is that, if the detailed circuit structure is known, we can immediately write its primitive connection matrix and reduce it to the output matrix; but, if only the transmission function of the matrix is known, we can write only the output matrix with certainty. The process of expanding an output matrix to a primitive connection matrix confronts us once again with the problem of making successful choices. Nevertheless the impressive potential of the method demands our attention.

In this discussion we will consider only matrices of two-terminal networks.† Let us first write the primitive connection matrix for the bridge circuit of Fig. 8–15, as shown.

		To node: 1	2	3	4
From node:	1	1	0	A	C
	2	0	1	B	D
	3	A	B	1	E
	4	C	D	E	1

We should observe that each entry in the matrix represents the connection between a pair of nodes and *not,* in general, the internode transmission. Thus, the connection between nodes 3 and 4 is simply E, while the transmission between nodes 3 and 4 would include elements in paths passing through nodes 1 and 2. Again, there is certainly a transmission function between the output terminals 1 and 2, but there is no connection between these nodes, so the corresponding entry in the matrix must be 0.

* F. E. Hohn and L. R. Schissler, "Boolean Matrices and the Design of Combinational Relay Switching Circuits," *Bell System Technical Journal,* Vol. 34, January 1955, pp. 177–202.

† Hohn and Schissler treat the subject more broadly to develop the mathematical background required for further research in this field.

On the principal diagonal each entry represents a connection between a node and itself; hence all these entries are 1's. We observe that the matrix is symmetrical about the principal diagonal. This is true of all matrices written for networks containing only bilateral elements. If we restrict ourselves to such networks, it is not necessary to specify that an entry is a connection "from" one node "to" another. However, if we write matrices for networks containing, say, contacts and rectifier elements, the direction must be specified and the matrix will not be symmetrical about the principal diagonal.

The output matrix of a two-terminal network is simply

$$\begin{bmatrix} 1 & T \\ T & 1 \end{bmatrix}$$

where T is the transmission function of the entire network. We can reduce a primitive connection matrix to an output matrix by a process of node removal.*

If we want to remove, say, node 3 in the matrix written for the circuit of Fig. 8–15, then in a new matrix containing only three rows and columns, an entry representing a connection between nodes 1 and 4 must be of the form $E_{14} = C_{14} + C_{13}C_{34}$, where E_{ij} represents an entry in a reduced matrix, and C_{ij} represents an entry in a matrix having one more row and column.

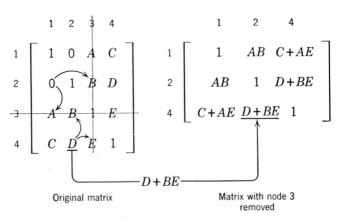

Original matrix   Matrix with node 3 removed

Fig. 8–23   Formation of a reduced matrix.

The typical entry of a reduced matrix can readily be found by using the construction shown in Fig. 8–23. In the original matrix the row

---

* The reduction can also be performed by a method analogous to the evaluation of determinants. We use the node-removal method because it is a process which is more easily reversed and hence leads more readily to synthesis.

and column corresponding to a node to be removed are ruled out. In the reduced matrix 1's are entered on the principal diagonal. The remaining entries are found as indicated in Fig. 8–23. For example, in row 4, column 2, we find the entry $D + BE$. This consists of the entry D of row 4, column 2 in the original matrix, plus the product of the entries in row 4, column 2, that are ruled out. The reader may verify that this entry corresponds to $E_{42} = C_{42} + C_{43}C_{32}$. The new entry for row 2, column 1, is found to be $0 + AB = AB$. Physically, this says that when node 3 is removed, we must consider the A and B contacts in series as a connection* between nodes 1 and 2.

We may now start with the reduced matrix of Fig. 8–23 and perform another reduction to remove node 4. In the final output matrix, 1's are again entered on the principal diagonal and the remaining entries are given by

$$T = AB + (C + AE)(D + BE)$$
$$= AB + CD + ADE + BCE$$

Thus we see that the primitive connection matrix not only describes explicitly how a network is built, but also contains a description of the terminal action of the network. For the purpose of synthesis we must ask whether the analytic procedures described above are reversible. Since the network structure does not become fully specified until the connection matrix is expanded to its primitive form, our problem is to learn how to distribute the literals of a non-primitive entry by *adding* nodes.

From the analysis performed above, it might be supposed that synthesis involves no more than converting each non-primitive entry into the form $x + yz$, and then making y and z entries in an added row and column. If we had been required to synthesize a network to realize the transmission function of the bridge, $T = AB + CD + ADE + BCE$, it is unlikely that we would have written the factored form, $T = AB + (C + AE)(D + BE)$. Let us assume, however, that we do start a matrix synthesis with this advantage.

Example 8–9

Expand the output matrix

$$\begin{bmatrix} 1 & AB + (C + AE)(D + BE) \\ AB + (C + AE)(D + BE) & 1 \end{bmatrix}$$

to a primitive connection matrix.

* A distinction is made between a connection matrix and a primitive connection matrix. In a connection matrix the entries are the transmission functions of two-

We first add a node, by adding a row and a column, and enter the terms $(C + AE)$ and $(D + BE)$ in the positions shown. It makes no difference which term is placed in the new row or which is placed in the new column. This step gives us the matrix

$$\begin{bmatrix} 1 & AB & C + AE \\ AB & 1 & D + BE \\ C + AE & D + BE & 1 \end{bmatrix}$$

Next we add another row and column to receive the components of the products AE and BE. Here, however, we are careful to place E in the column or row that allows it to contribute to both products. This step results in the matrix

$$\begin{bmatrix} 1 & AB & C & A \\ AB & 1 & D & B \\ C & D & 1 & E \\ A & B & E & 1 \end{bmatrix}$$

At this point we use a new tactic to eliminate the AB entry from this non-primitive matrix. We note that there is already a connection A from node 1 to node 4, and a connection B from node 4 to node 2. Hence there is already a connection AB from node 1 to node 2 and the entry AB is redundant. Replacing AB by 0's, we obtain a primitive connection matrix, and indeed, as Hohn and Schissler remark, "a wiring diagram for the bridge circuit" of Fig. 8–15.

Redundant matrix entries are of several types. The type found in the example given is probably the most common. It is important in synthesis to understand that the treatment of redundant entries is not necessarily to discard them. At times it is even advantageous to insert a redundant term, temporarily, in order to render other terms redundant.

Several redundancies may be found in the matrix shown here. If

$$\begin{bmatrix} 1 & A + B & B & A'D \\ A + B & 1 & B & A + C \\ B & B & 1 & BDE \\ A'D & A + C & BDE & 1 \end{bmatrix}$$

$B = 1$ there is a connection from node 1 to node 3, and from node 2 to node 3. Hence there is a connection from node 1 to node 2 and the B in the $A + B$ term is redundant. Or, since any two of the B entries

---

terminal networks which are between the selected nodes. In a primitive connection matrix the entries represent either single contacts or contacts connected in parallel.

suffice to establish the 1 to 2 to 3 connection, we can regard any one of the B entries as redundant.

Assume that we have removed the B in the 1, 2 entry. Then from 1 to 2 we have A and from 2 to 4 we have $A + C$. This series connection gives us from 1 to 4, $A(A + C) = A$. But the 1, 4 entry is $A'D$ and this is a connection which is in parallel with A. Since $A + A'D = A + D$, the A' is redundant.

With A' removed, we have the connection D from 1 to 4, the connection B from 3 to 1, hence the series connection BD from 3 to 4. Since BD contains BDE, the entire 3, 4 entry is redundant and may be replaced by 0.

We observe further that the connection $C_{12} = A$ and that there is another path from 1 to 2 comprising $C_{14}C_{42} = D(A + C)$. Hence between 1 and 2 we have contacts which represent $A + AD + CD = A + CD$. Thus the A contact in the connection $C_{42} = A + C$ is redundant. The final matrix is then

$$
\begin{bmatrix}
1 & A & B & D \\
A & 1 & B & C \\
B & B & 1 & 0 \\
D & C & 0 & 1
\end{bmatrix}
$$

The following example illustrates the matrix synthesis procedure on a function in five variables, described by a standard sum composed of numbers selected at random.

Example 8–10

The function to be realized is

$$
T = \Sigma(7, 8, 15, 18, 19, 21, 24, 29)
$$

This leads to the minimum sum

$$
\begin{aligned}
T &= BC'D'E' + AB'C'D + A'CDE + ACD'E \\
&= (AB'C' + A'CE)D + (BC'E' + ACE)D' \\
&= (D + BC'E' + ACE)(D' + AB'C' + A'CE)
\end{aligned}
$$

The final factored form of the function is such as to permit the output matrix to be expanded to a three-node matrix in the step

$$
\begin{vmatrix} 1 & T \\ T & 1 \end{vmatrix} \rightarrow
\begin{vmatrix}
1 & 0 & (D+BC'E'+ACE) \\
0 & 1 & (D'+AB'C'+A'CE) \\
(D+BC'E'+ACE) & (D'+AB'C'+A'CE) & 1
\end{vmatrix}
$$

We observe now that both the 1,3 entry and the 2,3 entry contain CE as a factor of one term. This permits us to add a fourth node in the next step.

$$\begin{bmatrix} 1 & 0 & D + BC'E' & A \\ 0 & 1 & D' + AB'C' & A' \\ D + BC'E' & D' + AB'C' & 1 & CE \\ A & A' & CE & 1 \end{bmatrix}$$

In adding a fifth node we take advantage of the C' which is present in both the 1,3 and the 2,3 entries and obtain the matrix

$$\begin{bmatrix} 1 & 0 & D & A & BE' \\ 0 & 1 & D' & A' & AB' \\ D & D' & 1 & CE & C' \\ A & A' & CE & 1 & 0 \\ BE' & AB' & C' & 0 & 1 \end{bmatrix}$$

In this matrix it is necessary to introduce a 0 entry between nodes 4 and 5 in order to prevent the formation of improper terms when the matrix is reduced.

This final matrix is not in the primitive form as defined by Hohn and Schissler. Further node addition, however, does not lead to any better result than the network of Fig. 8–24, which is described by the matrix shown.

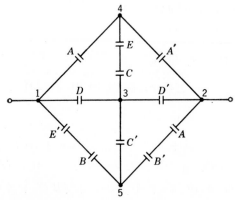

Fig. 8–24. Network synthesized in Example 8–10.

The matrix method operates without prejudice as to the form of a circuit, but the final result does depend upon the sequence of steps taken in obtaining a primitive connection matrix. The simple exercise in Example 8–11 is instructive.

Example 8–11

Synthesize a network to realize $S_1(A, B, C')$ using the matrix method. This symmetric function with mixed variables of symmetry is written

$$T = AB'C + A'BC + A'B'C'$$
$$= AB'C + A'(BC + B'C')$$

The output matrix is

$$\begin{bmatrix} 1 & AB'C + A'(BC + B'C') \\ AB'C + A'(BC + B'C') & 1 \end{bmatrix}$$

This augments to

$$\begin{bmatrix} 1 & AB'C & BC + B'C' \\ AB'C & 1 & A' \\ BC + B'C' & A' & 1 \end{bmatrix}$$

In the next step we use the relations

$$AB'C = 0 + (B')(AC) \quad \text{and} \quad BC + B'C' = (BC) + (B')(C')$$

and the matrix becomes

$$\begin{bmatrix} 1 & 0 & BC & B' \\ 0 & 1 & A' & AC \\ BC & A' & 1 & C' \\ B' & AC & C' & 1 \end{bmatrix}$$

In the next two matrices, first the BC entry and then the AC entry from the preceding matrix are broken down. Note the 0 entries which are used to prevent spurious product terms from being implied in previous entries.

$$\begin{bmatrix} 1 & 0 & 0 & B' & B \\ 0 & 1 & A' & AC & 0 \\ 0 & A' & 1 & C' & C \\ B' & AC & C' & 1 & 0 \\ B & 0 & C & 0 & 1 \end{bmatrix}$$

$$\begin{bmatrix} 1 & 0 & 0 & B' & B & 0 \\ 0 & 1 & A' & 0 & 0 & A \\ 0 & A' & 1 & C' & C & 0 \\ B' & 0 & C' & 1 & 0 & C \\ B & 0 & C & 0 & 1 & 0 \\ 0 & A & 0 & C & 0 & 1 \end{bmatrix}$$

The final matrix was developed entirely from the algebraic description, and with no preconceived idea of the structure except that the internode connections should be single literals, when not 0 or 1. The circuit in Fig. 8–25 shows the result. It is a valid circuit and it realizes the trans-mission function, but the distribution of variables and the renumbering of the nodes is hardly conventional. These were fixed by the particular series of steps we chose to take.

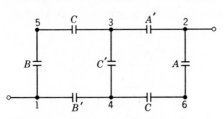

Fig. 8–25. Symmetric circuit derived by the matrix method.

Suppose now we remove the $A'B'C'$ term in the function, which is equivalent to remov-ing the C' contact between nodes 3 and 4. Writing the function $T = C(AB' + A'B)$ we can augment the output matrix by the steps shown.

$$\begin{bmatrix} 1 & C(AB' + A'B) \\ C(AB' + A'B) & 1 \end{bmatrix} \quad \begin{bmatrix} 1 & 0 & C \\ 0 & 1 & AB' + A'B \\ C & AB' + A'B & 1 \end{bmatrix}$$

$$\begin{bmatrix} 1 & 0 & C & 0 \\ 0 & 1 & AB' & B \\ C & AB' & 1 & A' \\ 0 & B & A' & 1 \end{bmatrix} \quad \begin{bmatrix} 1 & 0 & C & 0 & 0 \\ 0 & 1 & 0 & B & A \\ C & 0 & 1 & A' & B' \\ 0 & B & A' & 1 & 0 \\ 0 & A & B' & 0 & 1 \end{bmatrix}$$

The primitive connection matrix represents the network of Fig. 8–26(a). We observe that the matrix method does not necessarily arrange contacts so that transfer contacts can be used, but it is more

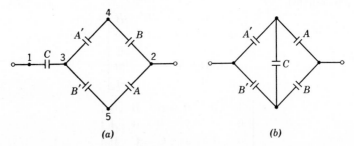

(a)   (b)

Fig. 8–26. Matrix synthesis is series-parallel, although there is an equally economical non-series-parallel form.

interesting to note that the non-series-parallel circuit of Fig. 8–26(b) is another realization. The synthesis gives no obvious clue to the existence of this form of the network. The student will find it instructive to reduce the primitive connection matrix for Fig. 8–26(b), and examine the steps required to obtain that matrix by augmentation.

8.4 Synthesis by Path Accumulation

The elusive character of the problem of designing non-series-parallel networks is especially evident in the process to be discussed in this article. Research efforts have done much to make the procedures systematic,* but we still find it difficult to discern a firm method within the process.

In this approach to synthesis the general idea is to realize a transmission function, expressed as a minimum sum, by building up a network term by term. At each step we try to add another term of the minimum sum, using as many existing contacts as possible. Before describing the procedure suggested by McCluskey, an example will illustrate some of the difficulties encountered.

Example 8–12

The transmission function $T = \sum(0, 1, 2, 3, 4, 7, 8, 13)$ is to be synthesized by path accumulation. A map of the function is given in Fig. 8–27. From the map the function can be written as the minimum sum

$$T = A'B' + A'C'D' + A'CD$$
$$+ B'C'D' + ABC'D$$

We note also that because the term $A'B'$ accounts for terms in the *standard* sum which are also accounted for by other terms in the *minimum* sum, we need not adhere strictly to the minimum sum in realizing the function. In the function

$$T = A'B' + A'(B)C'D'$$
$$+ A'(B)CD + (A)B'C'D' + ABC'D$$

the variables enclosed in parentheses may be represented by specific contacts in a tie path, or not, without changing the terminal action of the network. Our purpose here is to determine and specify what latitude of design is available. Usually this determination is made only when there is need for it. In this example we do it at the outset for increased awareness.

We observe in the minimum-sum form of the transmission function that the literals A and B appear in only one term, namely, $ABC'D$. This particular term must be present in full as a tie set and there is

	AB			
CD	00	01	11	10
00	1	1		1
01	1		1	
11	1	1		
10	1			

Fig. 8–27. Map of a function to be synthesized by path accumulation.

* McCluskey. See Reference in Art. 5.5.

no alternative form. There is no compelling reason for the selection of any particular one of the remaining terms of the minimum sum to combine with the $ABC'D$ term. In Fig. 8–28(a) we have chosen to add the path represented by the term $B'C'D'$.

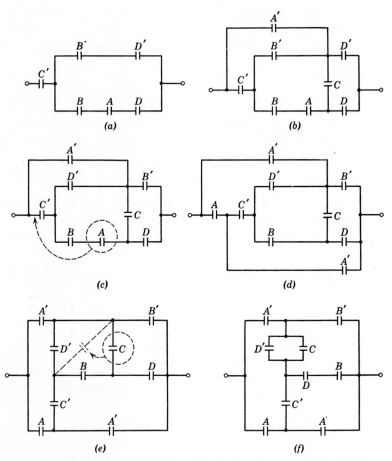

Fig. 8–28. Successive steps in the realization of the switching function of Example 8–12 by path accumulation.

Since there is a C' contact in series with the remainder of the network, we know from the absorption method that we can connect a C contact across any pair of points in the network of Fig. 8–28(a) without changing the transmission between external terminals. In Fig. 8–28(b) a C contact is added, and then in an attempt to establish the path represented by the term $A'CD$, an A' contact also is added. Unfortunately, the addition of the A' contact establishes the path $A'D'$ which is not a term of the transmission function. However, the term $A'B'$ is in the transmission function, and a simple interchange of the B' and D' contacts produces the network of Fig. 8–28(c) in which we have added not only the term $A'CD$ but also the term $A'B'$.

At this point the last path to be added to the network is that represented by the term $A'C'D'$. We observe that beginning at the left-hand terminal there is a path which proceeds through contacts A', D', and C' and returns to the left-hand terminal. Also, we note that there is an A contact (encircled in Fig. 8–28(c)) which might be moved to the position shown by the dotted arrow. If the A contact is moved, the term $ABC'D$ is not changed, but the term $B'C'D'$ becomes $AB'C'D'$. However, the modified expression for the transmission function found at the beginning of this example shows that the term $AB'C'D'$ may be substituted for the term $B'C'D'$ without changing the transmission. After the A contact is thus moved, it becomes possible to insert a duplicate A' contact as shown in Fig. 8–28(d), to realize the final term $A'C'D'$.

We now redraw the circuit diagram as in Fig. 8–28(e), and there we observe that only one pair of contacts can be combined into a transfer contact. However, if instead of providing a path for the term $A'CD$, we provide instead a path for the equally acceptable substitute term $A'BCD$, it becomes possible to shift the C contact to the position indicated by dotted lines in Fig. 8–28(e). After this is done, the B and D contacts may be interchanged, and, as we see in the circuit of Fig. 8–28(f), we are able to combine four complementary pairs of contacts into transfer contacts and have left only one A' contact which is not so combined. The final network realizes the required function with 9 contacts and 14 springs.

After a network such as that of Fig. 8–28(f) has been designed, it is a relatively simple matter to determine whether the paths were combined in the most expeditious order. At the beginning of this example we tried to find some rational basis for starting the synthesis, and this led us to the point represented by Fig. 8–28(a). However, in Fig. 8–29 it appears that if the paths to be accumulated are chosen in a different order, the network can be synthesized in fewer steps. In Fig. 8–29(a) the terms $A'B'$ and $(A)B'C'D'$ are first combined. In part (b) of Fig. 8–29 the term $ABC'D$ is added. The term $A'(B)CD$ is added in Fig. 8–29(c) and the term $A'C'D'$ in Fig. 8–29(d). It may readily be verified that the last figure is identical to Fig. 8–28(f).

It is apparent from the preceding example that this synthesis procedure is one that requires skill in circuit manipulation, and alertness

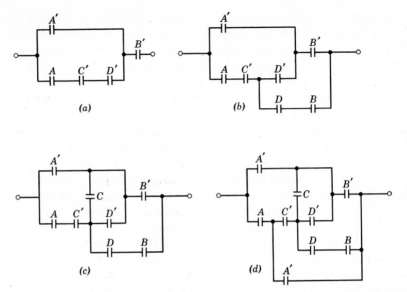

Fig. 8–29. The network of Fig. 8–28 is derived in fewer steps by accumulating paths in a different order.

in the advantageous use of redundancy, rather than the mere elimination of redundant items. In Example 8–12 we were concerned only with redundant literals, but we shall see in Example 8–13 that we may find redundant terms useful.

The remainder of this article deals with some of the work of McCluskey in synthesis by path accumulation. He provides a procedure which within each step is systematic, or at least can be made so. Hence, a synthesis need not necessarily be subject to the skill of the designer, but it usually can be helped by such skill.

McCluskey does not assume a form for the network. He starts with the transmission function written as a minimum sum. The terms of the sum are designated as M_i, and the function as $\sum M_i$. We know that in forming $\sum M_i$ all possible eliminations of literals have been made. Hence any literal in $\sum M_i$ must appear as a contact designator in any network which represents $\sum M_i$. We shall therefore call all literals in $\sum M_i$ *essential literals*. All other literals are non-essential.

A network in which each essential literal appears as the designator of one and only one contact, and no other literals appear, is an optimum network. Usually we cannot form optimum networks. The extra contacts in networks represent either repetition of an essential literal or the appearance of non-essential literals. The simple function $T = D'C + A(B + C)$ is represented by the networks in Fig. 8–30. If the function is synthesized as in network (a) it becomes necessary to use a repeated contact for the variable C. When we avoid the repetition of the C contact, it becomes necessary to introduce the non-essential B' contact in network (b).

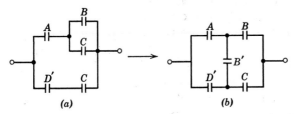

(a)   (b)

Fig. 8–30. A repeated contact in (a) is replaced by a non-essential contact in (b).

The first step in a synthesis by path accumulation is to form a network with a transmission given by the sum of two of the terms of $\sum M_i$. Such a network can always be realized without either contact repetition or the addition of non-essential contacts. This is true because all literals common to the two terms can be factored, and after all common literals have been factored the remaining variables can have no repetitions. We cannot say with certainty which two terms of the minimum sum should be used as the starting point. We can be guided somewhat by the fact that our general procedure will be to try to provide contacts in a partially developed network that can be used in additional desired paths.

The next step is to form a desired contact path between a pair of nodes of the partial network. This is illustrated in Fig. 8–31 which shows the

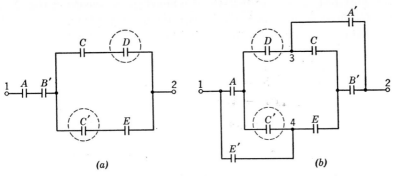

(a)   (b)

Fig. 8–31. Network rearranged to form a contact path.

steps in the synthesis of the function $T = AB'(CD + C'E) + A'C'DE'$. Figure 8–31(a) is a network which represents two terms of the minimum sum expressed in factored form. The contacts C' and D in this network are encircled because we want to use these contacts in a path that will enable us to add the term $A'C'DE'$. It may be necessary to rearrange the partial network to form a desired contact path, but the contact path is an essential requirement of the method. In Fig. 8–31(b) the desired contact path has been formed by rearrangement and the final term of the function to be synthesized is realized by adding the A' and E' contacts shown. It may be verified that this network contains no paths other than those specified by the minimum sum.

There are two ways to add a path which makes additional use of contacts within the partial network, as can be seen in the two parts of Fig. 8–32. In each of these we assume there is a desired contact path

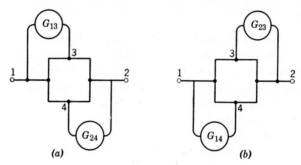

Fig. 8–32. A path can be added in two ways.

between nodes 3 and 4 of the network. Considering Fig. 8–32(a), we then want to add contacts between nodes 1 and 3 and between nodes 2 and 4, as indicated by the transmissions G_{13} and G_{24}, respectively. We must test to be sure that the combined transmissions of G_{13}, T_{34}, and G_{24} in series represents the term of the minimum sum to be added. Furthermore, we must be sure that the combination of the transmissions G_{13} and T_{32} in series, and the combination of G_{24} and T_{14} in series, do not introduce false transmission terms between the terminals 1 and 2.

These requirements have been summarized by McCluskey as follows:

(8–1) $G_{13}G_{24}T_{34} = M_i(aT)$ $G_{14}G_{23}T_{34} = M_i(aT)$

(8–2) $G_{13}T_{23} = 0 \ (aT)$ $G_{14}T_{24} = 0(aT)$

(8–3) $G_{24}T_{14} = 0(aT)$ $G_{23}T_{13} = 0(aT)$

The symbol (aT) is to be read "add T." In equation 8–1 it signifies that the product of the two G terms and T_{34} must contain the minimum sum term M_i, but it may also contain any additional term which is present in the standard sum of the transmission function T from which the M_i are derived. Likewise, the "anti-sneak" provisions represented by equations 8–2 and 8–3 mean that if the indicated products are not 0 then they must represent terms of the transmission function being realized.

In the network of Fig. 8–31(b), before the external contacts are added we find $T_{34} = C'D + CE$, $T_{24} = B'E$, $T_{13} = AD$. The added contacts represent $G_{14} = E'$, and $G_{23} = A'$. When these values are substituted in the appropriate set of equations 8–1, 8–2, and 8–3 we find

$$G_{14}G_{23}T_{34} = E'A'(C'D + CE) = A'C'DE' = M_i$$

$$G_{14}T_{24} = E' \cdot B'E = 0$$

$$G_{23}T_{13} = A' \cdot AD = 0$$

We will find it convenient at times to discuss what added contacts are required before deciding to which terminals they should be connected. For this purpose we will use the term "GG product." The importance of the (aT) provision is well brought out in the next example.

Example 8–13

The function $\sum(1, 3, 7, 15, 17, 19, 20, 21, 22, 23)$ reduces to the minimum sum

$$T = B'C'E + AB'C + A'CDE$$

We note that the first two terms contain the literals E and C, respectively, which both appear in the third term. We hence form the contact network shown in Fig. 8–33(a) and add a path for the third term as in Fig. 8–33(b).

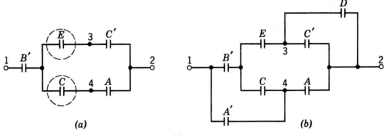

(a)   (b)

Fig. 8–33. The added path introduces an allowed "sneak" path.

For this circuit we have

$$G_{14}G_{23}T_{34} = A'D(EC + AC') = A'CDE = M_i$$

$$G_{14}T_{24} = A' \cdot A = 0$$

$$G_{23}T_{13} = D \cdot B'E$$

The term $B'DE$ when written in binary form is $-0{-}11$, and this corresponds to the decimal numbers 3, 7, 19, 23. Since these terms are all present in the standard sum, it is clear that the term $B'DE$ is an implicant of the function, but is not required in the minimum sum. This type of "sneak" path may, of course, be allowed. It is one of the reasons for the (aT) qualification of equations 8–1, 8–2, and 8–3.

Generally we make use of desired contacts in a path between interior nodes 3 and 4 as illustrated in Fig. 8–32. This need not necessarily be so, as can be seen in the next example.

Example 8–14

The transmission to be realized is

$$T = A'CD' + AB'C + BC'D'$$

In Fig. 8–34 the terms $A'CD'$ and $AB'C$ form the partial network, and the circled D' contact which is to be used in forming an added path

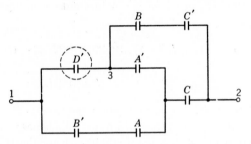

Fig. 8–34. Modified procedure when a contact in a desired path is connected to an output terminal.

is between the terminal 1 and node 3. The transmission between node 3 and terminal 1 is simply D' and the contacts added between terminal 2 and node 3 give us

$$G_{23}T_{31} = BC'D'$$

It is always possible to add to a partial network a path corresponding to another term in the minimum sum, but it may be necessary to use repeated contacts or non-essential contacts in doing so.

Example 8–15

For the transmission function

$$T = ABDE' + AB'D'E' + A'B'C'DE$$

a partial network is formed as in Fig. 8–35, using the first two terms of the minimum sum. For this network we have, before adding any external contacts,

$$T_{34} = BD' + B'D$$

$$T_{13} = AB; \quad T_{14} = AD'$$

$$T_{23} = DE'; \quad T_{24} = B'E'$$

In order to add the third term, the GG product must contain $A'C'E$, and either B' or D must be repeated in order to remove the term BD' which is present in T_{34}. We can either place B' in G_{23} or place D

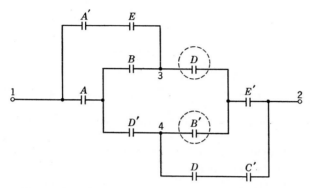

Fig. 8–35. The added path contains a repeated D contact to avoid false transmission.

in G_{24}. In Fig. 8–35 we have chosen to place D in G_{24}. With a D contact in G_{24}, it becomes necessary to place the E contact in G_{13} so that the product $G_{13}T_{23}$ goes to 0. The location of the A' and C' contacts is not critical.

It is not always possible to avoid introducing a "sneak" path by the use of repeated contacts or non-essential contacts. McCluskey has proven, however, that it is always possible either to avoid introducing the "sneak" path or to convert it to an allowable path. The proof requires an exhaustive examination of all possible situations and will not be given here. Example 8–16 illustrates the conversion of a spurious transmission term to an allowable one.

Example 8–16

The transmission function to be realized is

$$T = AC'D'E + AB'C'E + AB'CD + B'CD'E'$$

In Fig. 8–36 a partial network is formed using the terms $B'CD'E'$ and $AB'CD$. The contacts are arranged so that between nodes 3 and 4 we have a desired path AD' to use in forming the term $AC'D'E$. We find $T_{34} = AD' + DE'$, so the GG product is $C'E$. $T_{23} = CE'$, so we set $G_{13} = C'$. If $G_{24} = E$, we then have the product $G_{24}T_{14} = AB'E$, which is not allowed by the transmission function. However, by in-

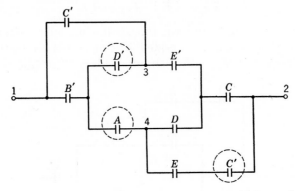

Fig. 8–36. The encircled C' contact converts a false term to an allowed term.

serting the repeated C' contact as shown in Fig. 8–36 this product becomes $AB'C'E$ and this is the remaining term required in the transmission function.

In a complex synthesis we may eventually reach the condition illustrated diagrammatically in Fig. 8–37. A number of paths have been

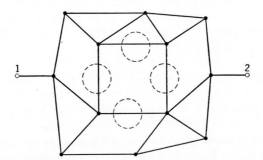

Fig. 8–37. Generalization of the problem of path accumulation.

accumulated and another is to be added. We find that the desired contacts to be used in the new path are connected in a loop as indicated in the diagram. This situation occurred in the synthesis shown in Fig. 8–28 where at the step represented by part (c) the desired contacts were found to be in a loop. The loop was opened by changing the position of an A contact. McCluskey discusses the mathematical treatment of this general problem. Figure 8–38 shows the steps in a synthesis by McCluskey in which the contacts of a desired path were arranged in a loop.

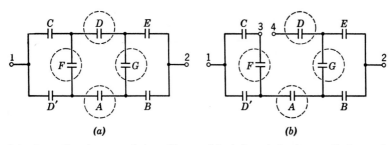

(a)   (b)

(a) A path of transmission $T =$ $AB'C'DE'FG$ is to be added to this network.

(b) A loop is broken so that a path containing the desired contacts exists between nodes 3 and 4.

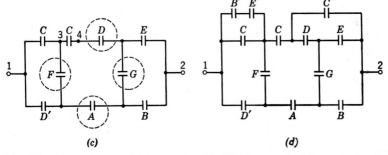

(c)   (d)

(c) When loop is reclosed by a C contact, correct transmission is restored between nodes 1 and 2.

(d) Final network with required path added.

Fig. 8–38. A more difficult example of path accumulation.

In the preceding discussion no special definition was given to inter-node transmissions of the type T_{ij} which are used in equations 8–1, 8–2, and 8–3. We may express the total transmission between a pair of nodes in terms of the transmission of the actual contacts connected between these nodes. Thus,

$$T_{34} = t_{34} + t_{13}t_{14} + t_{23}t_{24} + t_{23}t_{12}t_{14} + t_{13}t_{12}t_{24}$$

McCluskey shows that if equations 8–1, 8–2, and 8–3 are satisfied, then $T_{34} = t_{34}$. Similar proofs hold for T_{13}, T_{14}, etc. In general, these total transmissions may be replaced in equations 8–1, 8–2, and 8–3 by the transmissions of those paths between the designated nodes i and j which do not touch any other numbered node. In the relatively simple networks we have dealt with little is saved by the use of these special definitions, but in a complex synthesis the work is materially reduced.

8.5 Special Situations

There are a number of functions which fall into no particular category but which can be recognized as types which are frequently best synthesized by non-series-parallel networks. Among these we have:

(1) Functions which contain as factors one or more terms and their complements.

(2) Combinations of symmetric functions. By this we mean that parts of the given function are each symmetric functions but are not functions of the same variables.

(3) Incomplete symmetric functions. That is, these functions would be symmetric if one or more missing terms were added.

For functions in any of these categories it is well to look for non-series-parallel circuits but we cannot be sure that such realizations will be optimum. The examples which follow treat functions for which the non-series-parallel realization is advantageous.

Example 8–17

The transmission function

$$T = A'B'E + A'C'E + A'D'E + ABCD + BCDE'$$

may be factored to the form

$$T = A'E(B' + C' + D') + (A + E')BCD$$

The complementary relations between the factors of this function are quite obvious and suggest a synthesis of the pattern shown in Fig. 8–39.

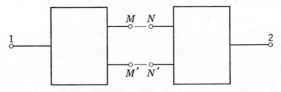

Fig. 8–39. A synthesis for functions containing products of complementary functions.

Since both component networks must be disjunctive at their output terminals, they may be connected terminal to terminal in the manner indicated, with no possibility of forming "sneak" paths. Figure 8–40 shows the contact network for the function synthesized in this way. Since every literal of the function appears as a designator of one and only one contact this network is in optimum form.

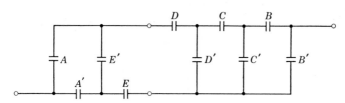

Fig. 8–40. An optimum network for the function of Example 8–17.

Example 8–18

Combinations of symmetric functions are frequently recognizable. For the function of this example such recognition is advantageous but this is not always true.

The function

$$T = A'B' + A'C + B'C + ABC'$$

is shown in the map of Fig. 8–41.

From the map we readily find that this function is represented by the sum of two symmetric functions, namely, $T = S_2(A, B, C) + S_{0,1}(A, B, C')$.

In Fig. 8–42 network (a) represents the symmetric $S_2(A, B, C)$ and network (b) represents the symmetric $S_{0,1}(A, B, C')$. In network (b) we observe that if the branch containing the contact C is swung upward to a vertical position,

	\multicolumn{4}{c}{AB}
C	OO	OI	II	IO
O	I			I
I	I	I		I

Fig. 8–41. Map of function containing two symmetric functions.

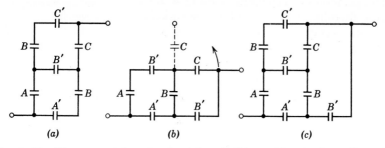

(a)   **(b)**   **(c)**

Fig. 8–42. The symmetric networks (a) and (b) combine to form the network (c).

then all contacts of network (b), except the B' contact in the lower level, are duplicated by contacts in network (a). These may be superposed to yield the network shown in Fig. 8–42(c).

This function can also be treated by writing it in the form

$$T = A'B' + C(AB)' + C'(AB)$$

Here we have a situation similar to that of the preceding example, except for the extraneous term $A'B'$, and the realization given in

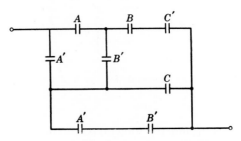

Fig. 8–43.   Another realization of the function mapped in Fig. 8–41.

Fig. 8–43 shows the network represented. Although this network contains the same number of contacts as that found in Fig. 8–42(c), the form based on the recognition of symmetric functions uses fewer springs because all its contacts are contained in transfer combinations.

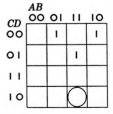

Fig. 8–44. Map of an incomplete symmetric function.

Example 8–19

An incomplete symmetric function is mapped in Fig. 8–44. If the cell which contains the circle contained a 1 entry we would have mapped the symmetric function $S_3(A, B, C', D')$. The term $ABCD'$, however, is missing. In Fig. 8–45(a) we have literally drawn a contact network for the complete symmetric function, and then accounted for the missing path by removing one C contact. After this is done, it becomes possible to bring a C' contact outside and draw the network diagram as in Fig. 8–45(b).

The transmission function represented by the map of Fig. 8–44 is

$$T = C'(AB'D' + A'BD' + ABD)$$

It is interesting to synthesize this function by using the path accumulation procedure of the preceding article. Figure 8–46 shows a network thus designed. This network and that of Fig. 8–45(b) contain the same number of contacts. However, the network based on a recognition of symmetry has all possible complementary literals combined into transfer contacts, and hence uses 13 springs instead of the 15 springs

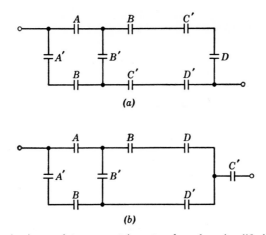

(a)

(b)

Fig. 8–45. An incomplete symmetric network and a simplified form of it.

used in the network of Fig. 8–46 where only one transfer combination is present.

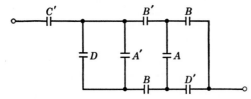

Fig. 8–46. The incomplete symmetric synthesized by path accumulation.

PROBLEMS

8.1 Reduce the given contact network to a minimum form by the synthesis of a new network (10 springs are sufficient).

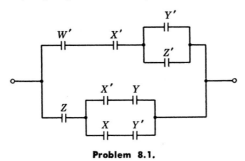

Problem 8.1.

8.2 A disjunctive-tree synthesis leads to the circuit given. Find the circuit derived by expansion about the variables w and y.

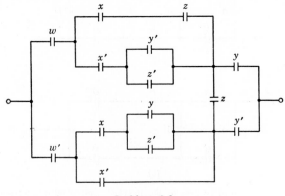

Problem 8.2.

8.3 For the contact network shown
1. Write the transmission function in minimal factored form. If more than one minimal form exists, write all such expressions.
2. Design a simpler contact network which has the same transmission as the original network.

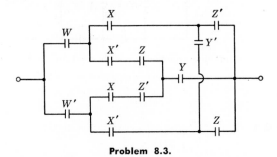

Problem 8.3.

8.4 Design a minimum contact network having the transmission described by the map shown. (A network can be built with 10 contacts and 16 springs. Another network with 9 contacts uses 17 springs.)

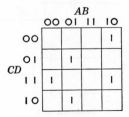

Problem 8.4.

8.5 Design minimized contact networks for the following transmission functions. The indicated numbers of contacts and springs are sufficient but not necessarily the minimums ("c" = contact, "s" = spring).

1. $T = \sum (0, 3, 5, 14)$ 10c/15s
2. $T = \sum (0, 1, 2, 5, 14)$ 8c/13s
3. $T = \sum (0, 2, 7, 8, 10, 12, 13, 15)$ 7c/11s
4. $T = \sum (0, 1, 2, 5, 6, 11, 13)$ 9c/15s
5. $T = \sum (0, 2, 8, 13, 14, 15)$ 8c/12s
6. $T = \sum (0, 1, 4, 6, 7, 8, 9, 10, 11, 12, 13, 15)$ 8c/12s
7. $T = \sum (4, 5, 20, 21, 23, 25, 29, 31)$ 6c/11s
8. $T = \sum (0, 2, 3, 6, 7, 8, 9, 13, 16, 17, 20, 22, 24, 25, 27)$ 14c/24s
9. $T = \sum (0, 1, 2, 5, 6, 7, 8, 10, 12, 13, 14, 15, 41, 57)$ 14c/25s

8.6 Synthesize a network to realize the transmission function described by the standard product

$$T = \Pi(1, 3, 4, 5, 6, 7, 9, 10, 11, 12, 17, 19, 20, 21, 22, 23, 25, 26, 27, 28).$$

A non-series-parallel solution exists, with 8 contacts and 12 springs.

8.7 Synthesize by the method of path accumulation a network to realize the transmission function

$$T = ABC + ABDE + ACE' + B'CDE' + A'B'C'$$

(9 contacts, 17 springs are sufficient).

8.8 Three independent switching circuits each contain two relays and a contact network built on their own relays. The transmission functions of the circuits are:

$$T_1 = A' + B; \qquad T_2 = PQ'; \qquad T_3 = YZ + Y'Z'$$

The circuits are interconnected so that the output T_1 becomes the "Y" input of the No. 3 circuit, and the output T_2 becomes the "Z" input.

1. Determine the transmission function T_3 in terms of the variables A, B, P, Q.
2. Express this function in both standard sum and standard product form.
3. Draw a map which shows the transmission represented by the standard sum.
4. Design a new contact network which has the same transmission but which uses only the relays $A, B, P,$ and Q (4 transfer contacts are sufficient.)

8.9 Redesign or modify the circuit shown so that X and Y maintain their original functional dependence on $a, b, c, d, e,$ and f, and so that no rectifiers are used. You are to keep the number of springs to a minimum.

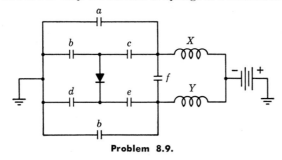

Problem 8.9.

8.10   Design a contact network having the transmission function

$$T = CD(A'B' + AB) + A'B'C + ABC' + B'DXY + B'C'XY$$

(One network requires 9 contacts and 18 springs.   Another network uses 10 contacts and 17 springs.)

8.11   Use the disjunctive-tree method to design a minimum contact network for each of the transmission functions described.

1. $T = \sum (0, 5, 10, 12, 15)$;   2. $T = \sum (1, 6, 8, 13)$

8.12   Repeat Problem 8.11 using the absorption method.

8.13   Repeat Problem 8.11 using Boolean matrices.

8.14   Repeat Problem 8.11 using the method of path accumulation.

8.15   Design a multi-terminal contact network to realize the transmission functions

$$T_1 = W + X + Y + Z; \qquad T_2 = W' + X + Y'Z'$$

(7 contacts, 11 springs are sufficient.)

CHAPTER 9

Electronic and solid state devices in combinational switching circuits

The theory of switching circuits was first developed as a means of expressing mathematically the operating characteristics of circuits containing contacts, and as a means of improving the synthesis of such circuits. Since then other types of devices have been found to exhibit switching properties, that is, they have modes of operation which can be described as binary. Among these, vacuum and gas tubes, rectifiers, transistors, and magnetic cores have found important applications. Most of these devices are capable of switching operations at much higher speeds than relays and some are considerably more reliable and more durable.

Although we can describe certain modes of operation of these devices as binary, their application in switching circuits is not one of simple substitution for relay contacts. We must adapt and specialize the algebraic treatment to achieve the synthesis of circuits using these newer elements. Many of the more modern devices have become especially important in the design of sequential switching circuits. In this chapter we shall study their combinational aspects in preparation for their application to sequential circuits.

A special Bibliography is included at the end of this chapter. It is not intended to be a complete Bibliography, but it does contain a selection of items which are pertinent to the subject and a number of them contain additional references. The work of this chapter should be considered as a background for more extensive reading of current literature.

9.1   Gate Elements in Network Synthesis

In contrast with contact networks in which we can readily perceive paths that conduct current, most of the circuits we will consider in this chapter operate by controlling the levels of electrical potential. The block diagram of a combinational switching circuit shown in Fig. 9–1

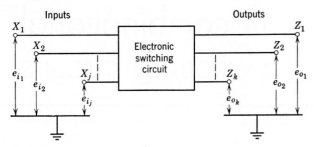

Fig. 9–1. Switching variables are represented by voltages at inputs and outputs.

is a reminder to us that we do not consider "paths" existing between inputs and outputs. This was not even true for relay switching circuits. As we can see in Fig. 9–1 both the input and output variables are defined as electric potentials relative to some datum.

We first examine the problem of synthesis using logical gates, or simply *gates*. A gate is a switching device which operates on one or more input variables, and which delivers an output bearing a prescribed functional relation to the input or inputs. It is convenient to describe three types of gates, corresponding to the Boolean operations of addition, multiplication, and complementation. Symbolic representations of these gates are shown in Fig. 9–2, where they are identified as Add, Multiply, and Complement gates. These are the gates which commonly are called "or," "and," and "not" gates, respectively, in much of the literature of switching circuits. We have already seen that, given a set of Boolean variables, a switching function can be formed from these variables by the use of the operations of addition, multiplication, and complementation. Hence, if we have a set of Boolean variables represented by voltages, and gates which are capable

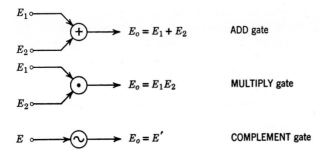

Fig. 9-2. Symbolic representation of gates which perform three basic Boolean operations.

of carrying out on those voltages operations corresponding to addition, multiplication, and complementation, we can realize any switching function of the variables we care to write. Actually, as is demonstrated in Fig. 9–3, we can realize any function if we have only the Complement

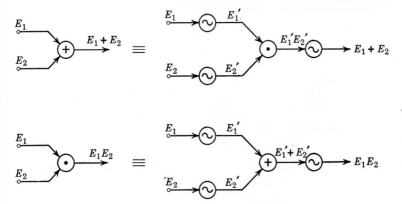

Fig. 9-3. Only two of the three gates shown in Fig. 9-2 are basically needed.

gate and either the Add gate or the Multiply gate, since either of the latter gates can be converted to the other by inserting Complement gates in all input and output connections.

Example 9-1

Synthesize a switching circuit using the gates of Fig. 9–2 to realize the function

$$T = A(BC + D) + A'D'(B' + C')$$

Determine how many additional Complement gates would be required to realize the function

(a) using only Multiply and Complement gates

(b) using only Add and Complement gates.

We observe that the function contains the term $(BC + D)$ and its complement $D'(B' + C')$. The function is hence of the form

$$T = AQ + A'Q' = (A + Q')(A' + Q)$$

where $Q = BC + D$.

In Fig. 9–4(a) the function is realized in the form $AQ + A'Q'$, and in Fig. 9–4(b) the form $(A + Q')(A' + Q)$ is realized. In both cir-

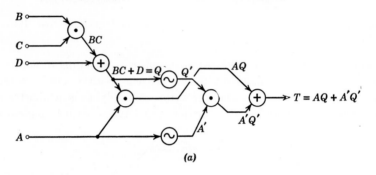

(a)

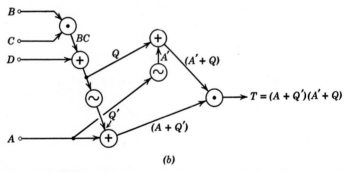

(b)

Fig. 9–4. Two realizations of the function of Example 9–1 using the basic gates.

cuits two Complement gates are required, and five Add and Multiply gates. We observe also in these circuits that a voltage which represents a given variable may be used as the input to more than one gate. The voltage representing $BC + D$ and the voltage representing A are thus used. In both circuits the A variable becomes the input of a Complement gate, to produce A'. If one of the circuits of Fig. 9–4 is the only circuit to use the variable A', it is then properly charged with the cost of the Complement gate required. More frequently, however, this circuit will be part of a larger system in which it shares the need for complemented input variables. It is common, therefore, to assume that all input variables *and their complements* are available. We hence would count a total of only six gates in each of the circuits of Fig. 9–4.

In determining the number of additional Complement gates required if only Multiply gates or only Add gates are used, it will be instructive to retain in the count the gates required to produce A' in Fig. 9–4.

(a) If only Multiply and Complement gates are to be used, it will be necessary to convert two Add gates in Fig. 9–4(a) and this will require a total of six additional Complement gates. However, we see in Fig. 9–5 that when the Add gate which produces $(D + BC)$ is

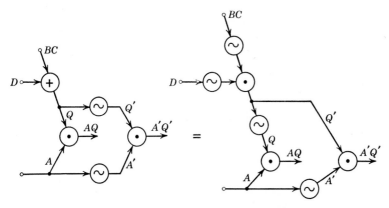

Fig. 9–5. Replacement of an Add gate by a Multiply gate.

converted, the Complement gate in its output is required only for the production of Q, and the Complement gate formerly required to produce Q' is no longer needed. Effectively, so far as the realization of Q' is concerned, two Complement gates in series eliminate the need for any gate. The net requirement then is for five additional gates.

In Fig. 9–4(b) there are three Add gates, which would require nine Complement gates for conversion. These are shown in Fig. 9–6(a) in which dotted lines enclose the combinations of Multiply and Complement gates which replace each Add gate. In Fig. 9–6(b), however, we see that five Complement gates can be eliminated, so the conversion requires a net of four additional gates.

(b) It will be left as an exercise for the student to verify that if the function is to be realized using only Add and Complement gates, the circuit of Fig. 9–4(a) requires seven additional Complement gates, whereas the circuit of Fig. 9–4(b) requires six additional gates.

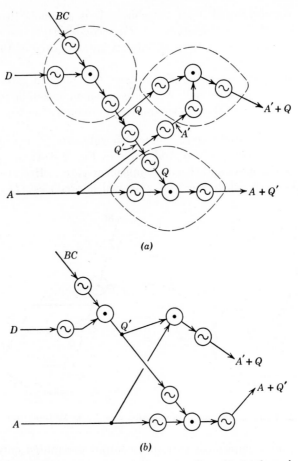

Fig. 9–6. Complement gates are combined to reduce the total number required.

The gate concept as we have so far developed it is roughly analogous to the series-parallel concept in relay contact networks. Both forms of synthesis depend solely on the operations of addition, multiplication, and complementation. However, relay contacts can conduct in either direction and this makes it possible to synthesize non-series-parallel networks. The action of a gate is not reversible and the concept of non-series-parallel synthesis using gates is meaningless. On the other hand, a potential which represents a given variable, or a term, can be used as an input to more than one gate, with the restriction that the voltage source concerned must be adequate to supply all the loads imposed upon it. Our freedom to use a voltage as more than one input is not subject to the hazard of setting up a "sneak" path such as we encountered in contact networks.

The restriction noted regarding the amount of load that may be placed upon the output of a given gate is typical of the precautions which must be taken in the actual design of gate switching circuits. We can readily design a wide variety of gate circuits using only the logical symbols, but we must keep in mind that these logical symbols do not prevail over engineering limitations.

9.2 Analysis of Gate Circuits

At this point we will confine our attention to circuits in which switching variables are represented by voltage or current *levels* rather than by voltage or current pulses. Specifically, we will consider only voltage levels. The question then is: what level of voltage represents a 1 and what level represents a 0? From the logical viewpoint any two different voltage levels may be chosen, but the engineering viewpoint also becomes important. The two levels must be sufficiently different that they are not ambiguous in their effects. For example, as the grid inputs to vacuum tubes, one level is commonly chosen as that which permits saturation current in the plate circuit, and the other level is that which causes cut off of plate current.

In deciding which level is to represent a 1 and which a 0, the convention usually adopted is that the higher voltage in the positive direction of polarity represents a 1. Note that this does not mean that 1 must be represented by a positive voltage level—it must merely be more positive than the level which represents 0. Thus we may have 0 volts representing a 1, with perhaps -20 volts representing a 0. We shall speak of the 1 as represented by the *high* level and the 0 as represented by the *low* level.

Compared to other forms of electronic switching circuits, those which are shown schematically in terms of the three basic gates are in general not difficult to analyze. Consider the circuit shown in Fig. 9–7, where the input variables are given and the types of gates are indicated. The output of gate number 1 is BC'. This is added to D' in gate 2 and in gate 3 we multiply $D' + BC'$ by A, giving $A(BC' + D')$ as one input to gate 8. In gate 4 we form the product $A'B$ and in gate 5 the product CD. These terms are added in gate 6 and the sum is multiplied by E in gate 7 to produce $E(A'B + CD)$ as a second input to gate 8. The final output is then

$$T = A(BC' + D') + E(A'B + CD)$$

If we had written this expression as the transmission function of a relay contact network, we would readily recognize the terms ABC', AD', $A'BE$, and CDE as the tie sets of the function. In the gate circuit these sets represent input voltages which, when high, cause the output to be high. Thus, tracing back through the circuit of Fig. 9–7, we see that the output will be high if either input of gate 8

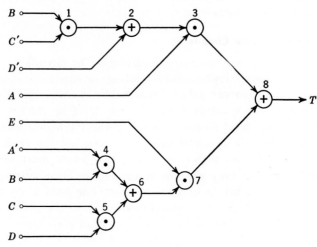

Fig. 9–7. A gate circuit to be analyzed.

is high. If we continue back along the upper branch, we see that both inputs of gate number 3 must be high, and hence the input A must be high. The output of gate 2 must be high and this requires either of its inputs to be high. If D' is high, the condition is satisfied, so AD' is one set of input variables which when high causes the output to be high, regardless of the condition of the other input variables. The other input of gate 2 is high if both B and C' are high. Hence, ABC' is another set of input variables which independently can cause the output to be high, regardless of the state of the remaining variables. A similar analysis made by tracing back along the lower branch discloses that the terms $A'BE$ and CDE have the same properties.

The analogy to the tie sets and cut sets of relay contact networks will be complete when we find minimum sets of input variables which when low cause the output to be low regardless of the condition of the remaining variables. It is desirable also to have better names for these sets than tie sets and cut sets. For switching circuits in which the variables are represented by voltage levels, Huffman* has suggested that we replace the names tie set and cut set by *lift set* and *drop set*, respectively. Thus, when in Fig. 9–7 we seek an analogue of the cut sets of a contact network, we look for minimum sets of input variables which when low (dropped) ensure that the output will be low and these we will call the drop sets. The sets ABC', AD', $A'BE$, and CDE, found in the preceding analysis, are the lift sets of the circuit.

To find the drop sets in Fig. 9–7, we observe first that in order to have a low output voltage, both inputs to gate **8** must be low. These inputs are the outputs of gates **3** and **7**. For both the latter gates the output is low if either input is low. Hence we can readily recognize $(A + E)$ as a drop set since A is an input to gate **3** and E is an input to gate **7**. If E is high and A is low, we can still get a low output from gate **7** if both inputs of gate **6** are low. Considering gate **4**, we see that since A' is high, B must be low. From gate **5** we get a low output if either C or D is low. Hence, we have the two additional drop sets $(A + B + C)$ and $(A + B + D)$. By similar reasoning, we find that with A high, $(B + D' + E)$ and $(C' + D' + E)$ are drop sets. If both A and E are high, the output will be low for the set $(B + C + D')$. In terms of the drop sets, we can therefore write the transmission

$$T = (A + E)(A + B + C)(A + B + D)(B + D' + E)$$
$$(C' + D' + E)(B + C + D')$$

It is interesting to observe in this analysis that no drop set includes the variable A', or rather, the drop set $(A' + B + C + D')$ is contained in the drop set $(B + C + D')$. The circuit shown in Fig. 9–7 does not realize a minimum sum. Consequently, if the product of the drop sets is multiplied out, the lift sets thereby found will not be exactly the same as those found by direct analysis of Fig. 9–7.

Example 9–2

Determine the lift sets and the drop sets of the gate circuit of Fig. 9–8.

LIFT SETS. At gate **7**, both inputs must be high. The output of gate **5** is high if either input is high, and the output of gate **6** is high if any one of the three inputs is high. (Note that gate **6** is the first example we have seen of a basic gate with more than two inputs.) The output of gate **3** is high if W is high or if both Y and Z are

* D. A. Huffman, "The Design and Use of Hazard-Free Switching Networks," *Journal of the Association for Computing Machinery*, Vol. 4, January 1957, pp. 47–62

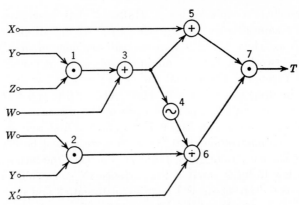

Fig. 9–8. Gate circuit of Example 9–2.

high. The output of gate 2 is high if W and Y are high. We note also that when the output of gate 3 is high, one input to gate 6 is low because a complement is formed at gate 4.

If W is high, the output of gate 3 is high, and hence the output of gate 5 is high. The output of gate 2, and hence of gate 6 will be high if Y also is high. Thus one lift set is WY. The output of gate 6 will be high if X' is high, so WX' is a lift set.

If Y and Z are high, the outputs of gates 3 and 5 are high, and with X' high the output of gate 6 is high. Hence $X'YZ$ is a lift set.

If X is high the output of gate 5 is high, and the X' input to gate 6 is low. If W and Y are also high the output of gate 2 is high, and hence the output of gate 6. The set WXY is not a lift set, however, because the lift set WY exists, so WXY is not a minimum set. The only lift sets containing X must therefore be associated with a low output of gate 3, which through the complementing action of gate 4 causes a high input to gate 6. Gate 3 has a low output when W' is high and either Y' or Z' is high. Hence there are two additional lift sets, $W'XY'$ and $W'XZ'$.

DROP SETS. To determine the drop sets, we observe that either input to gate 7 must be low, so we want to find minimum sets which produce low output at either gate 5 or gate 6.

For gate 5 to have a low output, X must be low, W must be low, and either Y or Z must be low. Hence two of the drop sets are $(W + X + Y)$ and $(W + X + Z)$.

For gate 6 to have a low output, three inputs must be low. The input X' must be low, at gate 2 either W or Y must be low, and the input to gate 4 must be high. The input to gate 4 is high if W is high (W' is low) or if Y and Z are high (Y' and Z' are low). Some of the combinations are incompatible. We cannot have W high at gate 3 and low at gate 2, nor Y high at gate 1 and low at gate 2. However, there is no harm in writing such drop sets since they vanish algebraically. The remaining drop sets are $(W' + X' + Y)$ and $(W + X' + Y' + Z')$.

From this determination of the lift sets and the drop sets, the transmission of the circuit in Fig. 9–8 may be written in either of two forms:

$$T = WY + WX' + X'YZ + W'XY' + W'XZ'$$

$$T = (W + X + Y)(W + X + Z)(W' + X' + Y)(W + X' + Y' + Z')$$

9.3 Rectifier and Resistor Gates

Various types of rectifiers have long been used in switching circuits. They are frequently inserted in relay contact networks to take advantage of their unilateral conduction properties to eliminate "sneak" circuits. This discussion, however, will be centered on the switching properties of the rectifier itself.

For use in switching circuits which have voltage levels at both the inputs and the outputs, it is possible to use any of the standard types of rectifiers. However, the selenium and the copper oxide types are rather bulky and, except in special circumstances, their ability to handle relatively high power is not needed. They have the disadvantage, if voltages change rapidly, as in pulse circuits, that the equivalent capacitance of the rectifier is also relatively high. For general switching purposes the germanium rectifier is more satisfactory. The silicon rectifier is attracting attention as a switching rectifier because it combines the small dimensions of the germanium rectifier with higher current-carrying capacity.

The switching properties of the rectifier are due to its voltage-current characteristic which is shown in Fig. 9–9. In the "forward" direction, the rectifier conducts a relatively large current with a relatively small voltage drop, and its forward resistance is low. In the

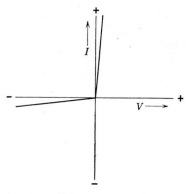

Fig. 9–9. Voltage-current characteristic of a rectifier.

"back" direction, the current conducted is relatively small and the voltage drop is large, so the back resistance is high. It is not difficult with rectifiers to get a ratio of back resistance to forward resistance of one thousand. Although these resistances, and the current and voltage ratings of the rectifier must be kept in mind in the actual design of a rectifier switching circuit,* for the purpose of logical design it is convenient to assume that the forward resistance is zero and the back resistance is infinite.

In rectifier gate circuits we are limited to the use of Add and Multiply gates, since no way has been found to form a complement by means of rectifiers alone. Hence all input variables and any of their complements which are needed must be available as input voltages.

Figure 9–10(a) shows the construction of a typical rectifier Multiply gate and Fig. 9–10(b) shows the construction of a typical rectifier

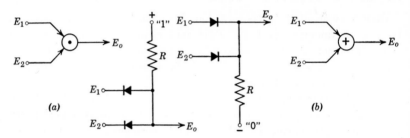

Fig. 9–10. Multiply and Add gates using rectifiers.

Add gate. In both these gates only two inputs are shown. Actually there may be a large numbers of inputs to either gate, with each new input requiring another rectifier. Two inputs are sufficient to discuss the switching properties of either gate. The Multiply gate is supplied by a source of positive voltage, representing the 1 state, through a resistor R. The rectifiers are oriented so that current can pass through the resistor R and then through any rectifier to the corresponding input terminal. Suitable provision must be made at the sources of input voltages to accept the current passing through the rectifier when the input is low. The resistor R is made large compared to the forward resistance of any rectifier. Since we are assuming that the forward resistance of the rectifier is small enough to be considered a zero resistance, if any input to the Multiply gate is low the output will, in effect, be connected directly to the low voltage and hence the output will be low. In order to have a high output voltage every input of the gate must be high. Since the only condition which produces a high output is that for which every input is high, the output represents the logical product of the inputs.

The gate of Fig. 9–10(b) has the input rectifiers reversed, so that current flows from the input sources to the resistor R and then to a

* See Reference 8 in the Bibliography at the end of this chapter.

negative voltage which represents the 0 state. For this connection, if any input is high the output is connected to the high potential. The only way we can obtain a low potential at the output is to drop all the inputs to the low potential. In this condition, no current flows into the resistor R and the output voltage has the low value corresponding to the 0 state. Since this is the only condition for which the output is low we can equate the output to the drop set composed of the sum of the inputs.

In Fig. 9–11(a) a schematic is shown for realizing the function $T = D(C + AB)$ with gate elements, and in Fig. 9–11(b) the corresponding gate elements made up from rectifiers are used.

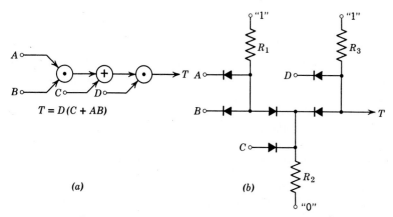

$$T = D(C + AB)$$

(a) (b)

Fig. 9–11. Rectifier circuit for the realization of a factored function.

We observe in the diagram of Fig. 9–11(b) that the gate which multiplies A and B is supplied from the high level of voltage which represents the 1 state and that its output becomes one of the inputs of the Add gate, forming the function $C + AB$. The resistance R_2 of the Add gate is connected to the 0 level of voltage. If $A = B = 1$, we observe that effectively R_1 and R_2 are in series between the high and low voltages. If R_1 is finite, even though the product $AB = 1$ (and the output of the Add gate should therefore be 1) this output voltage can never quite reach the excitation voltage supplied to R_1, but is determined by the relative sizes of R_1 and R_2. In practice, it is necessary to make R_2 large compared with R_1 in order that a suitable distinction between the 1 and 0 states, as represented by output voltages, be maintained.

In the next stage of the circuit the output of the Add gate becomes one of the inputs of the final Multiply gate. If all input variables to the Add gate are low, the resistors R_3 and R_2 are connected between the high voltage and the low voltage. In this condition, if the low output voltage is to be nearly as low as the excitation voltage supplied to R_2, it is necessary that R_3 be much larger than R_2.

It is apparent that it is never necessary to connect rectifier Multiply gates in series or rectifier Add gates in parallel, because for each of these combinations the same effect can always be obtained with a single gate carrying all the inputs. When functions are realized by multiple stages of rectifier gates there will hence always be an alternation of Add and Multiply gates as indicated in Fig. 9–11. Under these conditions, it becomes necessary to increase the size of the gate resistor by a large factor for each stage that is added. The condition is so serious that most rectifier switching is done in two stages.* If necessary, it is possible to build rectifier circuits with more than two stages. It requires careful design and well-selected components. Generally speaking, it is also necessary to accept a smaller difference in the voltages which represent the 1 state and the 0 state at the output.

The immediate consequence of using two-stage rectifier circuits is that we write all transmission functions as minimum sums or minimum products and build the circuits directly from that form without factoring. It is apparent in Fig. 9–11 that even the simple factoring shown requires the addition of another rectifier stage.

Example 9–3

The function $T = ABC + A'B'C'$ is to be realized using rectifier gates. Design the circuit required.

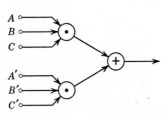

Fig. 9–12. A two-stage rectifier circuit in symbolic form.

Since this function cannot be reduced, it is in minimum sum form. A two-stage circuit is required because the function cannot be factored. Figure 9–12 shows the circuit as described by gate symbols.

The total number of rectifiers is equal to the total number of gate inputs, and it can be seen that this function requires 8 rectifiers. When a function is realized in two-stage form, we start with either a minimum sum or a minimum product. In the first stage each term of the function is generated, and one rectifier is required for each literal in the function. In the second stage the terms are combined to generate the

---

* What we here call stages are sometimes called levels. We prefer to retain the word "level" as part of the distinction between voltage levels and pulses.

final output, and one rectifier is required for each term of the function. Hence, a two-stage rectifier realization always requires a total number of rectifiers equal to the sum of the number of literals and the number of terms in the function.

The complement of the function $T = ABC + A'B'C'$ is $T' = (A' + B' + C')(A + B + C)$. In the circuit of Fig. 9–12, it happens that the complement can be generated by merely replacing Add gates by Multiply gates, and vice versa. In general, however, the complementary circuit requires that all gates be changed as indicated, and that all input variables be replaced by their complements.

It was pointed out at the beginning of this article that rectifiers are used in combination with relay contact elements. They are also used quite frequently in combination with other types of switching components, and in certain types of multiple output circuits, as will be discussed in Art. 9.6.

Rectifier gates are frequently found at the inputs of vacuum tubes where they serve to form an input which is the sum or product of two or more variables. In many of these applications rectifiers can be replaced by ordinary resistors, but we must be careful in defining the voltage levels which represent 1 and 0 values. Consider the circuit shown at the left of Fig. 9–13 in which the positive voltage E represents the 1 value. Let ground potential represent the 0 value.

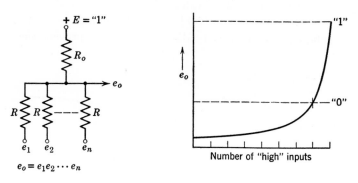

Fig. 9–13. A Multiply gate using resistors.

If the inputs $e_1, e_2, \ldots, e_n$ are applied through rectifiers oriented so that no current can flow from a "high" input to ground at one or more "low" inputs, the circuit behaves as though each input is controlled by a switch. When the switch is closed the input is grounded, and opening the switch removes the connection to ground. The output e_o then varies as shown at the right of Fig. 9–13. We must define 0 as the output voltage found with only one input grounded and all others ungrounded. When the last input is ungrounded the output voltage rises to E, the 1 value, and we observe that this is a Multiply gate. The separation between the 0 and 1 values increases as the ratio of R_o to R increases.

An entirely different mode of operation is found if the input resistors are connected permanently to sources which apply 1 or 0 values. The resistor R of each input at the 1 value is effectively connected in parallel with the resistor R_o. Analysis shows that under these conditions the output e_o increases linearly with the number of high inputs. For a resistance gate with n inputs, $n - 1$ of which are high, the ratio e_o/E is given by

$$\frac{e_o}{E} = 1 - \frac{R_o}{R + nR_o}$$

If $R_o \gg R$ this ratio reduces to approximately $1 - \dfrac{1}{n}$. Hence for a two-input gate the output voltage level corresponding to the 0 value is about one-half the voltage level at the 1 value. As the number of inputs increases the output voltage at the 0 value approaches the voltage E. We conclude that unless the inputs to this type of gate are applied through switches, the number of inputs must be kept very small and we must be able to accept a smaller difference in the voltage levels which represent 1 and 0 values.

Similar remarks apply to the Add gate circuit in Fig. 9–14. If actual switches or properly oriented rectifiers are used to prevent the input

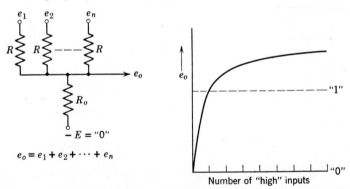

$$e_o = e_1 + e_2 + \cdots + e_n$$

Fig. 9–14. An Add gate using resistors.

resistors of low inputs from being connected, effectively, in parallel with R_o, the distinction between 0 and 1 values will be as indicated in the curve at the right of Fig. 9–14. Otherwise the output voltage variation will be linear and we must accept the same limitations that we found in the resistance-type Multiply gate.

9.4   Vacuum-Tube and Transistor Gates

In discussing vacuum-tube gates we will consider only those which are formed from triodes and pentodes. Although vacuum-tube diodes are excellent for use in rectifier gates, they have been almost entirely displaced by germanium and silicon rectifiers.

As a switching device, the vacuum tube is generally operated so that when high values of input voltage are applied to the grid, or grids, the plate current has a value at or near saturation, and when low input voltages are applied to the grid, or grids, the plate current is cut off. This is because it is desirable that output voltages be relatively insensitive to small variations in the input voltages which represent the 1 state and the 0 state.   Unlike rectifier circuits, it is not necessary to restrict vacuum-tube circuits to two stages. Because the vacuum tube has gain available, it is not necessary to increase the output impedance level from stage to stage.

Complementation is readily obtained by means of a single triode, as shown in Fig. 9–15. The plate is supplied through a plate resistor

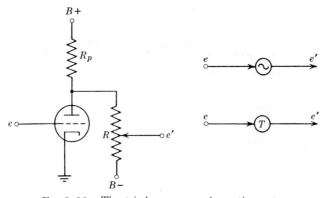

Fig. 9–15.   The triode as a complementing gate.

R_p, and the plate terminal is then connected to a low supply voltage through the potentiometer R.   When the grid voltage e is at its high value, a high plate current flows and the plate voltage drops.   When the grid voltage goes to a low value, the plate current is cut off, and the plate voltage goes to the value of the positive supply voltage.   Thus, the variation of the grid voltage causes a change in the plate voltage in the opposite direction, so the output voltage e' is the complement of the grid voltage. The potentiometer R permits the adjustment of the level of the output voltage e' relative to ground. At the right of the circuit diagram in Fig. 9–15 two symbolic representations are shown for the single triode used as a complementing gate. Either symbol may be used, but the lower symbol specifically identifies the gate as a triode gate. The lower symbol will be used to represent this gate in the remainder of this book.

When triodes are connected so that their plates are supplied through a common plate resistor, we make the plate resistor R_p large relative to the tube plate resistances. Then, if either input grid voltage is at its high value, the corresponding tube will conduct and the plate voltage will be at its low value. Only when both input voltages are at their low values, and both tubes are cut off, will the output voltage rise to its high value. If we represent a high input voltage or a high output voltage by 1, and any low voltage by 0, the table of combinations may be written as shown.

Table of Combinations for Two Triodes

e_1	e_2	e_o
0	0	1
0	1	0
1	0	0
1	1	0

It is apparent from this table that the switching function generated by triodes connected as in Fig. 9–16 is given by $e_o = e_1' e_2'$. At the

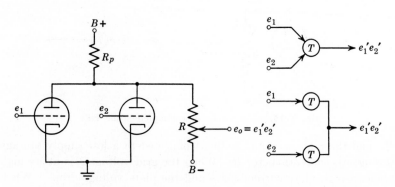

Fig. 9–16. Triodes supplied through a common plate resistor.

right of Fig. 9–16 two symbolic forms are shown, both of which represent two triodes with independent inputs, but with a common plate resistor. This type of connection is not limited to a connection of two triodes. If n triodes are operated with a common plate resistor and independent inputs, the output voltage is given by $e_o = e_1'e_2' \ldots e_n'$.

If we call a pair of triodes connected as in Fig. 9–16 a *triode gate*, then in Fig. 9–17 we see that the three basic gates can all be built by

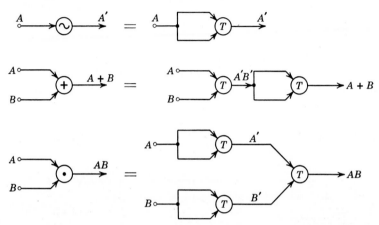

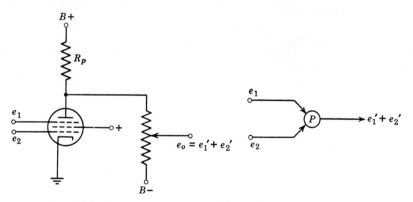

Fig. 9–17. All three basic gates can be realized by means of a single type of triode gate.

using only the triode gate. This demonstrates that any switching function can be realized using only triodes.

A pentode gate is shown both by circuit diagram and by symbolic representation in Fig. 9–18. Physically, the pentode is cut off if either

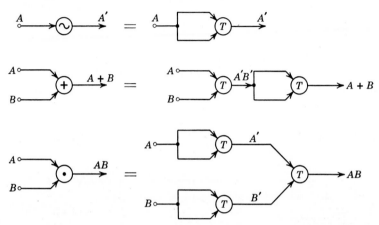

Fig. 9–18. The pentode gate and its symbolic representation.

or both of its input voltages are low, and conducts only when both input voltages are high. Hence, for the pentode we write the table of combinations shown.

Table of Combinations for a Pentode

e_1	e_2	e_o
0	0	1
0	1	1
1	0	1
1	1	0

The switching function generated by the pentode gate may be written from the table as $e_o = e_1' + e_2'$. Unlike that of the triode gate, this function cannot be extended to include n input variables, since we have no tube containing n grids which conducts only when all input variables have their high values. A number of pentodes may, however, be operated with a common plate resistor, as shown in Fig. 9–19.

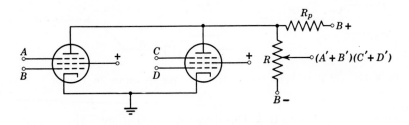

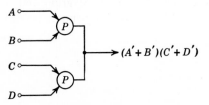

Fig. 9–19. Pentodes supplied through a common plate resistor.

If either, or both, of the pentodes conducts, the output voltage will be low. If the output voltage represents the transmission function of the circuit, the zeros of transmission are obtained for the conditions shown in the table. This table expresses the physical fact that the output

A	B	C	D	T
ϕ	ϕ	1	1	0
1	1	ϕ	ϕ	0

voltage will be low if inputs C and D are high, regardless of the values assumed by inputs A and B. Likewise, if A and B are high, the output voltage is low regardless of the values of C and D. These relations clearly lead to the transmission $T = (A' + B')(C' + D')$. Thus we see that when two pentodes are operated with a common plate resistor, the output function is the product of the outputs which the individual pentodes have when operated with individual plate resistors. A symbolic representation of the connection of pentodes with a common plate resistor is shown below the circuit diagram in Fig. 9–19.

It is possible to realize all the basic gates by the use of pentode gates alone, as the symbolic equivalents shown in Fig. 9–20 demonstrate. Hence we know that any switching function can be realized by using pentode gates only.

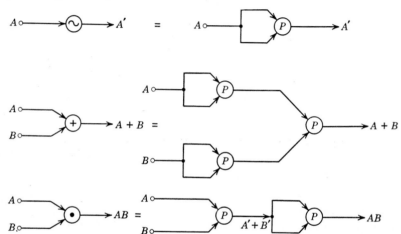

Fig. 9–20. The three basic gates realized by means of the pentode gate.

Triodes and pentodes may be supplied in combination through a common plate resistor as shown in Fig. 9–21. In this circuit, two triodes having the inputs A and B are operated in parallel with a pentode having the inputs C and D. A symbolic representation of this connection is shown below the circuit diagram. By writing a table of combinations it may readily be found that the output function of this circuit consists of the products of the outputs of each tube when supplied through an individual plate resistor. Hence, for the connection of Fig. 9–21, the output function is $T = A'B'(C' + D')$. The student may verify this result by constructing the table of combinations.

The multiplying property of the common plate resistor is related to that of the resistance gate of Fig. 9–13. A common plate resistor corresponds to the resistance R_o, and the input resistors R of Fig. 9–13

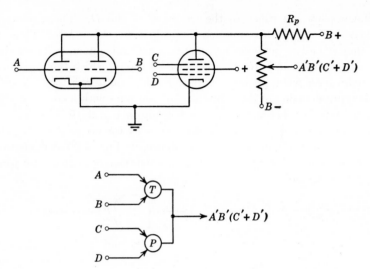

Fig. 9–21. The common plate resistor permits logical multiplication of the outputs of triodes and pentodes.

correspond to the plate resistances of the tubes in Fig. 9–21. We note also that each tube supplies the rectifier action required to keep multiple inputs mutually isolated.

When a single triode is used as a cathode follower, an output voltage may be taken from the cathode to ground which substantially repeats the input grid voltage. This connection may occasionally be useful, but a more interesting use of the cathode follower is shown in Fig. 9–22.

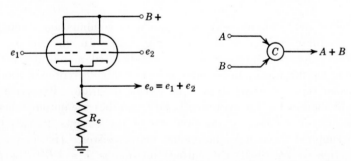

Fig. 9–22. Triodes used as cathode followers perform logical addition.

There, two cathode followers with independent inputs are supplied through a common cathode resistor. For this connection, the output voltage is high if either grid voltage is high and the output is low only if both grid voltages are low, as summarized in the table. From this table, the output voltage is given by $e_o = e_1 + e_2$. A symbolic

Table of Combinations for Two Cathode Followers

e_1	e_2	e_o
0	0	0
0	1	1
1	0	1
1	1	1

representation of this connection is given to the right of the circuit diagram in Fig. 9–22. We may also connect a larger number of cathode followers in parallel and obtain the output $e_o = e_1 + e_2 + \ldots + e_n$. Just as the common plate resistor of triodes and pentodes operating in parallel gives the effect of multiplication, the common cathode resistor of cathode followers operating in parallel gives the effect of addition. It may be seen that the effect is related to the performance of the resistance gate of Fig. 9–14. For the cathode follower gate, the common cathode resistance R_c must be much greater than the plate resistances of the individual tubes.

It is never necessary to use cathode followers for their switching properties. They are used largely for their qualities as output devices, and as convenient means for changing impedance levels.

In this discussion of vacuum-tube gates the symbolic forms for representing the individual gates do not indicate the restrictions which are present. An extreme example might be given in terms of the function $T = (A' + B')(A + B)$. We could readily show a symbolic diagram in which the term $(A' + B')$ is generated by a pentode having the inputs A and B, and the term $(A + B)$ is generated by two cathode followers having the inputs A and B. We might also indicate by the schematic connection that the multiplication of these terms was to be obtained by using a common resistor. This, of course, makes no sense in any physical circuit, but it certainly can be indicated symbolically.

It has been shown that either triodes or pentodes alone can be used to construct the three basic gates, and that hence any switching circuit may be realized using either triodes or pentodes alone. It is instructive to study the realization of a switching function using just one type of vacuum tube, but not necessarily depending on the rigid process of providing either triode or pentode versions of the three standard gates. Rather, we shall here attempt to make use of the specific switching property of each tube gate in a more advantageous way.

Example 9–4

The function found by analysis in Example 9–2 is to be resynthesized using two-input triode gates only. Assume that all variables and their complements are available as input voltages.

It is convenient when using triode gates to work with the function in the form given by the drop sets.

$$f = (W + X + Y)(W + X + Z)(W' + X' + Y)(W + X' + Y' + Z')$$
$$= (W + X + YZ)[X' + (W' + Y)(W + Y' + Z')]$$

If this expression is to be derived from two triodes with a common plate resistor, then as inputs to the grids we must have

$$A = (W + X + YZ)' = W'X'(YZ)'$$

$$B = [X' + (W' + Y)(W + Y' + Z')]'$$
$$= X(WY' + W'YZ)$$

If A is to be the output of a triode gate, the inputs should preferably be

$$C = (W'X')'$$

$$D = YZ$$

We may derive B from a triode gate by using the inputs

$$E = X'$$

$$F = (WY' + W'YZ)'$$
$$= (W' + Y)(W + Y' + Z')$$

Finally, the inputs to the triode gate which produces F are:

$$G = WY'$$

$$H = W'YZ = W'(YZ)$$

In Fig. 9–23 the complete circuit is shown, with intermediate functions identified by the letters $A, B, C, \ldots, H$ used above. If we examine the realization of this function shown in Fig. 9–8, and use the equivalent gates of Fig. 9–17, we find that the general gate method requires 16 gates, with 32 triode grids. The circuit of Fig. 9–23 uses 10 gates, with 20 grids. Although we limited this solution to the use of triode gates, we obtained a more economical realization of the function because we took advantage of the specific switching property of the triode gate, rather than use the derived properties shown in Fig. 9–17.

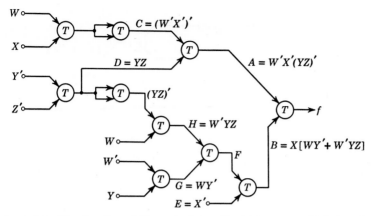

Fig. 9–23. The function of Example 9–4 realized by means of triode gates.

Example 9–5

Synthesize an electronic network to realize the function found in Example 9–2, using pentode gates only. Assume that all variables and their complements are available as input voltages.

We shall take advantage of the specific switching property of the pentode gate rather than the derived properties shown in Fig. 9–20. Hence, we prefer to begin with the function as determined from the lift sets:

$$
\begin{aligned}
T &= WY + WX' + X'YZ + W'XY' + W'XZ' \\
&= X'YZ + W(X' + Y) + W'X(Y' + Z') \\
&= (X + Y' + Z')' + [(W' + XY')(W + X' + YZ)]' \\
&= A' + B'
\end{aligned}
$$

In the steps shown, the function has been so manipulated that it will be produced as the output of a pentode gate which has the inputs

$$
A = X + Y' + Z'
$$

$$
B = (W' + XY')(W + X' + YZ)
$$

If we write $A = (X')' + (YZ)'$, the pentode inputs required are X' and YZ. Since YZ is required also in generating B, it is developed by first producing $Y' + Z'$ and then taking the complement, as shown in Fig. 9–24.

The input B may be written, by theorem 17,

$$
B = W'(X' + YZ) + WXY'
$$

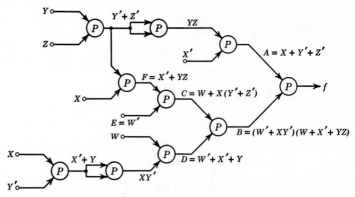

Fig. 9–24. The function of Example 9–5 realized by means of pentode gates.

This function will be delivered as the output of a pentode to which the inputs are

$$C = W + X(Y' + Z')$$
$$D = W' + X' + Y$$

The function C is the output of a pentode to which the inputs are

$$E = W'$$
$$F = X' + YZ$$

and F is the output of a pentode which has the inputs X and $(Y' + Z')$.

The function D can be obtained in three ways, all requiring the same number of pentodes. For one of these ways we write

$$D = W' + (XY')'$$
$$XY' = (X' + Y)'$$

In the foregoing manipulation the required transmission function has been broken down so that it can be generated in a series of steps, each of which requires a pentode gate. The circuit of Fig. 9–24 is obtained by assembling the component networks represented by the separate steps. As in the preceding example it is found necessary to use ten gates when we are restricted to the use of the pentode gate only. In the next article we shall work with this function again, and realize it by using a mixture of gates.

Transistors of many types are applicable in a wide variety of switching circuits. We shall restrict the discussion here to the use of p-n-p type transistors, and in most of the circuits we will use the grounded emitter connection, with input signals applied to the bases. Thus restricted, transistor switching gates exhibit a number of aspects of

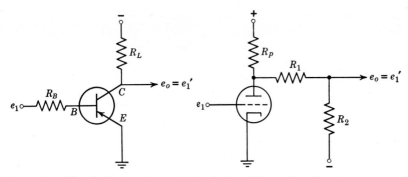

Fig. 9–25. The single transistor and the single triode used as Complement gates.

duality with triode gates. In Fig. 9–25 we see that either the single
transistor or the single triode can be used as a Complement gate. The
collector is supplied from a negative source through the resistance R_L,
whereas the plate of the vacuum tube is supplied from a positive source
through a resistor R_p. Corresponding to the grid of the triode, we have
the base of the transistor to which the input signal e_1 is supplied. We
can determine the switching action of the transistor from the physical
fact that when the base voltage becomes positive relative to the emitter,
the emitter current and hence the collector current are essentially cut
off. In this condition, the output voltage e_o goes to the value of the negative collector voltage. When the base voltage goes negative relative
to the emitter, current flows from the collector and the output voltage
e_o rises to ground potential. Hence, we may write $e_o = e_1'$. We must
observe, however, that all potentials are opposite in polarity to those
in the triode circuit. This significantly affects the switching properties
of p-n-p transistors used in combination.

A parallel combination of transistors is shown in Fig. 9–26. Nega-

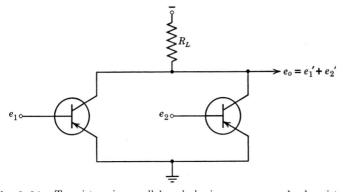

Fig. 9–26. Transistors in parallel and sharing a common load resistor.

tive potential is supplied through a common resistor R_L to both col-lectors, and both emitters are connected to ground. For switching purposes the base voltages will either be at negative values or at essen-tially ground potential. This causes collector voltages which are either at ground potential or at negative values, respectively. If we associate the higher voltage (ground) with the 1 state and the lower voltage (negative) with the 0 state, we may then write a table of combinations.

Parallel Connection—Grounded Emitter

e_1	e_2	e_o
0	0	1
0	1	1
1	0	1
1	1	0

This table is written by observing that if R_L is large enough, when either base is at negative potential the corresponding transistor is conducting and the collector voltage rises to ground potential. Only when both bases are high are both transistors cut off, and for this condition the collector voltage goes to the value of the negative supply voltage. The table of combinations shows that the output of transistors connected in parallel as in Fig. 9–26 may be written $e_o = e_1' + e_2'$. For two transistors in parallel we observe that the switching action is the same as that given by a single pentode. However, unlike the pen-tode gate, we can connect additional transistors in the parallel circuit and get the switching action described by $e_o = e_1' + e_2' + \ldots + e_n'$. We may also note that, except for the complementation of all input variables, the additive property of the common load resistance R_L is similar to that obtained from the resistance gate in Fig. 9–14. The transistors, of course, supply the rectifier action required when the number of inputs is large.

Transistors may also be connected in series as shown in Fig. 9–27. This type of connection is rarely used in vacuum-tube circuits, largely because of the difficulties associated with power supply, bias voltages,

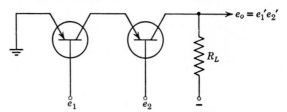

Fig. 9–27. A series connection of transistors.

and the problems of insulating cathodes from heaters. When transistors are operated in series, if either base voltage is high the corresponding transistor is cut off and consequently there will be no current in the load resistor R_L. If both base voltages are low, both transistors conduct and the output voltage rises to substantially ground potential. A table of combinations for two transistors in series follows.

Series Connection—Grounded Emitter

e_1	e_2	e_o
0	0	1
0	1	0
1	0	0
1	1	0

From the table of combinations, we write as the output of two transistors in series $e_o = e_1'e_2'$. Thus the switching action of transistors connected in series is found to be the same as that of triodes operating in parallel and supplied through a common plate resistor. Just as we may add additional triodes in parallel, we may add additional transistors in the series circuit and obtain the switching action described by $e_o = e_1'e_2' \ldots e_n'$.

From the transistor circuits of Figs. 9–26 and 9–27 we see that a transistor acts much like a contact which is closed when the base voltage is in the 0 state and is open when the base voltage goes to the 1 state.

Transistor switching operation is not limited to the grounded-emitter connection discussed above. A circuit using the grounded-base mode of operation is shown in Fig. 9–28. The input signals, e_1 and e_2, are

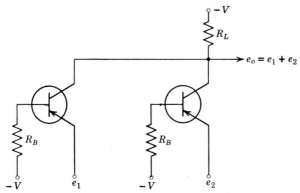

Fig. 9–28. A parallel connection of transistors with inputs applied to the emitters.

applied to the emitters. If either emitter is high relative to the base, there will be collector current flow and the output will hence be high. This is shown in the table of combinations, from which we find that the switching action of the circuit is given by $e_o = e_1 + e_2$.

Parallel Connection—Grounded Base

e_1	e_2	e_o
0	0	0
0	1	1
1	0	1
1	1	1

Additional transistors may be connected in the circuit of Fig. 9–28 to produce the function given by $e_o = e_1 + e_2 + \ldots + e_n$.

It is apparent from the preceding discussion that the transistor can be connected so as to deliver all the gate functions of triodes and pentodes combined. Therefore, any synthesis which has been achieved in terms of triodes and pentodes may be duplicated by means of transistors.

9.5 Factoring Problems in the Synthesis of Electronic Circuits

It became evident in the preceding article that it was not particularly economical to use electronic components to form basic gates and then to synthesize a given switching function from these gates. One common method for measuring the effectiveness of our use of vacuum tubes is to count the number of grids required, assuming that voltages are available to represent all input variables and their complements. This method of measurement puts a premium, of course, on the use of techniques which perform Boolean operations without using grids. An example of this process is the use of a common plate resistor in vacuum tube circuits to perform multiplication. This in turn makes it necessary to find functional forms which exploit the use of multiplication of vacuum-tube outputs.*

The need to express functions, if possible, as products of terms each of which is realizable by a vacuum-tube configuration, makes factoring an operation of some importance. It also suggests that we examine closely minimum-product forms of functions rather than minimum-sum forms. The minimum-product form is not always the best one to use,

---

* Transistors are somewhat more versatile in this respect. Multiplication is obtained by the series connection of Fig. 9–27, and two forms of addition are available through the use of a common resistor in the collector circuit as indicated in Fig. 9–26 and Fig. 9–28.

but it is so frequently applicable that it should not be overlooked. Many switching functions require the realization of the disjuncts of two variables. In these, the variables may be literals of the function, or they may be combinations of literals. Almost always they are expressed in the form $f = (X + Y)(X' + Y')$, or, $f = (X + Y')(X' + Y)$. This disjunctive form is preferable because it is realized quite easily by pentode pairs as is shown in Fig. 9–29.

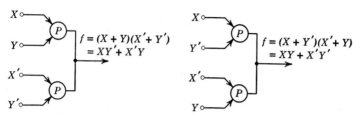

Fig. 9–29. The disjuncts of two variables realized by pentodes sharing a common plate resistor.

There is no need to make use of one kind of vacuum tube exclusively, or of one kind of circuit configuration. We should take full advantage of the special properties available in each component.

Symmetric functions can be quite troublesome in their realization by vacuum tubes because we have no standardized solutions such as we had for contact network realizations.

Example 9–6

An electronic network is to be used to realize the symmetric function $T = S_2(X, Y, Z)$. This function is mapped in Fig. 9–30. From the map we write for the 0's of transmission the minimum product

$$T = (Y + Z)(X + Y)(X + Z)(X' + Y' + Z')$$
$$= (Y + Z)(X + YZ)[X' + (YZ)']$$

The objectives of the factoring used here are first, to keep the function as a product of sums, and second, to produce the disjunct represented by the last two terms. The required circuit is

	XY			
	00	01	11	10
Z 0	0	0	1	0
1	0	1	0	1

Fig. 9–30. Map of the symmetric function of Example 9–6.

drawn in Fig. 9–31. Both triodes and pentodes are used in this realization, and two products are formed by using common plate resistors.

It will now be instructive to reexamine the switching function which we treated in Examples 9–2, 9–4, and 9–5. We will place no limitations

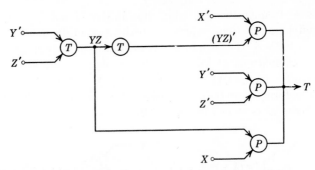

Fig. 9–31. Symbolic diagram of an electronic circuit for realizing a symmetric function.

or restrictions on the choice of the components used, but we will try to make sensible choices throughout.

Example 9–7

A map of the function to be realized is given in Fig. 9–32. Its minimum product can be written and manipulated as follows

$$T = (W + X + Y)(W + X + Z)$$
$$(W' + X' + Y)(W + X' + Y' + Z')$$
$$= (W + X + YZ)[W + X'$$
$$+ (YZ)'](W' + X' + Y)$$
$$= [W + (X + Q)(X' + Q')]$$
$$(W' + X' + Y)$$

$$Q = YZ$$

Fig. 9–32. Map of the function of Example 9–7.

		WX			
		00	01	11	10
	00	0	1	0	1
	01	0	1	0	1
YZ	11	1	0	1	1
	10	0	1	1	1

This function can be generated as the output of two triodes with a common plate resistor. That is,

$$T = [W'(X'Q' + XQ)]'(WXY')'$$

The input WXY' is obtained as the output of three triodes in parallel. The other input is derived from two triodes in parallel, with inputs W and $(X + Q)(X' + Q')$. We use two pentodes to form the disjunct. Finally, we may either generate YZ with two triodes, and take its complement, or generate $Y' + Z'$ with a pentode and take the complement. The circuit of Fig. 9–33 uses the second method.

It requires 14 grids to realize the function by this synthesis. We may now write, from the map of Fig. 9–32, a minimum sum for the function in the form

$$T = WX' + WY + X'YZ + W'XY' + (W'XZ' \text{ or } XYZ')$$

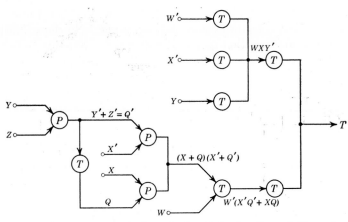

Fig. 9–33. A more economical synthesis of the function of Example 9–2.

We choose the term $W'XZ'$, and write the factored form

$$T = WY + W'X(Y' + Z') + X'(W + YZ)$$

If $Q = W'(Y' + Z')$, this reduces to

$$T = WY + XQ + X'Q' = WY + (X + Q')(X' + Q)$$

We now observe that $Q' = W + YZ$, and the product

$$(X + Q')WY = (X + W + YZ)WY$$
$$= WY + WXY + WYZ = WY$$

This identity permits us to write the function in the form

$$T = (X + Q')(X' + Q + WY)$$

The circuit shown in Fig. 9–34 requires only 10 grids to realize this function, compared with 14 grids in Fig. 9–33 and 20 grids in Figs. 9–23 and 9–24.

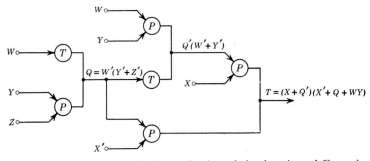

Fig. 9–34. Further economy in the realization of the function of Example 9–2 by improved factoring.

The preceding example makes it quite clear that the problem of obtaining optimum factoring is a challenging one. No general method applicable to any function is now known. If the function to be synthesized can be represented by a map, the procedure illustrated in Fig. 9–35 is a useful one. The map shown in the upper left-hand

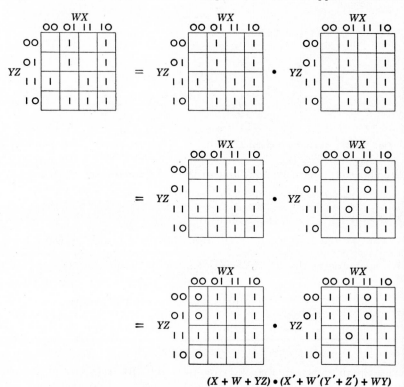

$$(X + W + YZ) \cdot (X' + W'(Y' + Z') + WY)$$

Fig. 9–35. Procedure for factoring a function represented on a map.

corner of the figure represents the function treated in Example 9–7. We assume that we want to express this function as the product of two terms each of which is represented by its own map. In Fig. 9–35 the map of the original function is shown as being equal to the product of two other maps, both of which in the upper row contain identical entries. This merely expresses the fact that the two component maps must contain all the 1's of the original map if their product is to be the desired function. In the remaining spaces of the component maps we can enter a 1 in either map provided we enter a 0 in the same cell of the other map. Hence, in the second row we have added 1's to the left-hand map in three cells, and 0's in the right-hand map in the same three cells. In the bottom row we have added 1's in the right-hand map and balanced them by 0 entries in the left-hand map. Our objective in this process is to attempt to make each of the component maps represent a simple function. The functions represented by each map are written below the bottom pair, and we can see that these are exactly the factors which were finally obtained in the example. The basic procedure here is essentially the same as that developed in Chapter 6 for synthesizing multi-terminal networks by the method of assumed form. It can be a powerful procedure for finding factors which are not immediately evident.

9.6 Multiple Output Circuits

Circuits which realize more than one output function are commonly encountered in electronic switching and offer many opportunities for economic synthesis. The theoretical concepts developed in Chapter 6 are applicable to electronic realizations, with appropriate modification where the nature of electronic components requires it. We have no electronic equivalent of the contact network path which can conduct in either direction. On the other hand, in an electronic network design a voltage representing a given term can be used freely in building up more than one output function without the need to guard against sneak paths.

A few examples will best serve to show the basic methods employed. In the examples which follow a network with two outputs will be synthesized by several methods so that comparisons can be made.

Example 9–8

An electronic circuit is to have two outputs for which the transmission functions are described by the standard sums

$$T_1 = \sum (2, 3, 4, 5, 6, 7, 11, 15)$$

$$T_2 = \sum (0, 1, 3, 4, 5, 7, 11, 15)$$

These functions are mapped in Fig. 9–36, using the variables A, B, C, D.

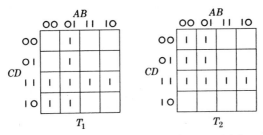

Fig. 9–36. Maps of functions to be realized by a multiple-output circuit.

The minimum sums corresponding to these maps are

$$T_1 = A'B + A'C + CD$$

$$T_2 = A'C' + CD$$

Both functions contain the term CD and it hence need be produced only once. If no complementing gates are required, the functions can be realized using rectifier gates only, as shown in Fig. 9–37.

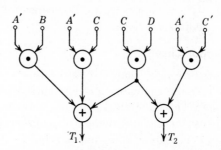

Fig. 9–37. A gate circuit to realize the functions mapped in Fig. 9–36.

These functions may also be written as the minimum products

$$T_1 = (A' + C)(B + C)(A' + D)$$

$$T_2 = (A' + C)(C' + D)$$

We observe that both products contain the term $(A' + C)$. Again the functions may be realized by the use of rectifier gates only, but it will be more instructive to examine triode and pentode circuits.

A circuit using triodes only is shown in Fig. 9–38. Thirteen grids are required and we shall soon see that we can do much better. But it

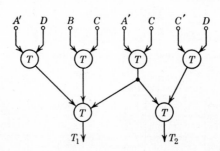

Fig. 9–38. Triode circuit to realize the functions of Example 9–8.

should be observed that eight triode grids are being used to obtain the four products AD', $B'C'$, AC', and CD'. These products can readily be supplied by rectifier gates. If this is done the resulting circuit uses only five grids.

Sometimes a more economic synthesis can be achieved by assuming the form which a multiple-output network will take, just as we assumed the form of multi-terminal contact networks. Two simple assumed forms for electronic networks are shown in Fig. 9–39. There are many

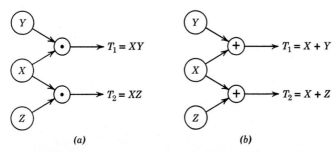

(a)   (b)

Fig. 9–39. Assumed forms of multiple-output circuits.

forms which can be assumed and an appropriate form might well be suggested by a study of the functions to be realized. Some additional forms for circuits with two outputs are described by

$$T_1 = XY \qquad T_2 = X + Z$$

$$T_1 = XY \qquad T_2 = X' + Z$$

$$T_1 = XY \qquad T_2 = X'Z$$

In using the method of assumed form, the manipulation of functions with the aid of maps is important. As we learned in Chapter 6, once the form of the circuit has been assumed the rules for making entries in the maps must be determined and applied. This will be illustrated in the next example.

Example 9–9

The functions treated in Example 9–8 are to be synthesized by using the form shown schematically in Fig. 9–39(a).

A map approach to this synthesis is given in Fig. 9–40. In the upper row of the maps, the two maps on the right contain the 1 entries of T_1 and T_2, respectively, while the left-hand map contains the combined 1 entries of T_1 and T_2. This left-hand map must contain at least all the 1's of T_1 and T_2, since it represents the function X of Fig. 9–39(a), and must be multiplied by functions Y and Z to obtain T_1 and T_2, respectively.

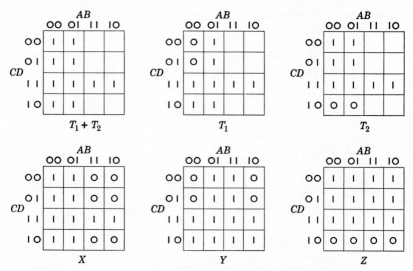

Fig. 9–40. Components of a multiple-output circuit found by maps.

The maps of T_1 and T_2 in the upper row must initially contain all the 1's of the respective functions, and must contain 0's wherever the map of $(T_1 + T_2)$ contains 1's which are not present in the respective functions. Thus the map of T_1 and the map of T_2 each contain two 0 entries which are needed to suppress 1's in the $(T_1 + T_2)$ map.

We may now enter additional 1's in the $(T_1 + T_2)$ map, if this is desirable, provided corresponding 0 entries are made in *both* the T_1 and the T_2 maps. In Fig. 9–40, the $(T_1 + T_2)$ map represents the function

$$X = A' + CD$$

and this is an acceptable function which makes it unnecessary to enter additional 1's in the $(T_1 + T_2)$ map. The X map in the lower row of Fig. 9–40 is hence the $(T_1 + T_2)$ map with the remaining cells containing 0 entries.

In forming the Y map from the T_1 map, and the Z map from the T_2 map, we may enter 1's in any cells for which the X-map has 0 entries, since these 1 entries will become 0's in the maps of the products XY and XZ. We have accordingly made additional 1 entries in the T_1 and T_2 maps to produce the Y and Z maps, respectively, shown in the lower row. These maps represent the functions

$$Y = B + C$$

$$Z = C' + D$$

A circuit based on this synthesis is given in Fig. 9–41. It requires 9 grids instead of the 13 grids of Fig. 9–38.

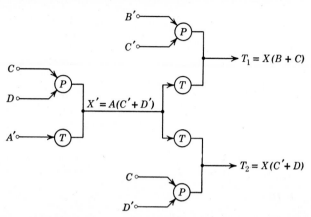

Fig. 9–41. Multiple-output circuit derived from the maps of Fig. 9–40.

In this example the maps were quite helpful as guides in forming the factors X, Y, and Z. In Example 9–8 we had the opportunity to select the same factors, but they were not so clearly evident. There we wrote the minimum products

$$T_1 = (A' + C)(B + C)(A' + D)$$
$$T_2 = (A' + C)(C' + D)$$

But, by theorem 16, the function T_2 can be written

$$T_2 = (A' + C)(C' + D)(A' + D)$$

and terms can be combined in both functions to give

$$T_1 = (A' + CD)(B + C) = XY$$
$$T_2 = (A' + CD)(C' + D) = XZ$$

An interesting variation of the method of assumed form is illustrated in Fig. 9–42. A transmission X is obtained as a function of A, B, C, D. Another transmission Y is a function of the same variables A, B, C, D, but it is also a function of the output X of the first network. It would appear that X is a function of four variables and Y is a function of five variables. This is not so, however, since X itself is a function of the input variables A, B, C, D.

Although this method of design may be useful in situations which require that an additional output be obtained from an already existing circuit, it is of more interest as a method for discovering relations

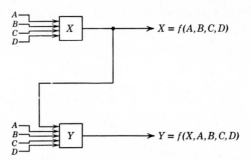

Fig. 9–42. Another assumed form of a multiple-output circuit.

between functions. In Example 9–10 the method will be applied to the same functions that were treated in the preceding two examples.

Example 9–10

For the transmission functions

$$T_1 = \sum(2, 3, 4, 5, 6, 7, 11, 15)$$

and

$$T_2 = \sum(0, 1, 3, 4, 5, 7, 11, 15)$$

determine the algebraic form of T_1 as a function of the variables (T_2, A, B, C, D).

If we examine the terms of the standard sum for T_1, we find that the decimal term 2 stands for binary 0010, or $A'B'CD'$. For these values of (A, B, C, D), T_2 is zero, so T_1 as a function of (T_2, A, B, C, D) has in its new standard sum the term $T_2'A'B'CD'$, which in binary form is 00010 and hence remains decimal 2. However, both T_1 and T_2 must equal 1 for the term $A'B'CD$ (decimal 3), so the new standard sum for T_1 must contain the term $T_2A'B'CD$. This in binary form is 10011 and is decimal 19. It should be apparent that when $T_1 = 1$ and $T_2 = 0$ the decimal designator of T_1 is unchanged, but when $T_1 = T_2 = 1$, an appropriate power of 2, in this instance 16, must be added to the designator of T_1. We may tabulate the process, as shown:

Terms of Standard Sum

$T_1(A, B, C, D)$	2	3	4	5	6	7	11	15
$T_2 =$		0	1	1	1	0	1	1	1
$T_1(T_2, A, B, C, D)$	2	19	20	21	6	23	27	31

The terms in the bottom row are those for which T_1 *must* equal 1. But the original standard sum for T_1 implied also the standard product

$$T_1 = \prod(0, 1, 8, 9, 10, 12, 13, 14)$$

The standard product form of T_2 is

$$T_2 = \prod(2, 6, 8, 9, 10, 12, 13, 14)$$

Again we must find new decimal designators for these terms. If $T_1 = T_2 = 0$, the corresponding decimal designator of the T_1 term remains unchanged, but if $T_1 = 0$ and $T_2 = 1$, we must add 16 to the corresponding designator of the T_1 term. The term 9 in the standard product of T_1 stands for binary 1001, or the algebraic term $(A' + B + C + D')$. Since for this combination T_2 also is 0, the term in the new standard product of T_1 must be $(T_2 + A' + B + C + D')$. This is the binary term 01001 and again is decimal 9. However, for decimal 1, $T_1 = 0$ and $T_2 = 1$. Hence the new term must be $(T_2' + A + B + C + D')$ and this corresponds to decimal 17. The tabulation shows the complete correction to the standard product form of T_1.

Terms of Standard Product

$T_1(A, B, C, D)$	0	1	8	9	10	12	13	14
$T_2 =$		1	1	0	0	0	0	0	0
$T_1(T_2, A, B, C, D)$	16	17	8	9	10	12	13	14

The terms in the bottom row are those for which T_1 *must* equal 0. From the two tabulations we can now specify

$$T_1 = 1 \text{ for the terms } 2, 6, 19, 20, 21, 23, 27, 31$$

and

$$T_1 = 0 \text{ for the terms } 8, 9, 10, 12, 13, 14, 16, 17$$

There are 32 possible combinations of (T_2, A, B, C, D), and the value of T_1 is specified for only 16 of these. The remaining combinations represent optional terms for which we can choose values that help to simplify the functional form of T_1. In this type of synthesis we will always have as many optional terms as there are specified terms. We have apparently added one more variable and thus doubled the number of possible terms, but the added variable is a fixed function of the original variables and physically there can be no more actual combinations than there were before.

The situation thus far is shown in the upper pair of maps in Fig. 9–43, where the left-hand and right-hand maps correspond to $T_2 = 0$ and $T_2 = 1$, respectively. The map entries correspond to the specified values of T_1. They can be derived directly from the standard sum and standard product forms of T_1, as a function of (A, B, C, D) by entering the map which corresponds to the value of T_2 for each combination. Thus the term 2 in the standard sum is represented by a

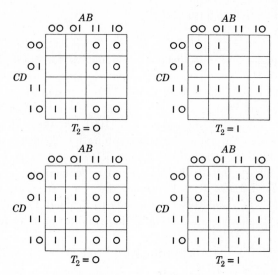

Fig. 9–43. Selection of optional terms by means of maps.

1 entry in the left-hand map, because for that term $T_2 = 0$, but the term 3 is represented by a 1 entry in the right-hand map because T_2 also contains that term in its standard sum. By the same process the 0's represented by the terms of the standard product are distributed between the maps.

All the blank cells in the upper pair of maps represent optional terms. In the lower pair of maps values have been chosen for the optional terms. These maps now represent

$$T_1 = T_2'A' + T_2(B + C)$$
$$= (T_2 + A')(T_2' + [B'C']')$$

The circuit of Fig. 9–44 is a realization of this functional form.

The result found in Example 9–10 leads to a generalization which materially reduces the amount of work involved in carrying out this type of synthesis. It may readily be seen that we can always write

$$T_1 = f_1(A, B, C, D) \cdot T_2' + f_2(A, B, C, D) \cdot T_2$$

where T_1, T_2, f_1, and f_2 are all functions of the same variables. Since T_2 and T_2' between them have the value 1 for all possible combinations of the input variables, we can always form functions f_1 and f_2 such that they will jointly derive from T_2 and T_2', respectively, all the 1's required by T_1. The procedure for forming the functions f_1 and f_2

requires that for all combinations of the input variables, A, B, C, D:

(a) if $T_1 = 0$, $f_1 = 0$ if $T_2' = 1$,   and f_2 is optional;

also $f_2 = 0$ if $T_2 = 1$,   and f_1 is optional;

(b) if $T_1 = 1$, $f_1 = 1$ if $T_2' = 1$,   and f_2 is optional;

also $f_2 = 1$ if $T_2 = 1$,   and f_1 is optional.

If T_1 is desired in product form we can write

$$T_1 = [f_1(A, B, C, D) + T_2][f_2(A, B, C, D) + T_2']$$

In forming the functions f_1 and f_2 we must make $f_1 = 1$ whenever $T_1 = 1$, and $T_2 = 0$, and we must make $f_2 = 1$ whenever $T_1 = 1$ and

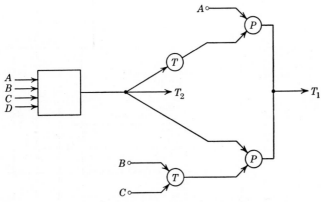

Fig. 9–44. The output T_2 serves as an input to the circuit which produces T_1.

$T_2' = 0$. We must make $f_1 = 0$ whenever $T_1 = 0$ and $T_2 = 0$, and make $f_2 = 0$ whenever $T_1 = 0$ and $T_2' = 0$. For all remaining com-

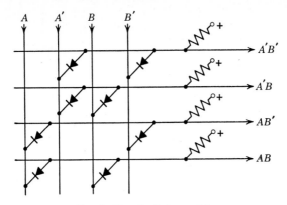

Fig. 9–45. A diode matrix.

binations of the input variables the values of f_1 and f_2 are optional.

A rather common type of multiple output network is in the form of a matrix array. This is illustrated by the two-variable diode matrix in Fig. 9–45. The four outputs represent the four combinations of the two variables and this is, of course, the set of outputs delivered by a contact tree.

It will be seen in Fig. 9–45 that eight diodes are required to provide four outputs. If we have n variables a matrix like that of Fig. 9–45

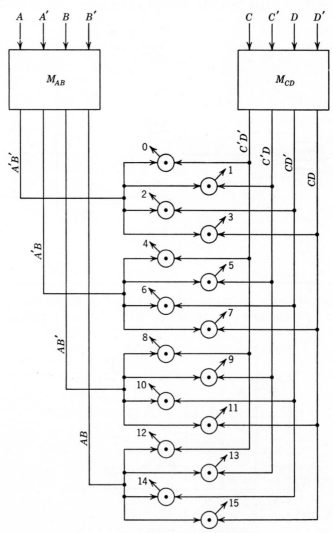

Fig. 9–46. A modified diode matrix.

for producing all the combinations of the input variables will require $n2^n$ diodes. Hence, for a four-variable matrix we would require 64 diodes.

The modified matrix circuit shown in Fig. 9–46 requires only 48 diodes to deliver the same outputs. Basically, we first generate all the combinations of (A, B) and all the combinations of (C, D) separately. This is done by using two-variable matrices of the form shown in 9–45. These are indicated schematically in Fig. 9–46 by the boxes M_{AB} and M_{CD}. In the remainder of the network there are 16 Multiply gates in which all the possible products of the terms in (A, B) and the terms in (C, D) are generated. The outputs of these gates are marked with the decimal numbers 0 to 15 to indicate the term generated at each gate. For a more complete study of networks which generate terms corresponding to all possible combinations of input variables, the student is referred to Reference 1 in the Bibliography at the end of this chapter.

9.7 Magnetic Switching Devices

Superior types of transistors and diodes are among the outstanding successes of research in solid-state physics. Another development, the magnetic core for switching, has been extensively used in the construction of high-speed memory devices, but has only recently begun to receive widespread recognition as an active switching element.

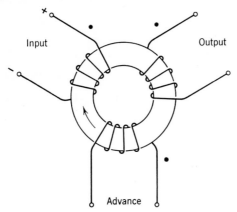

Fig. 9–47. A magnetic switching core and its basic windings.

A basic form of the switching core and its windings is shown in Fig. 9–47. With only the three windings shown, the core serves essentially as a memory device, but by adding other windings it can become a means for realizing switching functions.

The core is toroidal in shape, with a cross-section that is approximately rectangular. For a polarity convention we shall say that the core is in the 1 state when it is magnetized in the clockwise direction as shown in Fig. 9–47. A dot is placed near one terminal of each winding to indicate, for the input and advance windings, the terminals to which positive voltage is applied, and for the output winding the terminal at which the output voltage is positive.

For use as a switching device, the core is made with magnetization properties as indicated in Fig. 9–48. If the magnetizing force is slowly varied between the values of $+H_m$ and $-H_m$ and back again, the

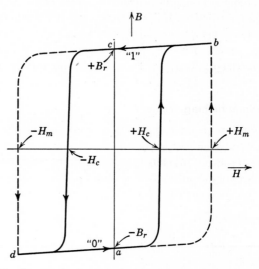

Fig. 9–48.   The hysteresis loop (solid lines) of a switching core is nearly rectangular.

flux-density variation is that indicated by the solid line of Fig. 9–48. If the inputs to the core are changes of voltage level, it is possible to operate the core in the manner indicated by this solid-line hysteresis loop, which has here the desirable property of being nearly rectangular in shape. In practice, however, the inputs to the core are almost always in the form of pulses.

It will be noted that the 1 state is defined as that corresponding to the positive value of the remanent flux density, $+B_r$, and the 0 state corresponds to $-B_r$. The 0 state is marked by a in Fig. 9–48 and the 1 state is marked by c. If the core is in the 0 state and its input winding receives a pulse of short duration having a maximum magnetizing value of $+H_m$, the core will be driven to a positive value of flux density as indicated by the point b. The path taken by the magnetizing curve in reaching this point will depend partly upon the shape of the pulse. If the variation of magnetizing force is slow, the path will be that indicated by the solid line, but the path followed in response to an extremely rapid change of magnetizing force is that indicated by the dotted line. Under practical working conditions the actual path taken will lie somewhere between these. The important point is that after a positive pulse is terminated the core remains in a state of positive magnetization, at the point c. If then a negative pulse is applied, the core is driven to the point d and finally remains at the point a after the negative pulse terminates. In the absence of any input pulse, the core will remain indefinitely in either the 0 state, at point a, or in the 1 state, at point c.

A finite time is required to reverse the direction of magnetization of a core. This "switching time" depends upon the core itself and upon the magnitude of the applied magnetizing force. It is given by the equation

$$\tau = \frac{C}{H - H_0}$$

where $\tau =$ the time required after the application of a current pulse until most of the flux reversal has been completed. This time is most conveniently measured by recording the output of another winding and measuring the width of the induced voltage pulse along the axis of zero voltage.

$H =$ the applied magnetizing force due to the current pulse.

$H_0 =$ a constant minimum magnetizing force which H must exceed. If $H = H_0$ the switching time becomes infinite. Physically, H_0 is slightly larger than the coercive force H_c.

$C =$ a constant depending upon the core material and dimensions.

We note from the above equation that $1/\tau$ varies linearly with H. If experimental data are thus plotted, the graph will be a straight line having a slope $1/C$ and an intercept on the H axis at the value H_0.

At this point we should consider exactly what we mean by the term "transmission" when we are dealing with inputs and outputs in terms of pulses. We cannot readily assign a magnitude of voltage or current to represent a 1 of transmission or a 0 of transmission. There are several ways to define the values of Boolean variables in pulse systems, of which two are commonly used. One method which is not used extensively is that of assigning pulses of opposite polarity to represent the

1 and the 0 values. This method has the attractive feature that the value intended is always indicated by the polarity of the pulse, but it is awkward to handle from an engineering point of view. A system in rather general use is to represent a 1 by the presence of a pulse and a 0 by the absence of a pulse. A complication of this system is that the question of whether or not a pulse is present must be determined in relationship to the presence of a clock pulse. That is, if at the time of a clock pulse, there is a pulse representing a variable, that variable has the value 1. If, however, there is no pulse representing the variable at the time of a clock pulse, the variable then has the value 0. A disadvantage of the system is that the absence of a pulse may mean that the variable has the value 0, but it may also mean that something has failed in the equipment. In a third method which is becoming more widely used, separate terminals are available for a variable and for its complement. If a pulse appears at the terminal corresponding to the variable itself, the value of the variable is 1, but if the pulse appears on the terminal corresponding to the complemented variable, the value of the variable is 0. This system avoids the ambiguity of whether the absence of a pulse has logical meaning or whether it signifies a failure of equipment, and it is well adapted to the requirements of magnetic switching.

It should also be pointed out that the operation of a magnetic core is not exactly ideal. This is true especially of situations in which the core output should be 0. Let us refer to Fig. 9–48 and suppose the core is in the 1 state, that is at point c on the magnetization curve, and that it receives a positive magnetizing pulse. The magnetic state will be driven to the right toward the point b and at the end of the pulse will return to c, the original state. If the magnetizing curve were strictly rectangular in shape, there would be no change of flux in going from point c to point b and back. However, in practice there is a small change in flux and there will be a corresponding induced voltage in any output winding. This voltage is, of course, small compared to that induced by a reversal of the core flux, but it is nevertheless sufficient to require its recognition as part of the "noise" of a core circuit. One of the important objectives of research in magnetic materials is to render the magnetizing curve as nearly rectangular as possible and thus reduce such spurious outputs.

An important aspect of magnetic core operation can be examined by referring to Fig. 9–47. Suppose that a pulse has been applied to the input winding to magnetize the core in the clockwise, or positive, direction. If now a pulse is applied to the advance winding with its positive potential at the dot terminal, the polarity is such that the direction of magnetization of the core will be reversed. In so doing, a voltage pulse will be induced in the output winding. If another pulse is now applied to the input winding, in the positive sense, the core flux will be again reversed and a pulse of opposite polarity will be induced in the output winding. Generally speaking, output pulses which are induced by the action of pulses on the input windings of a core are treated as spurious, and means must be provided in the output circuits to reject them. Only those output pulses induced by pulses applied to the advance winding are to be accepted. A practical way to accomplish this is to associate the core pulsing with two or more clock phases. In the simplest of systems there is an input phase and an output phase. As systems become more complex, however, and the outputs of one part of a system become the inputs to another part, either clock phase may be associated with input operation or output operation, depending upon the part of the system involved.

One of the first approaches to the design of general types of magnetic switching circuits is described by Minnick.* This method is characterized by the fact that it uses magnetic cores only, with no rectifiers. The increasing versatility and reliability of rectifiers now makes this restriction quite unnecessary, but for comparative purposes a brief examination of the Minnick method is instructive.

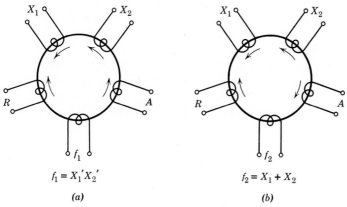

$$f_1 = X_1' X_2'$$

$$f_2 = X_1 + X_2$$

(a)

(b)

Fig. 9–49. Magnetic core realizations of a product and a sum. The polarity of the advance pulse determines which function is produced.

The basic core and winding configurations used by Minnick are shown in Fig. 9–49. In Fig. 9–49(a) there are two input windings X_1 and X_2, an advance winding A, a reset winding R, and an output winding at which the function f_1 is to be produced. Assume that there has

* See Reference 15 in the Bibliography at the end of this Chapter.

been a pulse applied to the reset winding which magnetizes the core in the clockwise direction as indicated. The arrows associated with the input windings, X_1 and X_2, indicate that if a pulse is applied to either of these windings the core will be set in the opposite, or counterclockwise, direction. The arrow associated with the advance winding indicates that the advance pulse also magnetizes the core in the counterclockwise direction. We now observe that after the reset winding pulse magnetizes the core in the clockwise direction, it will be magnetized in the counterclockwise direction if either or both input windings receive pulses. Under these conditions, an advance pulse finds the core already magnetized in the direction associated with the advance pulse, and it will induce no voltage in the output winding. The only circumstance which permits a voltage to be induced in the output winding is to have both inputs 0. Hence the output may be expressed as $f_1 = X_1'X_2'$. If only one of the input windings is used this configuration will supply an output which is the complement of the input. If, however, the core carries more than the two input windings shown in Fig. 9–49(a), the output will be $f_1 = X_1'X_2' \cdot \ldots \cdot X_n'$.

In Fig. 9–49(b), the only change made is that the magnetizing direction of the advance winding has been reversed. After the core has been magnetized clockwise by the reset winding, a pulse on either of the input windings will magnetize it in the counterclockwise direction. Since the advance winding now sets the core in the clockwise direction, an output voltage will be induced if either or both of the input windings have received pulses. Hence the output function is represented by $f_2 = X_1 + X_2$. If the core carries more than the two input windings shown in Fig. 9–49(b) the output will be given by $f_2 = X_1 + X_2 + \ldots + X_n$.

It is cumbersome to represent core and winding configurations by schematic diagrams of the type used in Fig. 9–49. Among other problems is that of accounting for relative polarities. The direction of magnetization depends on the direction of current, the terminal into which current is directed, and the sense of the winding. For the remainder of this discussion, the schematic symbols shown in Fig. 9–50 will be used. In this system, a core is represented by a vertical line, and if there is more than one core, each is identified by a number, or other identification, placed above its vertical line. Input or output leads are represented by horizontal lines which cross the line representing the core at right angles. If, associated with any input or output line, there is a winding on the core, it is represented by a line which passes through the intersection of the core line and the input (or output) line at an angle of 45° to both. The direction of the winding is

signified by having the winding line slope downward either from right
to left or from left to right.

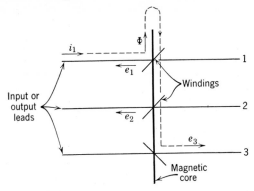

Fig. 9–50. Schematic representation of a magnetic core and its windings, using mirror symbols.

A schematic drawn as described uses the so-called mirror symbol.[*]
This method greatly facilitates the specification of the direction of
magnetization and the direction of induced voltage. It is assumed
that all input currents flow from left to right as indicated by the arrow
on i_1 in Fig. 9–50. When a current flowing from left to right encounters
the slanted line representing the winding, we visualize this line as the
plane of a mirror, and the reflection of the current from the surface of
the mirror indicates the direction of the magnetization thus produced,
as indicated by the arrow on Φ. Now, we know that the change of flux
produced by the current i_1 will induce a voltage e_1 in the direction
indicated by the arrow on e_1, that is, in a direction opposite to the
current which produced the flux change. The direction of induced
voltage is found for all windings by considering that the flux direction
becomes reversed, as shown, and then in passing down through all the
windings is reflected again at each as though by a mirror. When we
perform this second reflection, we see that e_1 is in the direction from
right to left, e_2 is in the direction from right to left, but e_3 is in the
direction from left to right. These directions are all clearly consistent
with Lenz's law and all are embodied in the conventions assumed for
using the mirror symbols.

* M. Karnaugh, "Pulse Switching Circuits Using Magnetic Cores." See Reference 16 in the Bibliography at the end of this chapter. Karnaugh credits the
mirror symbol to R. P. Mayer, "A Proposed Symbol for Magnetic Circuits,"
Engineering Note E-472, Digital Computer Laboratory, Massachusetts Institute
of Technology, August 14, 1952.

In terms of the mirror notation, the configurations shown originally in Fig. 9–49(a) and Fig. 9–49(b) are repeated in Fig. 9–51(a) and Fig. 9–51(b). In both these figures the reset pulse magnetizes the core

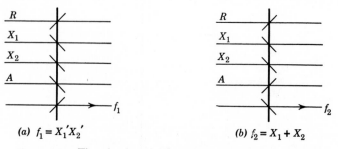

(a) $f_1 = X_1'X_2'$ (b) $f_2 = X_1 + X_2$

Fig. 9–51. The circuits of Fig. 9–49 using mirror symbols.

upward and any input pulse magnetizes it downward. However, in Fig. 9–51(a) the advance pulse magnetizes the core downward and there can be an output only if there has been no pulse on either input winding. In Fig. 9–51(b) the advance pulse magnetizes the core upward and there will be a change of flux, and hence an output, if either or both input windings have received pulses. We observe in these figures also that when the sense of the advance winding is reversed, the sense of the output winding must also be reversed if the polarity of the output pulse is to be unchanged.

We may combine the basic Multiply and Add circuits of Fig. 9–51 into a two-stage circuit of the type shown in Fig. 9–52. Cores 1 and 2 have as their outputs $g_1 = X_1'X_2'$, and $g_2 = X_3'X_4'$, respectively.

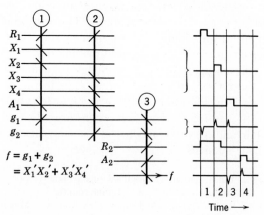

Fig. 9–52. A two-level circuit. Chart at the right indicates the timing of input and control pulses.

These outputs become in turn the inputs of core 3 where the function $f = g_1 + g_2$ is realized. Thus in a two-stage circuit, as represented, we can produce any switching function which is expressed as a minimum sum.

There are difficulties, however, associated with the timing of events in this type of circuit. A diagram to illustrate this fact is shown at the right of Fig. 9–52. In the first time interval we see that cores 1 and 2 are reset by the pulse R_1. This action can produce negative pulses in the output lines g_1 and g_2, and to prevent any disturbance to core 3 the reset pulse R_2 is maintained throughout the first time interval. In the second time interval the inputs X_1, X_2, X_3, and X_4 may be pulsed, and these pulses are in the direction to produce positive pulses in the outputs g_1 and g_2. In order to prevent a spurious input signal to core 3, the reset pulse R_2 is maintained into the second time interval and until after the pulses on g_1 and g_2 have terminated. In the third time interval, the advance pulse A_1 produces output pulses from cores 1 and 2 which are transmitted to core 3. These inputs to core 3 cause a negative pulse on its output, but it is assumed that proper precautions are taken to see that this negative pulse has no effect on the remainder of the system. Finally, in the fourth time interval the advance pulse A_2 produces the final output of the system in the form of a positive pulse on the f output lead. It is apparent from a study of Fig. 9–52 that when magnetic cores are used as switching devices without other means for guarding against spurious outputs, it becomes necessary to regulate both the lengths of pulses and the timing of pulses in a quite precise manner.

In larger and more complex circuits, such adjustments become more and more difficult and other methods have been devised to prevent undesired signals from propagating. Figure 9–53 illustrates some of the basic ideas. In this figure the output windings of cores 1 and 2 of

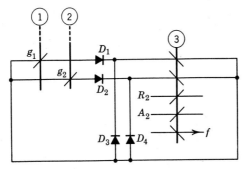

Fig. 9–53. Diodes used to avoid false outputs.

Fig. 9–52 are shown feeding the input windings of core 3, and the complete loop for the circulation of the output pulses from cores 1 and 2 is indicated. Instead of using a prolonged reset pulse on core 3 to prevent any effect from negative pulses on the output lines g_1 and g_2, diodes D_1 and D_2 are introduced to prevent the flow of current caused by these negative output pulses. It can also be seen that if there have been outputs on either g_1 or g_2 or both, so that core 3 has been set in a downward direction, the subsequent action of the advance pulse A_2 will not only induce a voltage in the output winding, but will also induce voltages in the two input windings of core 3. These voltages will be in the direction to circulate current clockwise around the loop and hence through the windings g_1 and g_2. Such backward feeding voltages are usually reduced considerably by proper proportioning of the windings concerned. In addition the diodes D_3 and D_4 can be used to present a low resistance to the back voltages and thus prevent them from establishing currents in the g_1 and g_2 windings on cores 1 and 2. At the same time, these diodes are so oriented that they present a high resistance to the output pulses of cores 1 and 2.

In core circuits of the type we have been studying an output pulse is obtained by transformer action when the advance winding receives a pulse. Karnaugh* has published an extensive treatment of this type of circuit, in which he particularly studies the problem of realizing a complete function with the use of only one magnetic core. For this purpose he allows input pulses to establish magnetizing forces in both

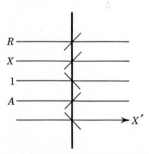

directions in the core, and calls the resultant magnetizing force the *input composite*. From the input composite is derived the *setting function*, which is the function represented by the core output.

A simple example of this approach is illustrated in Fig. 9–54 in which a complementary variable is produced. A reset pulse establishes upward magnetization of the core. The X input is synchronous with a unit pulse on the input line labeled 1. This unit pulse always occurs whether there is an X pulse or not. We note that the winding

Fig. 9–54. Input-composite method for obtaining the complement of a core input.

for the X input is in the direction to magnetize the core upward, while that associated with the unit pulse input magnetizes the core downward. When these two pulses occur simultaneously, their magnetomotive forces are opposed, and if we make the magnetomotive forces

* See Reference 16 in the Bibliography at the end of this chapter.

of equal magnitudes, the effect of the combined X input and unit input will be to cause no change in the core magnetization. Hence, following the X pulse, the advance pulse, which is in the direction to magnetize the core upward, finds the core already magnetized in that direction. Since there is then no change in core flux, there will be no output pulse. If, however, there is no X pulse, the unit pulse will magnetize the core in the downward direction, and the subsequent advance pulse in returning the core to upward magnetization will induce a voltage in the output winding. Since the output voltage is 0 when $X = 1$, and is 1 when $X = 0$, the setting function is recognized as $f = X'$. We also observe an opportunity to simplify the structure. Since the advance pulse always leaves the core magnetized in the upward direction, there is no need for a reset pulse to do the same thing. Hence the reset winding can be omitted.

With the reset winding eliminated core operation takes place in two time phases. These phases are established by appropriate clock pulses. For a given core, in the first phase it receives pulses at its input windings, and in the second phase it receives an advance pulse. The advance pulse is in the direction to leave the core again ready to receive input pulses in the next phase. When cores are interconnected so that the output of one becomes the input of another they are, of course, operating so that the output phase of one core is the input phase of another. In such systems, it becomes necessary to identify carefully the relative phases of various cores, particularly when delay elements are used to establish phase identity between signals from different paths in the system.

Although the input composite procedure alone cannot realize all switching functions, Karnaugh has shown that it can be applied to the realization of a large class of symmetric functions. This class may be described as that in which the symmetric function has *all* the a-numbers between j, the smallest a-number, and n, the number of variables, inclusive. We are particularly interested in two special cases which represent the extremes of this class. In the first, for which the smallest a-number is 1, the setting function reduces to $f = X_1 + X_2 + \ldots + X_n$. This function is realized, of course, by the circuit of Fig. 9–51 (b), with the reset winding omitted, and with additional input windings supplied.

In the other special case, the smallest a-number is n, and the function has the value 1 when all the variables have the value 1. The setting function is hence $f = X_1 X_2 \cdot \ldots \cdot X_n$. An input composite for this function is obtained by allowing any one of the variables to set the core down and allowing the *complements* of all remaining variables to set the core up. Thus, in Fig. 9–55, with the core initially magnetized upward, if all variables in the product have the value 1, there will be

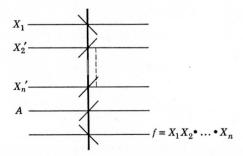

Fig. 9–55. Input composite for realization of a product.

a pulse on the X_1 line and no pulse on any line representing a complemented variable. Hence the X_1 pulse sets the core down, the advance pulse sets it up and there is an output pulse produced.

This method can be used to reduce the number of complementary variables required. Suppose we want to produce the term $f = X_1'X_2'X_3X_4$. We can use either X_3 or X_4 to set the core down, and then apply to the upward setting inputs either X_1, X_2, and X_4', or X_1, X_2, and X_3', respectively.

We are assuming in this discussion that all pulses are of equal amplitude and are applied to windings containing the same number of turns. In the circuit of Fig. 9–51(b) the input pulses need not be applied simultaneously since any one of them is sufficient to set the core down. However, in the circuit of Fig. 9–55, if the pulses are not simultaneous, the pulse on X_1 must precede all other inputs. If the X_1 pulse arrives late it can set the core down even though one or more other inputs were present to oppose it.

A quite different method for obtaining the output of a core circuit is that in which the advance pulse is used directly as the output pulse instead of being used to induce an output pulse by transformer action. Karnaugh[*] describes two basic procedures leading to either his type AF circuit or to the type AB circuit. We shall illustrate both types by using them in realizing the function $f = f_1 + f_2 = X_1'X_2 + X_1X_2'$.

A type AF realization is given in Fig. 9–56. Cores 1 and 2, respectively, are "set" by input composites for f_1 and f_2, respectively. By this we mean that if either f_1 or f_2 has the value 1 its core is magnetized downward. The advance pulse "resets" the core, that is, magnetizes it in the upward direction, and in so doing induces a voltage in the out-

─────────────

[*] See Reference 16 in the Bibliography at the end of this chapter.

put, or f, winding on any core that was previously set. If either f winding has a voltage induced in it, the advance-pulse current will flow through the path containing that winding because the induced voltage is in the forward direction relative to the advance-pulse current. Thus a voltage induced in either the f_1 winding or the f_2 winding in Fig. 9–56 requires the advance pulse to pass through the path containing that voltage and into the load impedance Z. A voltage pulse across the

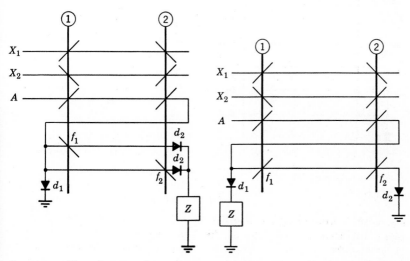

Fig. 9–56. The advance pulse used as an output pulse in the type AF circuit.

Fig. 9–57. Type AB circuit for using the advance pulse as an output pulse.

load represents a circuit output of value 1. If neither core is set most of the advance-pulse current passes through the low-impedance path containing the diode d_1 and the output then has the value 0. Since the output is high if either the path through f_1 or the path through f_2 conducts advance-pulse current, the output correctly represents $f = f_1 + f_2$.

In the type AB circuit of Fig. 9–57 the input composites are identical with those of Fig. 9–56 but the output windings f_1 and f_2 are of opposite sense and are connected in series. The voltages induced in the output windings when an advance pulse resets a core are in the direction to oppose the flow of advance-pulse current through the output windings. The windings are designed so that the magnitudes of induced voltages permit either the f_1 or the f_2 output to block the passage of the advance pulse. If either f_1 or f_2 is high the current of the advance pulse flows through the load Z and the circuit output is high. Thus again the output represents $f = f_1 + f_2$.

In both circuits diodes prevent the flow of induced current during the phase when the inputs receive pulses. In the type AB circuit diode d_2 prevents the flow of reverse current when a blocking potential is inducing in winding f_1 or f_2.

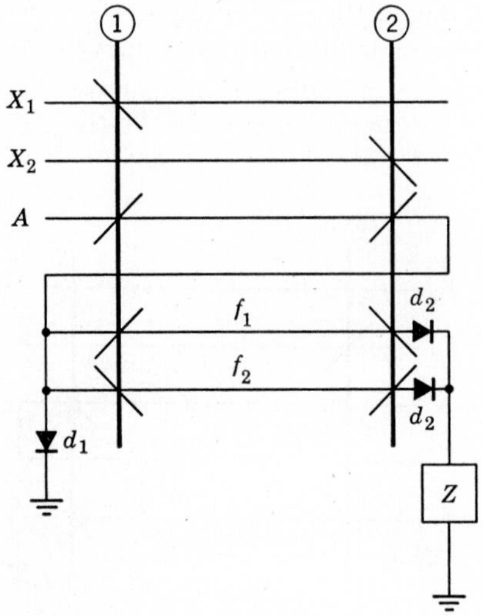

Fig. 9–58. Circuit using an output composite to determine the path of the advance current.

Another type of circuit which uses the advance pulse in the output circuit is described by Rosenfeld* and is shown in Fig. 9–58 where it is used to realize the same output function as the preceding two circuits. This circuit is similar to the type AF circuit in that the advance pulse is conducted through a path in which the induced voltage is in the forward direction. However, each core now represents the state of a single variable. The input windings are all in the same direction, but the output windings are connected to form an *output* composite.

We observe that the cores are set by the input variables X_1 and X_2 rather than by composite functions of those variables. In the output circuit which produces f_1 the induced voltage due to the advance pulse is in the forward direction in the winding on core 2 and in the backward direction in the winding on core 1. Hence because of the advance pulse the net voltage in this path is forward if core 1 is not set and core 2 is set. Thus the advance-pulse current takes the path through the f_1 windings to the load impedance Z if the input combination is $X_1'X_2$. When the input combination is X_1X_2' core 1 is set and core 2 is not set. The advance pulse induces forward voltage in the f_2 winding on core 1 and no voltage in the winding on core 2. Hence the advance-pulse current passes through the f_2 windings to the load Z. If neither core is set or if both are set, the net induced voltage in both the f_1 and the f_2 paths is zero. When this happens the advance pulse takes the low-impedance path through the diode d_1 and the circuit output is thus 0.

In performing a synthesis using the output-composite method certain restrictions must be observed. First, in order to simplify the engineering design, the advance-pulse current must not be allowed to divide

* See Reference 18 in the Bibliography at the end of this chapter.

among two or more paths in the output composite. Therefore the function to be realized must be written in a disjunctive form so that no two product terms have the value 1 for the same combination of variables. In Fig. 9–59 the same function is represented in both maps. If the minimum-sum terms indicated in Fig. 9–59(a) are chosen we

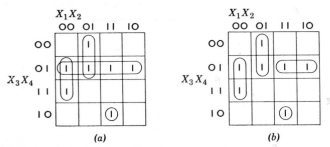

Fig. 9–59. A function to be realized in (a) the minimum-sum form and (b) disjunctive form.

find that the terms $X_3'X_4$ and $X_1'X_2X_3'$ both have the value 1 for the input combination 0101, and the terms $X_3'X_4$ and $X_1'X_2'X_4$ both have the value 1 for the input combination 0001. For both these input combinations the advance-pulse current would divide between two paths in the output composite. We avoid this by choosing terms which are represented by subcubes that do not overlap, as in Fig. 9–59(b). Hence we will perform the synthesis for the function written in the form $f = X_1'X_2'X_4 + X_1'X_2X_3' + X_1X_3'X_4 + X_1X_2X_3X_4'$.

The second restriction is that within each path in the output composite there must be one and only one winding polarized in the forward direction. This winding is located on a core set by some variable desired in the term. The remaining variables in the term are realized by placing backward-polarized windings on cores that are set by the *complements* of those variables.

We note that this restriction was observed in the circuit of Fig. 9–58. Using cores set by X_1 and X_2 we produce the terms $X_1'X_2$ and X_1X_2'. We cannot produce the term X_1X_2 on these cores because it would require the use of two forward-polarized windings in the same path. We can, however, use these cores if the product $X_1'X_2'$ is needed within a term, such as in $X_1'X_2'X_4$, provided the backward-polarized windings on cores 1 and 2 are contained in a path which has a forward-polarized winding on a core set by X_4.

An important minimizing step in the synthesis of an output composite is the choice of the variables that set the cores. Within each path complementation can be performed by reversing a winding polarity. Even though a variable and its complement are present in the algebraic expression for a function, it does not necessarily require the use of two cores. Accordingly we try to choose core variables which minimize the number of cores required.

For each pair of variables it is possible to realize three of the four product combinations with two cores, as has been demonstrated. A study of these combinations will frequently indicate for which variable or variables it will be most profitable to use whatever extra cores may be required. In the function written from the map of Fig. 9–59(b), the variable pairs X_1X_2, X_1X_3, and X_1X_4, each appear in three of their four possible product combinations. For each of the remaining pairs of variables only two product combinations are present. It may be verified that this function cannot be realized on four cores, one for each variable. As a first trial it would therefore seem desirable to supply cores for both X_1 and X_1' so that no forward-polarized winding need be used for either of these literals.

A chart of the form shown in Fig. 9–60 is helpful in choosing the cores to be used and in determining the locations of forward and

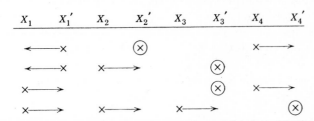

Fig. 9–60. Selection of cores for an output-composite synthesis.

backward-polarized windings. Each variable and its complement is represented by a column. Each product term of the function is entered as a row, by placing crosses under the variables in the term. Thus the term $X_1'X_2'X_4$ is entered in the first row by placing crosses in the X_1', X_2', and X_4 columns. If a cross remains in the column in which it was originally entered, that variable must be represented by a forward winding on the core. When a variable in a term is represented by a backward winding the cross in the chart must be shifted into the column of the complementary variable. An entry selected for representation by a forward winding is encircled in the chart and all remaining entries in the same row must be shifted, as indicated by the arrows. Our objective in this process is to get all the circled entries and the shifted entries into the minimum number of columns, under the condition that there be one and only one circled entry in each row. We note that in working out the selection for this synthesis we can ignore the entries in the first two columns because we have decided to supply cores for both X_1 and X_1'. Using the selection shown in Fig. 9–60 we can realize the function by an output composite on cores set by inputs X_1, X_1', X_2', X_3', and X_4'.

Once the cores have been selected the design of an output composite is greatly simplified by noting its resemblance to a relay-contact network. Multiplication is represented by connecting windings in series, and addition is represented by the parallel connection of paths. The polarity of a winding indicates whether the core-input variable or its complement is represented.

Before completing this synthesis let us look at Fig. 9–61, which shows the circuit of Fig. 9–58 in a simpler symbolic form. The mirror

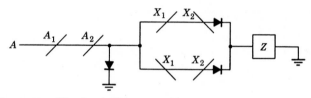

Fig. 9–61. Circuit of Fig. 9–58 using detached mirror symbols.

symbols are detached from the cores and only the advance-pulse circuit is shown. Advance-pulse windings are included in the drawing so that the direction of flux change resulting from an advance pulse can be determined.

For the function we have been synthesizing the output composite circuit is given in Fig. 9–62. Instead of showing the advance windings, we indicate by the symbol at the left that the advance pulse sets the cores upward and that, with the reflection as indicated, the direction

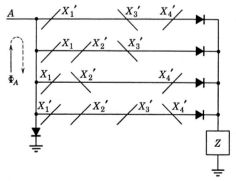

Fig. 9–62. Function mapped in Fig. 9–59 as realized by an output composite.

of polarization of windings is found by reflecting a downward-directed
flux arrow from the mirror symbols.

An output composite need not necessarily be in series-parallel form.
Any given winding may be shared by more than one path. However,
we must observe the restriction that each path contain one and only
one forward-polarized winding. Furthermore, we must insert rectifiers
so located and so oriented that they not only prevent the flow of
induced current during the application of input pulses, but that they
also prevent the circulation of current within network loops. It may
be verified that the non-series-parallel network of Fig. 9–63 contains

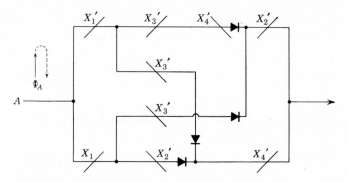

Fig. 9–63. A non-series-parallel version of the output composite.

in its paths all the terms of the function and that the diodes shown
prevent the flow of spurious currents. This circuit was obtained by
first designing a contact network to realize the function, using the
methods described in Chapter **8**. The contacts were then replaced by
windings, and the diodes were inserted to complete the synthesis. In
its original form the output composite required 13 windings, whereas
in the non-series-parallel form it uses 9 windings.

Magnetic-core switching is becoming increasingly important in industrial control. A number of "standard packages" are offered and
these, when assembled and used with appropriate power supply, make
possible static control circuits which are compact, reliable, and require
little or no maintenance.

In one widely used system the logical elements are built around the
magnetic amplifier developed by R. A. Ramey,* and shown in Fig.
9–64. The magnetic material used in this device has the rectangular
hysteresis loop which characterizes other types of switching cores. If
no signal voltage E_i is applied (but the input circuit is closed) the bias

* See Reference 11 in the Bibliography at the end of this chapter.

voltages E_{ac} and E_{ac}' alternately saturate the core in both directions. During the so-called reset half cycle, voltage E_{ac}' sets up a current *out of* the dot end of the input, or reset, winding while the diode d_1 prevents the flow of current in the output, or gate, winding. The core is hence saturated in the reset direction. During the next half cycle

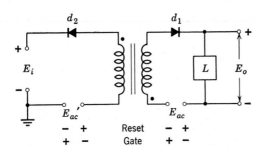

Fig. 9–64. Basic Ramey amplifier.

the diode d_2 prevents the flow of current in the reset winding and voltage E_{ac} establishes current *into* the dot end of the gate winding. This current reverses the flux and the core saturates in the opposite direction. Substantially all of the voltage E_{ac} is used in reversing the core flux and only a small voltage, due to the exciting current flowing through the load impedance, appears at the output.

If an input voltage E_i is now applied, and this voltage is larger than the reset bias voltage E_{ac}', no excitation current can flow in the reset circuit and the core flux does not reverse during the reset half cycle. During the gating half cycle the voltage E_{ac} is not used in reversing the core flux and almost the entire voltage appears across the load. The current that flows is limited only by the load impedance.

Thus, in response to a binary input E_i, the output voltage E_o is also binary, but it appears one half-cycle later than the input. Aside from this delay, the switching action is described algebraically by $E_o = E_i$.

For practical use the device requires the modification of the input circuit shown in Fig. 9–65. During

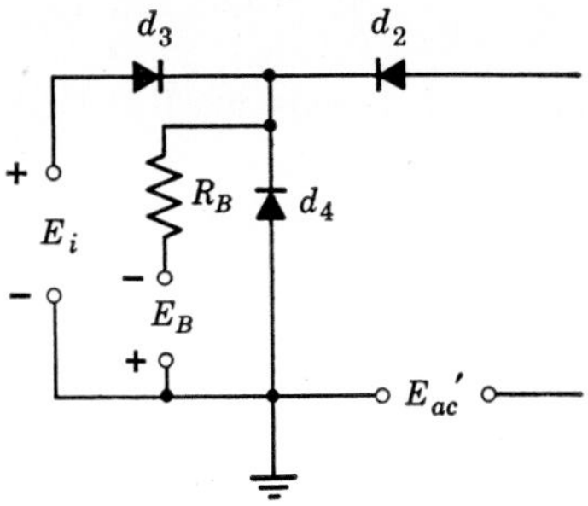

Fig. 9–65. Modification of the input circuit.

the reset half cycle we would like to have a low-impedance path for the exciting current and a relatively high-impedance path for the input signal. The voltage E_B and the resistor R_B establish a loop current through the diode d_4 which is slightly larger than the exciting current during the reset half cycle. If $E_i = 0$ the exciting current effectively sees only the *forward* resistance of the diode d_4 because the forward current is not quite reduced to zero by the opposing exciting current. If $E_i = 1$, the input source supplies current until the bias current in rectifier d_4 is exceeded. Thereafter the input source supplies a load consisting of the parallel combination of the back resistance of the diode d_4 and the resistance R_B. The diode d_3 prevents the flow of excitation current into the input source.

A circuit with two inputs and two of the bias circuits of Fig. 9–65 is shown in Fig. 9–66. If either input is low the excitation current during the reset half cycle can flow through the bias circuit of the low

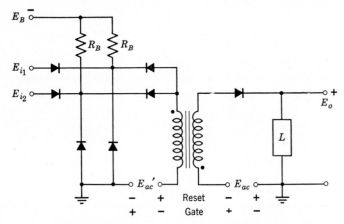

Fig. 9–66. Multiply gate using the Ramey amplifier.

input. It is only when both inputs are high that the core cannot reset and the output in the next half cycle becomes high. This circuit is thus a Multiply gate with two inputs. Other inputs can be added by supplying additional bias circuits and blocking diodes.

Add gates, in this system of standard components, make use of the conventional rectifier add circuit of Fig. 9–10(b). Because the Add gate does not include a magnetic amplifier element, the half-cycle time delay which is a feature of the Multiply gate is not present. Since a Multiply gate contains a source of energy, when we combine it with the passive Add gate we are not limited to a two-stage design as we are with rectifier gates. But when signals from several paths are combined in this system it may be necessary to equalize the delays in these paths.

Complementation of a variable is accomplished by the circuit of Fig. 9–67. A reset bias voltage is not supplied in this circuit. If there is no input signal the core does not reset and the output is high. But

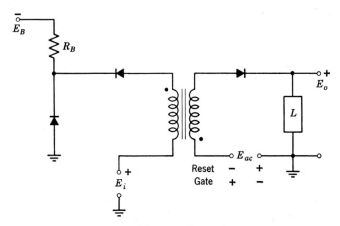

Fig. 9–67. The complementing gate.

when an input voltage of the polarity shown is applied, the core is reset by this input and the output is low. The input E_i is usually a half-wave voltage opposite in phase to the gating voltage.

These gates are sufficient, of course, to realize any combinational switching function. A special power supply must be used to provide voltages at the required levels and phases. The gates used to realize switching functions operate at a low energy level, but the outputs of the switching circuits can be supplied as inputs to magnetic amplifiers which in turn can supply substantial energy for control purposes.

Bibliography

1. Staff of the Computation Laboratory, *Synthesis of Electronic Computing and Control Circuits,* Harvard University Press, Cambridge, Mass., 1951.
2. S. H. Washburn, "An Application of Boolean Algebra to the Design of Electronic Switching Circuits," *A.I.E.E. Transactions, Part 1, Communication and Electronics,* Vol. 72, September 1953, pp. 380–388.
3. P. C. Sherertz, "Electronic Circuits of the NAREC Computer," *Proc. I.R.E.,* Vol. 41, No. 10, October 1953, pp. 1313–1320.
4. S. E. Gluck, H. J. Gray, Jr., C. T. Leondes, M. Rubinoff, "The Design of Logical OR-AND-OR Pyramids for Digital Computers," *Proc. I.R.E.,* Vol. 41, No. 10, October 1953, pp. 1388–1392.
5. P. F. Strong, "Rectifiers as Elements of Switching Circuits," *Proc. Assoc. for Computing Machinery,* Pittsburgh, Pa., May 2 and 3, 1952.
6. A. E. Anderson, "Transistors in Switching Circuits," *Proc. I.R.E.,* Vol. 40, No. 11, November 1952, pp. 1541–1558.

7. A. W. Lo, "Transistor Trigger Circuits," *Proc. I.R.E.*, Vol. 40, No. 11, November 1952, pp. 1531–1541.

8. L. W. Hussey, "Semiconductor Diode Gates," *Bell System Tech. Jour.*, Vol. 32, No. 5, September 1953, pp. 1137–1154.

9. R. F. Shea and others, *Transistor Circuits*, John Wiley and Sons, New York, 1953.

10. A. Wang, "Magnetic Triggers," *Proc. I.R.E.*, Vol. 38, No. 6, June 1950, pp. 626–629.

11. R. A. Ramey, "The Single-Core Magnetic Amplifier as a Computer Element," *A.I.E.E. Trans., Part 1, Communication and Electronics,* Vol. 71, 1952, pp. 442–446.

12. D. Katz, "A Magnetic Amplifier Switching Matrix," *A.I.E.E. Trans., Part 1, Communication and Electronics,* Vol. 75, May 1956, pp. 236–241.

13. C. Huang and E. Slobodzinski, "Power Transistor Switching Circuit," *A.I.E.E. Trans., Part 1, Communication and Electronics,* Vol. 75, July 1956, pp. 290–296.

14. R. L. Bright, "Junction Transistors Used as Switches," *A.I.E.E. Trans., Part 1, Communication and Electronics,* Vol. 74, March 1955, pp. 111–121.

15. R. C. Minnick, "Magnetic Switching Circuits," *J. of App. Phys.*, Vol. 25, No. 4, April 1954, pp. 479–485.

16. M. Karnaugh, "Pulse-Switching Circuits Using Magnetic Cores," *Proc. I.R.E.*, Vol. 43, No. 5, May 1955, pp. 570–584.

17. D. Loev, W. Miehle, J. Paivinen, and J. Wylen, "Magnetic Core Circuits for Digital Data-Processing Systems," *Proc. I.R.E.*, Vol. 44, No. 2, February 1956, pp. 154–162.

18. J. L. Rosenfeld, "Magnetic Core Pulse-Switching Circuits for Standard Packages," Master's thesis, Department of Electrical Engineering, Massachusetts Institute of Technology, June 1957.

PROBLEMS

9.1 Four input variables A, B, C, and D, but not their complements, are available to two electronic combinational circuits.

    1. In one circuit the function $F_1 = (A' + B' + C)(B + C)(C + D)$ is to be realized using only pentodes.

    2. In the other circuit the function $F_2 = A'B'C + BC + CD$ is to be realized using only triodes (but not as cathode followers).

    3. If you are given a functional diagram containing only pentodes, is it always true that a function which is dual in form (one in which the operations of addition and multiplication are interchanged) will be obtained by substituting triodes for the pentodes? Give proof of your answer.

    4. If you are given a functional diagram containing only triodes, is it always possible to obtain a function which is dual in form by substituting pentodes for the triodes? Give proof of your answer.

9.2 Design combinational electronic circuits which will realize the transmission functions given. Use only triodes and pentodes. The indicated numbers of grids are sufficient, but not necessarily minimum. Assume that both the primed and unprimed input variables are available. For part 1 draw a diagram showing all vacuum tubes and resistors required. For the remaining parts draw only a logical schematic diagram.

1. $T(A, B, C, D) = \sum (3, 7, 11, 14, 15)$ (5 grids)
2. $T(A, B, C, D) = \sum (0, 3, 7, 8, 11, 12, 15)$ (8 grids)
3. $T(A, B, C, D) = \sum (3, 7, 11, 12, 13, 14)$ (10 grids)
4. $T(A, B, C, D) = \sum (0, 3, 4, 7, 8, 11, 13, 14)$ (11 grids)

9.3 Show at least one realization of each of the transmission functions in Problem 9.2, utilizing diodes as well as vacuum tubes.

9.4 Reduce the following expression to a minimum form:

$$f(v, w, x, y, z) = v'w'x'y'z' + v'w'xy'z' + v'w'xy'z + v'wx'y'z'$$
$$+ vw'x'yz + vw'xyz' + vw'xyz + vwx'yz$$

Draw a schematic diagram of a minimal circuit using triodes and pentodes to realize the function.

9.5 An electronic combinational circuit is to realize two outputs, both functions of A, B, C, D. The outputs are given by:

$$T_1 = \sum (0, 1, 2, 7, 11, 15)$$
$$T_2 = \sum (8, 9, 10, 12, 13, 14)$$

Synthesize the circuit using triodes and pentodes. Assume that both primed and unprimed input variables are available. Minimize the number of grids otherwise required.

9.6 Design an electronic combinational switching circuit, using pentodes and triodes, which has three outputs, M, N, and S. M equals 1 if a majority of the four input variables, A, B, C, D are 1; N equals 1 if none of the input variables equals 1; S equals 1 if some of the input variables equal 1. Assume that voltage levels representing all the input variables and their complements are available. Minimize the number of grids used.

9.7 A combinational circuit has four inputs w, x, y, z and four outputs a, b, c, d. The inputs w, x represent in binary form a number M which can have decimal values from 0 to 3, and the inputs y, z represent another number N in exactly the same way. The outputs a, b, c, d are to represent in binary form the product P of M and N. Hence P can have decimal values from 0 to 9.

1. Derive expressions for the outputs a, b, c, d as functions of w, x, y, z.
2. The expressions found in (1) are to be realized by an electronic, multiple-output circuit which may contain both rectifiers and vacuum tubes. Rectifiers are to be used in preference to vacuum tubes wherever there is a choice. Draw a schematic diagram of the most economical circuit which produces a, b, c, d as a function of w, x, y, z only. (Note that complementary variables are not available at the inputs.) Write the algebraic expressions represented by the solution.

9.8 (a) A function of the variables A, B, C, D is represented by the standard sum $T_1 = \sum (0, 1, 2, 3, 8, 9, 10, 13)$. Synthesize a minimum network of triodes and/or pentodes which realizes this function.

(b) A second function of the variables A, B, C, D is given by the standard sum $T_2 = \sum (0, 1, 8, 11, 12, 14, 15)$. Synthesize a minimum network of triodes and/or pentodes which realizes T_2 as a function of (T_1, A, B, C, D).

9.9 Design combinational electronic circuits which will realize the following pairs of transmission functions. For each draw a logical schematic diagram only. Assume that both primed and unprimed input variables are available. Use only vacuum tubes.

1. $T_1(A, B, C, D) = \sum(2, 8, 10, 11)$; $T_2(A, B, C, D) = \sum(6, 12, 14, 15)$
(10 grids are sufficient)

2. $T_1(A, B, C, D) = \sum(11, 13, 14, 15)$; $T_2(A, B, C, D) = \sum(3, 6, 7)$
(12 grids are sufficient)

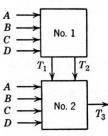

Problem 9.10.

9.10 In the block diagram circuit No. 1 is an electronic combinational switching circuit which realizes the functions T_1 and T_2 of the four variables A, B, C, and D. Synthesize an electronic combination circuit, No. 2, using only triodes and pentodes, which realizes the function T_3 as a function of T_1, T_2, and the four variables A, B, C, and D. You may assume that both primed and unprimed variables are available for A, B, C, and D, but not for T_1 and T_2.

$$T_1 = \sum(0, 1, 9, 13, 15)$$
$$T_2 = \sum(0, 1, 4, 6, 8, 9, 12)$$
$$T_3 = \sum(0, 2, 4, 5, 10, 13, 15)$$

9.11 The following standard sums represent functions of the variables A, B, C, and D. Circuits to realize these functions are to be synthesized using:
    (a) Vacuum tubes only.
    (b) Vacuum tubes and rectifiers.
    (c) Transistors.
    (d) Magnetic core circuits with output composites, as illustrated in Fig. 9–58.

  1. $\sum(0, 3, 6)$ 2. $\sum(0, 13, 14)$
  3. $\sum(0, 3, 6, 9)$ 4. $\sum(0, 5, 6, 11)$
  5. $\sum(0, 5, 6, 7, 12)$ 6. $\sum(0, 6, 10, 11, 12)$
  7. $\sum(1, 6, 10, 12, 15)$ 8. $\sum(4, 8, 11, 12, 13, 14)$
  9. $\sum(1, 6, 8, 9, 10, 12)$ 10. $\sum(2, 4, 5, 7, 9, 14)$
11. $\sum(3, 4, 5, 6, 9, 10)$ 12. $\sum(1, 2, 7, 8, 13, 14)$
13. $\sum(0, 1, 2, 3, 5, 6, 12)$ 14. $\sum(0, 1, 2, 3, 7, 8, 14)$
15. $\sum(0, 3, 4, 5, 6, 12, 15)$ 16. $\sum(1, 2, 4, 5, 7, 10, 14)$
17. $\sum(1, 4, 6, 7, 9, 10, 13)$ 18. $\sum(2, 3, 4, 5, 6, 7, 8, 15)$
19. $\sum(6, 7, 8, 9, 10, 11, 12, 13)$ 20. $\sum(1, 4, 7, 8, 9, 10, 11, 13)$
21. $\sum(1, 3, 7, 8, 10, 11, 13, 14)$ 22. $\sum(0, 2, 5, 6, 9, 10, 11, 15)$

CHAPTER 10

Switching aspects of codes

A code may be regarded as a system of symbols arbitrarily established to represent words, numbers, or other symbols. There are many kinds of codes, designed to accomplish a variety of purposes. In this chapter we shall discuss binary codes only, and among those the treatment will be limited to codes of three classes, each class having a different purpose or purposes.

The first class is that in which a decimal number is represented by a binary code. This class of codes is of particular interest to the designers of digital computers, for by the appropriate choice of a code various computational advantages may be derived. Our interest will not be in the computational aspects of these codes, but in the switching problems of encoding, decoding, and translation from one code to another.

In the second class the code again represents numerical values, but computational features are sacrificed in order to obtain advantageous code sequences. This class of codes is designated by several names: cyclic, progressive, or Gray codes. They are widely used in equipment which requires that information in analogue form be converted to digital form. In this chapter we will consider the problem of generating cyclic codes and also that of translation from cyclic codes to computational codes and vice versa.

Finally, there is a large class of codes which make possible either the detection of error in a transmitted code "word," or the detection and correction of error. From the viewpoint of combinational switching theory these codes present no serious problem of encoding and decoding. Our interest will be primarily in the structure of one type of error detecting and correcting code, and not merely because of that property, important as it is. This type of code is related to an aspect of the synthesis of sequential switching circuits, and the discussion in this chapter prepares us for some of the work of Chapter 13.

10.1 Decimal-Binary Codes

In the design of digital computing equipment one of the basic decisions which must be made is to specify what code or codes are to be used for the representation of decimal numbers. In certain kinds of special-purpose computers it may be desirable to convert the entire decimal number to its binary equivalent. In general-purpose types of computers, however, considerations of speed, reliability, and simplification of components usually require that each separate decimal digit be represented by a binary code.

It is apparent that in order to represent ten decimal digits it is necessary to use at least four digits in the binary code. Since there are sixteen available combinations of the four binary digits, of which only ten combinations are used, if all possible assignments of binary combinations to decimal digits are counted, it is possible to form $16!/6! = 2.9 \times 10^{10}$ codes.[*]

Not all of these codes are directly useful for computational purposes, although we shall see in Art. 10.3 that all of them can be translated into more suitable forms. The criterion of usefulness in the computational sense is that the decimal digit represented can be determined directly from the code digits. Although there are some exceptions, most of these codes are of the type called weighted codes.[†]

Among these weighted codes, we are already familiar with the one in which each decimal digit is represented by its exact binary equivalent. In that code the weights of $8, 4, 2, 1$ for the four binary digits are derived from 2^3, 2^2, 2^1, and 2^0.

A few examples of weighted, 4-digit codes are shown in Table 10–1. The weights of the binary digits are shown at the top of each column and the decimal digits represented by the code groups are shown at

---

[*] See Reference 1, Bibliography at the end of Chapter 9.

[†] R. K. Richards, *Arithmetic Operations in Digital Computers*, D. Van Nostrand Co., New York, 1955. In Chapter 6 of this Reference a listing of **70** weighted 4-digit codes is given.

Table 10–1

Some Weighted Binary Codes

	8 4 2 1	7 4 2 1	2 4 2 1	6 4 2 −3
0	0 0 0 0	0 0 0 0	0 0 0 0	0 0 0　0
1	0 0 0 1	0 0 0 1	0 0 0 1	0 1 0　1
2	0 0 1 0	0 0 1 0	0 0 1 0	0 0 1　0
3	0 0 1 1	0 0 1 1	0 0 1 1	1 0 0　1
4	0 1 0 0	0 1 0 0	0 1 0 0	0 1 0　0
5	0 1 0 1	0 1 0 1	1 0 1 1	1 0 1　1
6	0 1 1 0	0 1 1 0	1 1 0 0	0 1 1　0
7	0 1 1 1	1 0 0 0	1 1 0 1	1 1 0　1
8	1 0 0 0	1 0 0 1	1 1 1 0	1 0 1　0
9	1 0 0 1	1 0 1 0	1 1 1 1	1 1 1　1

the left of each row. For this set of codes, from each 4-digit code group the decimal digit can be derived directly as the sum of the weights in those binary positions for which 1's are entered. Thus, in the third column, for which the weights are $2, 4, 2, 1$, the code group for decimal 7 is 1101, corresponding to the sum $2 + 4 + 0 + 1 = 7$. The weights assigned to binary digits need not necessarily be positive, as we can see in the code shown in the fourth column where the weights are $6, 4, 2, -3$. In this code, decimal 5 is written 1011, corresponding to the sum $6 + 0 + 2 + (-3) = 5$.

In the codes listed in the third and fourth columns of Table 10–1 there appears to be some degree of choice in writing some of the code groups. For example, in the third column, for which the binary digit weights are $2, 4, 2, 1$, decimal 5 is written 1011, but it can also be written 0101. Similarly, in the fourth column, where the weights are $6, 4, 2, -3$, decimal 6 is written 0110, but it can also be written 1000. By choosing these entries as shown in the table we are able to preserve a feature of the codes which is important in computer application. Both codes as written are self-complementing. That is, when the code representation of any decimal digit is given, the code for its 9's complement is found by changing all the 0's to 1's and vice versa. It is important in the subtraction of decimal numbers to be able to obtain 9's complements readily. Thus, in the $2, 4, 2, 1$ code, decimal 3 is represented by 0011, and its 9's complement, or 6, is represented by 1100. In the $6, 4, 2, -3$ code, decimal 3 is represented by 1001 and decimal 6 by 0110. This feature is not present in the codes listed in the first and second columns, and if these codes are adopted it is necessary to use more elaborate methods to get 9's complements.

The $8, 4, 2, 1$ code can be transformed to a nonweighted code of considerable interest by adding the binary equivalent of decimal 3 to each entry, thus obtaining the so-called "excess-3" code which is shown in Table 10–2.

Table 10–2

Excess-3 Code

Decimal	Binary
0	0 0 1 1
1	0 1 0 0
2	0 1 0 1
3	0 1 1 0
4	0 1 1 1
5	1 0 0 0
6	1 0 0 1
7	1 0 1 0
8	1 0 1 1
9	1 1 0 0

We observe first that although it is a nonweighted code, the "excess-3" code is self-complementing and is thus potentially useful in subtraction. It has another interesting property when used for addition. We will investigate this by comparing the $8, 4, 2, 1$ code and the "excess-3" code in obtaining the sums $(4 + 3)$ and $(5 + 6)$. The steps are as follows:

```
    8 4 2 1                              Excess-3
    ‾‾‾‾‾‾‾                              ‾‾‾‾‾‾‾‾
    0 1 0 0          4                   0 1 1 1
  + 0 0 1 1         +3               +   0 1 1 0
  ‾‾‾‾‾‾‾‾‾                          ‾‾‾‾‾‾‾‾‾‾
    0 1 1 1 → 7                          1 1 0 1
                                    −   0 0 1 1      (binary 3)
                                    ‾‾‾‾‾‾‾‾‾‾
                                        1 0 1 0 → 7  (in excess-3 code)


    0 1 0 1          5                   1 0 0 0
  + 0 1 1 0         +6               +   1 0 0 1
  ‾‾‾‾‾‾‾‾‾                          ‾‾‾‾‾‾‾‾‾‾
    1 0 1 1 → 11                     (1) 0 0 0 1
  + 0 1 1 0                          +   0 0 1 1      (binary 3)
  ‾‾‾‾‾‾‾‾‾                          ‾‾‾‾‾‾‾‾‾‾
  (1) 0 0 0 1 → 1 (binary)           (1) 0 1 0 0 → 1  (in excess-3 code)
```

When the $8, 4, 2, 1$ code is used to obtain the sum $4 + 3$, the resulting binary number is the equivalent of decimal 7. When the excess-3 code is used, however, each element of the sum contains an excess 3, and we see that it is necessary to subtract binary 3 from the apparent sum to obtain the correct representation of decimal 7 in the excess-3 code. We note here that the sum of the two digits in this example is less than decimal *10*. In the next sum, 5 + 6, the sum of the digits is greater than *10* and the procedure is different. When the 8, 4, 2, 1 code is used, the sum obtained is the binary equivalent of decimal *11*, but since we are coding individual decimal digits we want to obtain the result in the form of the code for decimal *1* and a carry of *1*. However, in using the 8, 4, 2, 1 code, because the code combinations from 10 to 15 are not used, when the sum is equal to or greater than 10, we must add binary 6 to the indicated sum in order to obtain the required digit and carry. This is done in the example shown and the carry digit is placed in parentheses. When the excess-3 code is used, each element of the sum contains an excess of 3, so the sum of two digits contains an excess of 6. Hence, the sum which is first obtained contains an indication of the correct carry (shown by parentheses), but the remaining digits represent the required decimal digit *expressed as a binary equivalent*. To restore this result to a representation in excess-3 code, it is necessary to add binary 3.

These steps appear to make addition in the excess-3 code quite complex. However, we observe that in using the excess-3 code, if the sum is less than 10 no carry digit appears and this is a sufficient signal to apply the −3 correction. If, however, the sum is equal to or greater than 10, the carry digit appears *immediately,* and this is a sufficient indication to apply the +3 correction. In contrast, when addition is performed using the 8, 4, 2, 1 code, the result must first be tested to determine whether it should be accepted without change, or whether the +6 correction should be applied. A carry digit will not appear until after this correction is made, although the need for a 1 carry can be inferred from a test which shows that the sum is equal to or greater than 10. Summarizing, we see that in addition to its self-complementing property, the excess-3 code, when used for addition, provides immediate carry information, and the carry digit itself can control the direction of the ±3 correction.

In this discussion we have considered only 4-digit, decimal-binary codes. Although this is the smallest number of digits that can be used, we can also set up decimal-binary codes containing more than 4 digits. In Art. 10.4 we will discuss such codes and the reasons for using them.

10.2 Cyclic Codes

One of the problems encountered by the designers of computing equipment is that of converting information from an analogue form to its digital equivalent, and vice versa. For instance, it may be necessary to determine from a rotating shaft the value of a variable which is represented, to some scale, by the angle through which the shaft has turned. This information is to be supplied in digital form to a computer for further processing. The result of the computation is a digital value which it may be necessary to convert, through a servomechanism, to a shaft position.

Generally speaking, some type of coded commutator is mounted on the rotating shaft to act as the link between the continuously varying shaft position and the corresponding digital values which must change by discrete steps. There will be as many brushes making contact with the commutator as there are digits in the code, with each brush "reading" a separate track on which the 0's and 1's of the code are represented by, say, non-conducting and conducting segments.

If the commutator and the brush construction are perfect, and if all the devices controlled by the brush outputs have exactly the same response time, the commutator could be designed to represent any desired code. In practice, however, these conditions are not met. The brush and commutator assembly can be built only within certain tolerances and if the signals from two brushes are supposed to change simultaneously, they will actually be slightly out of phase. Furthermore, the response times of associated equipment will vary from channel to channel. For these reasons it becomes important that the code selected be one which avoids any ambiguity of response, even at the sacrifice of computational advantage.

The worst difficulty arises when a step between two code groups requires a change of more than one variable. Because of the normal variations in the construction of equipment, multiple changes of variables do not register simultaneously. For example, if we are required to make the change from 001 to 010 in one step, it becomes necessary to change both the second and the third digits simultaneously. With perfect adjustment of equipment, of course, we may do just that. What is more likely, however, is that in going from 001 to 010 we will momentarily go through either the combination 000 or 011. While these are only momentary, they are false code combinations which are supplied as outputs of the commutator. As the processing speeds of associated equipment increase, these momentary combinations can become more and more hazardous.

We may readily observe the existence of such multiple changes of variables in the codes shown in Table 10–1. In the 8, 4, 2, 1 code of the first column, the transition from decimal *1* to decimal *2* requires two variables to change; the transition from decimal *3* to decimal *4* requires three variables to change; and going from decimal *7* to decimal *8* requires a simultaneous change of all four variables. Similar observations may be made in all the codes shown in the table.

The problem is avoided by using commutator codes in which all consecutive code groups differ in only one digit. These are known as cyclic, progressive, or Gray codes.

A cyclic code may be complete or incomplete. A complete cyclic code in n variables contains all 2^n combinations of the variables in a cyclic sequence. The tabulation shown at the left of Fig. 10–1 is a complete cyclic code in 4 variables. It may be verified that in passing from any code group to an adjacent group, in either direction, the change of one variable only is required. This is true also of the transition from the bottom of the column back to the top where the 1000 code group at

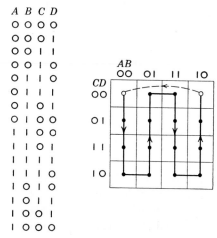

A B C D
O O O O
O O O I
O O I I
O O I O
O I I O
O I I I
O I O I
O I O O
I I O O
I I O I
I I I I
I I I O
I O I O
I O I I
I O O I
I O O O

Fig. 10–1. A complete cyclic code in 4 variables and its generation on a map.

the bottom differs from the 0000 code group at the top in the left-hand digit only. Hence this code can be built into a commutator in which the top and bottom groups become adjacent.

At the right of Fig. 10–1 is shown a Karnaugh map in which we start with an open circle in the 0000 cell and then trace the "route" followed by marking the successive cells of the map which are represented by the successive code groups. The sequence terminates in the 1000 cell from which a dotted line indicates the return to the 0000 cell by the change of a single variable.

It should be evident from the construction of this map that there are many ways in which a complete cyclic code can be generated. The basic idea is that any horizontal or vertical transition between adjacent cells of the map is always accomplished by a single change of variable. Consequently, any sequence of horizontal and vertical transitions within the Karnaugh map generates a cyclic code. If the sequence begins and ends in a pair of adjacent cells and passes through all the other cells, that sequence describes a complete cyclic code. In Fig. 10–2, two alternate forms of complete cyclic codes in four variables are shown. The beginning and the end of each code is indicated by open circles and the final connection is shown by a dotted line. Actually, however, it is not necessary to think of these codes as having either a beginning or an end. So long as the sequence closes on itself it can begin or end anywhere.

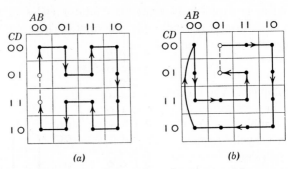

(a)   (b)

Fig. 10–2. Alternative complete cyclic codes generated by means of maps.

It may be desirable to form complete cyclic codes in more than four variables. This can readily be done by the use of multiple maps. Figure 10–3 shows how the code generated in Fig. 10–1 can be extended to five variables. Two four-variable maps are used, corresponding to the 0 and the 1 values of the fifth variable. Within each of these maps, a cyclic code is formed by a sequence of horizontal and vertical transitions as before. We can now continue the sequence into the other map by noting that a move from a cell of one map to exactly the same cell in the other map corresponds to a change in the fifth variable only. Thus, in Fig. 10–3 the move from the map for $E = 0$

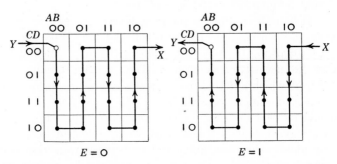

$E = O$ $E = 1$

Fig. 10–3. Generation of a complete cyclic code in five variables.

to the map for $E = 1$ is made by the transition marked X, and the cycle is closed by moving from the map for $E = 1$ to the map for $E = 0$ by way of the transition marked Y.

In Fig. 10–4, a group of four maps is arrayed to permit the generation of a cyclic code in six variables. Each of the component maps represents the variables A, B, C, D. The four separate maps correspond to values of the variables E and F of 00, 01, 11, and 10. The maps are so arranged that a transition from any map to another map by either a horizontal or vertical movement requires the change of only one variable. Of course, as in the five-variable example shown in Fig. 10–3, such transitions between maps must be accomplished by going from a given cell of one map to exactly the same cell of the other map.

For the particular type of cyclic code shown in Fig. 10–1, it is not necessary to use maps in order to extend the code to a larger number of variables. A very brief examination will reveal the pattern of the code and indicate how it can be extended to a larger number of variables by a routine procedure.

A cyclic code need not necessarily be a complete code. In particular, when a cyclic code is to be used to

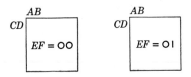

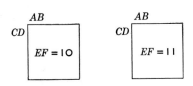

Fig. 10–4. Arrangement of maps to generate cyclic codes in six variables.

represent decimal digits, we need only ten code groups. It is usually desirable that the code form a closed cycle so that it can be generated by a continuously rotating commutator.* Other criteria may also enter into the selection of an incomplete code. For example, it may be desirable to minimize the average current in the commutator brushes. For this purpose we try to design the code so that the total

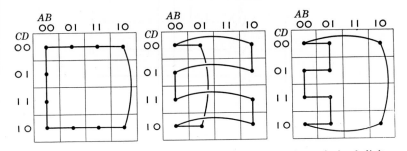

Fig. 10–5. A group of cyclic codes for representation of ten decimal digits.

number of 1's present in all the code groups is a minimum. The map method offers powerful guidance in making these selections. Figure 10–5 shows three incomplete codes, each containing ten code groups,

---

* J. A. O'Brien, "Cyclic Decimal Codes for Analogue to Digital Converters," *Trans. A.I.E.E.,* Part 1, Vol. 75, 1956, pp. 120–122. This paper discusses incomplete codes and the problem of selecting codes to simplify equipment design.

and each code containing a total of fifteen 1's.* These codes all close
on themselves, so no beginning or end is indicated.

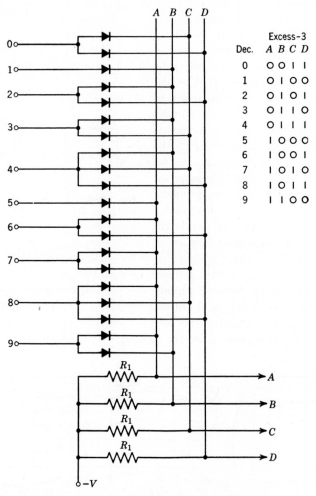

Fig. 10–6. Rectifier matrix for converting decimal digits to the excess-3 binary
code.

10.3 Code Conversion

One of the first problems of conversion is that of encoding decimal
digits in a selected binary code. Let us consider the problem of
converting decimal digits to the excess-3 code. This code is repeated
at the right of Fig. 10–6. Let the symbols $D_0, D_1, \ldots, D_9$ represent the

* J. A. O'Brien, op. cit.

decimal digits, only one of which is required at any one time. We can consider these symbols as binary variables (not binary numbers) such that if, for example, $D_5 = 1$, the input corresponding to decimal 5 carries a ground, and all other inputs represent 0's. The individual digits of the excess-3 code can then be written in terms of the decimal inputs in the form

$$A = D_5 + D_6 + D_7 + D_8 + D_9$$

$$B = D_1 + D_2 + D_3 + D_4 + D_9$$

$$C = D_0 + D_3 + D_4 + D_7 + D_8$$

$$D = D_0 + D_2 + D_4 + D_6 + D_8$$

Each digit of this binary code can be obtained as the output of an Add gate having five inputs. The realization can be in terms of rectifier gates as shown in Fig. 10–6. Any decimal digit to be represented will have a ground at its corresponding input terminal and through the action of the Add gates, grounds will then appear on the required combination of output terminals.

The conversion circuit of Fig. 10–6 indicates a code 1 by an output ground and a code 0 by a negative voltage. In computer work, it is generally preferable to have, say, an output pulse to represent a code 1 and the absence of a pulse to represent a code 0. If the pulse outputs are designated as A_P, B_P, C_P, and D_P, then we can write $A_P = A \cdot P$; $B_P = B \cdot P$; $C_P = C \cdot P$; $D_P = D \cdot P$, where P represents an input clock pulse. These relations indicate that an output pulse can be produced by allowing each voltage level output of Fig. 10–6 to become an input of a Multiply gate to which a clock pulse is supplied as the other input. A circuit for doing this is shown in Fig. 10–7.* The gates in Fig. 10–7 are shown supplied at ground potential, which is high relative to the negative voltage supplied to the Add gates in Fig. 10–6. Hence if the clock pulse rises momentarily from $-V$ to ground potential, the output pulse will vary between approximately the same values, assuming R_2 is large compared to R_1. (See Fig. 10–6.)

The problem of converting from a binary code to the decimal digits represented, assuming the code inputs are voltage levels, is that of designing a combinational circuit which has 4 inputs and 10 outputs. We can take advantage of the fact that only 10 of the 16 input com-

---

* We have, of course, oversimplified the problem. No input or output pulse-coupling circuits are shown, and it is here assumed that changes in level at the A, B, C, D inputs are completed before a pulse appears. The synchronization problem is discussed further in Chapter 15.

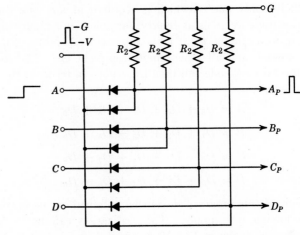

Fig. 10–7. The voltage levels produced in Fig. 10–6 can be used to control pulse outputs.

binations are possible. Hence the remaining 6 combinations may be used as optional states to simplify the network. Circuits having pulse inputs will not be discussed at this point since many of the practical circuits require the use of memory elements.

Perhaps the most important of the conversion problems is that of converting from one code to another. This is a straightforward combinational problem which will be discussed by means of two examples.

Example 10–1

A relay contact network has four inputs and four outputs. The inputs are the digits A, B, C, D of a decimal-binary $8, 4, 2, 1$ code. The outputs are to be the corresponding digits W, X, Y, Z of an excess-3 code. Design the contact network.

The given inputs and outputs form the table of combinations shown

	A	B	C	D	W	X	Y	Z
0	0	0	0	0	0	0	1	1
1	0	0	0	1	0	1	0	0
2	0	0	1	0	0	1	0	1
3	0	0	1	1	0	1	1	0
4	0	1	0	0	0	1	1	1
5	0	1	0	1	1	0	0	0
6	0	1	1	0	1	0	0	1
7	0	1	1	1	1	0	1	0
8	1	0	0	0	1	0	1	1
9	1	0	0	1	1	1	0	0

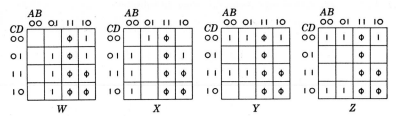

Fig. 10–8. Maps for the conversion of binary code to excess-3 code.

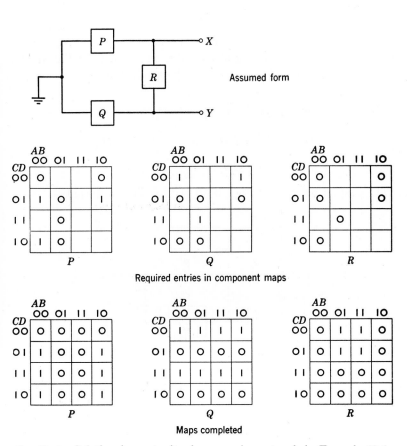

Fig. 10–9. Solution for part of code conversion network in Example 10–1.

The outputs W, X, Y, Z may be written as standard-sum functions of A, B, C, D, including optional terms, as follows:

$$W = \sum(5, 6, 7, 8, 9) + \sum_\phi(10, 11, 12, 13, 14, 15)$$

$$X = \sum(1, 2, 3, 4, 9) + \sum_\phi(10, 11, 12, 13, 14, 15)$$

$$Y = \sum(0, 3, 4, 7, 8) + \sum_\phi(10, 11, 12, 13, 14, 15)$$

$$Z = \sum(0, 2, 4, 6, 8) + \sum_\phi(10, 11, 12, 13, 14, 15)$$

Maps of these functions are given in Fig. 10–8. It is apparent that optional conditions can be chosen so that $Z = D'$. A reasonably good synthesis of the remaining network is found by developing $W = A + B(C + D)$, and then obtaining X and Y from a three-terminal network. The latter network is derived from the maps of Fig. 10–9.

For the transmission functions which satisfy the form assumed in Fig. 10–9 we write

$$P = B'(C + D)$$

$$Q = C'D' + CD = (C' + D)(C + D')$$

$$R = BC' \text{(or } BD')$$

The contact network of Fig. 10–10 realizes all four outputs.

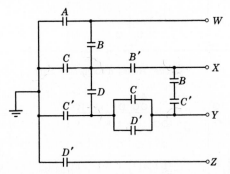

Fig. 10–10. Contact network for conversion of 8, 4, 2, 1 code to excess-3 code.

It will be instructive to examine a code conversion problem in which complete codes are used, so that there are no optional choices available.

Example 10–2

Design a relay contact network which converts a complete 8, 4, 2, 1 code to the cyclic code shown in Fig. 10–1, and another network which converts the cyclic code to the 8, 4, 2, 1 code.

We first tabulate the two codes:

| A | B | C | D | | W | X | Y | Z |
8	4	2	1			Cyclic		
0	0	0	0		0	0	0	0
0	0	0	1		0	0	0	1
0	0	1	0		0	0	1	1
0	0	1	1		0	0	1	0
0	1	0	0		0	1	1	0
0	1	0	1		0	1	1	1
0	1	1	0		0	1	0	1
0	1	1	1		0	1	0	0
1	0	0	0		1	1	0	0
1	0	0	1		1	1	0	1
1	0	1	0		1	1	1	1
1	0	1	1		1	1	1	0
1	1	0	0		1	0	1	0
1	1	0	1		1	0	1	1
1	1	1	0		1	0	0	1
1	1	1	1		1	0	0	0

In Fig. 10–11 the upper row of maps presents the cyclic code digits W, X, Y, Z as functions of A, B, C, D, and the lower row of maps shows the digits A, B, C, D as functions of W, X, Y, Z.

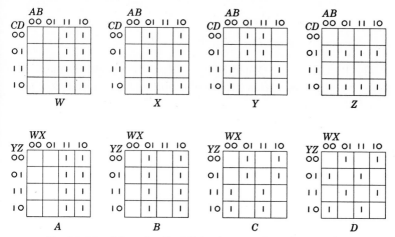

Fig. 10–11. Maps for the bilateral conversion of two codes.

We can write immediately from the upper row of maps, $W = A$; $X = A'B + AB'$; $Y = B'C + BC'$; and $Z = C'D + CD'$. These functions are realized by the network of Fig. 10–12.

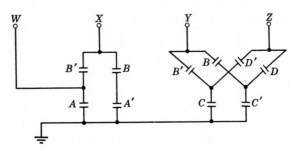

Fig. 10–12. Network for the conversion of a weighted code to a cyclic code.

The lower row of maps in Fig. 10–11 presents a very interesting situation. For A and B we can immediately write $A = W$, and $B = W'X + WX'$. For C the transmission function is $C = W'X'Y + W'XY' + WX'Y' + WXY$, and this function is readily recognized as $C = S_{1,3}(W, X, Y)$. The map of D demands realization as a symmetric function, and for it we write $D = S_{1,3}(W, X, Y, Z)$. This function can be produced as a folded symmetric. But we also note that we can summarize the transmission functions for all the digits in the form:

$$A = S_1(W)$$

$$B = S_1(W, X)$$

$$C = S_{1,3}(W, X, Y)$$

$$D = S_{1,3}(W, X, Y, Z)$$

In Fig. 10–13 we see that when the network which produces D is drawn, the $A, B,$ and C functions can be obtained at intermediate nodes of the D network.

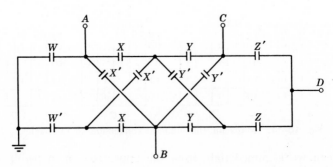

Fig. 10–13. A multiple output network for converting a cyclic code to a weighted code.

10.4   Detection of Error

In the codes we have so far examined, we have used the minimum number of digits needed to represent the desired information. Such codes, while adequate for *representation* of information, may not be suitable for *transmission* of information. We may transmit a code group correctly, but because of equipment failure or noise in the transmission channel there may be an error in the code group that is received. Our purpose in this article is to see how transmission errors can be detected.

If we are using a complete code, for which all combinations of digits are possible, any single error in the transmission of a digit will cause the reception of a false code group. In any practical transmission system there is always a finite probability of the occurrence of a single error. This probability should be and usually is quite small. Furthermore, the probability that two or more errors will occur simultaneously is very much smaller. Our simplest method for detecting the presence of a single error assumes that multiple errors do not occur. This method is called the parity check method.

The basic principle of the parity check is to transmit an extra digit with each code group. This digit is chosen so that the entire group, including the parity check digit, contains *either* an odd or an even number of *either* 1's or 0's. There are thus four ways in which the parity check can be applied. We will use only the *even* check on the 1's, (also called the even-one check); that is, to each code group we will add a parity digit chosen so that the total transmitted group always contains an even number of 1's.

This application of the parity check is illustrated in Table 10–3 where a 2, 4, 2, 1 weighted code is shown together with the augmented code ready for transmission. In the augmented code the parity digit is indicated by P in the tabulation. Of course, in making use of the received code, after it has been determined that the parity check is satisfied, the parity digit may be discarded since it carries no information other than the assurance that no single error has occurred.

The operation of the parity check may be examined more closely by looking at some possibly troublesome code groups. In the original code, decimal *2* and decimal *3* are represented by 0010 and 0011, respectively. These two code groups are separated by only a single change of variable. If in the transmission an error occurs in the fourth digit of either code group, the other group is received.

In the augmented code, these groups become 00101 and 00110, respectively. By the addition of the parity digits, the "distance"

Table 10–3

Application of the Parity Check

Original Code	Augmented Code
2 4 2 1	2 4 2 1 P
0 0 0 0	0 0 0 0 0
0 0 0 1	0 0 0 1 1
0 0 1 0	0 0 1 0 1
0 0 1 1	0 0 1 1 0
0 1 0 0	0 1 0 0 1
1 0 1 1	1 0 1 1 1
1 1 0 0	1 1 0 0 0
1 1 0 1	1 1 0 1 1
1 1 1 0	1 1 1 0 1
1 1 1 1	1 1 1 1 0

between groups has been increased. It now requires two changes of variable to go from one code group to the other. If a change occurs in the fourth digit, we will not know which group was originally transmitted, because we do not know that it is actually the fourth digit which has changed, but we do know that the group received contains an error. For example, if we receive the group 01000, the parity check tells us that something is wrong. Assuming that only one error has occurred, however, we do not know whether the original transmitted group was 00000, 01001, or 11000.

Although the simple parity check is not intended for the detection of multiple errors, it does actually detect any odd number of errors. When the code used is incomplete, an even number of errors may sometimes also be detected. This will be possible if the received code group is not a part of the code which is used. For example, in the code of Table 10–3 we transmit the augmented code for decimal 5 as 10111. Suppose we receive the group 10001, after two errors in transmission. The parity check is satisfied, but the errors can be detected from the fact that the received group is not a member of the code at all.

Codes using parity checks can be designed so that freedom from error is detected by relatively simple networks. Two codes of this type are shown in Table 10–4.

With the exception of the code group for decimal 0, the left-hand code of Table 10–4 is the same as the code in the second column of Table 10–1, and with the same exception it is a weighted code. The decimal 0 group has been changed so that when augmented by a parity check digit it becomes part of a 2-out-of-5 code. All ten possible combinations of five things taken two at a time have been formed, so a

Table 10–4
Parity-Check Codes

Decimal Digit	A 7	B 4	C 2	D 1	P 0	A 5	B 0	C 4	D 3	E 2	F 1	G 0
0	1	1	0	0	0	0	1	0	0	0	0	1
1	0	0	0	1	1	0	1	0	0	0	1	0
2	0	0	1	0	1	0	1	0	0	1	0	0
3	0	0	1	1	0	0	1	0	1	0	0	0
4	0	1	0	0	1	0	1	1	0	0	0	0
5	0	1	0	1	0	1	0	0	0	0	0	1
6	0	1	1	0	0	1	0	0	0	0	1	0
7	1	0	0	0	1	1	0	0	0	1	0	0
8	1	0	0	1	0	1	0	0	1	0	0	0
9	1	0	1	0	0	1	0	1	0	0	0	0

"free of error" signal can be derived as the output of a symmetric network which realizes the function $S_2(A, B, C, D, P)$.

The code shown at the right of Table 10–4 is the so-called biquinary code. In this code the digits A and B determine whether the decimal digit represented is less than 5 or is equal to or greater than 5. For decimal digits less than 5, code digit B is given the value 1, while for decimals of 5 or more, code digit $A = 1$. The code digits C, D, E, F, G determine which digit in each group of 5 is represented, and have the weights shown in Table 10–4. This is a 2-out-of-7 code, of course, but it can be treated also as a double code in which the A, B group is tested for parity by the symmetric function $S_1(A, B)$, and the C, D, E, F, G group is treated by $S_1(C, D, E, F, G)$. This code has been extensively used, particularly in relay computers. It shows promise of further application in computers using other components.*

10.5 Error Detection and Correction

This article is restricted to the examination of a single type of error detection and correction code.† While the derivation of the Hamming

* A 2-out-of-5 code-checking circuit using magnetic cores is given by M. Karnaugh, "Pulse Switching Circuits Using Magnetic Cores," *Proc. I.R.E.*, Vol. 43, No. 5, May 1955, pp. 570–584. There is an extensive discussion of the biquinary code and its application in W. Keister, A. E. Ritchie, and S. H. Washburn, *The Design of Switching Circuits*, D. Van Nostrand Co., New York, 1951.

† R. W. Hamming, "Error Detecting and Error Correcting Codes," *Bell System Technical Journal*, Vol. 29, April 1950, pp. 147–160. For a more general treatment of the subject, see D. Slepian, "A Class of Binary Signaling Alphabets," *Bell System Technical Journal*, Vol. 35, January 1956, pp. 203–234. A sequential treatment of the subject is given by D. A. Huffman, "A Linear Circuit Viewpoint

code is both interesting and instructive in itself, we will find in Chapter 13 that a procedure related to this code enables us to make a useful generalization on the problem of assigning secondary devices in sequential circuits.

For the detection and correction of a *single* error, the basic idea is:

(a) if we *know* an error has occurred (by parity check), and,

(b) if we know the *position* of the error, then by simply complementing the digit received in the "error position" we can correct the error.

Hamming proceeds as follows:

1. To the m message (or information) digits add k checking digits.

2. The k checking digits permit the development of a binary number, $D_a D_b D_c \ldots D_k$, the decimal equivalent of which gives the error position. We call this the *position number*.

3. The position number must contain enough digits to describe the location of a single error occurring in any of the $m + k$ positions, and must in addition permit the value $000 \ldots 0$ to describe the condition of "no error anywhere." These considerations define the magnitude of k for any m in accordance with $2^k \geqslant m + k + 1$.

Table 10–5 shows the maximum number of message digits m which can be monitored by k checking digits, for values of k up to 6. For

Table 10–5

k	m
1	0
2	1
3	4
4	11
5	26
6	57

values of m not contained in the table the next larger value of k must be used. For example, if there are 8 message digits, 4 checking digits will be required in forming the code.

Now we want to design k parity checks, all of which are of the type satisfied by an even number of 1's, and from a set of binary values associated with the success or failure of each parity check we build up the "position number" which reveals the location of any single error. We note at this time that an error may be present in any of the $n = m + k$ positions, and not merely in the m message positions.

---

on Error-Correcting Codes," *I.R.E. Trans. on Information Theory*, Vol. IT-2, No. 3, September 1956, pp. 20–28.

For each parity check that is made we report the results numerically in terms of the definitions

$$0 = \text{parity check satisfied (no error found)}$$

$$1 = \text{parity check fails (error in that parity check)}$$

Consider the application of these ideas to the specific code for which $m = 4$, and $k = 3$. There are $2^k = 8$ possible "position numbers." Of these the number 000 is reserved to mean "no error anywhere." This leaves 7 true position numbers available to reveal the location of single errors in any one of the $m + k = 4 + 3 = 7$ code digit positions. In accordance with our definition above, the presence of a 1 digit anywhere in a position number means that the parity check has failed in one of the positions which has a digit 1 in that part of its position number.

Specifically, suppose a 1 appears in the right-hand digit of the position number. This can mean a failure of the parity check in any of the four positions which contain a 1 in the right-hand digit of the position number. These are

Position Number	Decimal Equivalent
0 0 **1**	1
0 1 **1**	3
1 0 **1**	5
1 1 **1**	7

Hence, a parity failure in position 1, or 3, or 5, or 7 will produce a 1 in the right-hand digit of the position number. This we call the **1-3-5-7** parity check.

If a 1 appears in the middle digit of the position number, we note the following possibilities:

Position Number	Decimal Equivalent
0 **1** 0	2
0 **1** 1	3
1 **1** 0	6
1 **1** 1	7

Hence, a parity failure in position 2, or 3, or 6, or 7 will produce a 1 in the middle digit of the position number. We designate this as the **2-3-6-7** parity check.

Finally, if a 1 appears in the left-hand digit of the position number, we note

Position Number	Decimal Equivalent
1 0 0	4
1 0 1	5
1 1 0	6
1 1 1	7

A parity failure in position 4, or 5, or 6, or 7 thus produces a 1 in the left-hand digit of the position number. We designate this as the 4-5-6-7 parity check.

As an example of the use of this set of parity checks, we see that a single error in position 5 causes a failure of the parity checks in the first and third digits, but not in the second digit. Hence we write (using 1 = failure, and 0 = success) for the position number $1\ 0\ 1 \rightarrow 5$ (location of the error).

So far we have discussed the *number* of message digits and checking digits, and the constituents of the parity checks, but we have said nothing about which digits in the combined code are message digits and which are checking digits.

This selection of digit positions may be made quite arbitrary, and hence there are many possible Hamming codes. For example, suppose we let positions 1, 3, and 5 be checking positions, and 2, 4, 6, and 7 be message positions. We then wish to find the composite code for transmission of the message 1011. For this purpose we will number the "positions" arbitrarily from left to right, and carry out the encoding process as tabulated:

Position	1 2 3 4 5 6 7	
Digit Type	$k\ m\ k\ m\ k\ m\ m$	
"Message"	1 0 1 1	Step 1—cannot insert 1-3-5-7 parity digit
	1 1 0 1 1	Step 2—insert 2-3-6-7 parity digit
	1 1 0 0 1 1	Step 3—insert 4-5-6-7 parity digit
Coded message	0 1 1 0 0 1 1	Step 4—insert 1-3-5-7 parity digit

We note that for this assignment of message and checking positions, the parity digits are not found independently; that is, the checking digit placed in position 1 depends on the checking digits placed in positions 3 and 5.

A conventional Hamming code is one which uses the positions 1, 2, 4, (8, 16, and so on) for checking digits. The binary equivalent of each of these position numbers contains only a single 1 and hence it can appear in only *one* parity check. Each parity digit is thus determined independently. We will use these checking positions in developing the full Hamming code for $m = 4$, $k = 3$, as shown in Table 10–6.

Table 10–6

Hamming Code for $m = 4$, $k = 3$

Position	1 2 3 4 5 6 7	Equivalent Decimal
	k k m k m m m	Value of Message
	0 0 0 0 0 0 0	0
	1 1 0 1 0 0 1	1
	0 1 0 1 0 1 0	2
	1 0 0 0 0 1 1	3
	1 0 0 1 1 0 0	4
	0 1 0 0 1 0 1	5
	1 1 0 0 1 1 0	6
	0 0 0 1 1 1 1	7
	1 1 1 0 0 0 0	8
	0 0 1 1 0 0 1	9
	1 0 1 1 0 1 0	10
	0 1 1 0 0 1 1	11
	0 1 1 1 1 0 0	12
	1 0 1 0 1 0 1	13
	0 0 1 0 1 1 0	14
	1 1 1 1 1 1 1	15

As an example of the application of this code, suppose we transmit the message "12" with an error in the sixth position. We determine the location of the error by the following sequence of steps.

0 1 1 1 1 0 0	"Undisturbed" message
0 1 1 1 1 1 0	Message with error
1 1 1 0	4-5-6-7 parity check = 1
1 1 1 0	2-3-6-7 parity check = 1
0 1 1 0	1-3-5-7 parity check = 0

Position number = 110→6 = position in error.

A simple extension of the Hamming code provides single-error *correction* plus double-error *detection*. We start with the single-error correction code which has already been derived. To this we add one more position, using an even-1 parity check on *all* positions. Then the following possibilities exist:

1. No error: all parity checks, including the last one, are satisfied.
2. Single error anywhere:
   (a) the last parity check always fails, regardless of the position of the error;

  (b) the original position number gives the position of the detected
       error, but now the position number 000 signifies that the error
       is in the added position.
3. Two errors:
  (a) the last parity check is always satisfied;
  (b) the original position number indicates that there is some kind
       of error. If one of the errors is in the added position, the
       original position number actually locates the other error, but
       there is no way to know that this condition exists. Hence a
       double error can only be *detected* with certainty.

The process of error detection and correction can be given a geometrical interpretation. We have seen that the "distance" between two code points in n-dimensional space is given by the number of coordinates (or positions) in which they are different. Thus,

From:	To:	The "distance" is:
0 0 1	0 1 1	1
0 0 1	0 1 0	2
0 0 1	1 1 0	3

In terms of error detection and correction, "distance" means:

Minimum Distance	Meaning
1	Error cannot be detected
2	Single error detection
3	Single error correction
4	Single error correction and double error detection
5	Double error correction

Consider the code group for decimal 5 in Table 10–6, that is, 0100101. If we now compare this code group with all others in the table we find seven groups, corresponding to the equivalent decimals 0, 1, 6, 7, 11, 12, 13, which are at a "distance" 3 from the code group for decimal 5. If a single error is made in transmitting the code group for decimal 5, the new code group will be at a distance 1 from decimal 5 and at a distance of 2 from all the nearest neighbors of decimal 5. Hence there need never be any doubt, after a single error, about which code group is intended in the transmission of the message.

Finally, we may note that for a given minimum "distance" between code groups, some *correctability* may be exchanged for more *detectability*. For example, at a distance 5 we may have

  (a) Double error detection and correction.

(b) Single error correction and triple error detection.

(c) Quadruple error detection.

PROBLEMS

10.1 (a) Encode each of the ten decimal digits $0, 1, \ldots, 9$ by means of the following weighted binary codes:

$$
\begin{array}{lrrrr}
(1) & 7 & 4 & 2 & -1 \\
(2) & 8 & 4 & -2 & -1 \\
(3) & 4 & 4 & 1 & -2 \\
(4) & 7 & 5 & 3 & -6 \\
(5) & 8 & 7 & -4 & -2
\end{array}
$$

(b) Identify the codes of Part (a), if any, that are self-complementing.

(c) If a weighted binary code is self-complementing, what necessary condition is placed upon the sum of the weights of the code?

(d) Is this condition sufficient to ensure a self-complementing code? Give an example, or other demonstration, to justify your answer.

10.2 Use first the 8, 4, 2, 1 code, and then the "excess-3" code to demonstrate the steps in performing the following additions, when each digit of a decimal number is represented by one of the given binary codes.

1. $236 + 479$;   2. $632 + 974$;   3. $1 + 19 + 21 + 69$

10.3 Design a minimum contact network to serve as a three-digit binary-to-cyclic code converter. The table of combinations between the inputs A, B, C, and the outputs X, Y, Z is:

A	B	C	X	Y	Z
0	0	0	0	0	0
0	0	1	0	0	1
0	1	0	0	1	1
0	1	1	0	1	0
1	0	0	1	1	0
1	0	1	1	1	1
1	1	0	1	0	1
1	1	1	1	0	0

(7 contacts, 11 springs are sufficient)

10.4 In a code conversion network the input variables A, B, C, and D can have any of the combinations shown in the following table. Corresponding to each input combination there is a four-variable output combination, as shown in the columns marked W, X, Y, and Z. The input combinations which are not present in the tabulation under A, B, C, and D are impossible combinations which may be used to simplify the networks.

A	B	C	D		W	X	Y	Z
0	0	0	1		0	0	0	0
0	0	1	0		0	0	0	1
0	0	1	1		0	0	1	0
0	1	0	0		0	0	1	1
0	1	0	1		0	1	0	0
0	1	1	0		0	1	0	1
1	0	0	0		0	1	1	0
1	0	0	1		0	1	1	1
1	0	1	0		1	0	0	0
1	1	0	0		1	0	0	1

Derive transmission functions for the W, X, Y, and Z outputs, with each function expressed in minimal form. Design a minimal contact network to realize these functions.

10.5 (a) Design a minimum-spring contact network of the form shown for translating the following decimal-binary code into an 8, 4, 2, 1 code.

Decimal Digit	A	B	C	D
0	1	0	1	0
1	1	1	1	0
2	0	1	1	0
3	0	1	1	1
4	0	0	1	1
5	0	0	0	1
6	0	1	0	1
7	0	1	0	0
8	1	1	0	0
9	1	0	0	0

(b) Is the given code a cyclic code?

(c) How does the given code compare with a minimum average-brush-current code?

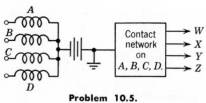

Problem 10.5.

10.6 The decimal number 1854* is to be converted to its binary equivalent and then is to be transmitted in a coded form which permits the detection and

* The year of publication of *The Laws of Thought*, by George Boole.

correction of any single error of transmission. Use the "even-1" parity check in the code.

(a) How many parity checks are required?

(b) What digit positions would preferably be occupied by the parity check digits?

(c) How are each of the digits of the position number found?

(d) What is the transmitted code for decimal 1854?

10.7 A seven-digit code is constructed by augmenting a four-digit cyclic code for the purpose of detecting and correcting any single error in any one of the binary encodings representing a decimal number $0, 1, \ldots, 9$. An even-1 parity check is used. All parity checks are independent of each other.

The encoded decimal numbers $0, 1, \ldots, 9$ are transmitted over a *noisy* channel and the table shown is received:

1. Assume that, at most, a single error of transmission has occurred in any of the received code groups. Correct any error present in the tabulation.

2. The four-digit cyclic code consists of the sequence of the correct message digits only as found in part 1. Construct a minimum-spring contact network on the variables A, B, C, and D, to convert this code to a weighted 8, 4, 2, 1 code. Consider the cyclic code to be on the variables A, B, C, and D and the weighted 8, 4, 2, 1 code to be on the variables W, X, Y, and Z.

Encoded Messages

Decimal Numbers	1 k_1	2 k_2	3 m_1	4 k_3	5 m_2	6 m_3	7 m_4	Position Type of Digit
0	I	I	O	I	O	O	I	
1	I	O	O	O	I	I	I	
2	O	I	I	O	O	O	I	
3	I	O	I	I	I	I	O	
4	O	I	O	I	O	I	O	
5	I	I	O	O	I	I	O	
6	I	O	I	I	I	O	O	
7	O	O	I	O	O	O	O	
8	I	I	I	O	O	O	O	
9	O	O	I	I	O	O	I	

Problem 10.7.

CHAPTER 11

Iterative
networks

In the preceding chapters we have learned to use tables of combinations, standard sums and products, maps, and other methods for the description of switching functions. Of course, when functions are simple enough we know that we can describe the terminal action of a network by verbal statements. But, with the exception of the symmetric functions and their associated circuits, verbal description of the action of complex circuits is neither precise nor elegant.

We have already seen, in Chapter 7, that symmetric networks may be synthesized by an iterative method. It was not necessary then to develop this method beyond the elementary level, however, because a more direct synthesis was possible by modifying a standard circuit.

Symmetric functions are characterized by the *number* of variables within a given group which have a specified behavior. These requirements are usually well adapted to verbal description. We now propose to examine another large class of functions for which contact networks can be most readily synthesized by the iterative method. For these functions the terminal action of the associated networks is described either in terms of the *positions* of variables having prescribed values, or in terms of a combined numerical and positional requirement. The number of variables involved may be very large, and the number of terms required in, say, a standard-sum description may be prohibitively large. Yet these functions, as a class, are realized by networks for which the terminal action can be described by relatively simple verbal statements.

Finally, we shall see that among the devices for describing the basic components of these networks, we can use a matrix which is closely related to the principal method we use for describing the terminal action of sequential circuits.

11.1 Switching Properties of Iterative Networks

As the name implies, an iterative network is one which contains a repeated structure. We have already studied in Chapter 7 iterative networks of the type represented by Fig. 11–1. This network transmits

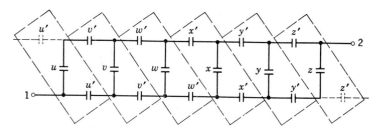

Fig. 11–1. Contact network of an iterative switching circuit, showing cell structure.

ground between terminals 1 and 2 when one and only one of the six relays is operated, and for no other condition of the input variables will there be 1 transmission. We do not specify that any particular relay must operate, but merely that one of the group must operate.

A set of rectangles, drawn in dashed lines, has been superposed on the contact network of Fig. 11–1. These rectangles divide the network into a group of cells, each of which contains contacts on one relay only. If we examine this structure, we find that except for the change of contact designators, each cell is the same as its neighbors. Thus the network is built up from a basic cell structure which is repeated as often as necessary, depending upon the number of variables to be included. The cells at the extreme ends of the network, corresponding to the variables u and z, were originally the same as the interior cells, but because there are no adjoining cells beyond the terminals, one contact in each of these terminal cells has no destination and can be eliminated. The unused contacts of the terminal cells are indicated by dotted lines.

We shall see from the discussion in this chapter that iterative networks perform highly useful switching duties, and this fact alone makes them important. To the circuit designer, however, their importance is enhanced by the fact that they can be expanded or contracted at will to operate with any desired number of variables. After the design of the contact cell has been determined, the network is formed by making a chain of cells, with suitable modifications at the terminal cells.

Another iterative network is shown in Fig. 11–2, with the cell boundaries again indicated. The transmission of this network between

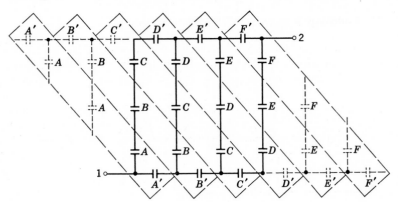

Fig. 11–2. An iterative contact network in which all the cells are incomplete.

terminals 1 and 2 requires that three and only three relays operate, but in addition, the three operated relays must occupy consecutive positions in the chain. We note again that each cell has the same structure, and if the network is to be built to include a larger number of variables, we merely add the required number of cells to the chain. Terminal cells are treated as before, by inserting a complete cell and then discarding contact elements that do not connect either to an adjacent cell or to a terminal.

The circuit of Fig. 11–2 is interesting in another respect. Although it is a true iterative circuit, the number of variables used is so small that none of the cells are complete. Hence it does not appear to be a repeated structure when confined to six variables. If built for seven variables, the circuit would have one complete cell.

Iterative methods are used to synthesize switching circuits of the form shown in Fig. 11–3. There are n input variables, and any one of the input relays is operated by grounding its input terminal. We see that the contact network is a two-terminal network which controls transmission between the terminals A and B. It is arranged as a chain of cells with multiple connections between pairs of cells. There are n contact cells, corresponding to the n input variables. This is the most common distribution, but we need not necessarily have only one input variable for each cell. In a later part of the discussion it will be shown that iterative networks can sometimes be built more economically by associating more than one variable with a single contact cell.

One of the interior cells in Fig. 11–3 is marked as the J cell. This cell will be referred to as a typical cell. It occupies an indefinite position in the interior of the chain, and the design of a typical cell is the central problem in the design of iterative networks.

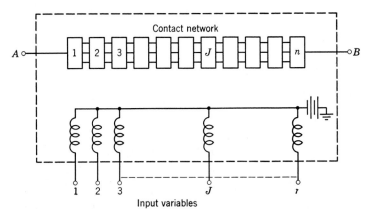

Fig. 11–3. Switching circuit containing an iterative contact network.

There is an indefinitely large number of networks which can be designed most effectively by the iterative approach. They are classified broadly into two types, but this is more a matter of convenience than of precise terminology. In one class, the transmission of the network is determined solely by the *number* of relays which are operated, regardless of where they are located in the chain. In Chapter 7 we identified this type of network as a symmetric network. In the other class of iterative networks the transmission is determined wholly or partly by the relative *positions* occupied by operated and unoperated relays in the chain. This type is known as a positional* network. An example of the description of a wholly positional network would be one for which the transmission is 1 when one or more of the input relays are operated, provided all the operated relays form a consecutive group in the chain. No limitation is placed on the number of operated relays except that there must be at least one. The circuit of Fig. 11–2 illustrates a network which is classified as positional because the operated relays must form a consecutive group, but it is not wholly positional because the number of relays allowed in the consecutive group is specified.

If the relative positions of operated and unoperated relays are involved in the description of circuit performance, whether the number of operated relays is specified or not, we must in general use the iterative approach in designing the network.

* See Reference 8, Bibliography at the end of Chapter 3.

It is instructive to examine the kinds of conditions encountered in the synthesis of positional iterative networks in terms of the sequence patterns of operated and unoperated relays which must be established. If 1 represents an operated relay in a chain and 0 represents an unoperated relay, the following sequences are typical of those for which a transmission of 1 may be specified.

(a) The sequences 00111110000000, and 00000111111111 would meet the requirement that any number of relays in a chain may be operated provided they form a consecutive group.

(b) The sequence 110111100011011111100 satisfies the condition that all the operated groups of relays contain an even number of members.

(c) In the sequence 101111100000110010 each operated group is followed by an unoperated group containing the same number of members.

In the design of an ordinary contact network each variable has its own identity, and in general the effect of a change in one variable is quite different from the effect of a change in some other variable. When we design an iterative network, however, we deal with a variable which is merely typical, and each variable is capable of the same switching duty as its neighbor on either side in the chain. The latter statement is modified when there is more than one variable in a cell, but for the present we will confine our attention to problems in which each cell contains contacts associated with a single variable.

We shall consider a switching circuit of the type illustrated in Fig. 11–3, with one input relay per contact cell. Terminal A of the contact network is connected to ground, and a network transmission of 1 will be indicated by the presence of ground potential at terminal B. When we discuss the appearance of ground potential on a particular connection between cells at an interior point in the chain, we may use the word "activate," and its derivatives, to signify that a particular connection is carrying ground potential. A distinction of this sort is necessary because a network may have 0 transmission between terminals A and B, while at the same time the chain permits ground potential to reach an intermediate point between the two terminals.

The structure of the contact network in the neighborhood of a typical cell is given in Fig. 11–4. In general there may be any number of connections between cells, but the iterative character of the circuit requires that the outputs of one cell become the inputs of the cell which follows it in the chain.

The significance of the multiple interconnections between cells can best be understood in terms of the concept of information. Information is furnished at the inputs of a cell by activating one or more of the input lines, or by the absence of activation on any input line. We shall be concerned initially with problems in which one and only one of the inputs to a typical cell is activated. For these, the input system of the typical cell permits only mutually exclusive signals. For example, if a

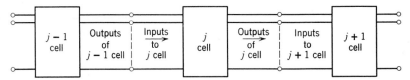

Fig. 11–4. Input and output relations within an iterative contact network.

ground on one input means that an odd number of relays preceding the typical cell is operated, and a ground on another input means that an even number is operated, only one of these inputs can be activated at any one time. The absence of ground on all inputs simply means that at some preceding point in the chain the conditions for transmission of 1 have been violated.

Since the outputs of a cell are connected directly to the inputs of the next cell, it must be true that the outputs represent the same information statements as the inputs. All that the relay of a typical cell can do is to switch activation from an input representing one statement of information to a corresponding output statement, or to an output representing a different statement of information, depending on the cell's condition of operation or non-operation. Thus by switching activation from one information statement to another, a typical cell is able to contribute its part of the total information recognized by the whole network.

If the input system of a cell is mutually exclusive, and if the outputs of one cell connect directly to the inputs of the next cell, it follows that the outputs of such a typical cell must be disjunctive with respect to all pairs of output leads. This does not imply that the input system of the cell is disjunctive. The internal contact network of the cell may at times connect two of its own inputs together, but it must never establish paths which could activate more than one output line.

11.2 Input-Output Specification of Typical Cells

We have seen that a positional iterative network may be required to respond to the operation of a specific number of relays, but its more general application is in responding to requirements based on patterns of operated and unoperated relays in a chain. For example, we may specify that an iterative network transmission is to be 1 if three or more of its relays operate, provided the operated relays form a single consecutive group. There is a numerical specification present, since at least three relays must operate, but there are also the additional specifications that the operated relays must form a continuous group within the chain, and that there can be only one such group. These additional specifications place a pattern constraint on the positional circuit which is not present in the symmetric circuit.

In describing the information available at the inputs and outputs of a typical cell of a symmetric network, it was sufficient to use a single word which indicated how many relays had been operated to the left of the typical cell. We can also use verbal statements to describe the information at the inputs and outputs of a typical cell in a positional network, but the information cannot always be described with precision by single words or short phrases. It will therefore be helpful to adopt certain symbols which can be used either alone or in combinations to represent the status of the relays in a positional circuit. These are not the only symbols that may be devised, nor is there any compulsion to use them. Almost always they must be interpreted within the context of the problem, but they do offer in most problems a compactness of description which verbal statements cannot duplicate.

The effective use of these symbols will depend upon the exact meanings of the words "adjacent" and "consecutive." For purposes of design we assume that an iterative contact network is composed of a chain of cells, as shown in Fig. 11–3. The relays of the circuit are assumed to be numbered from left to right in a continuous sequence $1, 2, 3, \ldots, j, \ldots,$ n. Terminal A of the contact network will be considered the source of activation, and terminal B will be activated if the transmission of the entire network is 1. The J cell of the network is considered to be a typical cell. If there is one relay associated with each cell, the relay *adjacent* to the J cell is the relay numbered $(J - 1)$, that is, the relay immediately to the left of the typical cell. If there is more than one relay in a typical cell, the relay *adjacent* to the typical cell is the highest numbered relay to the left of the typical cell. A *consecutive* group of relays is one whose numbers form an unbroken sequence, such as 4, 5, 6, 7. An *adjacent, consecutive* group is a consecutive group which extends to the relay immediately to the left of the typical cell.

We can also use alphabetic ordering instead of numerical ordering to form a sequence pattern which gives meaning to the words adjacent and consecutive. This is almost always done when the final network is assembled and contact designators are applied.

We shall now define the symbols which will be used to describe the information represented by the inputs and outputs of a typical cell in a positional network.

0—represents a single *unoperated* relay, adjacent to the cell on whose input terminal the symbol is placed. A specific number of adjacent, consecutive, unoperated relays is described by repetition of the symbol. Thus 000 stands for an adjacent, consecutive group of three unoperated relays.

1—represents a single *operated* relay, adjacent to the cell on whose input terminal the symbol is placed. A specific number of adjacent, consecutive, operated relays is described by repetition of the symbol. Thus 111 stands for an adjacent, consecutive group of three operated relays.

$\bar{0}$—represents an adjacent, consecutive group of unoperated relays, where the number of relays in the group is equal to or larger than a number which must be counted exactly.

$\bar{1}$—represents an adjacent, consecutive group of operated relays, where the number of relays in the group is equal to or larger than a number which must be counted exactly.

These symbols must frequently be used in combination. If we must have a "consecutive group of at least two operated relays" we would symbolize the existence of this group by $11\bar{1}$. The 11 part of the symbol guarantees that there are *exactly* two consecutive relays operated, while the $\bar{1}$ which follows indicates that the consecutive group *may* be larger than two, but that there is no need to take this number into account.

The $\bar{0}$ and $\bar{1}$ symbols used alone or in combination may refer to *any* number, including zero. If the requirements of a problem place no restrictions on the size of a group except that it be non-zero, we must use the combinations $0\bar{0}$ or $1\bar{1}$.

Some words cannot conveniently be replaced by symbols. We find the words "odd" and "even" useful in many situations as part of a symbolic description. There are also occasions when V, signifying "valid," is a useful symbol. It may be used also with subscripts so that V_c represents "conditionally valid" and V_a represents "absolutely valid." The latter symbol is used to represent a situation for which the transmission becomes 1 regardless of the behavior of the remainder of the chain. The V_c symbol indicates that up to the location of the typical cell the chain pattern calls for a network transmission of 1, but that this condition may still be destroyed in the remainder of the chain.

These concepts will become clearer after their use has been illustrated in a variety of problems.

11.3 Design of the Typical Cell

We now examine a number of specific examples of synthesis by the iterative method. All the examples in this article will be based on cells with disjunctive outputs. The first few examples will show the effect of changing the original statement of a problem in various ways.

Example 11–1

An iterative contact network is to have a transmission of 1 between its terminals if and only if there is a single consecutive group of three operated relays.

A typical cell of the required network is shown in Fig. 11–5. We assume that ground is applied at the left side of the chain and that it propagates through the chain from left to right, as shown by the arrow in Fig. 11–5, at levels determined by the states of operation of the

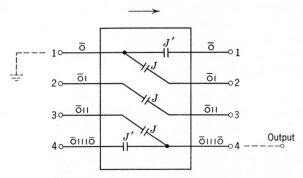

Fig. 11–5. Typical cell, Example 11–1. The arrow indicates the direction of propagation of ground through the iterative chain.

various relays. The input ground is indicated by a dotted connection at the left of the typical cell, on level 1, and the output connection from level 4 is shown dotted at the right of the typical cell.

Level 1 is marked at both input and output by the symbol $\bar{0}$. An input ground appearing at this level conveys the information that no relays to the left of the typical cell have operated. We do not know and we do not care *how many* have not operated, provided *none* have operated. Note that the $\bar{0}$ symbol thus used permits the typical cell to occupy any position in the chain. Specifically, if the typical cell is the first cell in the chain, no relays to the left of it can possibly be operated, so the $\bar{0}$ symbol is still appropriate. When applied to the input of the J cell, the symbol $\bar{0}$ assures us that the $(J-1)$ relays to the left of the J cell have not operated, regardless of the position occupied by the typical cell.

At the output of the typical cell, on the first level, the symbol $\bar{0}$ again appears. We need merely observe that this must be true if the J relay is not operated. By way of a J' contact the cell transfers an input ground meaning $\bar{0}$ to its output at the same level, and that output ground must convey the same information, namely $\bar{0}$, to the input at level 1 of the $(J + 1)$ cell.

Suppose that the relay numbered $(J - 1)$ has operated and that this is the first relay in the chain to operate. By definition, the $(J - 1)$ relay is adjacent to the typical cell, and since it is the first operated relay it may be preceded by any number of unoperated relays. The combined symbol for this state is $\bar{0}1$, as shown at the input of level 2. A ground appears at this input level if the first relay to operate is adjacent to the typical cell. Now we note that if the ground had appeared at level 1 of the J cell and the J relay had operated, we would have transferred the ground to the output at level 2, again with the symbolic description $\bar{0}1$.

We could continue to describe step-by-step the input-output symbols and the related contact structure of this typical cell, but it is important that we see a broader picture. Obviously, if there are, say, eight relays preceding the typical cell there are 2^8 possible states of these relays. Of this large number, we have chosen only four to be the possible inputs to the J cell. The reason for this, of course, lies in the fact that according to the problem statement the only state of the entire chain which permits the transmission to be 1 is that described by the symbol $\bar{0}111\bar{0}$ (note that $\bar{0}$ can refer to any number including zero). A typical cell must be applicable to any part of the chain. Hence it must provide inputs and outputs which represent any part of the development of the $\bar{0}111\bar{0}$ sequence. If we now examine the symbols on the inputs and outputs of the typical cell of Fig. 11–5 it will be apparent that all possible subsequences leading up to the $\bar{0}111\bar{0}$ sequence have been described, together with the conditionally valid sequence $\bar{0}111\bar{0}$ at level 4 (conditionally valid because there is always the possibility that a relay to the right of J will operate, and then the network transmission becomes 0). No other states of operation of the relays to the left of the J cell need be considered because none of them can lead to a valid sequence. Note that if either the $\bar{0}1$ or the $\bar{0}11$ input to the J cell is grounded, and the J relay is not operated, none of the outputs of the J cell will be grounded. Likewise if the $\bar{0}111\bar{0}$ input of the J cell is grounded, and the J relay operates, no output will carry a ground. In both these situations the J relay prevents the final formation of a valid sequence and its contact cell then halts the propagation of ground through the chain.

The actual contact structure of the typical cell of this example is readily designed by assuming a ground on each input and deciding what output, if any, should be grounded both for the J relay not operated, and for the J relay operated. Based on these decisions a normally open contact, or a normally closed contact, or no contact, is placed between the indicated input and output terminals.

Having designed a typical cell, we may then interconnect a group of cells, connecting the outputs of one to the corresponding inputs of the next. At the terminal cells we discard redundant contacts. It may be verified that the network of Fig. 11–2 was thus derived from the typical cell of Fig. 11–5.

Example 11–2

The preceding example is to be modified so that for a network transmission of 1 the operated relays must be in two consecutive groups, each group containing three operated relays, and the operated groups are to be separated by a group containing at least one unoperated relay.

For this network to transmit, the final state of operation of the entire chain must be described by the sequence symbol $\bar{0}11100\overline{1}111\bar{0}$. We may now break down this sequence symbol into the successive subsequences which must exist, as follows:

$\bar{0}$	No relays operated
$\bar{0}1$	First group of three started
$\bar{0}11$	First group of three continued
$\bar{0}111$	First group of three completed
$\bar{0}1110\bar{0}$	Separation group of non-operated relays established
$\bar{0}1110\bar{0}1$	Second group of three started
$\bar{0}1110\bar{0}11$	Second group of three continued
$\bar{0}1110\bar{0}111\bar{0}$	Second group of three completed

The basis on which these subsequences are written is that in passing from one symbol, say $\bar{0}11$, to the next symbol, $\bar{0}111$, the status of an additional relay must be taken into account. We note also that the symbol for the final system state, $\bar{0}1110\bar{0}111\bar{0}$, might be written first without the final $\bar{0}$, and we may then add the $\bar{0}$ to represent an additional state. This step is redundant, however, because $\bar{0}$ can mean a group of unoperated relays of any size, including zero size. In the typical cell of Fig. 11–6 we see that both of these two possible, valid final states are signified by a ground on the eighth level.

The design of the typical cell hardly needs further comment, once we have found the subsequences which must be recognized. It is a matter then of providing contacts which make all required transfers of input grounds for both the unoperated and the operated conditions of the J relay. Note that even though an input ground is supplied to only one terminal of the cell, inputs 4 and 5 are connected internally whenever the J relay is not operated. All output pairs of a typical cell, however, are disjunctive. The input and output connections to the complete network are shown by the dotted construction at levels 1 and 8, respectively, of Fig. 11–6. The assembly of a group of these cells into a complete circuit, and particularly the allowable modification of the terminal cells should be completed by the student.

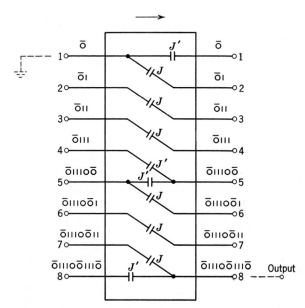

Fig. 11–6. A typical cell for Example 11-2.

Example 11–3

An iterative network is to have a transmission of 1 between its terminals when all its operated relays are contained in groups, each group containing exactly three consecutive members, and each group separated from any other group by at least one unoperated relay. If no relays are operated the transmission is to be 0.

In this example there is no limit on the number of operated groups allowed, although there must be at least one group of three operated. Suppose, now, that we have established the first group of three consecutive, operated relays, and have followed this by at least one unoperated relay. This sequence can be represented by the symbols $\bar{0}11100$. The subsequences leading up to this are $\bar{0}$, $\bar{0}1$, $\bar{0}11$, $\bar{0}111$, and $\bar{0}11100$.

If, further along the chain, another relay is operated we might describe the subsequence in the form $\bar{0}111\bar{0}01$. There is nothing logically wrong about this description, but there is a question in regard to the necessity of the step. And, since no limit is placed on the number of operated groups allowed, where do we stop adding groups of three to the description?

We can answer this question by comparing the formation of a second group of three with that of the first group. The steps may be tabulated as follows:

Formation of First Group		Formation of Second Group	
$\bar{0}$	$(T = 0)$		
$\bar{0}1$	$(T = 0)$	$\bar{0}111\bar{0}\bar{0}1$	$(T = 0)$
$\bar{0}11$	$(T = 0)$	$\bar{0}1110\bar{0}11$	$(T = 0)$
$\bar{0}111$	$(T = 1)$	$\bar{0}11\bar{0}\bar{0}111$	$(T = 1)$
$\bar{0}11100\bar{0}$	$(T = 1)$	$\bar{0}1110\bar{0}11100\bar{0}$	$(T = 1)$

Regardless of which group is being formed we see that the transmission is 0 if a group contains one or two operated relays, and becomes 1 when the third consecutive relay operates. Thus the two sets of descriptions are not distinguishable at the terminals of the network and the pairs of subsequences which occupy the same line in the tabulation may be regarded as equivalent. The subsequence $\bar{0}11100\bar{0}$ is a conditionally valid sequence. If no further relay operation occurs the transmission of the network will be 1, but if one more relay operates, the further steps needed to obtain a transmission of 1 are exactly as they were when the descriptive subsequence was $\bar{0}1$. Hence, we may say that for the requirements of this example, the subsequence $\bar{0}11100\bar{0}1$ is equivalent to the subsequence $\bar{0}1$. Or, in more general terms, after the completion of any conditionally valid sequence, the operation of one additional relay starts another operated group, and is equivalent to restoring the network to the condition represented by the subsequence $\bar{0}1$.

These considerations influence directly the design of the typical cell, shown in Fig. 11–7. If the input at level 5 is grounded, operation of the J relay transfers the ground to the output at level 2. Two more consecutive relays must then operate before a conditionally valid sequence is regained. The dotted connection is an alternative way to insert the J contact between the level 5 input and the level 2 output.

Particular attention should be paid to the connections at the terminal cells. Ground is applied at level 1 of the left-hand cell in the chain, but the output connection is taken from levels 4 and 5 of the right-hand cell. This is necessary because the right-hand cell may be the last cell in which a relay is operated, and an output must then be taken from level 4. If the right-hand relay is not operated the output, if any, will appear at level 5.

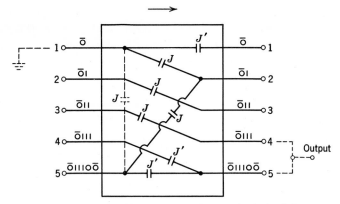

Fig. 11–7. Typical cell for Example 11–3. Output is derived from two levels of the right-hand terminal cell.

A network composed of a chain of these cells is shown in Fig. 11–8. Only the cell associated with the E relay is complete.

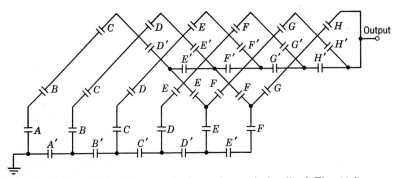

Fig. 11–8. Network derived from the typical cell of Fig. 11–7.

Example 11–4

Draw and compare the typical cells of the iterative networks which satisfy the following conditions:

(a) The network transmission is to be 1 if and only if the total number of operated relays is an odd number. Zero is to be considered an even number.

(b) The network transmission is to be 1 if and only if each operated group of consecutive relays contains an odd number of members. The transmission is 0 if no relays operate.

In part (a) there are only two kinds of subsequences. For any combination of operated and unoperated relays the number of operated relays is either even (including none operated), or odd. Hence the

typical cell of Fig. 11–9 has only two inputs and two outputs. If the
J relay does not operate, J' contacts connect each input to the output
at the same level. If the J relay operates, odd changes to even, and
vice versa, so crossover connections are made by J contacts.

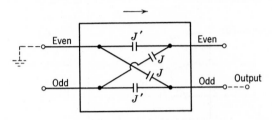

Fig. 11–9. Typical cell of Example 11–4, part (a).

A circuit made up from these cells is, strictly, not a positional circuit.
The same network can be derived by folding a symmetric circuit
designed to realize a function having all the odd a-numbers. It is
instructive, however, to see how the odd-even feature of part (b), which
is a positional problem, is treated in contrast with part (a).

We must first recognize the fact that there are many sequences
possible in which all operated groups of consecutive relays contain an
odd number of members. A description of these sequences by means
of the 0, $\bar{0}$, 1, $\bar{1}$, symbols alone would be hopeless. The alternatives
are either to use verbal statements, or to invent a special symbol and
define its meaning. We illustrate the second procedure by definition:

1_{odd} — a ground at this level means that up to this point the requirements for $T = 1$ have been satisfied.

1_{even} — a ground at this level means that except for the adjacent
operated group, which contains an even number of members, the
requirements for $T = 1$ have been satisfied.

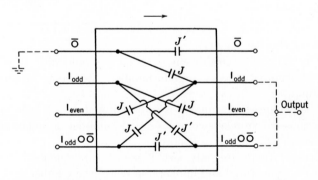

Fig. 11–10. Typical cell of Example 11–4, part (b).

With these symbols available, we see that there are only four subsequences which need be recognized, since no others can lead to a transmission of 1. These are identified as $\bar{0}$, 1_{odd}, 1_{even}, and $1_{odd}0\bar{0}$. The output in Fig. 11–10 is taken from the levels occupied by 1_{odd} and $1_{odd}0\bar{0}$. It should be noted that there is no level for $1_{even}0\bar{0}$. If any group *terminates* while it contains an even number of members, the propagation of ground must stop. On the other hand, if a group containing an odd number of members terminates, the level $1_{odd}0\bar{0}$ must be provided to propagate the ground through any number of unoperated cells. This level leads either to the network output, or through a *J* contact back to the 1_{odd} level to start a new group.

Sometimes the specifications of an iterative circuit are best realized by synthesizing a complementary network. If the network thus found is planar, its geometric complement will then satisfy the original specifications.

Example 11–5

A contact network built on six relays is to have 0 transmission if and only if there is a single consecutive group of operated relays containing exactly three members.

We recognize this specification as the complement of that given for Example 11–1. For that example the typical cell is given in Fig. 11–5, and a network built up from six of these cells is shown in Fig. 11–2. The geometric complement of the latter network is shown in Fig. 11–11.

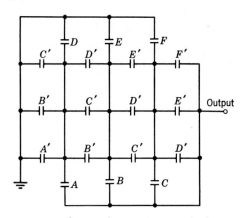

Fig. 11–11. Geometric complement of Fig. 11–2.

It is interesting to verify the fact that the transmission of this network is 1 for all combinations of the variables except those which contain a group of exactly three, consecutive, operated relays.

It is also possible to take the complement of a typical cell and build up the final network. In Fig. 11–12 the construction is given for taking the geometric complement of the typical cell in Fig. 11–5. Input

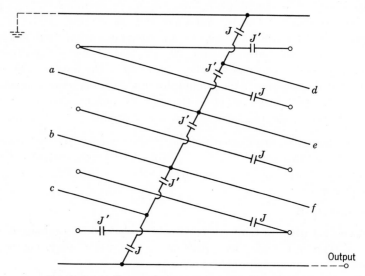

Fig. 11–12. Geometric complement of a typical cell.

ground is supplied to a solid conductor, or bus, which runs along the top for the full length of the chain. The output is taken from a similar bus at the bottom. Within each cell there are interior nodes which must connect with interior nodes of cells to the left and to the right of the typical cell. Thus, the nodes represented by the lines marked a, b, and c extend into the $(J - 1)$ cell, while the nodes represented by lines d, e, and f extend into the $(J + 1)$ cell. The placement of contacts between the pairs of interior nodes, and between interior nodes and exterior nodes, follows the usual procedure.

Many iterative cells and networks are non-planar, and geometric complements are hence unobtainable. It is interesting to find, however, that some cells which apparently lead to non-planar networks can be changed to planar form. An example of this is illustrated in Fig. 11–13. At the top of the figure a typical cell, J, is shown as it was first synthesized, and the next, or K, cell is also shown. Each cell has two crossovers which prevent the use of the geometric process for obtaining complements. In the lower half of the figure, however, the same two cells are shown with their input and output terminals permuted. It may readily be verified that when these cells are connected in pairs, as indicated by the dotted intercell connections, the contact structure between like-numbered terminals is identical with that of the upper part of the figure. For other typical cells it may be necessary to combine

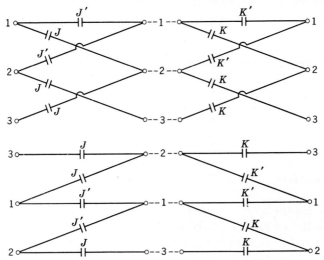

Fig. 11–13. Non-planar cells transformed to planar pairs of cells.

three or more cells in order to "unwind" the structure that leads to crossovers.

11.4   Multi-Element Cells

Most iterative networks are synthesized in terms of a typical cell containing contacts associated with a single variable. There is, however, a group (not well enough defined to call a class) of problems for which a more economical result is obtained when the typical cell contains contacts on two or more consecutive relays. The existence of this type of problem can best be demonstrated by some examples. Following this demonstration we will examine the structure of the problems for whatever enlightenment there may be as to why the multi-element cell is more economical, and for what kinds of problems we may expect the multi-element cell to be more suitable than the single-element cell.

Example 11–6

A two-terminal, iterative network is to have a transmission of 1 if and only if there is a single consecutive group of one or more relays operated.* The problem is readily solved, using a typical cell associated

---

* This problem and its analysis is the first published example of a more economical, multi-element, typical cell. It is given in W. Keister, A. E. Ritchie, and S. H. Washburn, *The Design of Switching Circuits*, D. Van Nostrand Co., New York, 1951.

with one relay, as drawn in Fig. 11–14. This structure contains 5 contacts, with 8 springs, per relay.

When we attempt to synthesize a typical cell containing contacts from two consecutive relays, the first question is again what subse-

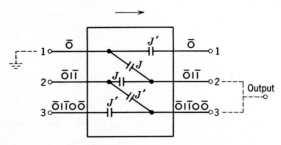

Fig. 11–14. Typical cell associated with one relay, Example 11-6.

quences are to be represented by grounds on the inputs and outputs of the cell. In Fig. 11–14 the subsequences described by the symbols, $\bar{0}$, $\bar{0}1\bar{1}$, and $\bar{0}1\bar{1}0\bar{0}$, have the following meanings, respectively:

(a) Up to this point in the chain no relays have been operated.

(b) A single consecutive group of operated relays, including the adjacent relay, has been established.

(c) A single consecutive group of operated relays has been established and terminated, and the adjacent relay is not operated.

These three statements describe the only conditions within the network that, with appropriate operation of relays beyond the typical cell, can possibly lead to a transmission of 1 for the entire network. They represent states of the network up to but not including the typical cell if they describe the inputs to the typical cell, and inclusive of the typical cell if they describe its outputs. Since these state descriptions do not apply to the entire network it is convenient to refer to them as *partial states*. Of course, if we think of the typical cell as occupying the extreme right-hand position in the chain, the descriptions of its outputs represent states of the entire network, and we provide output connections only to those cell outputs which correspond to valid total states.

An important feature of the concept of partial states is that the action of a typical cell can always transfer a ground from an input representing one partial state to an output representing another partial state. The concept of "distance" may be applied to partial states. It requires the action of only one relay to change the partial state from $\bar{0}$ to $\bar{0}1$, but it requires the action of two relays to change from $\bar{0}$ to $\bar{0}11$.

When we apply these ideas to the problem of describing the inputs ınd outputs of a multi-element typical cell, we realize that although the distance between the input partial state and the output partial state can be greater when more than one relay is associated with the cell, the partial states depend upon the requirements of the problem, and not on the contents of the typical cell. Hence we describe the inputs and outputs of the two-relay cell of this example by exactly the same symbols used for the single-relay cell of Fig. 11–14.

If J and K are the relays associated with the typical cell, we may tabulate, as shown in Table 11–1, the states of operation of these relays

Table 11–1

Partial States		Relay States		Contact Tie Sets
Input	Output	J	K	
$\bar{0}$	$\bar{0}$	0	0	$J'K'$
$\bar{0}$	$\bar{0}1\bar{1}$	$\begin{bmatrix} 0 & 1 \\ 1 & 1 \end{bmatrix}$		K
$\bar{0}$	$\bar{0}1\bar{1}0\bar{0}$	1	0	JK'
$\bar{0}1\bar{1}$	$\bar{0}1\bar{1}$	1	1	JK
$\bar{0}1\bar{1}$	$\bar{0}1\bar{1}0\bar{0}$	$\begin{bmatrix} 1 & 0 \\ 0 & 0 \end{bmatrix}$		K'
$\bar{0}1\bar{1}0\bar{0}$	$\bar{0}1\bar{1}0\bar{0}$	0	0	$J'K'$

required to make all possible input-output transitions. Corresponding to each required relay state the contact tie sets between input and output terminals can then be written.

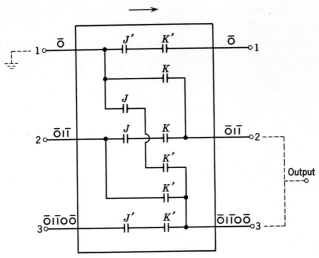

Fig. 11–15. Typical cell built on two relays, Example 11–6, before removal of redundant contacts.

In Fig. 11–15 a typical cell is shown with all the tie sets listed in Table 11–1 represented by separate sets of contacts. It is quite apparent in this figure that many of the contacts are redundant. In Fig. 11–16 all path consolidations have been made to remove redundant contacts,

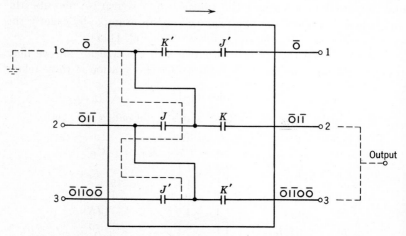

Fig. 11–16. Final design of two-relay typical cell, Example 11-6.

while maintaining disjunctivity between outputs. There are two points of special interest to be observed in the consolidated cell diagram. First, the tie set JK', which is required between input 1 and output 3, is obtained entirely by the use of contacts required in other paths. The route followed in establishing the JK' tie set is indicated in Fig. 11–16 by a dotted line. The second point of interest is the interchange in the positions of the J' and K' contacts in the path between input 1 and output 1. By this simple maneuver a transfer contact is made possible on the K relay, and the spring distributions on the J and K relays are made identical. Instead of the 8 springs per relay required by the single-relay typical cell, the cell built on 2 relays requires only 5 springs for each relay.

The dotted lines at the right of Fig. 11–16 indicate that the output of a complete network can be taken from either the $\overline{0}1\overline{1}$ or the $\overline{0}1\overline{1}0\overline{0}$ output of the right-hand terminal cell. In Fig. 11–17 four of these cells have been combined to form a complete network in eight variables. The input and output connections of this network should be compared with the connections indicated by dotted lines in Fig. 11–16 (note that the $\overline{0}$ level is at the bottom of the circuit in Fig. 11–17 instead of at the top). We also observe in Fig. 11–17 that some of the contacts found in a typical cell are not required in the left-hand and right-hand terminal cells. These contacts are shown by dotted lines.

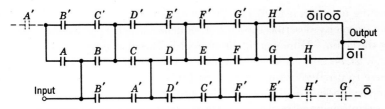

Fig. 11–17. Network based on the typical cell of Fig. 11–16.

In Example 11–7 we investigate the possibility of using more than two relays per cell advantageously.

Example 11–7

A two-terminal iterative contact network is to have a transmission of 1 if none of its relays are operated, or if each consecutive group of operated relays consists of no more than three members.

It is more difficult in this problem to write a precise description of the subsequences which can be considered partial states. The descriptions which will be used make sense only within the context of this problem.

Figure 11–18 contains two versions of the single-relay typical cell. In the left-hand diagram the partial states are described as $\bar{0}$, $\bar{0}1$, $\bar{0}11$, and $\bar{0}111$. These symbols describe adequately the formation of the

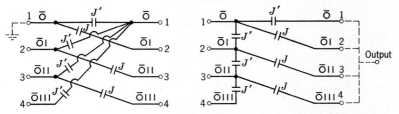

Fig. 11–18. Two versions of the single-relay typical cell, Example 11–7.

first operated group in the chain. But we observe that from the inputs $\bar{0}1$, $\bar{0}11$, and $\bar{0}111$ there are J' contacts leading to the $\bar{0}$ output. Since the final output is to be obtained by connecting all four outputs of the right-hand terminal cell together (see dotted construction in the right-hand cell of Fig. 11–18), after an operated group of three members or fewer is established, the non-operation of the next relay terminates the operated group and permits the start of another operated group.

The connections shown are correct but the descriptions of the partial states are now ambiguous. After an operated group of allowable size has been terminated, the ground at output 1 no longer represents merely $\bar{0}$. It contains in addition the idea of some other valid sequence having been formed. We might change the label to $V\bar{0}$, but this would not correctly describe the true $\bar{0}$ sequence which may exist at the left of the chain. Moreover, if the symbol V is used at input 1 and output 1, it must be used at levels 2, 3, and 4. To be strictly precise we would have to use descriptions like "$\bar{0}$ or $V\bar{0}$," "$\bar{0}1$ or $V\bar{0}1$," etc. There is no important gain to be derived by adding this detail. Effectively, the descriptions used in this example say that whenever an operated group of allowable size is terminated by an unoperated relay, the partial state of the network may be regarded, with respect to terminal conditions, as identical to the partial state in which no relays have been operated. The cell at the left of Fig. 11–18 has all its contacts located so as to make direct interterminal connections. In the right-hand cell the interterminal connections are exactly the same, but the diagram is made planar by connecting all the J' contacts in series. For this problem, it should also be noted that each of the partial states represents a condition for which the network transmission is 1.

We now examine the problem of designing a typical cell, for this example, based on two consecutive relays. The descriptions of the partial states will be the same as those used for the single-relay cell. All possible connections between inputs and outputs, and the contacts required, are listed in Table 11–2.

Table 11–2

Partial States		Relay States		Contact Tie Sets
Input	Output	J	K	
$\bar{0}$	$\bar{0}$	$\begin{bmatrix} 0 \\ 1 \end{bmatrix}$	$\begin{bmatrix} 0 \\ 0 \end{bmatrix}$	$J'K' + JK' = K'$
$\bar{0}$	$\bar{0}1$	0	1	$J'K$
$\bar{0}$	$\bar{0}11$	1	1	JK
$\bar{0}1$	$\bar{0}$	$\begin{bmatrix} 0 \\ 1 \end{bmatrix}$	$\begin{bmatrix} 0 \\ 0 \end{bmatrix}$	$J'K' + JK' = K'$
$\bar{0}1$	$\bar{0}1$	0	1	$J'K$
$\bar{0}1$	$\bar{0}111$	1	1	JK
$\bar{0}11$	$\bar{0}$	$\begin{bmatrix} 0 \\ 1 \end{bmatrix}$	$\begin{bmatrix} 0 \\ 0 \end{bmatrix}$	$J'K' + JK' = K'$
$\bar{0}11$	$\bar{0}1$	0	1	$J'K$
$\bar{0}111$	$\bar{0}$	0	0	$J'K'$
$\bar{0}111$	$\bar{0}1$	0	1	$J'K$

We note in Table 11–2 that no provision is made for a change from $\bar{0}1$ to $\bar{0}11$, or from $\bar{0}11$ to $\bar{0}111$. Both of these changes require that one operated relay be added to an existing group, but there is no way to do this with two relays.

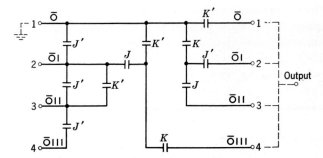

Fig. 11–19. A two-relay typical cell for Example 11–7.

A circuit for the typical cell specified in Table 11–2 is shown in Fig. 11–19. Although there are three places in the table where the interterminal tie set is $J'K' + JK' = K'$, little advantage can be

Table 11–3

Partial States		Relay States			Contact Tie Sets
Input	Output	J	K	L	
$\bar{0}$	$\bar{0}$	$\begin{bmatrix} 0 \\ 0 \\ 1 \\ 1 \end{bmatrix}$	$\begin{matrix} 0 \\ 1 \\ 0 \\ 1 \end{matrix}$	$\begin{matrix} 0 \\ 0 \\ 0 \\ 0 \end{matrix}$	L'
$\bar{0}$	$\bar{0}1$	$\begin{bmatrix} 0 \\ 1 \end{bmatrix}$	$\begin{matrix} 0 \\ 0 \end{matrix}$	$\begin{matrix} 1 \\ 1 \end{matrix}$	$K'L$
$\bar{0}$	$\bar{0}11$	0	1	1	$J'KL$
$\bar{0}$	$\bar{0}111$	1	1	1	JKL
$\bar{0}1$	$\bar{0}$	$\begin{bmatrix} 0 \\ 0 \\ 1 \\ 1 \end{bmatrix}$	$\begin{matrix} 0 \\ 1 \\ 0 \\ 1 \end{matrix}$	$\begin{matrix} 0 \\ 0 \\ 0 \\ 0 \end{matrix}$	L'
$\bar{0}1$	$\bar{0}1$	$\begin{bmatrix} 0 \\ 1 \end{bmatrix}$	$\begin{matrix} 0 \\ 0 \end{matrix}$	$\begin{matrix} 1 \\ 1 \end{matrix}$	$K'L$
$\bar{0}1$	$\bar{0}11$	0	1	1	$J'KL$
$\bar{0}11$	$\bar{0}$	$\begin{bmatrix} 0 \\ 0 \\ 1 \end{bmatrix}$	$\begin{matrix} 0 \\ 1 \\ 0 \end{matrix}$	$\begin{matrix} 0 \\ 0 \\ 0 \end{matrix}$	$(J' + K')L'$
$\bar{0}11$	$\bar{0}1$	$\begin{bmatrix} 0 \\ 1 \end{bmatrix}$	$\begin{matrix} 0 \\ 0 \end{matrix}$	$\begin{matrix} 1 \\ 1 \end{matrix}$	$K'L$
$\bar{0}11$	$\bar{0}11$	0	1	1	$J'KL$
$\bar{0}111$	$\bar{0}$	$\begin{bmatrix} 0 \\ 0 \end{bmatrix}$	$\begin{matrix} 0 \\ 1 \end{matrix}$	$\begin{matrix} 0 \\ 0 \end{matrix}$	$J'L'$
$\bar{0}111$	$\bar{0}1$	0	0	1	$J'K'L$
$\bar{0}111$	$\bar{0}11$	0	1	1	$J'KL$

derived from the algebraic reduction. Except for the $\bar{0}$ to $\bar{0}$ connection the complete tie sets must be used to avoid sneak paths.

We now investigate typical cells using more than two relays per cell. Table 11–3 tabulates the interterminal connections required for a typical cell containing three relays.

The typical cell using three relays per cell is given in Fig. 11–20. Figures 11–21 and 11–22 show typical cells containing four and five

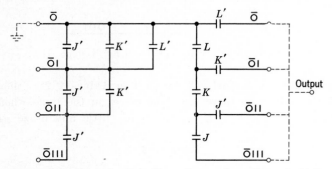

Fig. 11–20. Typical cell built on three relays, Example 11–7.

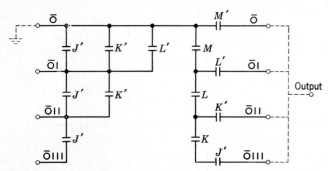

Fig. 11–21. Typical cell built on four relays, Example 11–7.

relays per cell, respectively. The effect of increasing the number of relays per cell is shown in Table 11–4.

Table 11–4

Number of Relays per Cell	Total Number of Contacts	Total Number of Springs	Contacts* per Relay	Springs* per Relay
1	7	11	7	11
2	11	18	5.5	9
3	12	21	4	7
4	13	23	3.25	5.75
5	17	31	3.4	6.2

*Average values

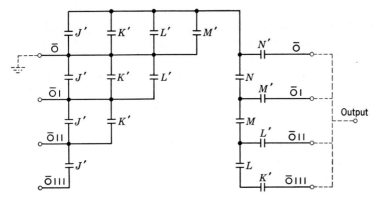

Fig. 11–22. Typical cell built on five relays, Example 11–7.

It is apparent from an examination of Table 11–4 that the average number of contacts per relay and the average number of springs per relay are both at a minimum when four relays per cell are used. But we shall see, in the next article, that even these figures can be reduced.

An examination of Examples 11–6 and 11–7 shows that they have one feature in common which suggests at least a partial reason for the improved economy of multi-element cells over single-element cells. For the multi-element cells of both problems the tabulations of the interterminal tie sets contain a number of transitions which are independent of the state of one or more of the cell variables. Sometimes a redundant variable must be retained in the circuit to prevent sneak paths, but some of the indicated saving can usually be realized.

The conditions for Example 11–6 are shown in Fig. 11–23 for a chain of indefinite length. We observe that when a single consecutive group of relays has operated, there are in general two points of discontinuity

J cell   K cell

---ooooo|o i|i i i i----i i i i|i o|ooo---

Fig. 11–23. Optional states at points of discontinuity.

within the chain. These discontinuities may occur within typical cells when the cell is associated with more than one relay. Thus, in Fig. 11–23, the change from 0 to 1 takes place within cell J, and the change from 1 to 0 occurs within cell K. The relays of cell J are actually in the state 01 (two relays per cell), but the network transmission would be the same if they were in the 11 state (or in the 00 state). Hence for the particular change of partial state involved it is not necessary to have a contact on the left-hand relay of the cell. A similar contact redundancy is present in cell K, where the actual relay state 10 leads to the same network transmission as the optional 00 or 11 states.

11.5 Non-Disjunctive Cells

All the cells of iterative networks that we have studied up to this point have had disjunctive outputs. Input grounds have therefore been mutually exclusive. This type of design is the most generally applicable that we know, but there are situations in which a non-disjunctive output system achieves economy not otherwise obtainable. There has not been enough investigation to permit a categorical description of the types of problems for which the non-disjunctive approach is advantageous. Example 11–8 is of the class in which the conditions for 0 or 1 transmission require that a particular consecutive group occur at least once.

Example 11–8

In Example 11–7 the network transmission is 1 if either no relays operate, or if each consecutive group of operated relays contains no more than three members. We can now write a complementary statement, namely, the transmission is 1 if and only if a consecutive group containing four or more members is operated. The geometric complement, if it exists, of a network which realizes the complementary statement is a network which satisfies the requirements of Example 11–7.

The complementary statement requires merely that somewhere within the network there be a consecutive group containing at least four operated relays. If this condition is satisfied the network transmission must be 1 regardless of the presence of any other subsequence in the chain. This is an example of the absolutely valid partial state that we symbolize by V_a. Since a group of four or more operated relays may begin at any point in the chain, we cannot permit the availability of ground to be determined by the action of relays to the left of the point where the valid sequence starts. This means that there must be a ground bus running along the chain and available to all cells.

These ideas are expressed in the typical cell of Fig. 11–24(a). At the top a ground bus extends from cell to cell without interruption. A similar bus, V_a, at the bottom of the cell insures that if an output ground is obtained by establishing at least one valid sequence, no circuit action to the right of the typical cell can remove the ground. The contacts within the cell transfer ground from any activated input to an output which represents one additional consecutive relay operated. We note at this point that the outputs of the typical cell which represent

1, 11, and 111 are disjunctive between all pairs, but that it is nevertheless possible to have grounds appearing on more than one output.

Since the typical cell of Fig. 11–24(a) is part of a network which provides transmission of 1 when four or more consecutive relays are operated, the geometric complement of this cell will be typical of a

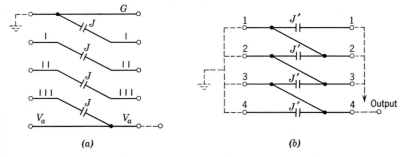

(a)   *(b)*

Fig. 11–24. Typical cell (*b*) is the geometric complement of cell (*a*). Cell (*a*) satisfies the complementary statement of the problem. See Example 11–8.

network for which the transmission is 1 when no relays are operated, or when each consecutive group of operated relays consists of no more than three members. The complementary cell is given in Fig. 11–24(b). When used to form an iterative chain this cell does the same work as the cell in Fig. 11–18.

The input ground at the left-hand terminal cell is supplied to all four of the cell inputs. If the first relay is not operated, ground appears on all four of the cell outputs. If the first relay is operated, ground is removed from the output 1, but remains at outputs 2, 3, and 4. In either case the outputs of the cell are not disjunctive.

Now, suppose the first relay is operated. Its contact cell supplies grounds at inputs 2, 3, and 4 of the second cell. If the second relay does not operate, grounds will appear again on all four of its cell outputs. But if the second relay operates, ground is removed from output 2, and outputs 3 and 4 remain grounded.

More generally, if ground is present at any cell input or inputs, and the associated relay does not operate, the contact structure is such that it restores ground to all outputs. If a consecutive group of relays operates, ground is removed from output 1 of the first cell, from outputs 1 and 2 of the second cell, and from outputs 1, 2, and 3 of the third cell. If the next relay does not operate, grounds are restored to all outputs of its contact cell. But if a fourth consecutive relay does operate, ground is removed from all outputs of that contact cell, and the entire network transmission becomes 0.

We note in Fig. 11–24(b) that the process of geometric complementation would ordinarily require that the output of the network be taken from all four of the cell outputs, as indicated by the dotted construction. However, it is clear from the analysis given in the preceding paragraph that if the network transmission is 1, output 4 will always be grounded. It is sufficient, therefore, to take the network output from output 4 of the right-hand terminal cell.

The partial states represented by the output grounds of the non-disjunctive typical cell may be described in tabular form.

Input or Output Leads Grounded	Partial State Represented
1, 2, 3, 4	No relays operated, or all sequences of operated relays terminated within allowable size
2, 3, 4	Single adjacent relay operated
3, 4	Two consecutive, adjacent relays operated
4	Three consecutive, adjacent relays operated
None	At least one consecutive group of operated relays contains more than three members

The disjunctive, complementary cell from which we derive the desired non-disjunctive typical cell may be based on two or more relays per cell. In Figs. 11–25, 11–26, 11–27, and 11–28, the left-hand cells—

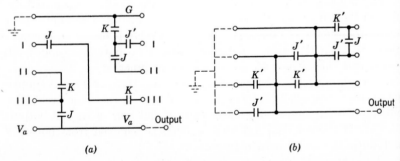

(a)   (b)

Fig. 11–25. The non-disjunctive typical cell (b) is built on two relays and is derived as the geometric complement of cell (a).

marked (a)—are complementary, disjunctive cells which perform the same duties as cell (a) in Fig. 11–24, but are built on 2, 3, 4, and 5 relays, respectively. In each figure, the right-hand cell—marked (b)— is the corresponding non-disjunctive typical cell found by taking the geometric complement. We can now tabulate the contact and spring requirements for the non-disjunctive cells.

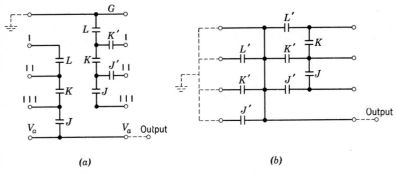

Fig. 11–26.   Non-disjunctive typical cell (*b*) is the complement of cell (*a*).

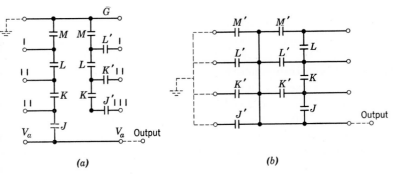

Fig. 11–27.   Complementary typical cells built on four relays.

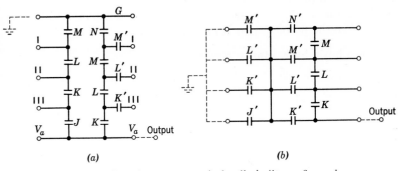

Fig. 11–28.   Complementary typical cells built on five relays.

A comparison of Table 11–5 with Table 11–4 indicates that for the requirements of this particular problem the non-disjunctive cell is much more economical in contacts and springs than the disjunctive cell. The student may verify that if the non-disjunctive cell is built on 6 relays per cell, a total of 19 contacts and 34 springs are required for

Table 11–5

Number of Relays per Cell	Total Number of Contacts	Total Number of Springs	Contacts* per Relay	Springs* per Relay
1	4	8	4	8
2	7	13	3.5	6.5
3	8	14	2.67	4.67
4	10	18	2.5	4.5
5	11	19	2.2	3.8

*Average values

each cell. Hence, the 5-relay-per-cell design minimizes the total contact and spring requirement.

The results demonstrated by this one example can hardly be called conclusive. Without a process of trial and error we are not aware of the applicability of the non-disjunctive cell approach. We have, however, demonstrated one thing which may be more generally applicable. If we regard the presence or absence of ground on the several inputs of a typical cell as a code which describes the partial state of the network to the left of the cell, then we see that the particular type of disjunctive design that we have been considering uses a code in which only one digit takes the value 1. When we design a non-disjunctive cell we use a code in which more than one digit can assume the 1 value. Efforts have been made to improve cell economy by improving the efficiency of input codes. Although the positive results obtained have not been impressive, there has been no proof that improvement is not possible, so the problem remains unsolved.

11.6 Synthesis by a Matrix Method*

We have seen that the relays of an iterative chain by operating or not operating form binary sequences. The associated contact network must be designed so that the transmission is 1 for certain specified sequences, or classes of sequences, and that it is 0 if the specifications are not satisfied. When a sequence is specified for all the members of a chain, we can speak about the total state of the chain. But we have found it useful also to speak of various partial states. These are states represented by sequences present in the part of a chain to the left of a typical cell. Since we are interested only in total states for which the transmission is 1, we use as inputs to the typical cell only those partial

---

* From a procedure developed by D. A. Huffman and based on the flow table used in his paper, "The Synthesis of Sequential Switching Circuits," *Journal of the Franklin Institute*, Vol., 257, March and April 1954, pp. 161-190 and 275-303.

states which by further action of the chain can be converted to valid total states.

In problems of practical interest there is a limited number of partial states and total states which we must take into account. Furthermore, the action of a typical cell can change these states in only a limited number of ways. It becomes possible, therefore, to relate the action of a typical cell to the changes of partial states thus produced, by means of a relatively compact matrix. For the moment let us restrict the discussion to disjunctive typical cells.

The rows of the matrix will represent either partial states or valid total states. These may simply be identified by arbitrary numbers. For each state number there must somewhere be a description of the state expressed either by symbols or by a word statement.

The columns of the matrix will represent the states of the relay or relays associated with the typical cell (0 = not operated; 1 = operated). In addition, a column headed Z specifies the network output as 0 or 1 for the state represented by each row.

A given input state (row) and a given state of the relay(s) of the typical cell (column) define an intersection which requires a matrix entry. The entry at any intersection specifies which output of the cell is to be grounded as a consequence of the transfer (if any) of input ground by the action of the typical cell. The entry is accomplished by inserting the number, previously defined, of the activated output state. A few examples of this procedure will help to clarify the details.

Example 11–9

An iterative network is to have transmission of 1 if and only if its operated relays are contained within two consecutive groups.

The only total state for which the transmission is 1 is represented by the sequence $\bar{0}1\bar{1}0\bar{0}1\bar{1}0$. Using a typical cell associated with a single relay we may break down this valid total state into partial states. The complete list of states, partial and total, are identified by arbitrary state numbers as follows:

State Number	State Description
1	$\bar{0}$
2	$\bar{0}1\bar{1}$
3	$\bar{0}1\bar{1}0\bar{0}$
4	$\bar{0}1\bar{1}0\bar{0}1\bar{1}$
5	$\bar{0}1\bar{1}0\bar{0}1\bar{1}0$

The matrix for the typical cell is also shown. Note that the 1 entries in the output column indicate that either state 4 or state 5 are valid total states.

State Number	J 0	1	Output Z
1	1	2	0
2	3	2	0
3	3	4	0
4	5	4	1
5	5	—	1

Let us examine a few entries in this table. In the second row, and in the column for $J = 0$ we find the entry 3. This means that if ground is present on input 2, for which the state is $\overline{0}1\overline{1}$, and the J relay does not operate $(J = 0)$, ground should appear on output 3, for which the state is $\overline{0}1\overline{1}0\overline{0}$. In the next entry down in the same column, if the input ground represents state 3 and the J relay does not operate, the output ground must also represent state 3.

At this same level in the next column, however, we see that if the input represents state 3, and the J relay operates $(J = 1)$, the output must represent state 4. This corresponds to an input ground which represents the state $\overline{0}1\overline{1}0\overline{0}$ transferring to an output ground which represents $\overline{0}1\overline{1}0\overline{0}1\overline{1}$, when the J relay operates. We note also that in the fifth row of the column for $J = 1$ that no entry is indicated. Once state 5 is reached, any further relay operation creates an invalid state. We make no provision in the contact structure of the typical cell for an invalid state, so no entry is required in the matrix.

The matrix of the iterative network is a complete wiring diagram of the typical cell. Inputs to the cell are represented by the state number. An entry at the intersection of a row representing an input state and the column for $J = 0$ indicates that a J' contact joins the input terminal having the specified state number and the output

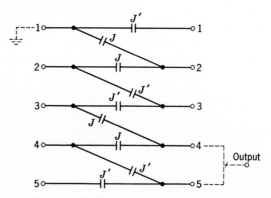

Fig. 11–29. Typical cell described by the matrix of Example 11–9.

terminal having the entry number. If the intersection is with the $J = 1$ column, the connection is made by a J contact. All connections specified by the matrix are shown in Fig. 11–29. The matrix contains the entry "4" at the intersection of row 3 and the column $J = 1$. In Fig. 11–29 this entry describes the J contact which connects input 3 to output 4. The J' contact which connects input 4 to output 5 is represented by the entry "5" in row 4 and in the column for $J = 0$.

In the next example we can show the application of the matrix method to the design of a typical cell with either one relay per cell or two relays per cell.

Example 11–10

The transmission of an iterative network is to be 1 if and only if each consecutive group of operated relays contains an odd number of members, or if no relays are operated.

For this problem we define a conditionally valid state, namely, either no relays are operated or all operated relays are contained in odd-numbered groups, with the last group followed by at least one unoperated relay. The symbol $V_c 1_{odd}$ means that a conditionally valid sequence is followed by an odd number of operated relays, and $V_c 1_{even}$ means that the conditionally valid sequence is followed by an even number of operated relays. With these definitions in mind we can immediately write the matrix for a single-relay typical cell. Note that there is a blank entry if a group terminates with an even number of operated relays, and the network transmission becomes 0. The single-relay typical cell described by this matrix is shown in Fig. 11–30.

	State Number	$J = 0$	$J = 1$	Z
V_c	1	1	2	1
$V_c 1_{odd}$	2	1	3	1
$V_c 1_{even}$	3	—	2	0

When more than one relay is associated with a typical cell the matrix description is modified by adding columns to represent all the possible

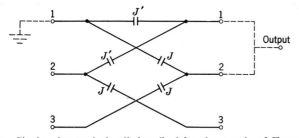

Fig. 11–30. Single-relay typical cell described by the matrix of Example 11–10.

combinations of the variables associated with the cell. In the next
matrix we describe, for this same problem, a typical cell with two
relays. The partial states are exactly as defined for the single-relay cell,
and are identified by the same numbers. Blank entries again are used
when the action of the cell leads to a network transmission of 0.

	State Number	00 $J'K'$	01 $J'K$	10 JK'	11 JK	Z
V_c	1	1	2	1	3	1
$V_c 1_{\text{odd}}$	2	1	2	—	2	1
$V_c 1_{\text{even}}$	3	—	—	1	3	0

From this matrix we see that between input 1 and output 1 we have
the tie sets $J'K' + JK' = K'$. From input 2 to output 2 we have
$J'K + JK = K$. Making these simplifications we can draw the two-
relay typical cell as in Fig. 11–31. The single-relay cell of Fig. 11–30

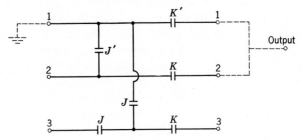

Fig. 11–31. Two-relay typical cell synthesized by the matrix method, Example 11–10.

uses 5 contacts, 8 springs per relay. In the two-relay cell these are
reduced to 3 contacts, 5.5 springs per relay.

Non-disjunctive cells can also be described by the matrix method.
To illustrate this point we will use the problem treated in Examples
11–7 and 11–8.

Example 11–11

Design a non-disjunctive typical cell on one relay for a network
which is to have a transmission of 1 if no relays operate, or if each
consecutive group of operated relays contains no more than three
members.

We will use the symbol V_c to represent either no relays operated, or
all operated groups terminated with three members or less. When V_c is
followed by 1, 11, or 111, the size of the next operated, but unterminated

group is indicated. The states of interest may be numbered

$$
\begin{array}{cl}
1 & V_c \\
2 & V_c 1 \\
3 & V_c 11 \\
4 & V_c 111
\end{array}
$$

Now, instead of having each state represented by a ground on one input, we will number the input leads and the output leads L_1, L_2, L_3, and L_4, and designate in the matrix what combination of leads is to be grounded for each state. The entries in the matrix again represent the destination states required by the action of the typical cell.

Leads Grounded	State Number and Description		$J = 0$	$J = 1$	Z
$L_1 L_2 L_3 L_4$	1	V_c	1	2	1
$L_2 L_3 L_4$	2	$V_c 1$	1	3	1
$L_3 L_4$	3	$V_c 11$	1	4	1
L_4	4	$V_c 111$	1	—	1

The construction of the typical cell is, of course, the same as in Fig. 11–24(b). We note in the first column that whenever $J = 0$ the circuit goes to state 1, and this requires that all four outputs be grounded. If all four of the inputs are grounded, the introduction of a J' contact between each pair of like-numbered input and output terminals satisfies this output requirement. The location of the diagonal connections is then dictated partly by the requirements of the transitions in the matrix column for $J = 1$. If this column alone was to be satisfied, we might be led to make these diagonal connections by means of J contacts. However, the need for solid connections is found when we try to satisfy the condition that if the input combination represents any one of the states 2, 3, or 4, and $J = 0$, ground must be restored to *all* output terminals. This places a J' contact in parallel with each J contact in the diagonal branches, and hence is the equivalent of a solid connection.

PROBLEMS

11.1 Design a network on nine relays for which the transmission is 1 if and only if all the operated relays are grouped in pairs of adjacent relays, with each operated pair separated from the next operated pair by at least one unoperated relay, and there is at least one operated pair.

11.2 Design a network which has a transmission function which is the complement of that realized in Problem 11.1. Compare the typical cell for this network with that found in Problem 11.1. How do you account for the difference in the number of information levels required in the two cells?

11.3 Design the typical cell and all incomplete end cells for an iterative contact network which is to have transmission 1 if and only if exactly two non-consecutive relays are operated. Each cell is to contain contacts from a single relay.

11.4 Design the typical cell and all incomplete end cells for an iterative contact network which is to have transmission 0 if and only if exactly two non-consecutive relays are operated. Each cell should contain contacts from a single relay.

11.5 Design the typical cell and all incomplete end cells for an iterative contact network which is to have transmission 1 if and only if there is a group of relays which includes the last relay and which contains an even number of consecutively operated relays.

11.6 Design the typical cell (one relay per cell) and show the end-cell connections for the iterative solution of the transmission statement given.

$T = 1$ if and only if all operated and all unoperated groups contain an odd number of members.

In your solution define clearly any code symbols used to describe the meaning of grounds at the various inputs and outputs of the typical cell.

11.7 An indefinitely long iterative network is to have a transmission of 1 if and only if there exists a single consecutive group of exactly two operated relays, or if there exists a single consecutive group of exactly three operated relays, or if both groups exist.

Design a typical, single-variable cell for the network required by the stated conditions. Indicate clearly the connections to the terminal cells of the network. The cell diagram should also be marked with a clearly explained code specifying the conditions for which each lead into the cell is grounded.

11.8 An iterative contact network is to be designed with *two* output terminals, A and B. There is to be a transmission of 1 at terminal A, if and only if there exists at least one group of consecutively operated relays which consists of an odd number of members. The transmission at terminal B is to be the complement of that at terminal A.

Design a typical, single-variable cell for the network required by the given conditions. Indicate clearly on the diagram of this cell which lead or leads should be grounded if the typical cell occupies the extreme left-hand position in the network, and which lead or leads should be connected to terminal A and which to terminal B if the typical cell occupies the extreme right-hand position in the network. The cell diagram should also be marked with a clearly explained code specifying the conditions for which each lead into the typical cell is grounded.

11.9 Design the iterative contact network which realizes the following requirements: $T = 1$ if and only if the odd-numbered groups of operated relays contain an odd number of members and the even-numbered groups of operated relays contain an even number of members. In addition, at least one relay must be operated for $T = 1$.

11.10 A two-terminal network is to be built on an indefinitely large number of relays. Its transmission is to be 1 if and only if (a) at least one

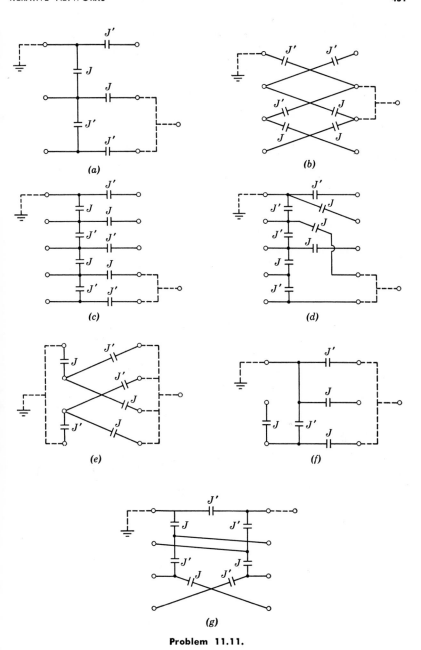

(a)

(b)

(c)

(d)

(e)

(f)

(g)

Problem 11.11.

relay is operated, (b) the positions of the operated relays correspond to a single pattern selected from the indefinitely large set, as shown:

0 1 0	One operated relay
0 1 0 1 0	Two operated relays
0 1 0 1 0 1 0	Three operated relays
0 1 0 1 0 1 0 1 0	Four operated relays
and so on	

Note that the pattern of operated relays may be preceded or followed by any number of unoperated relays.

Design a typical, single-variable cell and indicate the connections made to the network terminals on the cells at the extreme ends of the network. The inputs to the cell should be labeled so that the meaning of a ground at each input is clear.

11.11 Write a word description of the terminal action of an iterative, positional network based on each of the typical cells shown, taking into account the connections made at the left- and right-hand extremities of the circuit, as indicated by dotted lines in the diagrams.

CHAPTER 12

Synthesis
of
sequential circuits

In the preceding chapters our attention was concentrated on the problem of synthesizing combinational circuits, with economy if possible. It was a feature of every circuit specification, either expressed or implied, that the combination of input variables present at any moment completely determined the output or outputs of the circuit. Regardless of circuit complexity, we could always express, algebraically or otherwise, fixed functional relations between inputs and outputs. Of course, we realized that after a change of input conditions we would have to wait a short time for some of the switching devices to change state, but this was a rather minor qualification of the specified circuit performance.

We now undertake to study, and ultimately to synthesize, sequential switching circuits.* Outputs will no longer be directly related to the input conditions of the moment, but will depend also on what the input conditions have been in the past. We need no longer be limited in our specifications to the rigid constraints of the table of combinations. In

---

* The methods presented in this chapter are based on the work of D. A. Huffman, first reported in a Doctoral dissertation, "The Synthesis of Sequential Switching Circuits," Department of Electrical Engineering, Massachusetts Institute of Technology, 1953, and later published under the same title, *Journal of the Franklin Institute,* Vol. 257, Nos. 3 and 4, March and April 1954, pp. 161–190 and 275–303

Chapter 11 we introduced the concept of sequences in space, and we learned to design iterative circuits of great power, in the combinational sense. When this concept of sequence is extended to sequences in time, a whole new range of circuit properties and specifications is brought within reach of synthesis. Strangely enough, the objective we seek here is to reduce the general problem of sequential synthesis to one of combinational synthesis. In some problems the design of an appropriate and economical combinational circuit is the major task of a sequential synthesis. It is therefore another objective that the sequential synthesis procedure display with emphasis the alternatives of combinational design which satisfy the over-all specification.

Within this chapter we shall discuss circuits built on relays and contact networks. In Chapter 14 the ideas and methods developed will be applied with only minor modifications to circuits built with other types of switching devices.

12.1 General Properties of Sequential Circuits

In the design of sequential switching circuits we will encounter a number of problems which require the development of new procedures. The need for new methods is perhaps best shown by examining the nature of some elementary sequential circuits before we know how to design them.

A quite simple sequential circuit is present in Fig. 12–1. A relay A is controlled directly by a key K. Actually, the use of the relay A is in this instance a formality, because it carries only two contacts and these could just as well be mounted directly on the key. The other two relays, B and C, are controlled by a contact network containing contacts from all three of the relays A, B, and C. In order to distinguish between the relay coils and the contacts which are operated by the relay armatures, we designate the coils by capital letters and the contacts by lower-case letters. Furthermore, we will designate the transmission function which excites a relay coil by the same capital letter that identifies the coil itself. Using these conventions, we can write for the transmissions to relays B and C

$$B = (a + c)(a' + b)$$
$$C = (a + c)(a' + b')$$

There is also shown in Fig. 12–1 a tree network composed of contacts on relays B and C. This tree produces at its terminals the four outputs, Z_0, Z_1, Z_2, and Z_3, of the circuit.

In these expressions for the transmission to relays B and C we observe that each relay is at least partly controlled by one of its own contacts. We shall examine this point more fully a little later. Aside from this observation, however, we do not really learn much from the transmission expressions.

It will be much more instructive to examine step-by-step the changes which occur within this network as we attempt to influence it. The only way we can exert any influence on it is by the use of the key, K.

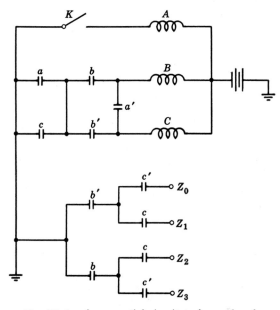

Fig. 12–1. A sequential circuit to be analyzed.

For simplicity let us assume that when the key K is closed the relay A operates immediately and that when K is opened, the relay A releases immediately.

Initially, we assume that K is open and all relays are unoperated. When K closes, A operates, and the a contact closes. Ground is thus applied through the path ab' to the relay C. When relay C operates it closes the contact c, thereby placing a short circuit across the contact a. Nothing further happens now as long as the key K is kept closed. If K is opened, relay A releases and opens the a contact through which relay C first operated. However, relay C is kept operated because its own contact c is still closed. As contact a is opened, contact a' closes, and through the path $cb'a'$ ground is applied to relay B. When relay B operates it opens the b' contact and closes the b contact, thereby maintaining transmission to its own coil through the path cb, and transmission to relay C through the path cba'. As long as we keep the key K open, this condition, with relays B and C both operated, will continue indefinitely. If we again close the key K, relay A in operating will close the a contact and open the a' contact. This operation maintains the transmission to the coil of relay B through the path ab, but since the contacts a' and b' are now both open, the transmission to relay C becomes 0 and it drops out, thereby opening the contact c. Finally, if we again open the key K and release relay A, contact a opens, and since contact c is already open, excitation to both relays B and C is removed and relay B will drop out. At this point, we note that we have returned to the starting condition with the key K open and all relays released.

The significance of this analysis can better be appreciated by summarizing the steps we have described, as shown in Table 12–1.

Table 12–1

Step Number	K	A	B	C	Output
1	0	0	0	0	Z_0
2	1	1	0	0	Z_0
3	1	1	0	1	Z_1
4	0	0	0	1	Z_1
5	0	0	1	1	Z_2
6	1	1	1	1	Z_2
7	1	1	1	0	Z_3
8	0	0	1	0	Z_3

(Return to step 1)

It should be noticed in Table 12–1 that with respect to relays B and C we make a distinction between the excitation of a relay and its operation. Thus, in step 2 relay A is operated by closing the key K. The effect of this is to apply a ground to relay C, but we do not indicate that C operates at the same time that A operates. Instead, we show that the operation of relay C follows that of relay A by indicating it in a separate step, that is, step 3. It is of no real consequence that the conditions existing in step 2 are of very short duration, whereas the conditions of step 3 can last for a long time. The important thing in the sequential problem is that we must account for the fact that events do happen in a time sequence.

Table 12–1 has a column that indicates the output terminal which is grounded at each step. The outputs listed for the even-numbered steps are of short duration, but those listed for the odd-numbered steps can last indefinitely. If we examine only the outputs of potentially long duration, we see that in steps 1 and 5 the key K is open, but the outputs are Z_0 and Z_2, respectively. Also, if we look at steps 3 and 7, we find the key K is closed in both steps, but the outputs are Z_1 and Z_3, respectively. The only input we have to this circuit is the key K. It is quite apparent, however, that the outputs are not governed solely by the position of the key. This dependence of the output on something other than the immediate input situation is one of the most important features of a sequential switching circuit.

It is apparent also that the state of operation of the relays B and C is not a function of the input conditions only. We will learn to refer to relays like B and C as *secondary* relays, which derive their control not only from the conditions at the input or inputs of the circuit, but also from conditions within the secondary system itself. Thus, we see that in step 3, when key K is closed, relay C is operated and relay B is released, but in step 7 when key K again is closed, relay B is operated and relay C is released.

We observed that some of the steps in Table 12–1 are of short duration, and that the others represent conditions which persist for as long as the position of key K is left undisturbed. The steps of short duration represent unstable conditions within the network and the other steps represent stable conditions. The intermixture of unstable and stable conditions is another important feature of sequential circuits, and one of the most important problems of design is the appropriate management of these conditions.

We can describe the operation of the circuit in Fig. 12–1 by noting that each time the key is closed or opened the output ground progresses from Z_0, to Z_1, to Z_2, to Z_3, and then back to Z_0. If we call each closing or opening of the key an event, the output of the circuit represents a counter which counts these events on a scale of four. Another way to use this circuit would be to take an output from either Z_1 or Z_3 and operate the key K at a uniform "frequency." From either of the designated outputs, a ground would be obtained for every second closure of K, and we could thereby designate the whole device as a frequency divider.

In carrying out the analysis which was summarized in Table 12–1, we went rather hastily over the transition from the conditions of step 4 to those of step 5. Previously, in step 3 relay A was operated and relay C was operated. In step 4, relay A was released and we said that this resulted in a ground being applied to the winding of relay B through the path $cb'a'$. In going then to step 5 we said that relay B operated and thereby transferred its excitation to the path cb, and continued the excitation of relay C through the path cba'. This is quite correct if the contacts on relay B have the ideal structure that we generally assume.

In the study of combinational circuits, we were able to overlook departures from the ideal because we never examined the transmission of a circuit until it had reached steady-state conditions. But in the circuit of Fig. 12–1, the possibility exists that the transfer contact on relay B will not operate in the ideal manner. Specifically, it is possible that when relay B operates, the b' contact might open before the b contact closes. If this interval is short enough, perhaps no harm will be done, but there always exists the possibility that relay B may try to operate and then lose its excitation for a period long enough that its armature starts to fall back. Worse still, during this period it may be possible for relay C to release. If this happens, the c contact opens and both B and C will release completely. We will defer further discussion of this point until later in this chapter, but it should be clear that the operation of a sequential circuit can involve more than the mere realization of the algebraic form of a transmission function. At first, we are going to assume that contacts do behave ideally; that is, all normally open contacts close simultaneously, all normally closed contacts open simultaneously, and there is a zero time interval between the opening and closing of the two parts of a transfer contact.

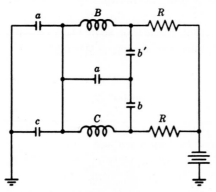

It may be somewhat reassuring to examine the circuit shown in Fig. 12–2. This circuit contains only the relays B and C and their control networks, and it can be used to replace the equivalent parts of Fig. 12–1. We can analyze the performance of the circuit by observing what happens as the A relay operates and releases. If we again start with all three relays released, the first operation of relay A applies ground to the coil of relay C through an a contact. Ground is also applied to the series control terminal of relay B, but at the same time ground is applied to the other side of the coil of B through the path ab', so that B cannot operate. When relay C operates it closes the c contact and maintains the ground at the control terminal of C. Now, when relay A releases, the shunt ground is removed from relay B and the series ground is applied to relay B through the already closed contact c. At this step we observe that the operation of relay B is free of any possibility of failure since it does

Fig. 12–2. Circuit which is equivalent to a part of the circuit in Fig. 12–1.

not involve any timing of the operation of a transfer contact. When relay A again operates, a shunt ground is applied to relay C, causing it to release, and thus open the c contact. Finally, when relay A again releases, all series excitation is removed and relay B releases. Thus, the operation of the relays B and C in Fig. 12–2 is the equivalent of the operation found in Fig. 12–1, but the performance of the circuit in Fig. 12–2 is independent of the exact timing of the associated contacts.

One method for displaying graphically the operation of a sequential circuit is illustrated by Fig. 12–3. This is known as a sequence diagram. Time is divided into non-uniform intervals which are indicated by the vertical lines numbered from 1 to 10. If one of the relays A, B, or C is operated during one of the time intervals, this fact is indicated by drawing a line through that interval opposite the designator of the relay. If the relay is not operated, a blank space is left. Another set of horizontal lines indicate the time intervals during which ground appears on each of the output terminals. The numbering of the time intervals corresponds to the step numbers given in Table 12–1. Thus, at step 1, A, B, and C are not operated. At step 2, relay A operates and at step 3 relay C operates. The time elapsing between step 1 and step 2 may be any length we choose, but the time elapsing between step 2 and step 3 is merely the time it requires for relay C to operate. In the sequence diagram, no distinction is made between the magnitudes of these two time intervals. The diagram records only the *order* in which events occur without indicating the relative time scale.

From the diagram of Fig. 12–3 it is possible to synthesize the control network for relays B and C. For example, since relay C becomes oper-

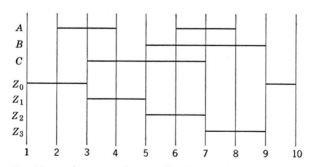

Fig. 12–3. Sequence diagram for the circuit of Fig. 12–1.

ated at step 3, the conditions which cause it to operate must exist in the interval between step 2 and step 3. The pertinent conditions are that relay A is operated and relay B is not operated. Hence, we might expect one term of the transmission C to be ab'. Relay C releases at step **7**, and it might therefore be expected that the conditions which cause it to remain operated are those which exist between step **3** and step 6, inclusive. Here we must take into account the fact that C itself is operated, together with the combinations of A and B which are present during this interval. The entire transmission to relay C is then given by

$$C = ab' + c(ab' + a'b' + a'b) = ab' + c(a' + b')$$

It can readily be verified that this algebraic statement of the transmission to relay C corresponds with the contact structure shown in Fig. 12–1. There is no question that from a properly drawn sequence diagram we can write the transmission expression for the secondary relays. If the problem is simple enough, we can usually draw an acceptable sequence diagram. But, for even a moderately complex problem, it becomes difficult to be sure that the sequence diagram takes into account all possible sequences, and even if this is accomplished, it is still more difficult to determine whether the secondary relays have been used in the most effective manner. These difficulties can be best appreciated by considering first a very simple problem, and then observing the effect of a slight change in specifications.

Referring to the block diagram at the left of Fig. 12–4, we want to design a circuit that has two inputs, X_1 and X_2, and a single output Z.

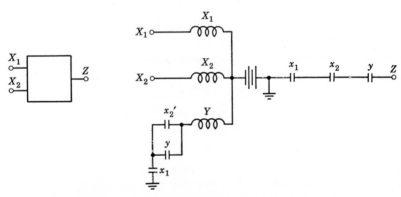

Fig. 12–4. Synthesis by use of operate and hold paths.

The requirements are that there is to be an output ground on Z if both X_1 and X_2 are grounded, but only if X_1 is grounded before X_2 is grounded. It is a simple matter to design the relay circuit shown in Fig. 12–4. We assign relays X_1 and X_2 to respond to grounds applied to inputs X_1 and X_2, respectively. We then use a secondary relay Y

which has a contact network containing the path $x_1 x_2'$. This path ensures that Y will operate only if X_1 is grounded and X_2 is not grounded, that is, input X_1 is applied before input X_2. After the relay Y is operated, we want it to continue to operate after the input X_2 is applied. To prevent the contact x_2' from releasing relay Y when X_2 is grounded, we place the contact y across the contact x_2'. This use of the contact y establishes a so-called holding circuit. Another way of saying it is that it permits relay Y to "remember" that X_1 was grounded before X_2. Finally, we ground X_2, and then through the circuit consisting of the contacts $x_1 x_2 y$ an output ground Z appears. This output circuit assures that both X_1 and X_2 are grounded, and through the y contact assures that X_1 was grounded before X_2.

The designer of the circuit in Fig. 12–4 now examines it a little more carefully. He sees that if, after the output ground Z is obtained, the ground is removed from X_1, relay Y will release. If ground is again applied to X_1, relay Y cannot operate because both the x_2' and the y contacts are now open. On the other hand, if after obtaining the output ground Z, the ground is removed from X_2, relay Y will not release. If the ground is again applied to X_2, the operation of relay X_2 will again produce a ground on the output Z. The designer decides that he does not like the situation in which the removal of one input ground causes the permanent loss of the output Z, but if the other input ground is removed and restored, the output Z is lost and then restored. He decides to change the specifications and require that, in addition to the original conditions to be satisfied by the circuit, it is to be designed so that if either of the input grounds is removed and then replaced, the output is to go to 0 and remain at 0 until after both input grounds have been removed and restored in the specified sequence.

The additional requirement which has been imposed is not a serious one. By struggling with a sequence diagram, it is possible to work out a network which operates in accordance with the revised specifications. It is doubtful, however, that this endeavor would carry with it any feeling of assurance that the solution obtained approached an optimum one. There would certainly be no assurance that the "method" used had a wide range of applicability.

A rather elegant solution of this problem is given in Fig. 12–5. If input X_1 is grounded before X_2, relay Y_2 will operate first, and then relay Y_1. This sequence will produce an output Z. If input X_2 is grounded before input X_1, relay Y_1 will operate first and prevent relay Y_2 from operating. An output ground will therefore not be obtained because the contact y_2 in the output circuit will remain open. If the

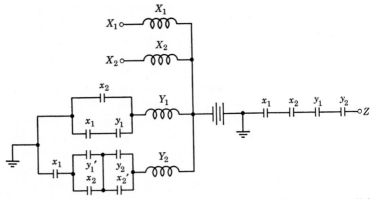

Fig. 12–5. More difficult synthesis required when specifications are slightly changed.

correct sequence has been followed and an output obtained, then when we remove the ground from X_1, relay Y_2 releases. If the ground is now reapplied at X_1, relay Y_2 cannot operate, and the output ground is not restored. If, instead of removing X_1, we remove the X_2 ground, the result is exactly the same. Relay Y_2 releases and cannot operate when ground is again applied to X_2. Hence it is not possible to restore the ground to the output after losing it, except by returning to the starting point, with both X_1 and X_2 ungrounded, and following the prescribed sequence.

We have been reasonably successful in analyzing the operation of the sequential circuits so far considered. It is essentially a verbal analysis in which we account for the conditions within the circuit from moment to moment as the inputs are changed. We have also made some use of tabulation, as shown in Table 12–1 and the sequence diagram of Fig. 12–3, in order to systematize the accounting. Let us now look at Fig. 12–8. This circuit shows two primary relays X_1 and and X_2 controlled by keys K_1 and K_2, respectively, and three secondary relays Y_1, Y_2, and Y_3, with their control networks. No output network is shown because we want to concentrate attention on the behavior of the three secondary relays as the input conditions are changed. It is quite evident that we are not going to learn very much about the behavior of this circuit by any process of keeping a record of what relays are operated, what relays are not operated, what contacts are open, and what contacts are closed. We shall have to develop a much more systematic procedure. This will be the subject of the next article.

12.2 Analysis Based on Stability Criteria; the Flow Matrix

The key to the analysis, and ultimately to the synthesis, of sequential circuits is the understanding derived from a systematic study of the stability or lack of stability associated with the states occupied by the secondary relays. Primary relays are all under the immediate control of the input variables, and they change their states of operation only in response to changes of state of the input variables. On the other hand, the control networks of the secondary relays may contain contacts associated with the primary relays and also contacts associated with the secondary relays. Thus, the secondary relays directly influence each other and the patterns of influence can become exceedingly complex.

Our basic ideas regarding stability can be derived from a study of Fig. 12–6. The key K can apply a ground to the terminal a, which we call the *control terminal* of relay R.

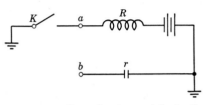

Fig. 12–6. Grounds at a and b signify excitation and operation, respectively, of the relay R.

Contact r is a normally open contact on relay R. If terminal a is grounded, R is *excited;* if terminal a is not grounded, R is not excited. If terminal b is grounded, R is *operated* (the normally open contact r is closed); if terminal b is not grounded, R is not operated.

If there are grounds on both terminals a and b, the relay R is both excited and operated. If neither a nor b is grounded, relay R is not excited and not operated.

Under what conditions can we have terminal a grounded and terminal b not grounded, or terminal a not grounded and terminal b grounded? To answer this we must take into account the finite time required for a relay to operate or release. If a is grounded and b is not grounded, it means that the relay is excited but that it has not yet had time to operate. Eventually, it will operate and both a and b will be grounded. Likewise, if a is not grounded and b is grounded, the relay is operated but not excited. The excitation has been removed and eventually the relay must return to the non-operated condition.

These observations are generalized by saying that if the conditions at terminals a and b are the same (either both grounded or both ungrounded), the relay R is in a stable state. Its state of excitation and its state of operation are identical, so there is no reason for it to change

state. If, however, the conditions at a and b are different, the relay
is in an unstable state. It must change its state of operation so that
it becomes the same as its state of excitation.

These considerations are so simple that they might appear to be
trivial. But by the application of these simple stability criteria our
analysis becomes revealing and our synthesis becomes systematic.

It will be instructive to apply these ideas to an analysis of the circuit
of Fig. 12–1. The first step is to determine algebraically the state of
excitation of the relays B and C. These excitation expressions are
simply the transmission functions of the contact network between the
ground bus and the control terminals of relays B and C, which may
be written

$$B = (a + c)(a' + b) = ab + a'c$$

$$C = (a + c)(a' + b') = ab' + a'c$$

We now display these transmissions on a map as functions of a, b, c,
in Fig. 12–7(a). Each entry in the map contains two binary digits

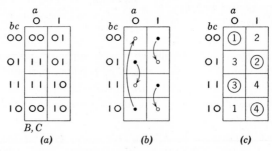

Fig. 12–7. Stability analysis of circuit in Fig. 12–1.

which correspond to the excitation values of B and C, respectively.
We assume, of course, that $1 =$ relay excited, and $0 =$ relay not excited.
Thus, for $a = b = c = 1$, $B = 1$ and $C = 0$, so the corresponding B, C
entry in the map is 10.

The map consequently contains a description of the excitation states
of B and C for all combinations of the values of a, b, c. We now note
that the rows of the map carry designators which represent the values
of b and c. The binary variables associated with the rows represent
the transmissions of normally open contacts b and c which are on
relays B and C, respectively. Hence, these designators represent the
states of operation of the relays B and C.

If a particular map entry is the same as the state represented by
the row designator, the relay is stable and no change of state will occur.
Thus, in the row $bc = 00$, under column $a = 0$, there is an entry 00;

this signifies that the excitation of both relays is 0 and the row designator $bc = 00$ indicates that neither relay is operated. Hence, this entry represents a stable state. At the intersection of the column $a = 1$ and the row $bc = 10$, the map entry is 10. We interpret this to mean that relay B is excited and operated while relay C is not excited and not operated, which again represents a stable state of the two secondary relays.

In the column $a = 0$, and the row $bc = 01$, the map entry is 11. This means that relay B is excited but not operated, but relay C is both excited and operated. Since one of the two secondary relays has a state of excitation which differs from the state of operation, the entry represents an unstable state of the secondary system. In this instance, the relay B must operate, and when it does so we move from the 11 entry in the row $bc = 01$ to the 11 entry in the row $bc = 11$, still in column $a = 0$. This transition in the map corresponds to the physical operation of relay B, and it restores stability to the system.

A somewhat more graphic version of the map presentation is shown in Fig. 12–7(b). Instead of entries which represent the states of excitation of the secondary relays, we enter simply a small open circle to indicate that the corresponding state in Fig. 12–7(a) is stable, or a dot to indicate that the corresponding state is unstable. From each of the unstable states we then draw lines with arrows indicating the stable state which must be reached from each of the unstable states.

Another way to present this information is shown in Fig. 12–7(c). This is a form which we will use extensively in synthesis. In this presentation the states of the secondary system are assigned the arbitrary numbers 1, 2, . . . , n. These numbers are assigned only to the stable states of the system and the positions of those stable states are indicated by encircling the numbers which represent them, as in Fig. 12–7(c). Unstable states are described by numbers without circles and the actual numbers assigned are those of the stable states which the system ultimately reaches from any given position. Thus, at the intersection of the column $a = 0$ and the row $bc = 01$, the entry is the number 3 without a circle around it. This means that the state represented is unstable and that a transition must occur to the position occupied by ③. The ③ is located in the row $bc = 11$ in column $a = 0$ and the transition from 3 to ③ is accomplished by the operation of relay B.

The mechanics of operation within the sequential circuit can be observed quite clearly in the presentation of Fig. 12–7(c). If we start at the time power is first applied to the circuit, and no relays are operated, the system is in the state represented by the entry ① at the top of the $a = 0$ column. Now we observe that the map is so organized that horizontal movement within the map is accomplished by a change of the primary variable, and vertical movement within the map is

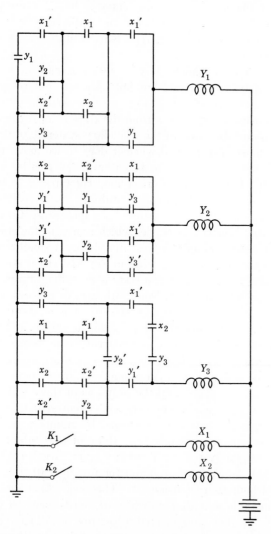

Fig. 12–8. A more complex sequential circuit to be analyzed.

accomplished by a change of secondary variables. We assume that after each change of primary variable we wait a sufficient time to permit all consequent changes of secondary variables to be completed. Starting with the state represented by ① in the map, we operate the primary relay and thus move to the column $a = 1$. Here we find the 2 entry (uncircled) which means that the secondary system is unstable. If we wait long enough, relay C will operate and we thus move to the ② entry, which is a stable state. If we now return to $a = 0$, the system state is represented by the unstable entry 3. This calls for the operation of relay B, which moves us to the stable ③ entry. If relay A again operates we move horizontally in the map to the 4 state and then vertically to the ④ stable state. Finally, when relay A is again released we move horizontally to the 1 entry and then vertically to the ① state which was the starting point.

Each time a change in the primary state is made we must wait for the secondary system to make any required change to a new stable state. In some instances no secondary change is necessary, but in general we must be prepared to allow time for a secondary response to a change in the primary state. We note here also that the system we have been studying is a relatively well-behaved one, in that each transition from an unstable state to a stable state involves the change of only a single secondary variable. Some systems require that two or more secondary variables change state in making such transitions. This is a subject which we will explore in more detail later.

The power of the map method for displaying the stabilities and instabilities of a sequential circuit can better be appreciated by using it in the analysis of the more difficult example represented by the circuit of Fig. 12–8. We begin the analysis by writing the contact network transmission functions which represent the excitations to the three secondary relays Y_1, Y_2, and Y_3.

$$Y_1 = x_1{}'y_3 + x_1{}'x_2y_2 + y_1(y_3 + x_1x_2{}' + x_1{}'x_2 + x_2y_2)$$

$$Y_2 = x_2y_1y_3 + x_1x_2{}'y_1{}' + y_2(x_1{}'y_1{}' + x_1{}'x_2{}' + y_1{}'y_3{}' + x_2{}'y_3{}')$$

$$Y_3 = x_2{}'y_1{}'y_2 + x_1x_2{}'y_1{}' + x_1{}'x_2y_1{}'y_2{}' + y_3(y_1{}'y_2{}' + x_1{}'x_2{}'y_1{}' + x_1{}'x_2)$$

The triple entries in the map of Fig. 12–9(a) represent the excitation values of Y_1, Y_2, and Y_3, respectively, as functions of x_1, x_2 (column variables) and y_1, y_2, y_3 (row variables). In Fig. 12–9(b) we have indicated those entries which represent stable states by open circles and those which represent unstable states by dots.

In the first column, starting with the dot in row 001, a solid line with an arrow indicates a transition to the row 101. The solid line signifies that this transition is accomplished by the change of a single secondary variable, in this instance the variable y_1. Row 101 also contains a dot, from which another solid line indicates the transition to

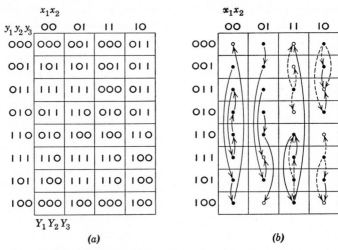

$y_1 y_2 y_3$	$x_1 x_2$			
	00	01	11	10
000	000	001	000	011
001	101	101	001	011
011	111	111	000	011
010	011	110	010	011
110	010	100	100	110
111	110	111	110	100
101	100	111	110	100
100	000	100	000	100

$Y_1 Y_2 Y_3$

(a)   *(b)*

Fig. 12–9.   Analysis of the circuit in Fig. 12–8.

row 100, by the change of the variable y_3. There is another dot in the 100 row so the indicated state is again unstable, and a solid line shows a transition to the row 000, by a change of the variable y_1. The last change terminates in a stable state. These transitions, as indicated in Fig. 12–9(b) should be verified by reference to the excitation values listed in Fig. 12–9(a).

Again within the first column, we find a group of rows, namely, 011, 010, 110, and 111, all occupied by dots representing unstable states. The excitations for these rows are such that the transitions made by the secondary relays form a closed cycle. The relay Y_2 remains operated throughout the cycle while the relays Y_1 and Y_3 successively occupy all their possible states of operation. Once the secondary system enters this cycle, it will continue indefinitely unless a change in the primary variables is made to break it. This is one of the "accidents" which can happen when sequential circuits are designed by methods which do not clearly display the stability conditions within the secondary system.

Going now to the second column, for which $x_1 x_2 = 01$, we find that there are two stable states represented. The stable state in row 111 is reached by one or more successive changes, each involving a single change of secondary variable, from the unstable states represented by rows 000, 001, 011, and 101. The stable state in row 100 is similarly reached from the unstable states in rows 010 and 110. No matter how we move into this second column by a change of primary variable the secondary system will always reach, without ambiguity, a state of ultimate stability. The mode of operation in this column is admittedly rather complex, but it is entirely acceptable if no more direct mode is available.

In the third and fourth columns we encounter secondary transitions which are classified as *races*. They are indicated by the dotted lines in these columns. A race occurs whenever a required secondary transition involves the change of two or more of the secondary variables simultaneously. Consider the race shown at the top of the column for $x_1x_2 = 11$. The dotted entry in row 011 is found, in Fig. 12–9(a), to correspond to an excitation of 000. Hence, relays Y_2 and Y_3 must both release. The destination intended is the stable state in row 000. One of the dotted lines leads from row 011 to row 000, since it is entirely possible that both changes of the secondary variables will occur simultaneously. On the other hand, if relay Y_2 releases before Y_3, we will have the transition indicated by the dotted arrow leading to the row 001. And if relay Y_3 releases before relay Y_2 the transition will take us to row 010, again indicated by a dotted arrow. If we reach either row 001 or row 010, we find that the excitations in these rows are stable and no further relay action will occur, despite the fact that the original intention was to reach row 000. Thus, the race condition in this instance can lead to false operation and we designate this as a *critical race*.

If we now look at the bottom of the $x_1x_2 = 11$ column we find another race condition originating in row 101. The indicated excitation requires us to go from row 101 to row 110, a change of the variables y_2 and y_3. One of the dotted arrows leading from row 101 goes to row 110, the intended destination, but the other dotted arrows lead to rows 111 and 100, depending upon whether relay Y_2 or Y_3 wins the race, respectively. We note now, however, that if the first transition reaches row 111, there is a solid-line arrow going to row 110, and another solid arrow going from there to row 100. Finally, there is a solid arrow from 100 to the stable state in row 000. Thus, in this race condition the final destination is always the stable state in 000, regardless of the relative speeds of the secondary relays. There is no ambiguity about the ultimate destination and this is a non-critical race.

In the fourth column, for which $x_1x_2 = 10$, there is a non-critical race at the top of the column and a critical race at the bottom of the column. In the synthesis of sequential circuits we will frequently use non-critical races to simplify contact structure, but the critical race must be avoided.

Considering the circuit of Fig. 12–8 as a whole, as described in Fig. 12–9, we see that except for the cycle present in the first column, any change of primary variables, causing a movement horizontally within the map, is followed by secondary changes which lead to conditions of ultimate stability. However, there are two critical races, and the operation of the circuit is, therefore, not fully determinate. It is not representative of good sequential circuit design.

12.3   The Flow Table

The circuits shown in Fig. 12–4 and Fig. 12–5 are solutions of a type of sequential switching problem in which an output is to be obtained in response to a specified sequence of input combinations. In specifying the sequence which led to the circuit of Fig. 12–4 we failed to state some of the requirements and found that the circuit did not do exactly as we wanted. After the operating requirements were more firmly fixed we found it necessary to use a circuit like that in Fig. 12–5. Such lack of clarity and completeness in circuit specification is by no means uncommon. We shall therefore begin in this article to develop a method for describing the performance of a sequential circuit which has the advantage of revealing the questions that must be answered before a circuit specification can be considered complete.

As originally stated, the requirements to be met by the circuit of Fig. 12–4 are that the output is to be grounded if inputs X_1 and X_2 are both grounded, but only if X_1 is grounded before X_2. We arrange these requirements in the tabular form shown.

X_1X_2

00	01	11	10	Z
①			2	0
		3	②	0
		③		1

In this table we note that a stable state ① is entered in the first row of the column for $X_1X_2 = 00$. At the extreme right of the table, in the column for the output Z, we enter a 0 since there is to be no output for the condition represented by the state ①. At this time, of course, we have no idea how many secondary relays may be required by the circuit, or what operative combination of the secondary relays will be used to represent any particular stable state. For the moment, we simply assume that each stable state occupies a separate row in the table we are forming and, if necessary, each row can correspond to a different secondary state.

We next enter in the table states to represent the response of the network when the input X_1 is grounded. These entries must, of course, be made in the 10 column. In the same row with ①, but in the 10 column, we enter the number 2 to indicate that the change that we have made in the primary variables has established an unstable secondary state. In the next row, immediately below the uncircled 2 we enter ② to represent the stable state finally assumed by the system in response to the first step of the required sequence. At the right of this circled entry we place a 0 in the output column to indicate that the sequence has not been completed and the output is still ungrounded. The next step in the specified sequence is that the input X_2 be grounded, which requires that we move horizontally in the second row until we reach the 11 column. There we enter an uncircled 3 to indicate that in response to this primary change, the system is again unstable. In the same column and immediately below the uncircled 3 we enter a ③ to identify the stable state reached after the last change of primary state. Since the state corresponding to ③ has been reached as the result of introducing the correct sequence of primary variables, a 1 is entered in the output column to indicate that the output terminal should be grounded.

The tabulation developed up to this point shows how we treat the introduction of the correct sequence, but we must also specify what is to happen if we use a sequence other than the one specified. Suppose, for example, that X_2 is grounded before X_1. The additional entries which must be made are shown in tabular form.

X_1X_2

00	01	11	10	Z
①	4		2	0
		3	②	0
		③		1
	④	5		0
		⑤		0

When input X_2 is grounded first we go through an uncircled 4 entry to the ④ entry, for which the output is 0. If X_1 is then grounded we enter the 11 column through an uncircled 5 entry, from which we reach the ⑤ entry and its associated output of 0. Hence, we make sure that this incorrect sequence cannot produce an output ground.

Up to this point our procedure has been one of tabulating the circuit action when the specified sequence occurs, and then trying to be certain that no other sequence can produce an output ground. The trouble is that there are many more incorrect sequences than correct ones. In a problem as simple as this, it is not particularly difficult to specify all the incorrect sequences, but the method in general is cumbersome. A better method is to go through the partly developed table and decide what the circuit action should be for each change of primary variables that we can make, starting from each of the existing stable entries. Whenever, in this process, we reach a stable entry, the next move must be another change of primary variables.

In many problems we specify that only one primary variable is to change at a time. We will apply this specification to the problem under consideration. Thus, we see that starting from the ① entry there are only two possible changes of primary variable, that is, to the 01 column or to the 10 column. We have already indicated by uncircled entries in those columns the stable states which should ultimately be reached because of these primary changes. Starting from the ② entry in the 10 column, we can go either to the 11 column or to the 00 column. The entry in the 11 column has already been made, so we need decide only what should happen if the primary variables return to the 00 combination. For this change, it seems sensible to direct the system back to the entry ①, and we hence enter an uncircled 1 in the 00 column of the row containing ②.

The tabulation given tells nothing about what happens if the circuit is in the state represented by the entry ③ when the primary variables change. We do know that we previously found it undesirable to allow a condition in which we could unground one of the inputs, thereby losing the output ground, and then by regrounding the same input obtain the output ground again. We therefore want to specify transitions which prevent this circuit response. If the changes in the primary state are restricted to those reached by a change of a single primary variable, when we leave the ③ state we can enter either the 01 column or the 10 column. If we unground X_1 and enter the 01 column we can direct the system to entry ④ by placing an uncircled 4 in the 01 column of the row containing ③. This entry insures that if the X_1 input is again grounded the system will go to the state represented by entry ⑤, for which the output is 0. A more troublesome situation exists if, starting from entry ③, we unground the input X_2 and enter the 10 column. In that column the only stable state available is represented by entry ②. If we enter an uncircled 2 opposite the entry ③ we simply guarantee that if the X_2 input is again grounded we will return to entry ③ and thus regain the output ground. To avoid this we define a new stable state, denoted by the entry ⑥, and place an uncircled 6 in the third row of the 10 column. The output corresponding to entry ⑥ is 0.

At this point we have developed all the stable states shown in the next table. The table is completed by entering the destination stable

$X_1 X_2$				
00	01	11	10	Z
①	4	—	2	0
1	—	3	②	0
—	4	③	6	1
1	④	5	—	0
—	4	⑤	6	0
1	—	5	⑥	0

states which are to be reached following any change of input variable as we leave entries ④, ⑤, and ⑥. States ④ and ⑥ can both reach the 00 column by a change of a single primary variable, so in this column we enter an uncircled 1 for each of these rows. States ④ and ⑥ can also enter the 11 column by a single change of primary variable. Here we direct the transitions to stable state ⑤ for which the output is 0. From stable state ⑤ we can enter either the 01 or the 10 column. In the former column we enter an uncircled 4, and in the latter an uncircled 6. The effect of these entries is to insure that once state ③ has been reached, and an output obtained, any further change of primary variables must eventually reach the 00 combination before a sequence leading to an output can again be effective. Blanks have been entered wherever the required change of primary variables is impossible.

The table we have just completed is called a *primitive flow table*. It is characteristic of a primitive flow table that each stable state occupies a row by itself, and that the output for any row is associated with the stable state of that row only. In the preceding table, if each of the six rows represents a different secondary state, we would require at least three secondary relays to differentiate among the rows. That is, we would use six of the $2^3 = 8$ combinations that would be available. Our objective in further manipulation of the flow table is to reduce the number of rows as far as possible. The important thing to remember at this point is that in setting up the primitive flow table, in a form which is frequently quite redundant, we are faced with the need to specify without ambiguity the response of the circuit to any input sequence it may receive. In this respect, the flow table does for sequential problems what the table of combinations does for combinational problems.

It is convenient in forming the primitive flow table to assign a different row to each entry which represents a stable state. However, if we also associate the rows of a flow table with operative combinations of secondary relays, we may use an unnecessarily large number of secondary relays, unless we can find some way to reduce the number of rows. For this reason we must adopt a different concept of what a circled entry in the flow table represents. We have indicated that the transition from an uncircled entry to a circled entry, within a given column, represents a change of state. It has been convenient to regard this as a change of secondary state. However, if we think of a circled entry as representing a stable *total state* of the system, that is, a state which includes both primary and secondary variables, we can achieve a change from one stable (total) state to another stable (total) state without necessarily making a change of secondary state. There would, of course, be two circled entries in the same row, but this simply means that the primary variables then differentiate between the two states.

The process of combining the rows of a primitive flow table is called *merger*. Mergers may be made in accordance with the following rules:

1. Two rows may be merged if the state numbers appearing in corresponding columns of each row are alike, or if the entry in one of the rows is blank.

2. When circled and uncircled entries of the same state number are to be combined, the resulting entry is circled. Thus if we have the two rows

$$\begin{array}{cccc} ③ & 5 & 6 & 8 \\ 3 & ⑤ & 6 & ⑧ \end{array}$$

they may combine to form the new row

$$\begin{array}{cccc} ③ & ⑤ & 6 & ⑧ \end{array}$$

A change from entry ③ to entry ⑤, or from entry ③ to entry ⑧ in the merged row, involves a change of the primary variables only, and there is no secondary transition. A change from entry ⑧ to entry 6 initiates a transition to the row containing entry ⑥, by way of a change of the secondary variables.

Consider the first two rows of the primitive flow table developed previously. These are

$$\begin{array}{cccc} ① & 4 & — & 2 \\ 1 & — & 3 & ② \end{array}$$

A merger of these rows in accordance with the rules yields the new row

$$\text{①} \quad 4 \quad 3 \quad \text{②}$$

It may appear that there is a contradiction present in this merged row. In the first row, as written in the primitive flow table, there is a blank in the 11 column which was inserted there to indicate that the change of primary variables from 00 to 11 was impossible. When the first two rows are merged, the 11 column is occupied by an uncircled 3, which appears to say that if the transition is made from the 00 column to the 11 column the system is directed to stable state ③. This is both true and false. In the merged row the double change of primary variable is still impossible. The entry which replaces the blank indicates what would happen if the transition from 00 to 11 were allowed, but since this transition cannot occur the indicated change to stable state ③ does not occur. The entry in the 11 column of the merged row does describe what happens when a primary change is made from the 10 column, where the system is in the state represented by entry ②, to the 11 column.

We have illustrated the process of merger by combining two of the rows of the primitive flow table. Further examination shows that a number of pairs of rows can thus be combined, but it is usually not the best procedure to simply start combining such pairs. Many problems offer more than one set of merger possibilities and these sets are not always of equal advantage. A sounder procedure is to display all the possible mergers before choosing those which are to be used. For this purpose we draw a merger diagram as illustrated in Fig. 12–10. This consists of an array of points each of which represents a row of the primitive flow table. The points are numbered to correspond with the numbers of the circled entries in the primitive flow table.

Fig. 12–10. A merger diagram.

We examine each pair of rows in the primitive flow table to see whether they can be merged in accordance with the rules of merger. If a pair can be merged, a line is drawn between the correspondingly numbered points in the merger diagram. Thus, we show in Fig. 12–10 that row 1 can be merged with row 2 or row 4, but not with row 3. Row 2 cannot merge with any additional row. Row 3 does not merge with any row. Row 4 merges with row 5 or row 6, and row 5 merges with row 6. This diagram must be used with care. For example, row 4 merges with row 1 or row 6, but since row 1 does not merge with row 6 we cannot combine these three rows. On the other hand, rows 4, 5, and 6 can be merged into a single row because all *pairs* of these rows can merge.

One possible set of mergers for this primitive flow table is to combine rows 1 and 2 to form a new row, enter row 3 as a separate row, and to combine rows 4, 5, and 6 as a third row. These mergers lead to the merged flow table shown.

X_1X_2

00	01	11	10
①	4	3	②
—	4	③	6
1	④	⑤	⑥
—	—	—	

It will be noticed that no output column is shown with the merged flow table. Regardless of merger, output values are still associated with circled entries, and the assignments made in the primitive flow table remain in force. Hence the output specifications of the primitive flow table must be retained, even though we base circuit design on the merged flow table.

In the merged form, the original six rows of the primitive flow table have been reduced to three rows. Each of these three rows must now be represented by a different secondary state. Since at least two secondary relays are needed, for which there are four secondary combinations, the fourth row of the table is indicated by blank entries. Later, in synthesizing a control network these blank entries can be treated as optional terms and used to simplify the network structure.

If we analyze the circuit shown in Fig. 12–5, it will be found that this circuit was derived from a merged flow table which differs from the one shown above. To derive the circuit of Fig. 12–5, we form a merged flow table which repeats rows 1, 2, and 3 of the primitive flow table, and then combines rows 4, 5, and 6 to form the fourth row of the merged flow table as shown.*

x_1x_2

00	01	11	10	
①	4	5	2	a
1	4	3	②	b
1	4	③	6	c
1	④	⑤	⑥	d

* In developing the flow table concept we have used capital letters to represent input variables. The next step converts the merged flow table to a map of the secondary excitation functions. Here we want the primary variables ex-

It will be observed that the entries that were blank in the primitive flow table for rows 1, 2, and 3 now contain a listing of unstable states. In particular, in row 1 and column 11 the blank entry is replaced by an uncircled 5. This seems to indicated that it was decided that if the double change of primary variable from 00 to 11 should occur, the system should be directed to stable state ⑤ for which the output is 0. This could very well be a sensible decision, but it is not the source of the entry we see in the table. Actually, this entry came about because the designer treated the blank entry as an optional term, and the values he ultimately inserted to simplify his network are those which would be required if the transition to state ⑤ were to occur.

We have noted in forming the primitive flow table and the merged flow table that we do not specifically identify the secondary states corresponding to the rows. We know that each circled entry represents a total state, and that those in the same row usually correspond to a specified secondary state.* Having established a merged flow table, we must now identify a set of row states (secondary states) such that all transitions required between rows can be achieved either by changing one secondary variable at a time, or by non-critical races.

In the merged table above we have identified the rows by the letters a, b, c, d, placed at the right of the table. We use these letters to represent the rows in the transition diagram of Fig. 12–11, where each of the four rows is represented by a point. A line joining two points in the transition diagram signifies that a transition present in the flow table requires that the secondary states of these two points differ in only one secondary variable. Thus, the transitions from uncircled 5 to ⑤, and from uncircled 3 to ③, in the 11 column, require the connections a-d and b-c, respectively. In the 10 column, the transition uncircled 2 to ② requires the connection a-b, and the transition uncircled 6 to ⑥ requires the connection c-d. It is not necessary to show in the transition diagram any connections for either the 00 or the 01 columns. Each of these columns contains only one stable state and the entries in all other rows direct the transitions to that stable state. For these columns we can safely set up secondary races, or any

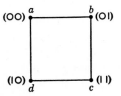

Fig. 12–11. A transition diagram.

---

*A given row in a merged flow table is sometimes represented by more than one secondary state. See Chapter 13.

other transition patterns which eventually reach the row containing the stable entry.

From the transition diagram of Fig. 12–11, we see that a reasonable assignment of secondary states is $a = 00$, $b = 01$, $c = 11$, $d = 10$. These assignments permit all the required transitions to be accomplished by the change of a single secondary variable. We now use the assignments to identify the secondary states of the rows of the merged flow table and thus obtain the completed flow matrix shown in Fig. 12–12(a).

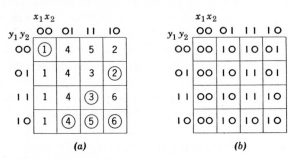

Fig. 12–12. Flow matrix at left converted to the excitation matrix at right.

The final step is to reverse a process we developed for analysis. In the map of Fig. 12–12(b) we first enter the secondary excitations which are required for all the stable states. Since for a stable state the excitation must be the same as the state of operation, the excitation required for any stable state shown in Fig. 12–12(a) is found from the values of $y_1 y_2$ assigned to the row in which that stable state is located. Thus, for ① we enter in the final map the excitation 00; for ② we enter 01; for ③ we enter 11; for ④, ⑤, and ⑥ we enter 10. It should be carefully verified that these entries are present in the correct places in the map of Fig. 12–12(b). We must next enter excitations for the uncircled entries. The uncircled entries represent unstable secondary states which must change to the secondary states associated with like-numbered circled entries. Thus, where an uncircled 5 is entered in the 00 row of column 11, we want the secondary state to change to the state 10, corresponding to the row in which the ⑤ is located. Hence we enter in the 00 row and the 11 column an excitation of 10, which will then require that the Y_1 relay operate. In the 01 row of the 11 column, the uncircled 3 entry directs the transition to the ③ in row 11. Therefore we must enter an excitation of 11 in the cell occupied by the uncircled 3. The continued application of this procedure accounts for the entries in the 10 column.

There is only one stable entry each in the 00 and in the 01 columns.

It will therefore be permissible to set up race conditions in controlling the secondary transitions in these columns because the races will be non-critical. The entries for these columns in Fig. 12–12(b) establish such races. This, however, is not the only way that we can direct the secondary action in these columns. For example, in the 01 column, instead of entering 10 in all the rows, we could have made the entries, reading from top to bottom, 10, 11, 10, and 10, respectively. These entries eliminate the race condition by specifying that a transition from the 01 row to the 10 row must follow the secondary-state sequence 01—11—10. This and other choices are all available to the designer. He may use them as needed, either to meet special requirements or to minimize control networks.

12.4 Some Synthesis Examples

In the preceding article we developed at least the outline of a method for synthesizing sequential circuits. In this article we will illustrate how the method is applied to typical problems. The steps in the method are first summarized as follows:

1. From a description of the problem given by word statements we write a primitive flow table which, by definition, includes a listing of the outputs associated with each stable state (circled entry).
2. We verify that the primitive flow table correctly describes the circuit performance for all possible input sequences. This is best done by specifying, for each stable state, what the circuit response must be after each allowed change of the primary variables.
3. Prepare a merger diagram and from it decide how the rows of the primitive flow table are to be merged in the final flow table.
4. Write the merged flow table.
5. Prepare a transition diagram and from it assign the row states (secondary relay states).
6. Write the excitation matrix.
7. Write the output matrix. Note that the identification of output states with stable states is contained in the primitive flow table.
8. Write the excitation and output functions from their respective matrices and design the combinational circuits thus specified.

In some of the more difficult problems we encounter later it will be necessary to modify this procedure somewhat, but there are many simple problems which can be treated immediately by the steps outlined. We note that steps 6 and 7 complete the process of converting the problem of sequential synthesis to a problem of combinational synthesis. The combinational methods developed in the preceding chapters apply directly to the synthesis of suitable networks either from the functional expressions found in step 8 or directly from the maps found in steps 6 and 7.

In Art. 12.3 we discussed the type of problem in which a specified input sequence leads to an output ground, and for which all other input sequences fail to produce an output ground. A more general type of sequential problem is one in which the output depends upon certain properties of the input sequence rather than upon a specified form.

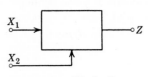

The examples we will use in the following discussion are all of the latter type. We start with a very simple example.

Fig. 12–13. Block diagram of a clamp-gate circuit.

Example 12–1

A sequential circuit of the form indicated in Fig. 12–13 is to be designed so that if $X_2 = 1$, the output Z is the same as the X_1 input, but if $X_2 = 0$, the output is to remain fixed at its last value prior to X_2 becoming 0. No more than one input variable is to change at one time.

It is immediately clear that no particular sequence of input variables is more closely associated with an output of 1 than any other sequence. A more useful attack is to determine, for each *combination* of input variables, what output or outputs can be associated with that combination. We must assign a separate stable state in each column for each possible output condition. This point is illustrated by the tabulation of stable states given in Fig. 12–14.

In the 00 column stable states ① and ② are entered, with outputs 0 and 1, respectively. In this column, $x_2 = 0$ and the output must therefore represent the value which x_1 had just before this column was reached. The 00 column can be reached from the 01 column or from the 10 column by a single change of input variable. If the system was previously

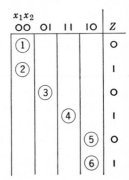

x_1x_2				
00	01	11	10	Z
①				0
②				1
		③		0
			④	1
			⑤	0
			⑥	1

Fig. 12–14. Table of stable entries, Example 12–1.

in the 01 column, the previous value of x_1 is 0 and after a change to the 00 column the output should be 0. If, however, the system was previously in the 10 column, where $x_1 = 1$, a shift to the 00 column might require an output of 1.

In the 01 column, $x_2 = 1$, and the output therefore is the same as x_1. Hence, this column contains only the single state ③ with an output of

0 corresponding to $x_1 = 0$. For exactly the same reason, the 11 column contains only the stable state ④ which is associated with an output of 1. Here, $x_1 = x_2 = 1$ and the output must therefore be the same as x_1.

In the 10 column, x_2 is again equal to 0 and the output must show the previous value of x_1. If the 10 column is reached from the 00 column, and if the output was previously 0, the output associated with ⑤ must be 0. If the 10 column is reached from the 11 column, the previous value of x_1 is 1, and the output associated with ⑥ is therefore 1.

The primitive flow table is completed by inserting the unstable entries and the blank entries shown in Fig. 12–15. It is a simple matter to make the entries of unstable states in the 01 and 11 columns since each of these columns contains a single stable state. In the 00 and 10 columns, however, care must be taken to direct each transition to its correct destination. Thus, if we start from entry ① in the 00 column and change to the 10 column, since x_2 remains at the 0 value during this

$x_1 x_2$				
00	01	11	10	Z
①	3	–	5	0
②	3	–	6	1
1	③	4	–	0
–	3	④	6	1
1	–	4	⑤	0
2	–	4	⑥	1

Fig. 12–15. Completed primitive flow table, Example 12–1.

transition, the output must not change. Hence we direct the transition to stable state ⑤ for which the output remains at 0. Starting from the ② state, for which the output is 1, we direct the transition in the 10 column to the ⑥ state for which the output remains 1. When the primary variables change from 10 to 00, the ⑤ state leads to the ① state through the uncircled 1 entry, and the ⑥ state leads to the ② state through the uncircled 2 entry. Each of these transitions keeps the output constant. The transition from the 01 column to the 00 column requires that the output remain 0 because the value of x_1 is 0 in both columns and the x_2 value changes from 1 to 0. Hence, the ③ entry leads, by way of the uncircled 1 entry, to the ① state. Similarly, when the primary variables change from 11 to 10, the starting point is the ④ state, and this leads by way of the uncircled 6 entry to the ⑥ state, thereby keeping the output 1 as required.

Blank entries are made in all positions of the primitive flow table which correspond to a change of more than one of the primary variables. After these entries have been made, it is apparent that all the spaces in the primitive flow table are occupied either by numbers or by deliberately inserted blanks. It is by this process that we verify that the primitive flow table specifies the circuit performance for all possible sequences of the input variables. Starting from any of the circled entries in the table, we have answered the question, "What happens when any allowable change of input variables is made?"

The merger diagram for this flow table is developed in Fig. 12–16. It contains two triangular groups consisting of rows 1, 3, and 5 and rows 2, 4, and 6. Within each of these groups all *pairs* of rows can be merged, so each of the groups can be merged to a single row. The resultant two-row, merged flow matrix is shown in Fig. 12–17. The

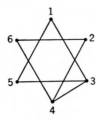

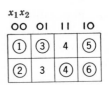

Fig. 12–16. Merger diagram for flow table of Fig. 12–15.

Fig. 12–17. Merged flow table of Example 12–1.

possible merger between rows 3 and 4 is of no advantage.

Ordinarily the next step is to draw a transition diagram and use it to select a suitable set of row states. Since there are only two rows in the merged flow table, only one secondary relay is needed. However, the corresponding secondary assignment can be made in two ways. In Fig. 12–18, the maps on the left-hand side result from assigning $y = 0$ to the top row, and the maps at the right result from assigning $y = 0$ to the bottom row, of Fig. 12–17.

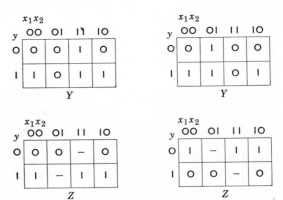

Fig. 12–18. Excitation and output matrices for two assignments of secondary states, Example 12–1.

The top maps in Fig. 12–18 describe the two alternative forms of the excitation function of the secondary relay. The bottom maps represent the respective forms of the output function. It will be noted in the ouput maps that each contains six definite entries, corresponding to the outputs associated with the six stable states of Fig. 12–15. The remaining two entries in each of the output maps are blanks and may be used as optional values. Consider the left-hand Z map in Fig. 12–18. The blank entry in the 11 column corresponds to the uncircled entry 4 in the flow matrix, Fig. 12–17. If we enter a 0 in this blank space it means that the output will not become 1 until the secondary relay operates and changes the network to the ④ state. If we want to obtain the output 1, associated with the circled state, as soon as possible, we enter a 1 in the Z map in the cell occupied by uncircled 4 in the flow matrix. Similar considerations apply to the choice of a 0 or 1 entry in the blank cell in the 01 column. If a 1 is entered, the output does not change to 0 until the ③ state is reached. By entering a 0 the ultimate output is obtained as early as possible.

The assignment of output values to unstable states can be a more complex problem than the one illustrated by this example. It is a topic which will be discussed later in this chapter. In this example we decide that the early appearance of the outputs associated ultimately with states ③ and ④ is not important, so we fill in the optional points in the Z maps with entries which lead to the simplest networks.

We finally write the excitation and output functions, for the left-hand maps

$$Y = x_1 x_2 + x_2' y; \qquad Z = y$$

and for the right-hand maps

$$Y = x_1' x_2 + x_2' y; \qquad Z = y'$$

The functions for the right-hand maps require the contacts x_1', x_2, x_2', y and y'. Those for the left-hand maps require x_1, x_2, x_2', and y. Furthermore since no x_1' contact is required, and only one x_1 contact, the functions of the left-hand maps can be realized without using an X_1 relay. The circuit for this is shown in Fig. 12–19. Instead

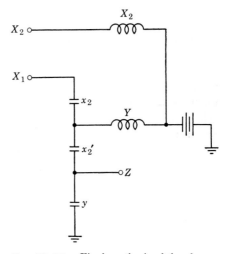

Fig. 12–19. Final synthesis of the clamp-gate circuit.

of supplying ground through an x_1 contact, the ground corresponding to the X_1 input is used directly. In obtaining the output Z by taking it from the excitation network, there is one possible disadvantage. For the condition $x_2 = 0$ and $y = 0$, the output terminal is connected through the secondary relay coil to the battery. There is hence battery voltage on the Z terminal, which may or may not be allowable. If this cannot be tolerated it is necessary to use a separate y contact to supply the output.

The sequential circuits we have been studying, both in analysis and in synthesis, have the structural form shown in Fig. 12–20. At the terminals of a sequential circuit we have inputs $X_1, X_2, \ldots, X_m$, and the

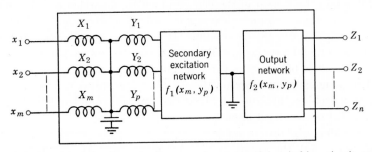

Fig. 12–20. General schematic diagram of a sequential switching circuit using relays and contact networks.

outputs $Z_1, Z_2, \ldots, Z_n$. The inputs have direct control of the operation of the primary relays $X_1, \ldots, X_m$. An unknown number of secondary relays, $Y_1, Y_2, \ldots, Y_p$ is controlled by a contact network, the secondary excitation network, which contains contacts on both the primary and the secondary relays. Another contact network, the output network, also contains contacts on both the primary and the secondary relays, and realizes the n outputs. Occasionally, as in the example just completed, one or more of the primary relays can be eliminated by using the primary input grounds directly. However, the general situation is that shown in Fig. 12–20. Our central problem in the synthesis of a sequential circuit is to convert the terminal requirements of the circuit to the specifications of the two internal combinational contact networks. Externally, we specify only the circuit inputs and outputs.

Example 12–2

A sequential circuit has two inputs X_1 and X_2, and two corresponding outputs, Z_1 and Z_2. At the inputs one variable only may change at a time, and there is to be a ground on only one output at a time. Whenever an input variable changes from 0 to 1, the corresponding output is to become grounded, and the other output ungrounded. A change of any input variable from 1 to 0 is to cause no change in the output.

The only allowable outputs in this example are 01 and 10. We can readily show that either output is possible for every combination of input variables, and that each column of the primitive flow table must therefore contain two stable states. The 11 column can be entered from either the 01 or the 10 column. These changes produce outputs of 10 and 01, respectively, and hence we require two stable states in the 11 column. We can go from either of these stable states in the 11 column to either the 01 or the 10 column. Since there must be no change of output for these transitions, there must be two stable states in both the 01 and the 10 columns. Finally, transitions from the 01 and the 10 columns to the 00 column must occur with no change of output, and since both outputs are thus possible in the 00 column it must contain two stable states.

x_1x_2				
OO	OI	II	IO	Z
①	3	–	8	O I
②	3	–	8	I O
1	③	6	–	O I
2	④	6	–	I O
–	3	⑤	7	O I
–	4	⑥	8	I O
1	–	5	⑦	O I
2	–	5	⑧	I O

Fig. 12–21. The primitive flow table for Example 12-2.

In Fig. 12–21 the primitive flow table is drawn with the stable entries as discussed above. The student should verify the remaining unstable and blank entries, particularly noting that the unstable entries must be chosen so that they lead to stable states which produce the outputs required by the circuit specifications.

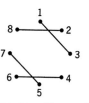

Fig. 12–22. Merger diagram, Example 12-2.

The merger diagram of Fig. 12–22 shows that the eight rows of the primitive flow table combine into four pairs, giving us the merged flow table of Fig. 12–23. Also in Fig. 12–23 is the transition diagram showing the row-to-row secondary state changes which must be accomplished by the change of a single secondary variable. We should note that the transition diagram is determined entirely by the requirements of the 00 and the 11 columns. In the 01 column the entry ③ can be reached directly from the 3 in row d by a single change of variable. The entry 3 in row c can reach the entry ③ by a transition first to row d and then to row a. A similar situation is present in the 10

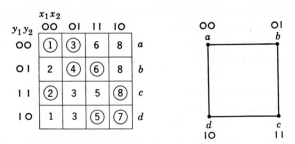

Fig. 12–23. Merged flow table at left, transition diagram with selected secondary states at right, Example 12–2.

column. The secondary states selected in the transition diagram are shown at the left of the merged flow table.

Figure 12–24 shows both the excitation matrix and the output matrix. All circled entries are assigned excitation values in the excitation

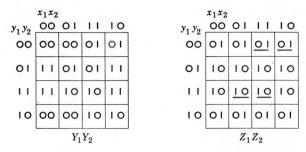

Fig. 12–24. Excitation matrix and output matrix of Example 12–2.

matrix corresponding to the secondary state designators of the row states in which they are located. In the 00 and 11 columns of the excitation matrix unstable entries are assigned excitations which are the same as those of the circled entries of the same number. In the 01 and 10 columns one unstable state is assigned the same excitation values as the corresponding stable state. The other unstable state is directed by a single change of variable to the first unstable state, from which the corresponding stable state is then reached.

The output matrix presents some points of interest. Referring to the primitive flow table of Fig. 12–21, we see that all odd-numbered stable states have the output 01 and all even-numbered stable states have the output 10. These entries are transferred first to the output matrix of Fig. 12–24. Next, by reference to the merged flow table (Fig. 12–23) we see that some possible transitions (odd number to odd number, or even number to even number) permit no change in output. These transitions require definite entries in the output matrix for the particular unstable states involved. The remaining unstable states are passed through by transitions which require a change of output. Hence we can either retain the original output a little longer, or produce the new output a little earlier. The underlined entries in the output matrix show the choices that were made in these positions. It is evident that the selections shown contribute to the simplification of the output network.

An almost routine application of the methods of combinational synthesis discussed in earlier chapters leads to the excitation and output networks of Fig. 12–25. It may be noted that although the circuit is

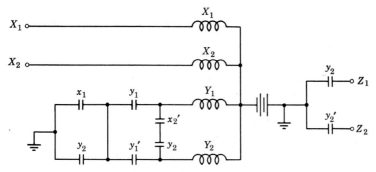

Fig. 12–25.   Completed circuit of Example 12–2.

drawn to conform with the general schematic diagram of a sequential circuit shown in Fig. 12–20, it is possible to eliminate the X_1 relay. This modification can readily be made by the student. The student will also find it interesting and instructive to visualize step-by-step the operation of this circuit and how it produces its required outputs as the input variables are changed in any arbitrary sequence.

One of the applications of these methods of analysis and synthesis is in the simplification of existing circuits. Many sequential circuits are designed by first satisfying one objective and then adding whatever relays and contact networks are required to satisfy additional objectives. It is entirely possible, and indeed likely, that redundancy is present in circuits thus designed. The next example does not illustrate this particular point but is intended to show how the combined analysis-synthesis process may be used to reduce circuit complexity.

Example 12–3

The circuit of Fig. 12–26 is to be used under conditions that never permit changes in both input variables at the same time. Redesign the circuit so that its terminal action remains the same, but obtain whatever economy is possible.

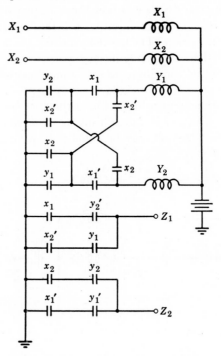

Fig. 12–26. A circuit to be simplified.

We first write expressions for the excitation functions of the secondary relays and for the output functions.

$$Y_1 = x_1x_2' + x_1y_2 + x_2'y_1$$

$$Y_2 = x_1'x_2 + x_1'y_1 + x_2y_2$$

$$Z_1 = x_1y_2' + x_2'y_1$$

$$Z_2 = x_2y_2 + x_1'y_1'$$

From these functions we prepare the excitation and output matrices of Fig. 12–27. The excitation matrix is then converted to the flow matrix at the left of Fig. 12–28. Since the flow matrix contains some rows having more than one circled entry, we know that mergers have taken place. Our next step, then, is to "unmerge" the flow matrix. At the right of Fig. 12–28 the corresponding primitive flow table is developed. To do this, we first assign one row of the primitive flow table to each circled entry of the flow matrix, and in the output column we insert the output values specified for those circled entries by the output matrix of Fig. 12–27. Next, the blank entries, corresponding to

$x_1 x_2$

$y_1 y_2$	00	01	11	10
00	00	01	00	10
01	00	01	11	10
11	11	01	11	10
10	11	01	00	10

$Y_1 Y_2$

$x_1 x_2$

$y_1 y_2$	00	01	11	10
00	01	01	10	10
01	01	01	01	00
11	10	01	01	10
10	10	00	10	10

$Z_1 Z_2$

Fig. 12–27. Excitation and output matrices of circuit in Fig. 12–26.

double changes of the input variables, are entered in the primitive flow table. The remaining entries must be uncircled state numbers, all of which are specified in the flow matrix.

$x_1 x_2$

$y_1 y_2$	00	01	11	10
00	①	3	②	6
01	1	③	5	6
11	④	3	⑤	6
10	4	3	2	⑥

$x_1 x_2$

00	01	11	10	$Z_1 Z_2$
①	3	–	6	01
–	3	②	6	10
1	③	5	–	01
④	3	–	6	10
–	3	⑤	6	01
4	–	2	⑥	10

Fig. 12–28. The flow matrix at the left is expanded to primitive form.

We now treat the primitive flow table in accordance with the normal synthesis procedure. In Fig. 12–29, the merger diagram shows that a two-row flow table can be obtained by merging rows 1, 3, and 5, and

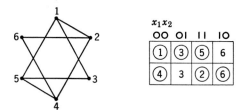

$x_1 x_2$

00	01	11	10
①	③	⑤	6
④	3	②	⑥

Fig 12–29. Merger diagram shows flow table can be reduced to two rows.

2, 4, and 6 of the primitive flow table. The resultant merged flow table is at the right of Fig. 12–29. Two different assignments of the secondary variable can be made. The excitation and output matrices

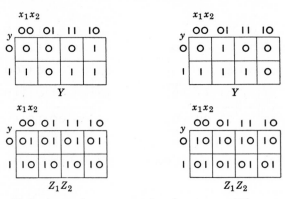

Fig. 12–30. Excitation and output matrices for two possible secondary assignments.

corresponding to these assignments are given in Fig. 12–30. Optional values in the output matrices have been chosen so as to simplify the required contact network. In Fig. 12–31 the circuit corresponding to the left-hand maps of Fig. 12–30 is drawn. Two of the relays of Fig. 12–26 are eliminated, and the contact networks have been reduced from 16 contacts, 28 springs to 6 contacts, 10 springs.

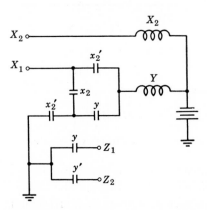

Fig. 12–31. Circuit which is the equivalent of Fig. 12–26.

12.5 Equivalent States; Unique Reductions

In writing a primitive flow table we determine for each input state the number of stable states that are required to represent all possible output conditions. Frequently the stable states within a given column are associated with different output conditions, but there are circumstances which require that two stable states within the same column be associated with the same output condition. If the flow table has been carefully constructed, these states do not represent identical circuit conditions, but it is possible to write flow tables which contain stable states that duplicate each other.

When complex circuits are designed such duplications may occur simply because, at the time they are entered, it is not clear that they are duplicates. They may be the result of error or of caution. In circuits designed by other procedures it is possible to have duplicate, and hence redundant, states because there is no obvious indication that redundancy exists.

Regardless of how equivalent states originate they can be detected by a well-defined process. The removal of equivalent states immediately reduces the number of rows in a primitive flow table. We will first examine an existing network to see how equivalent states may be found in it.

Example 12–4

In Fig. 12–32 the secondary control network and the output network of a sequential circuit are given. Write the excitation and control

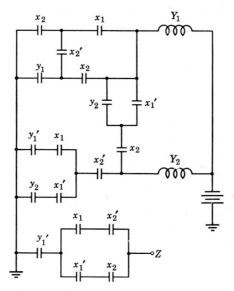

Fig. 12–32. Circuit analyzed in Example 12–4.

matrices and simplify these if possible. Only one input variable is allowed to change at a time.

The excitation and output functions are

$$Y_1 = x_1x_2 + x_1y_1 + x_2y_1$$

$$Y_2 = x_1x_2'y_1' + x_1'x_2y_1 + y_2(x_1'x_2' + x_1x_2 + x_2y_1)$$

$$Z = y_1'(x_1x_2' + x_1'x_2)$$

x_1x_2

y_1y_2	00	01	11	10
00	00	00	10	01
01	01	00	11	01
11	01	11	11	10
10	00	11	10	10

Y_1Y_2

x_1x_2

y_1y_2	00	01	11	10
00	0	1	0	1
01	0	1	0	1
11	0	0	0	0
10	0	0	0	0

Z

Fig. 12–33. Original excitation and output matrices, Example 12–4.

These functions are mapped in the excitation and output matrices of Fig. 12–33; the flow matrix is given in Fig. 12–34. Examination of the flow matrix shows that each row contains two circled entries, or stable states. In reconstructing the primitive flow table at the left of Fig. 12–35, each circled entry is assigned a separate row. The output matrix is used to enter in the primitive flow table the outputs associated with all stable states. We need not take into account the entries in the output matrix that are associated with uncircled entries in the flow table, for we know that these output values are not defined in a primitive flow table, but are added to complete the output matrix.

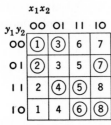

Fig. 12–34. Flow matrix for the circuit of Fig. 12–32.

After blanks are inserted to account for input changes which are not allowed, the uncircled entries in the primitive flow table are entered in

x_1x_2

	00	01	11	10	Z
	①	3	—	7	0
	②	3	—	7	0
	1	③	6	—	1
	2	④	5	—	0
	—	4	⑤	8	0
	—	4	⑥	8	0
	2	—	5	⑦	1
	1	—	6	⑧	0

x_1x_2

	00	01	11	10	Z
	①	3	—	7	0
	1	③	5	—	1
	1	④	5	—	0
	—	4	⑤	8	0
	1	—	5	⑦	1
	1	—	5	⑧	0

Fig. 12–35. Primitive flow table at left is reduced to form at right by removing redundant states.

accordance with the transitions shown in the flow matrix. Thus, in the flow matrix, Fig. 12–34, the first row contains both ① and ③. This means that starting in the state ① an input change from 00 to 01 puts the system in the ③ state without any change of a secondary variable. But when we return to the form of the primitive flow table, the circled entries are located in separate rows. Eventually we may again merge some of these rows, but we cannot assume this will happen. Hence we must add uncircled entries which provide a means for passing from one circled entry to another. Therefore in the primitive flow table the first row, 01 column, must contain an uncircled 3 entry so that after a change of the primary variables from 00 to 01 the system goes to the ③ state.

We now note that each column of the primitive flow table contains two circled entries. In the 01 column these entries are ③ and ④, and the outputs associated with them are 1 and 0, respectively. Since the outputs are different, for the same input combination, these entries must represent two entirely different states of the circuit. A similar situation exists in the 10 column where the entries ⑦ and ⑧ correspond to outputs of 1 and 0, respectively.

In the 00 column the two circled entries are ① and ②, and the output is 0 for both of these. This is not necessarily wrong, for it may be that after some further input changes, the states ① and ② lead to stable states for which the outputs are different. We can examine this question directly by finding the possible sequences that begin with states ① and ②. If we change the input from 00 to 01, regardless of whether we start from ① or ② the destination state is ③. If we change the inputs from 00 to 10, from either starting point we reach the destination state ⑦. Since these are the only input changes we can make, it is apparent that a sequence that starts from ① cannot be distinguished, at the input or the output terminals, from a sequence that starts from ②. We likewise find, in the 11 column, that entries ⑤ and ⑥ both lead to identical destination states when all allowable primary changes are made.

We conclude that states ① and ② are equivalent states, and that ⑤ and ⑥ are also equivalent. One state of each pair is redundant in the primitive flow table. It is convenient to discard the higher numbered state in each pair. A ① is substituted for ②, and an uncircled 1 for an uncircled 2. State ⑤ is written instead of ⑥, and uncircled 5 instead of uncircled 6. After these changes are made, the second row becomes identical with the first row and can be discarded. Likewise the sixth row is discarded. This reduces the primitive flow table to the six-row version shown at the right of Fig. 12–35.

Note carefully the difference between this new process and that of merger. When states are found to be equivalent, the total number of states is reduced, and we need fewer rows *in the primitive flow table.* Merger reduces the number of rows *in the merged flow table,* but does not reduce the number of states. After merger, some of the differentiation between states must be accomplished by the primary variables instead of by the secondary variables.

To continue with the example, the reduced primitive flow table has the merger diagram of Fig. 12–36. The obvious choice is to merge the rows containing the stable states (1, 3, 7), and the rows containing the stable states (4, 5, 8). We then have the two-row merged flow

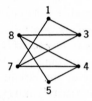

Fig. 12–36. Merger diagram of the reduced primitive flow table.

Fig. 12–37. Simplified flow matrix, Example 12–4.

table shown in Fig. 12–37. Two assignments of the single secondary variable are possible and these lead to the excitation and output matrices at the left and at the right of Fig. 12–38.

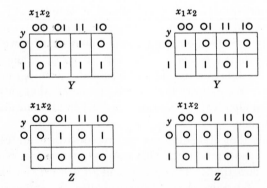

Fig. 12–38. Alternative excitation and output matrices derived from the reduced flow matrix.

The situation found in the preceding example is a very simple one. Two pairs of states were found to be equivalent by elementary reasoning. In general, the existence of equivalent states is not quite so obvious. If redundancy is extensive within a flow table, a number of steps may be needed to complete the necessary testing. Before showing this in an example, it is well here to summarize the conditions which must be met before two states can be called equivalent.

Within a primitive flow table, two stable states are equivalent if:
  (a) their input states are the same,
  (b) their output states are the same,
  (c) and if, for any sequence of input states the sequence of output states is the same, regardless of which stable state is used as a starting point.

Expressed another way, if two stable states of a primitive flow table are in the same input column (same input states), and are associated with the same output state, they may be considered equivalent unless there exists an input sequence for which the output sequence, starting from one stable state, is not the same as the sequence found after starting from the other stable state.

Example 12–5

A hypothetical flow table in primitive form is written at the left of Fig. 12–39. It is to be tested for equivalence, and redundant states are to be removed.

In the first column there are four stable states, three of which have the same output, 01. Let us first test to see whether states ② and ⑥ are equivalent. It will be found convenient to refer to the diagram of Fig. 12–40 as the test proceeds.

At the left of Fig. 12–40 we start with stable states ② and ⑥. From either of these as the starting point, one primary transition leads to state ③ and another leads to state ⑤. These changes are indicated by dotted arrows. Arrows drawn with solid lines lead from state ② to state ④ and from state ⑥ to state ⑪. We conclude, then, that states ② and ⑥ are equivalent if states ④ and ⑪ are equivalent.

States ④ and ⑪ are both in the 10 column of Fig. 12–39 and both are associated with the output 00. We find, however, that states ④ and ⑪ lead to states ③ and ⑩ in the 11 column, and to states ② and ⑧, respectively, in the 00 column. Hence, ④ and ⑪ are equivalent if states ③ and ⑩ are equivalent and if states ② and ⑧ are equivalent.

Let us defer for the moment any consideration of the equivalence of states ③ and ⑩, and consider the possible equivalence of states ② and ⑧. These states are both in the 00 column of Fig. 12–39 and both are associated with the output 01. One primary transition leads both ② and ⑧ to state ③, and another primary transition leads both states to state ④. These transitions are indicated again by dotted lines in

$x_1 x_2$				
00	01	11	10	$Z_1 Z_2$
①	7	9	4	11
②	5	3	4	01
1	7	③	11	10
2	–	3	④	00
6	⑤	9	–	11
⑥	5	3	11	01
1	⑦	14	–	10
⑧	12	3	4	01
1	7	⑨	13	01
1	7	⑩	4	10
8	–	10	⑪	00
6	⑫	9	–	11
8	–	14	⑬	11
2	12	⑭	11	00

$x_1 x_2$				
00	01	11	10	$Z_1 Z_2$
①	7	9	4	11
②	5	3	4	01
1	7	③	4	10
2	–	3	④	00
2	⑤	9	–	11
1	⑦	14	–	10
1	7	⑨	13	01
2	–	14	⑬	11
2	5	⑭	4	00

Fig. 12–39. A flow table and its reduced form after removing redundant states.

Fig. 12–40. However, a third primary transition leads states ② and ⑧ to states ⑤ and ⑫, respectively, so it becomes necessary to determine whether states ⑤ and ⑫ are equivalent.

States ⑤ and ⑫ are both in the 01 column and both are associated with the output 11. From both states ⑤ and ⑫ one allowed primary transition leads to state ⑥ and the other to state ⑨. Thus, states ⑤ and ⑫ satisfy the requirements for equivalence.

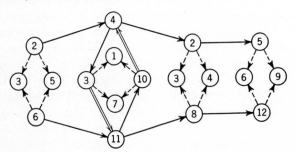

Fig. 12–40. Equivalence relations in the flow table of Fig. 12–39.

Since states ⑤ and ⑫ are equivalent, all primary transitions from states ② and ⑧ lead to identical sequences, and states ② and ⑧ are also equivalent. This in turn satisfies one of the conditions placed upon the equivalence of states ④ and ⑪. It remains only to determine whether states ③ and ⑩ are equivalent.

Referring to Fig. 12–40, we see that dotted lines lead from states ③ and ⑩ to states ① and ⑦, so the requirements for equivalence are partially met. We find, however, that state ③ leads to state ⑪ and state ⑩ leads to state ④. We are therefore saying that states ④ and ⑪ are equivalent if states ③ and ⑩ are equivalent, but that states ③ and ⑩ are equivalent if states ④ and ⑪ are equivalent. If we now examine the terminal action of the circuit when it is operated through any sequences involving the states in question, we find that we obtain the identical action whether we say the states are not equivalent or that they are equivalent. It is clearly to our advantage, then, to say that state ③ is equivalent to state ⑩ and that state ④ is equivalent to state ⑪. This in turn removes the final condition placed upon the equivalence of states ② and ⑥.

A practical method to remove redundancies in a flow table is to replace the number of one member of an equivalent pair by the number of the other member. We choose here to retain the lower number of each pair. Hence, in the flow table at the left of Fig. 12–39, the number 6 is replaced wherever it appears by the number 2, 11 is replaced by 4, 10 is replaced by 3, 8 is replaced by 2, and 12 is replaced by 5. When the flow table is thus modified, it is found that some rows—in this example, five of them—are exact duplicates of other rows and may be removed. We thus obtain the flow table at the right of Fig. 12–39. This table is still in its primitive form, in that there is only one circled entry in each row. The process described removes redundant rows but it does not merge any rows.

We may note in this example that we happened to start by comparing entries ② and ⑥, but we could have started with any pair and reached the same results. In fact, if we had started with entries ⑤ and ⑫, and worked backwards through the comparisons indicated in Fig. 12–40, we could have answered all questions of equivalence immediately instead of postponing most of them.

When the condensed primitive flow table we obtain by removing equivalent states is independent of the order in which the redundancies are eliminated, the flow table is unique. In the flow table of Fig. 12–39, it will be observed that for any pair of stable entries in any column, the allowable changes of primary variables are identical. These allowable changes may differ in number or type from column to column, but this is of no consequence since we compare only pairs of states that are in the same input column. The allowable primary transitions are fixed for any given starting point. Under

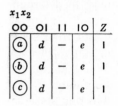

Fig. 12–41. A set of equivalent states which lead to a unique reduction.

these conditions, it makes no difference in what order the comparisons between states are made.

Consider, for example, the three states represented by the rows of Fig. 12–41. Regardless of the order we use in comparing the stable entries $\textcircled{a}$, $\textcircled{b}$, and $\textcircled{c}$, we must conclude that all three are mutually equivalent and that, hence, any two of the three may be discarded as redundant. The key point is that starting from the common input state 00, all three rows show allowable input transitions to states 01 and 10 only.

In contrast, Fig. 12–42 shows at the left a part of a flow table in which the two stable entries have the same input state and the same

$x_1 x_2$				
00	01	11	10	Z
$\textcircled{a}$	d	f	—	1
$\textcircled{b}$	—	f	e	1

$x_1 x_2$				
00	01	11	10	Z
$\textcircled{a}$	d	f	e	1

Fig. 12–42. Reduction of pseudo-equivalent states.

output state, but from which the allowable primary transitions are not the same. From either stable state a primary change from the column 00 to the column 11 leads to the state $\textcircled{f}$, but one row has a blank entry in the 01 column and the other is blank in the 10 column. There is present here a kind of equivalence which Huffman calls *pseudo-equivalence*. Suppose the stable state $\textcircled{a}$ is equivalent to the state $\textcircled{b}$. If we replace $\textcircled{b}$ by $\textcircled{a}$ the rows may then be *merged*, as shown at the right of Fig. 12–42. This final row describes exactly the same circuit action as the original two rows. But we note that the number of rows is reduced not by removing a redundant row, but by a process in which we first recognize pseudo-equivalence and then merge the rows containing the stable entries involved.

It may appear from the reduction shown in Fig. 12–42 that there is little point in writing two separate rows to be treated in this way. However, in Fig. 12–43 we see why the rows are first written separately. In the left-hand table of Fig. 12–43 we have the same two rows found in Fig. 12–42, and in addition a third row in which a stable state $\textcircled{c}$

has the same inputs and output as (a) and (b). We see that there is pseudo-equivalence between states (a) and (b), and also between states (b) and (c). In the upper right-hand table of Fig. 12–43 we

x_1x_2				
OO OI II IO				**Z**
(a)	d	f	e	I
(c)	g	$-$	e	I

x_1x_2				
OO OI II IO				**Z**
(a)	d	f	$-$	I
(b)	$-$	f	e	I
(c)	g	$-$	e	I

x_1x_2				
OO OI II IO				**Z**
(a)	d	f	$-$	I
(c)	g	f	e	I

Fig. 12–43. Two possible reductions of pseudo-equivalent states.

have combined (a) and (b) as before, and after this is done the third row clearly does not satisfy the conditions for equivalence. In the lower right-hand table, we have combined (b) and (c), and the row containing (a) clearly can not become part of a combined row. Of course, if states "d" and "g" lead to equivalent stable states, both tables reduce to a single row.

These illustrations demonstrate that when the allowable primary transitions from a given column are not the same for each stable entry in the column, a condensed flow table is not necessarily unique. Its final form may depend on the order in which equivalent states are combined.

Input restrictions of the type discussed above may arise because of mechanical design or because restrictions are imposed by manual operators. They can also arise when the inputs are derived from or modified by another sequential circuit.

Example 12–6

The primitive flow table of Fig. 12–44 is to be reduced by the advantageous use of equivalence consolidation and row mergers.

In column 10, states (7) and (10) have different outputs and hence cannot be equivalent. In column 01, states (3) and (9) likewise have

x_1x_2				
OO	**OI**	**II**	**IO**	Z_1Z_2
(1)	$-$	4	7	I O
(2)	3	5	$-$	I O
8	(3)	5	$-$	I I
$-$	9	(4)	7	O I
$-$	3	(5)	7	O I
(6)	3	$-$	7	I O
1	$-$	4	(7)	OO
(8)	$-$	5	10	I O
6	(9)	4	$-$	OO
2	$-$	5	(10)	I I

Fig. 12–44. A flow table to be tested for redundant states.

different outputs and cannot be equivalent. In column 11, states ④ and ⑤ have the same outputs, but they lead to states ⑨ and ③, respectively. Since these destination states are not equivalent, ④ and ⑤ cannot be equivalent.

In column 00, states ①, ②, ⑥, and ⑧ have the same outputs. Comparison shows that there is pseudo-equivalence between ① and ⑥, between ② and ⑥, and beween ② and ⑧. If we combine ① and ⑥ first, we can then combine ② and ⑧. The result of this reduction is the flow table of Fig. 12–45(a). If, however, we first combine ② and

x_1x_2				
00	01	11	10	Z_1Z_2
①	3	4	7	1 0
②	3	5	10	1 0
2	③	5	—	1 1
—	9	④	7	0 1
—	3	⑤	7	0 1
1	—	4	⑦	0 0
1	⑨	4	—	0 0
2	—	5	⑩	0 1

(a)

x_1x_2				
00	01	11	10	Z_1Z_2
①	—	4	7	1 0
②	3	5	7	1 0
8	③	5	—	1 1
—	9	④	7	0 1
—	3	⑤	7	0 1
1	—	4	⑦	0 0
⑧	—	5	10	1 0
2	⑨	4	—	0 0
2	—	5	⑩	1 1

(b)

Fig. 12–45. Two forms of the non-redundant primitive flow table derived from Fig. 12–44.

⑥, it becomes impossible to make any further combinations. The resulting flow table is in Fig. 12–45(b).

The merger diagrams of Fig. 12–46(a) and Fig. 12–46(b) apply to the corresponding flow tables in Fig. 12–45. From the merger diagram of Fig. 12–46(a) we see that the rows of the flow table, as identified by the numbers of the corresponding stable states, may be merged into the four groups (1), (2, 3, 10), (4, 7, 9), and (5). In Fig. 12–46(b), however, we see that the less advantageous equivalence reduction of the flow table in Fig. 12–45(b) also reduces the number of mergers that can be made. Consequently, the merged flow table must contain additional rows. The merger diagram of Fig. 12–46(b) reveals two 5-row mergers, namely, those consisting of the row groups (1, 4, 7), (2, 5), (3, 8), (9), (10), and, (1, 7), (2, 5), (3, 8), (4, 9), (10).

A given primitive flow table which contains no equivalent states still does not necessarily yield a unique flow table. If there are no blank entries in the primitive flow table, any two rows which merge

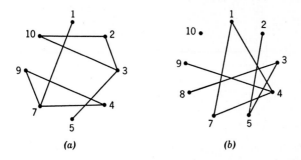

Fig. 12–46. Merger diagrams for the flow tables of Fig. 12–45.

must contain identical numbers, circled or not circled. All combinations of this type are unique. If, however, restrictions are placed on the primary transitions allowed, so that blank entries are present, there is not necessarily a unique merged flow table.

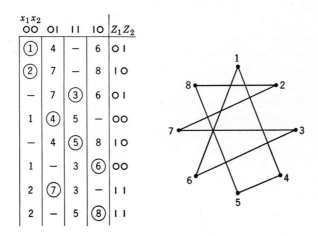

$x_1 x_2$				
OO	OI	II	IO	$Z_1 Z_2$
①	4	–	6	O I
②	7	–	8	I O
–	7	③	6	O I
1	④	5	–	OO
–	4	⑤	8	I O
1	–	3	⑥	OO
2	⑦	3	–	I I
2	–	5	⑧	I I

Fig. 12–47. A flow table and its merger diagram.

A flow table and its merger diagram are given in Fig. 12–47. It is apparent from the diagram that we can merge the rows either in the groups (1, 4), (5, 8), (2, 7), (3, 6) or in the groups (1, 6), (3, 7), (2, 8), (4, 5). The merged flow tables corresponding to these groupings are at the left and right, respectively, of Fig. 12–48.

x_1x_2

00	01	11	10
①	④	5	6
②	⑦	3	8
1	7	③	⑥
2	4	⑤	⑧

x_1x_2

00	01	11	10
①	4	3	⑥
②	7	5	⑧
2	⑦	③	6
1	④	⑤	8

Fig. 12–48. Two merged flow tables derived from the primitive flow table of Fig. 12–47.

12.6   The Output Matrix

Once the flow matrix of a sequential circuit is written, the dimensions of, and some of the entries in the output matrix become fixed. That is, the columns and rows of the output matrix carry the same input-variable and secondary-variable values as those of the flow matrix, and the output entries corresponding to the circled entries of the flow matrix are those specified in the primitive flow table. To complete the output matrix, values must be entered in the positions which correspond to uncircled entries in the flow matrix.

The degree of restriction encountered in completing the output matrix varies widely. It depends both on the output changes specified, and on certain design objectives, which must be stated in advance.

One general principle applies to the design of almost all output circuits. When a sequential circuit changes from one stable state, with a given output, to another stable state having a different output, there must be no momentary false output. For example, if a circuit output is 00 prior to a change of state, and is to be 11 after the change of state, it must not momentarily deliver an output of 01 or 10. Of course, we have not defined here what we mean by "momentary." Consider the change of state represented by the transition ⓐ → b → ⓑ, where the states ⓐ and ⓑ are in different columns. Let the outputs associated with ⓐ and ⓑ be 00 and 11, respectively. It is conceivable that a simpler output matrix might be formed if the output associated with the uncircled entry b is made 01, so that the output sequence becomes 00 → 01 → 11 instead of 00 → 11. It is this type of irregularity that we regard as a momentary false output. It is "built into" the circuit and is not the result of differences in the timing of contact changes. The latter effects can be treated by methods to be discussed in Art. 12.7. Relatively, they are of such brief duration that they often can be disregarded.

There can always be a relaxation of the provision against momentary false outputs, if other circuit conditions permit it. For example, the response time of the load supplied by the output signals may be long enough, compared with the duration of the false output, to justify relaxation of the principle. However, it should be emphasized that it is never *necessary* to permit the appearance of momentary false outputs.

In many instances, the entries to be made in an output matrix, for those positions occupied by unstable entries in the flow matrix, permit more or less freedom of choice. These choices are usually made in accordance with one of the following general objectives.

(a) The output network is to be minimized.

(b) All output changes are to occur as soon as possible.

(c) All output changes are to occur as late as possible.

(d) The relative timing of each output change is individually specified.

(e) For some output changes the relative timing is specified, but for all others the relative timing is not important and network minimizing entries may be made.

We will illustrate the application of some of these objectives in the examples that follow. All examples start with the flow matrix of Fig. 12–49, but there will be different assignments of the output values corresponding to stable entries. All examples will enforce the provision against momentary false outputs.

Example 12–7

The partially completed matrix of Fig. 12–50(a) contains the outputs specified for the circled entries of Fig. 12–49. The remaining entries of the matrix are to be completed with no restrictions imposed, except that there are to be no momentary false outputs.

In the first row of the flow matrix the uncircled 3 entry can be reached from either the entry ① or the entry ⑤. A change from the state represented by ① to that represented by ③ requires a change of output from 00 to 10. Only the Z_1 output need be changed in this process. However, in going from ⑤ to ③, the output changes from 11 to 10, and this requires a change of Z_2. If we enter the output 00 in the matrix position occupied by the uncircled 3, it would be satisfactory for the transition from ① to ③, but it would constitute a false output for the transition

$x_1 x_2$

$y_1 y_2$	00	01	11	10
00	①	3	⑤	8
01	2	③	5	⑦
11	②	4	⑥	7
10	1	④	6	⑧

Fig. 12–49. Flow matrix used to illustrate the development of several output matrices.

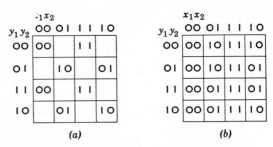

Fig. 12–50. An output matrix in which no optional entries are possible.

⑤ to ③. Similarly, an entry of 11 would satisfy the transition from ⑤ to ③ but would be a false output for the transition from ① to ③. The only entry which prevents a false output is 10, which is the entry made in Fig. 12–50(b).

An examination of the remaining entries to be made in Fig. 12–50(a) shows that it is necessary to enter the output corresponding to the destination state in every position in order to avoid false outputs. This example, therefore, is one in which there is absolutely no freedom of choice. Incidentally, all output changes are made as soon as possible, that is, as soon as the primary variables change and regardless of the time required for secondary changes to occur.

Example 12–8

In Fig. 12–51(a) a set of output values is specified for the stable entries of Fig. 12–49. The output matrix is to be completed in a manner which simplifies the output network as much as possible.

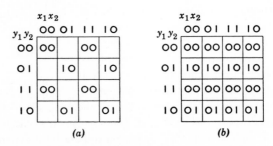

Fig. 12–51. An output matrix which satisfies two design objectives.

We note that for each row the outputs corresponding to the stable states are identical. Therefore any entry which is made to satisfy the transition from one of these states will satisfy the transition from the other. In Fig. 12–51(b) it is found that the entries which lead to minimized output networks are also those which satisfy the objective of having the ouput change as late as possible for each transition.

Example 12–9

For the set of required outputs shown in Fig. 12–52(a), we wish to compare the output networks which are obtained, first by making all

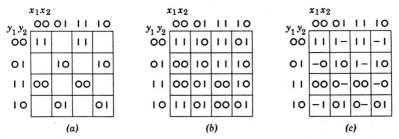

Fig. 12–52. Output matrices which demonstrate that different design objectives may require radically different networks.

output changes as soon as possible, and second by making use of whatever optional entries may be available to reduce the output network complexity.

When the output entries corresponding to the uncircled entries in the flow matrix are given the same values as the outputs for the respective circled entries, all output changes are accomplished as quickly as possible. For this condition, the resulting matrix is shown in Fig. 12–52(b). The output functions derived from this matrix are

$$Z_1 = x_2 y_1' + x_1' x_2' y_2' + x_1 x_2' y_2$$

$$Z_2 = x_2' y_2' + x_1 x_2 y_1' + x_1' x_2 y_1$$

When we permit the output entries to have all possible optional values, the matrix of Fig. 12–52(c) is obtained. Consider the transition from state ① or state ⑤ to state ③. The output is 11 for both ① and ⑤, and is 10 for state ③. The only output which changes is Z_2, and since this change may occur either before or after the change of the secondary variable, the output entry in the position occupied by uncircled 3 is 1–. Similar options are found in every position of this matrix corresponding to the position of an uncircled entry in the flow matrix. When the options are exercised most advantageously, the resultant output functions are $Z_1 = y_1'$, and $Z_2 = y_2'$. It should be noted, incidentally, that the choices made in arriving at these functions are those for which all output changes are made as late as possible.

Example 12–10

The outputs entered in Fig. 12–53(a) correspond to the stable entries in Fig. 12–49. An output matrix is to be completed so that the most economical output network can be realized.

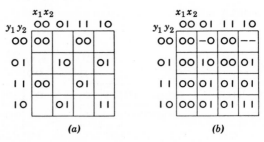

Fig. 12–53. An output matrix containing a restricted option.

In the completed output matrix of Fig. 12–53(b) it can readily be verified that, in all positions except those of the entries corresponding to the locations of uncircled 3 and uncircled 8 in the flow matrix, the necessity for preventing false outputs makes the full entries shown mandatory. The output for the uncircled 3 state contains an optional provision for Z_1. The interesting circumstance is the double option shown for the output corresponding to the uncircled 8 state. This entry provides for the transition from ① or ⑤, both of which have the output 00, to state ⑧, which has the output 11. The entry shown is optional only in the sense that it may be made either 00 or 11, but cannot be either 01 or 10. This is a restricted option.

12.7 Hazards in Contact Networks

In discussing the operation of the circuit in Fig. 12–1 we noted briefly that in passing from step 4 to step 5 of Table 12–1 there is the possibility of malfunction if the transfer contact on relay B does not operate in an ideal manner. This circuit is said to contain a hazard. On the other hand, the circuit of Fig. 12–2 is identical, in its terminal action and in the response of its secondary relays, with that of Fig. 12–1, but analysis of the operation of this circuit fails to show any hazard. We propose to examine this situation in more detail, first to see how we can discover the presence of hazard, and then to see how we can prevent or remove a hazard.*

---

* D. A. Huffman, "The Design and Use of Hazard-Free Switching Networks," *Journal of the Association for Computing Machinery*, Vol. 4, No. 1, January 1957, pp. 47–62.

The excitation functions of the secondary relays in Fig. 12–1 are

$$B = (a + c)(b + a'b') = ab + bc + a'b'c$$
$$C = (a + c)(b' + a'b) = ab' + b'c + a'bc$$

When these functions are reduced algebraically, we have

$$B = ab + bc + a'c$$
$$C = ab' + b'c + a'c$$

For the network of Fig. 12–2 the excitation functions are

$$B = (a + c)(ab')' = (a + c)(a' + b) = ab + bc + a'c$$
$$C = (a + c)(ab)' = (a + c)(a' + b') = ab' + b'c + a'c$$

It is apparent that algebraically the excitation functions of the two circuits are identical. The only point of difference is that the functions for the circuit of Fig. 12–1 require algebraic reduction.

We can compare these circuits further by examining the maps in Fig. 12–54. On the left are shown the excitation functions for the

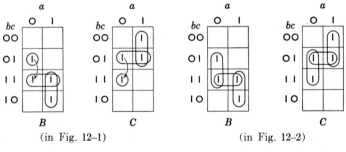

Fig. 12–54. Maps showing the origin of the hazard in Fig. 12–1.

circuit of Fig. 12–1, and those for the circuit of Fig. 12–2 are on the right. For corresponding relays the pattern of entries is identical in the two sets of maps. However, there is a vital difference in the ways in which the entries are grouped to represent tie sets in the network. Consider the excitation of relay B. In the left-hand map, we observe that in passing from the 001 cell to the 011 cell, we leave a subcube containing one term and enter a subcube containing two terms. In the right-hand map for relay B the same transition occurs *within* a subcube containing two terms. Since each subcube represents a tie set in the contact network, the mapping at the left of Fig. 12–54 means that relay B is initially excited by the tie set $a'b'c$ (in cell 001), but that after B operates, its excitation is maintained by the tie set bc. During this transition a transfer contact on relay B must change from the condition $b' = 1$ to the condition $b = 1$. It is a basic assumption of Boolean algebra that this is a perfect process; that the normally open contact closes just as the normally closed contact opens. In the circuit under consideration there will be a hazard if the normally closed contact opens for an appreciable time before the normally open contact closes.

If we now look at the right-hand map of the excitation of relay B, we find that the transition in question takes place within the tie set $a'c$. That is, when $a = 0$ and $c = 1$, relay B becomes excited. During the operation of B, the excitation remains the same. Since the transition from a state of excitation to a state of operation is independent of the action of any contacts on B, it is independent of the perfection or lack of perfection in the timing of the contact operation.

The excitation and operation of relay C is subject to exactly the same kind of hazard, as is shown by the left-hand map in Fig. 12–54, and is free of hazard when the excitation function described by the right-hand map is used.

It can be argued that the hazard described can be avoided by using a continuity transfer contact on the B relay, and this is true for the particular situation described. There are other situations, however, in which such corrective action relieves one hazard and aggravates another. Hence we must seek a deeper understanding of the problem.

Consider the circuit shown in Fig. 12–55 for which the transmission is given by $T = ab + a'c$. When $b = c = 1$, the transmission function requires that $T = 1$ regardless of the value of the variable a. This requirement is satisfied in the steady state condition for either $a = 1$ or $a = 0$. However, during a period when the relay carrying the a contacts is either operating or releasing, if there is a short period when

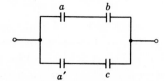

Fig. 12–55. Network with a hazard in the tie sets.

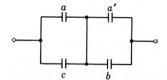

Fig. 12–56. Network with a hazard in the cut sets.

both the a and the a' contacts are open, the transmission will start with the value 1, then go to 0, and finally return to 1. Of course, this hazard can be avoided by using a continuity transfer contact so that there is a brief period when both the a and a' contacts are closed.

Let us look now, however, at the circuit of Fig. 12–56, for which the transmission is given by $T = (a + c)(a' + b)$. If $b = c = 0$, the transmission function requires that $T = 0$ regardless of the value of a. If, however, we happen to be using the continuity transfer contact suggested in the preceding paragraph, during a change from $a = 0$ to $a = 1$, or vice versa, there will be a period during which the a contact and the a' contact are both closed. Hence, the transmission will start with a value 0, then go to a value 1, and finally return to the value 0 during a period when the relay carrying the a contact is operating or releasing. To avoid this hazard, we must be sure that the transfer contact is *not* of the continuity type.

In the map of Fig. 12–57 the transmission function of the circuit of Fig. 12–55 is presented with all tie sets and cut sets marked. We see that for all changes of a variable which require that the transmission begin and end with a 0 value, the change takes place within a cut set, so that the 0 value is firmly maintained regardless of the timing of any contacts. On the other hand, when $b = c = 1$, a change of the value

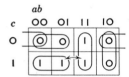

Fig. 12–57. Map showing a hazard in the tie sets.

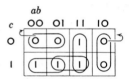

Fig. 12–58. Map showing a hazard in the cut sets.

of a requires that the transmission begin and end with the value 1. On the map, we see that this change begins within one tie set and ends within another, but that there is no tie set which assures that the transmission will remain 1 regardless of the timing of the contacts on relay A.

In Fig. 12–58, the map represents the transmission of the network of Fig. 12–56. Here we see that for any change of a variable which requires that the transmission be 1 before and after the change, the change takes place within a tie set and the transmission is not affected by the variable which is changing. On the other hand, when $b = c = 0$, a change in the variable a requires a shift from the cut set $(a + c)$ to the cut set $(a' + b)$, or vice versa. Since the cut set $(b + c)$ is not present, the required change is not independent of the timing of the contacts on relay A.

Two alternative circuits are shown in Fig. 12–59, each of which removes the hazard which is present in the circuit of Fig. 12–55. For either circuit, the transmission is given by $T = ab + a'c + bc$. The

presence of the bc tie set means that when $b = c = 1$, the circuit transmission is 1 regardless of the timing of the contacts on relay A.

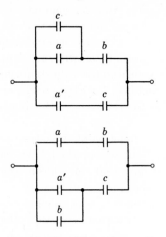

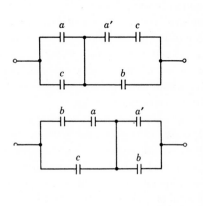

Fig. 12–59. Alternative methods for removing a hazard in
the tie sets.

Fig. 12–60. Alternative methods for
removing a hazard in the cut sets.

Similarly, in Fig. 12–60, the two circuits shown are alternative circuits for removing the hazard present in the circuit of Fig. 12–56. For
both alternative circuits the network transmission is $T = (a + c)$
$(a' + b)(b + c)$. The presence of the cut set $(b + c)$ assures us that
when $b = c = 0$, the network transmission is 0 regardless of the timing
of the contacts on relay A.

The map shown in Fig. 12–61 applies to any of the circuits given in
Fig. 12–59 and Fig. 12–60. When the change of any variable requires
that the network transmission be 1 before and

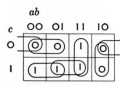

Fig. 12–61. Map of circuit with tie sets and cut
sets to prevent hazards.

after the change, that change takes place
within a tie set which guarantees that the
transmission is independent of the value of
the variable which is changing. Likewise,
when any change of a variable requires that
the network transmission be 0 before and after
that change, the change takes place within a
cut set which guarantees that the transmission

is 0 regardless of the value of the variable which is changing. Since in
either case the network transmission is independent of the value of the
variable which is changing, there can be no hazard due to contact timing.

Hazards of the type discussed above are classified by Huffman* as

* Huffman, *op. cit.*

static hazards. The network transmission is supposed to remain "static" at the value of either 0 or 1, but the hazard causes a momentary change in transmission when one variable changes state. In contrast, the term dynamic hazard refers to the situation in which the transmission is supposed to change from 0 to 1, or vice versa, but does not do so in one step. The example given in Fig. 12–62 is from Huffman's description.

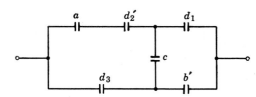

Fig. 12–62. A circuit which may have a dynamic hazard.

The network is built on the relays A, B, C, and D. Subscripts are shown on the d contacts, but these are for identification purposes only; these contacts are all on one D relay. In the map of Fig. 12–63 all the cut sets and tie sets of the network are marked. Dotted arrows in this map indicate that there are two static hazards. Our interest, however, is in the transition marked on the map by a solid arrow.

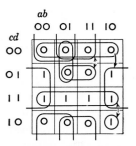

Fig. 12–63. Map showing tie sets and cut sets of Fig. 12–62.

Throughout the change thus indicated, we have $a = 1$, $b = 0$, and $c = 0$. We assume that d starts at the value 0 and then goes to the value 1 as shown by the direction of the arrow in the map. Effectively, during this transition, since $c = 0$ the upper branch of the circuit in Fig. 12–62 is simply in parallel with the lower branch. Since $a = 1$, the upper branch effectively consists of the d_2' contact in series with the d_1 contact, and since $b = 0$, the lower branch effectively consists of the d_3 contact. Now, let the D relay operate, and let the d contacts change their states in the order given by their subscripts. Initially the transmission of the network is 0, and then d_1 closes before d_2 opens, whereupon the transmission becomes 1. Then, when d_2' opens before d_3 closes, the transmission again becomes 0. Finally, d_3 closes and the transmission returns to the 1 value.

This is perhaps a rather extreme example of what may happen because of "contact stagger." We do not necessarily eliminate dynamic hazard by eliminating static hazards, but practically speaking, dynamic hazard is of much less consequence than static hazard. Hence, if static hazards have been eliminated from a circuit we shall call it hazard-free.

While the elimination of static hazard does not guarantee that dynamic hazard is eliminated, if we have designed a circuit, as in Fig. 12–59, which contains no hazard in its tie sets, the circuit will be free of hazard in its cut sets. If a circuit is designed, as in Fig. 12–60, to be free of hazard in its cut sets, it is also free of hazards in its tie sets. Figure 12–64 represents part of a circuit which consists of its tie sets all connected in parallel, and with the tie sets required to avoid static hazard all present. The question is, "Is this network also free of hazards in its cut sets"? Consider the situation in which any relay, say the J relay, is changing its state. Two tie sets, one containing a j contact and the other containing a j' contact are shown in Fig. 12–64. We know that since the network is hazard-free in its tie sets, some other tie set must be present to avoid a hazard due to the transfer contact on the J relay when it is changing state while the transmission is supposed to remain 1. Now let us consider the situation when J starts in the unoperated state and becomes operated, with the further requirement that the transmission of the network be 0 before and after the change. Before the J relay operates, $j = 0$ and in the tie set which contains the j' contact that contact is closed. If $T = 0$, however, some other contact in the tie set must be open. After the J relay operates, $j = 1$ and in the tie set containing the j contact that contact is closed. If $T = 0$, however, some other contact in the tie set must be open. Since j is the only variable which changes, the "other" contacts in these two tie sets must remain open throughout the change, and thus maintain $T = 0$ regardless of the change of j. A similar argument holds for any other pair of contacts which form a transfer contact. If the circuit is designed on a tie-set basis, and is free of hazard in its tie sets, it must also be free of hazard in its cut sets. It can likewise be demonstrated that if a circuit is designed on a cut-set basis, and is free of hazards in its cut sets, it will also be free of hazards in its tie sets.

In a practical sense, the treatment of static hazards discussed above places us in a dilemma. From the point of view of circuit minimization, we try to realize a given transmission in the form of a minimum

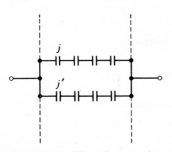

Fig. 12–64. Two tie sets of a hazard-free network.

sum or a minimum product. But since these forms, by definition, contain as few tie sets or cut sets, respectively, as are absolutely essential, if we design a circuit on that basis we probably design one which contains static hazards. The resolution of the dilemma does not necessarily require a major redesign of a circuit. Sometimes whatever additional tie sets or cut sets are required may be obtained by the addition of relatively few contacts. In other situations, because we can make a complete analysis, it may be possible to use such devices as continuity contacts with safety. Finally, in the excitation networks for the secondary relays of sequential circuits, a potential hazard as indicated by a map may not actually exist, because it may require a transition which the sequential circuit does not permit. We can always design a circuit which is free of static hazard, but with an understanding of the nature of the problem it may not be necessary to use extreme measures to achieve this freedom.

PROBLEMS

12.1 A sequential circuit contains the primary relays X_1, X_2, and X_3, and the secondary relays Y_1 and Y_2. The control networks for the secondary relays are shown.

1. Derive the flow matrix for this circuit, and from this draw a transition diagram.
2. Are there any race conditions present in the system? Discuss with the aid of the transition diagram the possible modes of operation, and particularly whether any critical race conditions exist.
3. Under what conditions does this circuit have a sustained cycle of operation? Show the sequence of operation during the cycle.

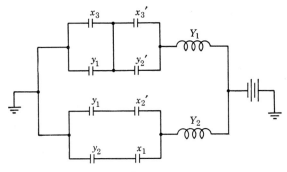

Problem 12.1.

12.2   Derive the flow table for the circuit given, and with the aid of this table and the output matrix develop a precise word description of the terminal action of the circuit.

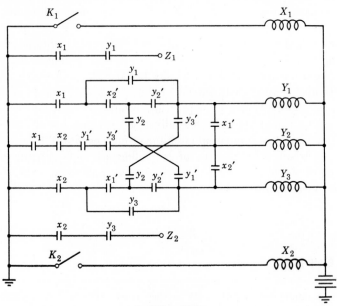

Problem 12.2.

12.3   In the primitive flow table shown blanks in the output data indicate outputs that may be chosen arbitrarily.

 1. Derive another primitive flow table in which there are no equivalences of any kind.

$X_1 X_2$				$Z_1 Z_2$
00	01	11	10	
8	2	7	①	1 0
4	②	7	6	1 -
8	2	③	1	0 -
④	9	7	6	0 0
4	⑤	3	6	1 1
8	5	3	⑥	- 0
8	5	⑦	1	- 1
⑧	2	7	6	0 0
8	⑨	7	6	1 0

Problem 12.3.

2. Is the table found in part 1 unique? If the answer is "yes," explain why. If "no," derive another primitive flow table (with its associated output data) from the original table.

12.4 A sequential switching circuit has two inputs and two outputs. All possible input sequences and the required output sequences are tabulated as follows:

(a)   Input Sequence: $00 \rightarrow 10 \rightarrow 11 \rightarrow 01 \rightarrow 00$
      Output Sequence: 00   00   10   00   00

(b)   Input Sequence: $00 \rightarrow 01 \rightarrow 11 \rightarrow 10 \rightarrow 00$
      Output Sequence: 00   00   01   00   00

(c)   Input Sequence: $00 \rightarrow 10 \rightarrow 00 \rightarrow 01 \rightarrow 00$
      Output Sequence: 00   00   00   00   00

(d)   Input Sequence: $00 \rightarrow 01 \rightarrow 00 \rightarrow 10 \rightarrow 00$
      Output Sequence: 00   00   00   00   00

Synthesize a relay control unit which will satisfy the requirements shown. Your design should use the least possible number of secondary relays and should have the simplest possible contact configurations in the Y and Z networks.

12.5 A relay control unit is to be designed which has two inputs (X_1 and X_2) and a single output, Z. Assume only single changes of variable occur at the input.

The output, after it has been ungrounded, may be grounded again only by removing both input grounds and then reapplying them in the order: X_1, X_2. The output, after it has been grounded, may be ungrounded again only by applying both input grounds and then removing them in the order: X_1, X_2.

1. Derive a primitive flow table, with its associated output data. The primitive flow table should have no equivalences in it.
2. Draw a merger diagram and from it derive all minimum-row condensed flow tables.
3. Derive Y and Z matrices corresponding to the best table found in part 2. Any spaces in the Y and Z matrices which correspond to non-occurring total relay states may be filled arbitrarily. Spaces in the Z matrix which correspond to uncircled entries in the condensed flow table may be filled arbitrarily, provided no "false" output is produced.
4. Derive minimized transmission expressions for the output network and for the control of any secondary relay or relays.

12.6 The input to the circuit shown never changes in both variables at the same time. This circuit is to be redesigned in such a way that its terminal action remains the same, but so that the circuit has improved economy. Each step in the analysis and resynthesis should be fully explained.

12.7 In the circuit shown, primary relay coils are omitted. The circuit is used under conditions which prevent a double change of input variables when the input state is $X_1X_2 = 00$, but the double change is possible for all other situations.

Resynthesize the circuit so that the same terminal action results, and so that ultimate simplicity is achieved. False outputs must be prevented, but it is not necessary to isolate the output from the secondary control network.

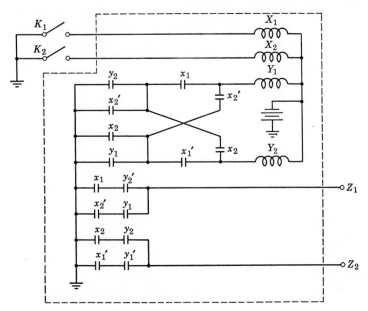

Problem 12.6.

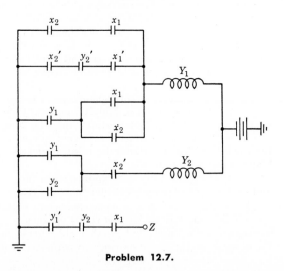

Problem 12.7.

12.8 A two-input, two-output sequential circuit is to have terminal action in accordance with the following word description: With all possible changes of input state allowed, an output is to indicate by becoming grounded which input or inputs last changed state. An output becomes ungrounded if the correspondingly numbered input does not change state when the other input does change.

1. Construct a primitive flow table and make any possible mergers.
2. Make an assignment of secondary states to the rows of the flow table found in part 1.
3. Write the excitation matrix for part 2.

12.9 A sequential circuit with two inputs and two outputs has the following properties (only single changes of input variable are permitted):

(a) After any *change* of input state, the output state is always either the initial input state or the final input state.

(b) When the input states are represented in binary form, an input change which increases the equivalent decimal value of the binary input causes an output of either 00 or 11. If the equivalent decimal value decreases, the output is either 01 or 10.

1. Write a primitive flow table for this circuit.
2. Draw a merger diagram for the flow table.
3. How many minimum-row flow tables are indicated by the merger diagram?

12.10 A two-input one-output sequential circuit is to be designed for use as an "accumulator." The X_1 input cycles $0 \rightarrow 1 \rightarrow 0$ while $X_2 = 0$ and X_2 cycles $0 \rightarrow 1 \rightarrow 0$ while $X_1 = 0$. The function of the circuit is to "remember" the number of times X_1 cycled while X_2 was zero and then give an output for each cycle of X_2 ($Z = 1$ while $X_2 = 1$) for as many cycles of X_2 as X_1 had cycled. The circuit is to "remember" a maximum of three cycles of X_1 between cycles of X_2. If an accumulation of X_1 cycles greater than three occurs then this information is lost. This accumulation of "remembered" X_1 cycles need not be cleared by X_2 cycles before X_1 is permitted to cycle again.

The time sequence of inputs and output illustrated represent normal operation and two ways of losing information. Three secondary variables are sufficient.

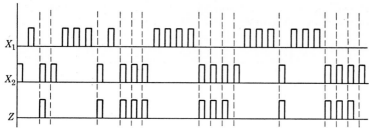

Problem 12.10.

12.11 The sequential circuit shown is designed around a two-winding secondary relay. This relay has the following characteristics. If neither winding is energized the relay will be unoperated. If the relay is unoperated, the energization of just one of its windings will not cause relay operation. Energization of both windings will cause relay operation. If the relay is operated, it will continue to be operated even if one of the windings is de-energized.

1. Derive a flow table which describes the terminal action of the circuit.

2. Redesign the circuit using an ordinary single-winding secondary relay (or relays) so that the circuit will have the same terminal characteristics as before.

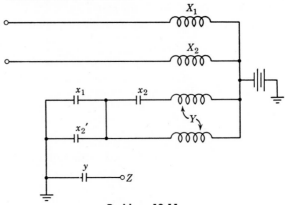

Problem 12.11.

12.12 A sequential relay circuit is controlled by two keys, K_1 and K_2, and has a single output, Z. Either key, when depressed, remains depressed for a fixed interval of time, d. (Assume that no double changes of input state occur). The output Z changes state only when either K_1 or K_2 is depressed (no output change occurs when a key is released). The closing of K_1 assures that Z changes to (or remains at) the 0 state. The closing of K_2 assures that Z changes to (or remains at) the 1 state. Typical input changes and the associated output responses are illustrated.

Synthesize an economical relay circuit satisfying the stated terminal requirements. No isolation is necessary between inputs and output or between the secondary relay control network(s) and the output. (A total of two coils and nine springs is sufficient for realization.)

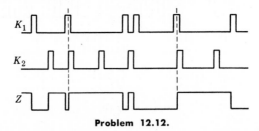

Problem 12.12.

12.13 Two identical switching circuits, S_1 and S_2, are interconnected as shown. Each of the inputs X_1, X_2, Y_1, and Y_2 controls a relay. The contact networks within S_1 and S_2 produce the functions:

$$Z_1 = x_1y_1' = Y_2 \qquad \text{and} \qquad Z_2 = x_2y_2' = Y_1$$

In addition, a network S_3 uses contacts from the relays in both S_1 and S_2 to provide the output $Z_0 = x_1x_2y_1'y_2$.

Assume that, (a) no double changes of the input variables X_1 and X_2 will ever occur and, (b) between changes of input variables there will always be sufficient time for the total state of the circuit to become stable.

1. Write a matrix for this circuit showing the secondary excitation and the output data.
2. Write the flow table for the circuit.
3. Synthesize a circuit which gives the same terminal action but which contains a minimal number of coils and springs. It is not necessary to isolate the output from the inputs or from the secondary control network(s). (Two coils and five springs are sufficient.)

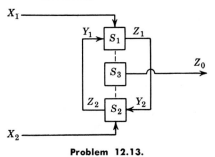

Problem 12.13.

x_1x_2				
OO	OI	II	IO	Z_1Z_2
①	11	4	10	OI
5	②		3	II
5	2	13	③	II
12	④	15		OO
⑤	8			IO
14	⑥		10	II
⑦	6	8	3	OI
7	⑧	3		OO
⑨	11	13	10	OI
12	6	13	⑩	II
5	⑪		3	II
⑫	2	4	15	OI
1	⑬	10		OO
⑭	8			IO
1	6	4	⑮	II

Problem 12.14.

12.14 In the primitive flow table shown determine whether there are any equivalences, and reduce the table accordingly. Complete the reduction by row merger. Is there a unique, minimum-row flow table? If not, how many minimum-row forms exist?

12.15 A three-input, one-output sequential relay circuit has the terminal requirements: $Z = 1$ whenever $X_2 = X_3 = 1$, provided X_1 had not become 1 since X_2 and X_3 had last been simultaneously equal to 1. The restrictions on the inputs are: there are no multiple simultaneous changes of the input signals, and X_1 is never equal to 1 when either or both X_2 and X_3 are equal to 1.

1. Construct the primitive flow table and the merged flow table.
2. Construct the Y and Z matrices.
3. Draw a contact network realization of the Y and Z circuits, which need not necessarily be hazard free (9 contacts and 16 springs are sufficient, but a solution exists with 8 contacts and 13 springs).

12.16 A sequential relay circuit has two inputs X_1 and X_2 and one output, Z. Changes of input state always occur in one variable at a time. If a change of secondary state is initiated, it is always completed before the input state again changes.

This circuit is to have the terminal action:

    (a) Whenever a *change* of X_1 is followed by a *change* of X_2 the output is to be *momentarily* grounded. In other words, after X_1 *changes* the output is 0, but on a change of X_2 which follows, the output goes to 1 and then back to 0.

    (b) For all other input sequences the output is to be 0.

Assume that the duration of the momentary output in part (a) is determined by the response times of the relays used.

    1. Write a primitive flow table showing how you obtain the required output changes.

    2. Write the merged flow table, the excitation matrix and the output matrix.

    3. Write the excitation functions and the output function. (Two secondary relays are sufficient for this synthesis.)

12.17 For the flow matrix and the output matrix given:

    1. Design an output network which is free of static hazards.

    2. Construct the excitation matrix.

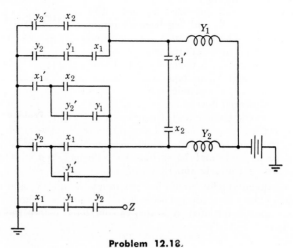

Flow matrix Z_1Z_2

Problem 12.17.

12.18 The sequential circuit shown (with primary relays omitted) is to be resynthesized with as much reduction as possible in the number of secondary relays and contacts.

Problem 12.18.

Design a minimal circuit which has the same terminal action and is free of static hazards.

12.19 The sequential circuit shown operates with input restrictions that prevent the double change of input state X_1X_2 $00 \leftrightarrow 11$, but which allow the double change of input state X_1X_2 $01 \leftrightarrow 10$.

    1. Resynthesize the given network to obtain the same output action with fewer relays and contacts, if possible. In constructing the new output contact network use the design criterion of a minimum-contact network consistent with no static hazards.

    2. Write a statement in words which describes the output action of the network.

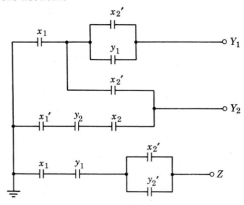

Problem 12.19.

12.20 The given circuit operates under conditions which prevent the double change of input state from 01 to 10 and vice versa, but permits the change $00 \leftrightarrow 11$.

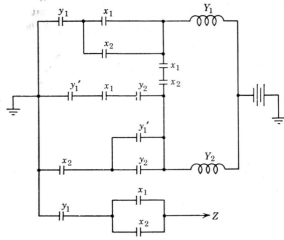

Problem 12.20.

1. Resynthesize the circuit so as to obtain the same output action using the fewest relays and contacts. The resynthesized circuit is to be free of static hazard.
2. Give a word statement which describes the output action of the circuit.

12.21 Synthesize a hazard-free, two-input, one-output sequential relay circuit whose output is 1 at the end of the input sequence $X_1X_2 = 00, 10, 11$ and maintains this output for all input variations until the input completes the sequence $X_1X_2 = 11, 10, 00$, at which time the output becomes 0. At most, a single input variable is changing at any time.

Indicate in the excitation and output matrices those transitions which can lead to hazards and indicate also any redundancy you must introduce to eliminate these hazards.

12.22 A two-input, two-output sequential relay circuit is required to deliver a ground at the output terminal which corresponds (by number) to the input terminal at which the last *change* of state occurred. Only one input variable can change state at a time, and the only possible outputs are 01 and 10.

1. Prepare a primitive flow table.
2. Derive a minimum-row merged flow table. Is this merger unique?
3. Prepare a secondary excitation matrix and an output matrix.
4. Write algebraic expressions for the secondary excitation and the outputs which lead to contact networks containing no hazards, and which under this restriction are also minimal in form.

12.23 A rotating shaft carries a circular slip ring. The ring is made up of two 180° sectors, one of which is a non-conducting material, and the other of which is metallic and connected to ground. Two brushes, separated by a 90° angle, are in contact with this ring, and these brushes are connected to the two input leads of a relay switching circuit. The shaft position illustrated gives the input state $X_1X_2 = 01$.

The single output of the circuit is connected to an indicator lamp which is to be lighted when the shaft is rotating clockwise (in the view given in the diagram) and is to be extinguished when the shaft is rotating counterclockwise. If the direction of rotation of the shaft changes, the output indication should change as soon as possible (within one-quarter of a revolution).

1. Derive a primitive flow table, merged flow table with proper assignment of secondary states, Y and Z matrices, and minimal algebraic expressions for the transmissions of the Y and Z contact networks.

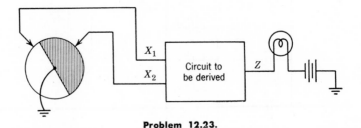

Problem 12.23.

2. Design Y and Z contact networks, using the results of part 1 but paying particular attention to avoiding situations in which the lamp either flickers on when it should be off, or momentarily goes off when it should be on.

CHAPTER 13

Secondary assignment methods

In the preceding chapter the development of a basic method for the design of sequential switching circuits placed major emphasis on the writing of a flow table and its reduction to more compact forms through either the recognition of equivalent states or the application of the merger process, or through a combination of these. A final step was the writing of the excitation and output matrices, which reduced the original sequential problem to the familiar combinational problem.

Before this last step could be taken, however, it became necessary to assign a set of secondary states to represent the rows of the reduced flow table. For this purpose we used a transition diagram which exhibited, in a convenient form, the pairs of rows for which secondary states could differ pairwise in only a single variable. In the examples presented it was a simple matter to assign an appropriate set of secondary states because these examples were selected for their simplicity in this respect.

We now propose to consider in more detail the problems of secondary assignment and some of the methods that are applicable to them. These problems fall broadly into two classes. First, there is the problem of making a secondary assignment for a specific flow table, without regard to the complexity of the requirements imposed in the table. The second type of problem is the general one of making assignments which satisfy any possible requirements of a flow table of a given number of rows.

13.1 Minimum-Row Matrices

When we assign S secondary states to represent the n rows of a flow table, the smallest number of secondary variables we can possibly use is given by $S = S_0$, where $2^{S_0} \geqslant n$.

If all the requirements of a minimum-row flow table are satisfied by the assignment of secondary states derived from S_0 variables, and if there are no more rows in the flow matrix than there are in the flow table, the resulting flow matrix is a minimum-row matrix. The requirements of a flow table are satisfied if each interrow transition is accomplished either by a change of secondary state in which only one secondary variable changes, or by a change of secondary state in which a multiple change of secondary variables does not involve a critical race.

Secondary states which differ in only a single variable are said to be adjacent states. For a geometrical interpretation of adjacent states, we can arrange four rows of a flow table, a, b, c, and d, as in the transition diagrams of Fig. 13–1. In these diagrams, each row is represented

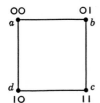 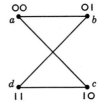

Fig. 13–1. Geometrical representation of adjacent secondary states in a four-row flow table.

by a node, and a line joining nodes indicates that an interrow transition is required. The problem then is to assign secondary states so that each connected pair of nodes is represented by an adjacent pair of secondary states. When this type of assignment is possible, the pattern of connections for a four-row flow table will have one of the forms shown in Fig. 13–1. The nodes in each of these diagrams have been labeled with the binary representations of one set of secondary states which have the required adjacencies.

We may note in passing that if a flow table can be reduced to three rows, its requirements can *always* be satisfied by two secondary variables. The worst condition with respect to required adjacencies is shown in Fig. 13–2(a), where it may be seen that all possible connections are required between three pairs of rows. For this pattern as it stands no proper assignment of secondary variables can be made. When two secondary states are adjacent, the binary designators of those states must contain for one state an even number of 1's and for the other state an odd number of 1's (zero is considered an even

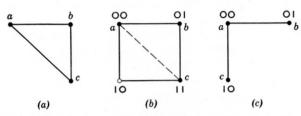

Fig. 13–2. A three-row flow table never requires more than two secondary variables.

number). If in Fig. 13–2(a), node a is represented by a secondary state with an even number of 1's, node b must contain an odd number of 1's, and node c must then contain an even number of 1's. However, this requires both node a and node c to contain an even number of 1's and at the same time to be adjacent. The odd-even rule is hence violated and appropriate secondary states cannot be assigned to this pattern. In Fig. 13–2(b), the direct connection between nodes a and c is replaced by one which passes through the fourth available node. This assignment avoids any need to have a race in passing between nodes a and c. Such a race would be critical in that it might result in a transition to node b. No increase in the number of secondary variables is required by using the fourth node because the secondary state represented by this node is already available. Another typical situation found in flow tables with three rows is illustrated by Fig. 13–2(c). Only two interrow connections are required and these are readily satisfied by an assignment like the one shown.

We have demonstrated that it is always possible to find a secondary assignment using two variables when the flow table contains three rows. If the flow table contains four rows, and if the interrow connections are represented by one of the patterns shown in Fig. 13–1, the requirements can also be satisfied with two secondary variables. However, many four-row flow tables require additional connections beyond those shown in Fig. 13–1 and it becomes necessary to use more than S_0 secondary variables. This situation will be studied further in the next two articles of this chapter.

For three secondary variables, adjacent secondary states may be represented by vertices of a cube which are joined by a line representing an edge, as shown in Fig. 13–3(a). An alternate representation is made available by the use of a map as shown in Fig. 13–3(b). The coordinates of the map are the binary representations of the *secondary*

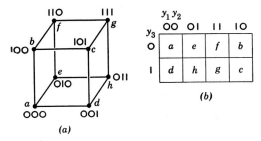

(a)

(b)

Fig. 13–3. Adjacent secondary states in three variables represented, (a) as the vertices of a cube, and (b) as cells in a map.

variables. Any pair of map cells that are adjacent either horizontally or vertically then represent adjacent secondary states. Whether we use the cube or the map representation, all possible adjacencies among the secondary states are displayed.

These geometric aids are useful only as guides in making secondary state assignments. There is a wide variation in the degree of difficulty involved in finding minimum-row assignments of secondary variables. The following examples illustrate the problems that arise in making assignments in three and four secondary variables.

Example 13–1

A sequential switching circuit has two inputs and one output. All input changes are permitted, and for any input sequence the output is to be alternately grounded and ungrounded. Write a minimum-row excitation matrix for this circuit.

Since both input variables may change simultaneously, or either input variable may change separately, either output may be obtained for any input state. There must hence be two stable states in each column of the primitive flow table, which is completed in Fig. 13–4.

$x_1 x_2$				
00	01	11	10	Z
①	4	6	8	O
②	3	5	7	1
2	③	6	8	O
1	④	5	7	1
2	4	⑤	8	O
1	3	⑥	7	1
2	4	6	⑦	O
1	3	5	⑧	1

Fig. 13–4. Primitive flow table of Example 13–1.

There are no possible row mergers in the primitive flow table, and since the pairs of circled entries in each column are associated with different output states, there are no equivalences. Hence the flow table as written in Fig. 13–4 cannot be reduced. A minimum of three secondary relays will be required.

In the transition diagram of Fig. 13–5(a), the node numbers correspond to the circled-entry numbers for each row. We observe that

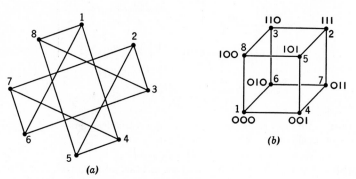

Fig. 13–5. (*a*) The transition diagram for the flow table of Fig. 13–4, and (*b*), an assignment of secondary states on a cube pattern.

there are exactly three transitions from each node and that there are no violations of the odd-even rule. It is not necessary in this example to represent the secondary states as the vertices of a cube, as shown in Fig. 13–5(b), but it is frequently a useful step in visualizing the adjacencies required. The map of Fig. 13–6(a) represents the same secondary assignment as that given in Fig. 13–5(b), while the map of Fig. 13–6(b) represents another valid assignment of secondary states. A map may be prepared from the transition diagram, or directly from the flow table. The map of Fig. 13–6(a) was prepared by first enter-

y_3	$y_1 y_2$ 00	01	11	10
0	1	6	3	8
1	4	7	2	5

(a)

y_3	$y_1 y_2$ 00	01	11	10
0	4	7	6	1
1	5	2	3	8

(b)

Fig. 13–6. Secondary state assignments derived from maps.

ing the "1" in the cell corresponding to $y_1 y_2 y_3 = 000$. Then the entries for rows 4, 6, and 8, all of which must be adjacent to row 1, were completed. Row 7 must then be placed adjacent to rows 4 and 6; row 5 is adjacent to rows 4 and 8; and row 3 is adjacent to rows 6 and 8. The remaining cell is for row 2 which is adjacent to rows 3, 5, and 7.

When the secondary values found in Fig. 13–6(a) are applied to the flow table, and the rows are rearranged in a cyclic ordering, the flow matrix of Fig. 13–7(a) is obtained and from this we write the excitation matrix of Fig. 13–7(b).

$y_1 y_2 y_3$ \ $x_1 x_2$	00	01	11	10
000	(1)	4	6	8
001	1	(4)	5	7
011	2	4	6	(7)
010	1	3	(6)	7
110	2	(3)	6	8
111	(2)	3	5	7
101	2	4	(5)	8
100	1	3	5	(8)

(a)

$y_1 y_2 y_3$ \ $x_1 x_2$	00	01	11	10
000	000	001	010	100
001	000	001	101	011
011	111	001	010	011
010	000	110	010	011
110	111	110	010	100
111	111	110	101	011
101	111	001	101	100
100	000	110	101	100

(b)

Fig. 13–7. Minimum-row flow matrix and excitation matrix of Example 13–1.

The transition diagram can become quite complex as the number of rows in a flow table increases. In the preceding example the transition diagram, although relatively simple, was of some help in making map entries. The next example illustrates the use of the transition diagram in a quite complex situation. It is possible to make the final secondary state assignments directly from the flow table, but the transition diagram enables us to visualize systematic properties of some importance.

Example 13–2

A sequential circuit has two inputs and two outputs, and only one input variable can change at a time. If the sequence of input combinations is numbered serially in ascending order, then when the jth input combination appears, the output combination is to be the $(j - 2)$ input combination, for all values of j. Prepare a minimum-row flow matrix.

With the restriction that any input change can involve only a single variable, the number of stable states required for each column of the flow table can be seen from a study of the diagrams in Fig. 13–8. These diagrams show the four ways in which a *present* input state of 00 can be reached by two input changes, each involving the change of a

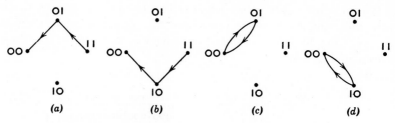

Fig. 13–8. Study of input sequences, Example 13–2.

x_1x_2 OO	OI	II	IO	Z_1Z_2
①	5	—	15	OO
②	7	—	13	OO
③	5	—	15	II
④	7	—	13	II
1	⑤	11	—	OI
3	⑥	9	—	OI
1	⑦	11	—	IO
3	⑧	9	—	IO
—	6	⑨	16	II
—	8	⑩	14	II
—	6	⑪	16	OO
—	8	⑫	14	OO
2	—	12	⑬	IO
4	—	10	⑭	IO
2	—	12	⑮	OI
4	—	10	⑯	OI

Fig. 13–9. Primitive flow table, Example 13–2.

x_1x_2 OO	OI	II	IO	Row
①	⑤	11	15	A
②	7	12	⑬	B
③	5	—	15	C
④	7	—	13	D
3	⑥	⑨	16	E
1	⑦	11	—	F
3	⑧	9	—	G
4	8	⑩	⑭	H
—	6	⑪	16	J
—	8	⑫	14	K
2	—	12	⑮	L
4	—	10	⑯	M

Fig. 13–10. Merged flow table, Example 13–2.

single variable. First, as shown in parts (a) and (b), we can start at $X_1X_2 = 11$ and reach $X_1X_2 = 00$ by way of either $X_1X_2 = 01$ or $X_1X_2 = 10$, respectively. For either of these the output must be $Z_1Z_2 = 11$ when $X_1X_2 = 00$. In parts (c) and (d) we change from $X_1X_2 = 00$ to $X_1X_2 = 01$ or $X_1X_2 = 10$, respectively, and then return to $X_1X_2 = 00$. In either of these sequences the output must be $Z_1Z_2 = 00$ after the input state returns to $X_1X_2 = 00$. However, in the 00 column we must provide two stable entries with the output 11 and two more stable entries with the output 00, because starting from either pair *the next output must be either* 01 *or* 10 depending upon the input state just before the $X_1X_2 = 00$ state.

Similar considerations apply to the other input states, so we must have four stable states in each column, or a total of sixteen rows in the primitive flow table, as shown in Fig. 13–9.

It is not worthwhile to draw a merger diagram, for examination of the primitive flow table shows that only the row pairs 1 and 5, 2 and 13, 6 and 9, and 10 and 14 may be merged. When these mergers are completed, the merged flow table is as given in Fig. 13–10. The twelve rows in it are identified by letters of the alphabet.

The transition diagram of Fig. 13–11 is drawn with both solid and broken lines. These distinguish between two types of transitions which we can observe in Fig. 13–10. Consider row A from which transitions are required to row J (state 11) and to row L (state 15).

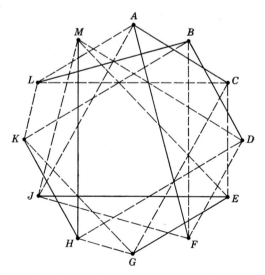

Fig. 13–11. Transition diagram for Example 13–2. Solid lines indicate required connections. Broken lines indicate connections for which alternate routes exist.

However, note that the transition from row A to the entry ⑪ in row J may be made either directly or by way of the uncircled 11 entry in row F. Furthermore, the transition from row F to the entry ⑪ in row J may be made directly or by way of row A. We are not at the moment certain which route, if any, is possible. Similarly the transition from row A to the entry ⑮ in row L may be direct or by way of row C.

In contrast, consider the required transition from row C to the entry ⑤ in row A. The uncircled 5 entry appears only once in the column so this transition must be direct, unless we choose to take advantage of the blank spaces in rows L and M of the same column to add an alternative route. Until it becomes necessary we will not make additional entries of this type in the flow table.

The solid lines in Fig. 13–11 represent those transitions which must be accomplished by a single route. Broken lines represent the transitions for which there are alternate routes. We know that any successful assignment of secondary states must satisfy the solid-line connections, and these become our first concern.

Inspection of the transition diagram reveals that every node is connected by a solid line to at least one other node. Only the nodes representing rows A, B, E, and H have two solid-line connections to other nodes. This group of solid-line connections breaks down into four independent groups, namely:

> Row A must be adjacent to row C and to row F
> Row B must be adjacent to row D and to row L
> Row E must be adjacent to row G and to row J
> Row H must be adjacent to row K and to row M

Each of these four groups is independent in the sense that no solid-line connections exist between members of different groups. There are, of course, many connections between these groups represented by broken lines, which we now examine.

Consider the nodes representing rows A, C, and L. There is a solid line from A to C and there are broken lines from A to L and from C to L. The three nodes are connected in a triangular pattern and thus violate the odd-even rule. Hence in any valid secondary assignment we make, the solid-line connection must be retained but one of the broken-line connections must be discarded. Referring to the merged flow table in Fig. 13–10, we see that the solid line indicates the required connection from row C to the entry ⑤ in row A. The broken line connections indicate that from both A and C it must be possible to reach the entry ⑮ in row L. But since a direct connection is already provided between A and C, only one of these rows need connect directly to row L. The transition from the other row will then require two changes of secondary state.

A similar pattern is found for all the broken-line connections in Fig. 13–11 and we may summarize the requirements they impose as follows:

Requirement

(Must be adjacent to *either* of the

Row	rows listed, but *not* to both)	
J	A	F
L	A	C
F	B	D
K	B	L
C	E	G
M	E	J
D	H	M
G	H	K

We can use a four-variable cyclic map to represent the various secondary states, taking advantage of the fact that adjacent states are represented by cells of the map that are adjacent either horizontally or vertically. The solid-line connections will be established by vertical adjacencies and we will attempt to satisfy the broken-line connections in the rows of the map. In Fig. 13–12(a), the entries in

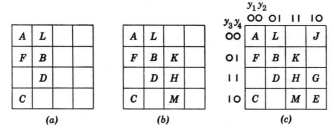

Fig. 13–12. Development of the secondary assignment map. Example 13–2.

the left-hand column make row A adjacent to row F and to row C as required. In the second column we must make row B adjacent to rows D and L, as required by the solid-line connections. By the arrangement shown, however, we also establish broken-line connections between A and L and between B and F. In Fig. 13–12(b) we add a column in which row H is adjacent to row K and to row M (solid-line connections), and we also establish the broken-line connections between *B* and *K* and between *H* and *D*. Finally, in Fig. 13–12(c) the map is completed by adding the *E, G, J* group with the required adjacencies vertically and horizontally. The student should verify carefully the relations thus established.

$y_1y_2y_3y_4$ \ x_1x_2	00	01	11	10	
0000	①	⑤	11	15	*A*
0001	1	⑦	11	—	*F*
0011	—	—	—	—	
0010	③	5	—	15	*C*
0110	—	—	—	—	
0111	④	7	—	13	*D*
0101	②	7	12	⑬	*B*
0100	2	—	12	⑮	*L*
1100	—	—	—	—	
1101	—	8	⑫	14	*K*
1111	4	8	⑩	⑭	*H*
1110	4	—	10	⑯	*M*
1010	3	⑥	⑨	16	*E*
1011	3	⑧	9	—	*G*
1001	—	—	—	—	
1000	—	6	⑪	16	*J*

Fig. 13–13. Minimum-row flow matrix of Example 13–2.

With the map completed and the coordinates labeled, the secondary states to be applied to each row of the flow table may be read directly from the map. Figure 13–13 shows the final minimum-row flow matrix. Note that the rows are rearranged so that the secondary states are in a cyclic order.

It will be observed in this flow matrix that there are numerous opportunities for effective network design. For example, in the 11 column, for the transition from uncircled 11 in the 0001 row to the ⑪ in the 1000 row a race can be permitted since it is non-critical. A number of similar opportunities can readily be found.*

13.2 Augmented Matrices

In the preceding article we discussed the assignment of secondary states to a three-row flow table for which the transition diagram had the triangular pattern of Fig. 13–2(a). We treated this situation by adding a fourth node to the transition diagram, or in effect, a fourth row to the flow table. Although this procedure did augment the final flow matrix in the sense that it contained more rows than the reduced flow table, it did not increase the number of secondary relays. Augmentation can be an important technique when thus used, but we are

* In the secondary assignment map of Fig. 13–12(c) the flow table rows *A, B, E,* and *H* are placed in different map rows, since no adjacencies are required among these flow table rows. However, another type of secondary assignment can be made in which the flow table rows, *A, B, E,* and *H* are all placed in the same row (or column) of the map. This leads to a secondary assignment in which the races are critical.

more concerned with situations which require an increase in the number of secondary variables. When the interrow transitions demanded in the flow table cannot be satisfied by using the minimum number, S_0, of secondary variables, we would like to achieve a satisfactory assignment with as little increase in the number as possible. Augmentation does not offer a general solution to this type of problem, but in specific situations it should always be tried first in preference to accepting a general method which may be less economic.

To examine this problem in terms of a specific situation, let us consider a sequential circuit which has two inputs and two outputs. For the input combination $X_1X_2 = 00$, the output is given by $Z_1Z_2 = 00$. Only one output is to be grounded at any one time and that output is to indicate which input became grounded first. If both inputs are grounded simultaneously, the output is to be $Z_1Z_2 = 00$ and is to remain at that value until one of the inputs is ungrounded and regrounded. The output is then to indicate which input was thus regrounded. To simplify the flow table we will permit the double change of input state from 00 to 11, in either direction, but we will not permit the double change of input state from 01 to 10, or vice versa.

The primitive flow table shown in Fig. 13–14 requires no discussion. In the same figure the merger diagram indicates that there is a unique

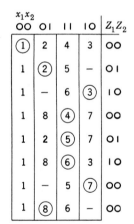
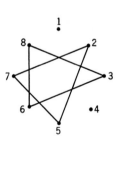

Fig. 13–14. A primitive flow table and its merger diagram.

merger of rows 2, 5, and 7, and of rows 3, 6, and 8. Rows 1 and 4 do not combine with any other rows. The merged flow table is at the left of Fig. 13–15 and the corresponding transition diagram is at the right. In the transition diagram the states written in parentheses indicate which columns of the merged flow table require the transitions

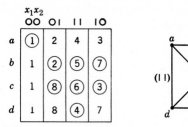

Fig. 13–15.   The merged flow table and its transition diagram.

thus marked. We observe that the transition diagram contains one triangular pattern connecting rows a, b, d, and another connecting rows a, c, d. Although for this situation, $S_0 = 2$, we do not have available an unused combination of secondary variables that we can introduce as an extra node to break up the triangular patterns. There is no possible assignment of two secondary relays which can satisfy the requirements of this flow table. Sometimes we can accept an assignment which requires multiple changes of secondary variables by making one or more of the secondary relays a slow-operate or slow-release type, so that the outcome of a race becomes predictable and hence noncritical. Even this relief cannot be permitted for the problem under consideration because it would bias the circuit to favor one input over another and hence would not satisfy the requirement that the output must show which input is grounded first.

It should be noted that although a triangular connection pattern in a transition diagram indicates that there will be trouble in trying to assign secondary states without setting up critical race conditions, the difficulty is not limited to the triangular pattern. In Fig. 13–16

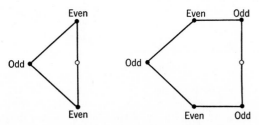

Fig. 13–16.   Patterns which do not satisfy the odd-even rule until an additional node (open circle) is introduced.

we see that the odd-even rule is violated by any connection pattern that has an odd number of sides. In both patterns the open circle indicates that a single node may be added to resolve the difficulty. The

existence of these patterns is not necessarily obvious, for they may
be embedded within a transition diagram.

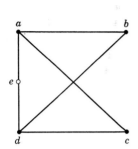

Fig. 13–17. The node
added at e breaks up
both triangular patterns
of Fig. 13–15.

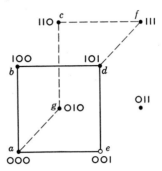

Fig. 13–18. The node added
at e requires nodes at f and g.

Suppose we try to overcome the difficulty of secondary assignment
in Fig. 13–15 by adding the node e as shown by the open circle in Fig.
13–17. This seems to be a reasonable procedure since this one node
breaks up both of the original triangular
patterns. In Fig. 13–18 we use a cube
representation to make the actual secondary assignments. We start by placing
node e adjacent to both a and d in accordance with the indications of Fig. 13–17.
However, we see that no matter how
we do this, we can have only one more
node adjacent to both a and d. From the
transition diagram, however, both b and
c are indicated as being adjacent to a
and d. Since we can satisfy only one of
these requirements, in Fig. 13–18 we
place node b adjacent to a and d. The
best we can do with node c is to locate it
so that it is equidistant from both a and
d. Either of the transitions to node c
requires two changes of secondary state.
Thus we see that in trying to augment the
transition diagram of Fig. 13–15 by add-

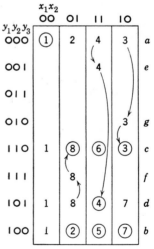

Fig. 13–19. Augmented flow
matrix showing multiple changes
of secondary state.

ing only one node, we must eventually add three nodes. From the
assignment selected we obtain the flow matrix of Fig. 13–19. Whenever

a change of secondary state requires that two secondary variables change, we accomplish this in two steps. The multiple changes of secondary state required in Fig. 13–19 are indicated by arrows. The final excitation matrix is not shown, but in writing it we can assign optional excitation values for all positions in the flow matrix which are not occupied by entries, either circled or uncircled. These optional entries usually offer an excellent opportunity to simplify the excitation network.

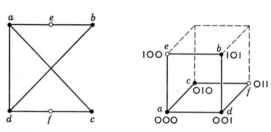

Fig. 13–20. All transitions are satisfied by adding two nodes.

We can avoid some of the difficulties previously discussed. If instead of trying to break up the triangular patterns of the transition diagram by adding a single node, we add two nodes as shown at the

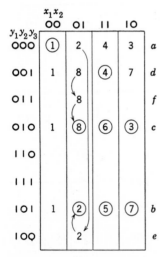

Fig. 13–21. Flow matrix augmented as in Fig. 13–20.

left of Fig. 13–20, a set of secondary assignments can be made as illustrated at the right of Fig. 13–20 in which only six of the vertices of a cube are needed to satisfy all requirements. The flow matrix resulting from this assignment is given in Fig. 13–21, and the multiple changes of secondary state are indicated by arrows.

Evidently the augmentation procedure can be carried out in a number of ways and the question arises whether the number of nodes we must add is of any importance. If we must add (at least) one secondary variable, the important question is not how many extra nodes we introduce in a transition diagram, but whether the required transitions of the flow table can be satisfied at all, using the additional nodes made available by the additional secondary variable. If all requirements *can* thus be satisfied, we may then examine the question of how to use the augmentation process most effectively.

Frequently, we may want to use augmentation so that the final network will be as simple as possible. In the problem we have been studying, however, it is more important to find a secondary assignment which most effectively satisfies the input-output requirements of the network. Physically, the circuit we are trying to design is supposed to have an output which indicates the winner in a race between two inputs. Hence, if we assume that the operating and release times of our secondary devices are identical, we should make sure that the secondary response time is the same regardless of which input is grounded first. Neither of the previous assignments has this property. In the assignment shown in Fig. 13–18 the secondary system responds more quickly to the grounding of input X_2, while in the assignment of Fig. 13–20 the response is quicker when input X_1 is grounded.

We can equalize the response time by the assignment shown in Fig. 13–22. First, we note that rows b and c contain the entries which

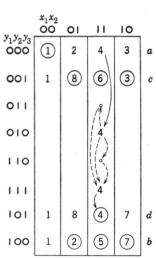

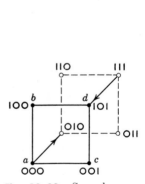

Fig. 13–22. Secondary assignment which equalizes secondary response times. A non-critical race is indicated by dotted lines.

Fig. 13–23. Flow matrix for secondary assignment of Fig. 13–22. Note the non-critical race.

indicate that inputs X_2 and X_1, respectively, win the race. Hence, we want to reach either of these rows in equal times, starting from either row a or row d. This requires that we place rows b and c adjacent to row a, and also adjacent to row d, as shown in the cube representation of Fig. 13–22. In doing this, we find it necessary to separate rows a and d by four changes of secondary variables, but this is of no real concern, and the output does not change in going from a to d or vice versa. Also, it is possible to reduce the time required for a transition between a and d by making use of the non-critical race which is indicated by the dotted connections in Fig. 13–22. For example, in going from a to d, we indicate a change from the secondary state 000 to the state 010 by the change of a single variable. Next, we must reach the state 111 and for this change we permit a race between y_1 and y_3. Finally, we reach row d by the single change of variable from secondary state 111 to state 101. The final flow matrix is shown in Fig. 13–23, and the non-critical race is indicated in the third column by the use of dotted connections. The arrows on solid lines indicate the changes that are accomplished by changing a single secondary variable.

13.3   General Assignments for Four-Row Flow Tables

It will be instructive to consider in some detail the various ways in which secondary states can be assigned to a four-row table that requires all possible transitions between rows. By a study of some of the ways to do this we can develop ideas and methods which will be helpful in the management of problems of much larger size where frequently the elements of a solution become confused by the sheer mass of detailed specification. Although it is important to be able to handle specific problems by the methods previously discussed, an understanding of the nature of more general types of solutions promotes a better understanding of the basic problem. We can also establish certain bounds which indicate in specific problems whether or not additional effort is likely to produce significantly better results.

In developing a group of secondary assignments applicable to the general four-row flow table, we will use as a running example the flow table and transition diagram of Fig. 13–24. No output specifica-

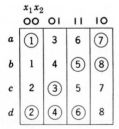
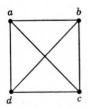

Fig. 13–24.   A flow table, and its transition diagram, in which all possible inter-row transitions are required.

tions are given for this particular flow table and we will assume that no equivalent pairs of states are present in it. In the transition diagram we see that all pairs of rows must be connected. Since this cannot be accomplished by using two secondary variables, we must examine the ways in which we can assign at least three secondary variables to satisfy these requirements.

The transition diagram shown in Fig. 13–24 describes the most severe requirements that can be imposed by a four-row flow table, but because of its severity it contains a useful symmetry in that the transitions required by starting from any one node are no more severe than those required by starting from any other node. Any solution we find for this problem can be applied directly to any four-row table. We will call secondary assignments which satisfy these requirements *general assignments.** For convenience of reference the assignments to be described will be numbered. At the end of the discussion a few additional assignments are presented without detailed description.

GENERAL ASSIGNMENT 1. In Fig. 13–25 a cube representation is shown for a secondary assignment applicable to the flow table of

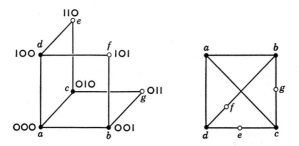

Fig. 13–25. A general assignment of secondary variables for a four-row flow table. (Assignment 1.)

Fig. 13–24 in which node a is placed adjacent to each of nodes b, c, and d. Three more nodes, e, f, and g, are added to make possible all transitions between pairs of the nodes b, c, and d. An equivalent augmentation of the transition diagram is shown at the right of Fig. 13–25. The flow matrix corresponding to this assignment is given in

* The assignments discussed here are general with respect to four-row flow tables of the type so far discussed. The flow table of Fig. 13–24 represents the most demanding of this type. However, some of the assignments can not be used without modification if the flow table requires secondary action which is cyclic. This problem is discussed in the next article.

Fig. 13–26. Each column of the flow matrix contains one transition which requires the operate or release time of only a single relay, and one other transition which requires the response time of two relays, or other secondary elements. Arrows are placed in each column wherever two changes of secondary state are required, to show the sequence in which these changes take place. The student should complete the preparation of the corresponding excitation matrix. An examination of the flow matrix for this assignment shows that there is a relatively large number of possible matrix entries which are not used. This large number of optional entries, when carried over to the excitation matrix, indicates the possibility, although not the certainty, that a relatively simple control network can be designed.

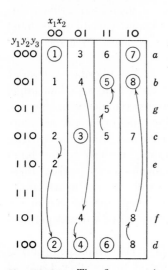

Fig. 13–26. The flow matrix using the secondary state assignment of Fig. 13–25. (Assignment 1.)

GENERAL ASSIGNMENT 2. This assignment is described by the cube representation of Fig. 13–27. Node b is placed adjacent to nodes a and c, while node c is made adjacent to b and d. The transition between nodes a and c takes place by way of node e, which has been added, and the transition between nodes b and d takes place by way of the added node f.

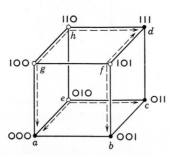

Fig. 13–27. General assignment 2.

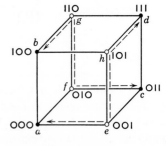

Fig. 13–28. General assignment 3.

Both of these transitions require two changes of secondary state. Finally, the transition between nodes a and d requires three changes of secondary state and takes place by way of the added nodes g and h. This is a general type of assignment which can have particular utility in situations that require wide variations in the time of secondary response, perhaps to control time delay in making output changes.

GENERAL ASSIGNMENT 3. The assignment shown in the cube representation of Fig. 13–28 is another of the type which contains widely different response times in the secondary system. One secondary response time is required for the transitions between nodes a and b or between nodes c and d. Two secondary response times are required for transitions between nodes a and c or between nodes b and d. Three response times are required for transitions between nodes a and d or between nodes b and c. One feature of this assignment is interesting because it involves a limitation on the generality of the assignment which will be discussed in the next article. We note that there are two possible routes for the transition between nodes a and d, and two possible routes for the transition between nodes b and c. We can choose simultaneous routes for these extreme transitions which do not conflict, as indicated by the dotted arrows in Fig. 13–28. However, when we try to add routes to be used for the transitions between nodes a and c, or between nodes b and d, we find it necessary to use some edges of the cube in common with paths which have already been established. This situation presents no difficulty when conflicting requirements occur in different columns, as in the flow table of Fig. 13–24.

GENERAL ASSIGNMENT 4. This assignment of secondary variables is described by the cube representation of Fig. 13–29. It is based on a choice of four vertices of the cube, each pair of which are located at the diagonally opposite corners of a face of the cube. None of the secondary states represented by these vertices are adjacent. If the four selected vertices are assigned as the secondary states applicable to the four rows of the flow table in Fig. 13–24, it is apparent that all transitions between rows require two changes of secondary state, and the assignment is completely symmetrical in this respect. This particular assignment is also interesting because it is the first assignment which has been proven to be general for *any* four-row flow table.*

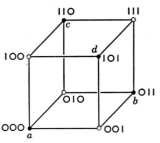

Fig. 13–29. General assignment 4.

* R. E. Wengert, "Minimizing Realization of Sequential Relay Circuits," Master's thesis, Department of Electrical Engineering, Massachusetts Institute of Technology, Cambridge, Massachusetts, June, 1953.

It can be observed either in the cube representation of Fig. 13–29 or in the flow matrix of Fig. 13–30(a) that all the transitions between

(a)

$y_1y_2y_3$ \ x_1x_2	00	01	11	10	
000	(1)	3	6	(7)	*a*
001					
011	1	4	(5)	(8)	*b*
010					
110	2	(3)	5	7	*c*
111					
101	(2)	(4)	(6)	8	*d*
100					

(b)

$y_1y_2y_3$ \ x_1x_2	00	01	11	10
000	000	110	101	000
001	000	101	101	011
011	000	101	011	011
010	000	110	011	000
110	101	110	011	000
111	101	101	011	011
101	101	101	101	011
100	101	110	101	000

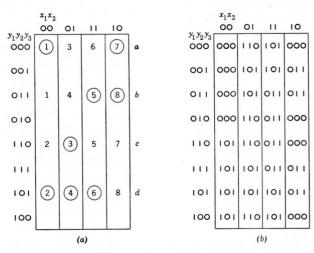

Fig. 13–30. Flow matrix and excitation matrix based on Assignment 4.

rows involve possible secondary races. It can also be verified that all these races are allowed because none is critical. An excitation matrix which contains all possible races is given in Fig. 13–30(b).

General Assignment 5. The secondary assignment shown in the cube representation of Fig. 13–31 is radically different from any previously described. We note that row *a* is assigned to vertex 000 and also to vertex 111. In a similar manner all rows of the original flow table are assigned to diagonally opposite pairs of vertices.

Fig. 13–31. General assignment 5.

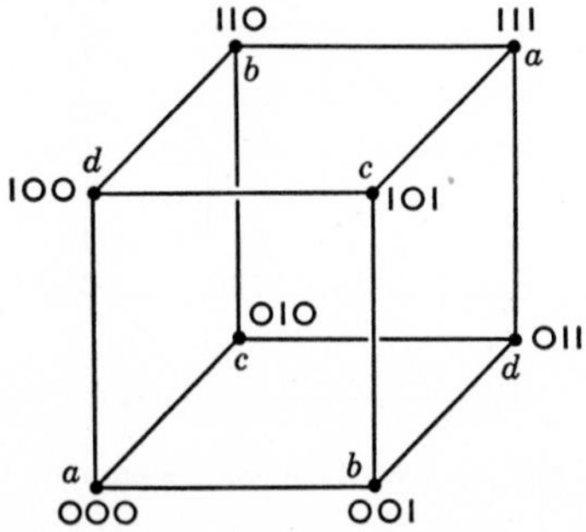

What does it mean when a single row in a flow table is represented by two different secondary states? This is simply a special case of the more general situation that we will encounter in which a single row of a flow table may be represented by any number of secondary states. Out of all the possible secondary states we may select any number of states to represent a given row and this selection constitutes a *set* of secondary states which we call a *row set*. In Fig. 13–31, from the eight available secondary states

we have selected four row sets, each set consisting of two secondary states, and each set representing one row.

Physically, it makes no difference which of the two secondary states of a row set is occupied at a given moment provided the output corresponding to the circled entry represented is that originally defined for that circled entry in the primitive flow table, and provided the same output is furnished for either secondary state in the row set.

In Fig. 13–32 we have specified the members of the row set applicable to each row. Then, in Fig. 13–33, the individual secondary states are listed in cyclic order and each circled entry is repeated (within a given

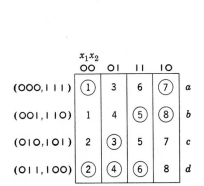

Fig. 13–33 flow matrix ($y_1 y_2 y_3$ rows, $x_1 x_2$ columns OO OI II IO):

$y_1 y_2 y_3$	OO	OI	II	IO
OOO	(1₁)	3₁	6₂	(7₁)
OOI	1₁	4₁	(5₁)	(8₁)
OII	(2₁)	(4₁)	(6₁)	8₁
OIO	2₁	(3₁)	5₂	7₁
IIO	1₂	4₂	(5₂)	(8₂)
III	(1₂)	3₂	6₁	(7₂)
IOI	2₂	(3₂)	5₁	7₂
IOO	(2₂)	(4₂)	(6₂)	8₂

Fig. 13–32 flow table ($x_1 x_2$ columns OO OI II IO):

row set	OO	OI	II	IO	
(000,111)	(1)	3	6	(7)	a
(001,110)	1	4	(5)	(8)	b
(010,101)	2	(3)	5	7	c
(011,100)	(2)	(4)	(6)	8	d

Fig. 13–32. The flow table with row sets assigned according to Assignment 5.

Fig. 13–33. Flow matrix derived from Assignment 5.

column) for each secondary state contained in the corresponding row set. Subscripts are used to distinguish between the circled entries that correspond to the same row set. Appropriate subscripts are also placed on the uncircled entries to direct each transition to the *adjacent* circled entry.

Returning to Fig. 13–31, we can see geometrically that starting from any vertex there is always *one member* of all other row sets at an adjacent vertex. Consequently, all transitions *between row sets* require just one time of operate or release. Although the individual rows in the final flow matrix are not necessarily adjacent, each pair of row sets is adjacent at two points.

The output matrix to be derived from the flow matrix of Fig. 13–33 presents no special difficulties. A circled entry of a given number appears not once but twice in each column. At the positions corresponding to each appearance, the output must be that specified for the corresponding circled entry, regardless of subscript, in the primitive flow table. After the outputs corresponding to the circled entries are entered, the usual decisions regarding the times at which output values change must be made for each uncircled entry.

GENERAL ASSIGNMENT 6. In Fig. 13–34(a) a cube diagram shows another way in which specific secondary states are selected to form

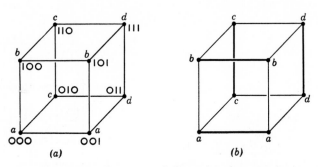

Fig. 13–34. Row sets of General assignment 6.

row sets that represent the four rows of the flow table. The nature of this assignment and its mode of operation may be visualized somewhat more clearly in Fig. 13–34(b). Heavy lines are used to connect the vertices of the cube which are members of the same row set, and light lines are used to show the adjacencies between row sets.

In contrast with the structure of Assignment 5, we see that in this assignment the members of each row set are adjacent. Starting from any secondary state a transition can be made to the other state which is in the same row set by the change of a single variable. This is a special case of the kind of row set we call a *connected row set*. As in Assignment 5, each row set again has some point of adjacency with each other row set.

Consider a transition from row b, state 100, to row d. The state of origin, 100, is not adjacent to either of the states which are contained in the d row set. However, in the excitation matrix we can direct a transition, with no change of output, to the other member of the b row set, namely, state 101; this state is adjacent to state 111, which is a member of the d row set. Since a transition has been made to the d row set the required output is now obtained and there is no need for a further change of secondary state. If we are going from row b to row a, no transition within the row set of origin is required, but for a transition from row b to either row c or row d it may be necessary to move first within the b row set, until the state is reached which is adjacent to a state in the destination row set. When we deal with connected row sets containing more than two members, the mode of operation almost always requires that a transition be made within the row set of origin before the final transition to the row set of destination.

The row sets assigned in Fig. 13–34 are applied to the original flow table in Fig. 13–35, and the detailed structure of the flow matrix is then given in Fig. 13–36. In the latter, arrows indicate where transi-

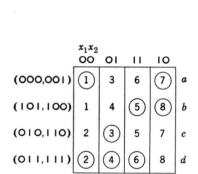

x_1x_2	OO	OI	II	IO	
(000,001)	①	3	6	⑦	a
(101,100)	1	4	⑤	⑧	b
(010,110)	2	③	5	7	c
(011,111)	②	④	⑥	8	d

Fig. 13–35. Row sets of Assignment 6 applied to the flow table of Fig. 13–24.

$y_1y_2y_3$ $\backslash$ x_1x_2	OO	OI	II	IO
OOO	①$_1$	3$_1$	6$_1$	⑦$_1$
OOI	①$_2$	3$_1$	6$_1$	⑦$_2$
OII	②$_1$	④$_1$	⑥$_1$	8$_1$
OIO	2$_1$	③$_1$	5$_2$	7$_1$
IIO	2$_2$	③$_2$	5$_2$	7$_1$
III	②$_2$	④$_2$	⑥$_2$	8$_1$
IOI	1$_2$	4$_2$	⑤$_1$	⑧$_1$
IOO	1$_1$	4$_2$	⑤$_2$	⑧$_2$

Fig. 13–36. Flow matrix derived from Assignment 6.

tions occur within row sets prior to the transition to the destination state. No arrows are shown for any of the transitions in the first column because these all involve transitions either from row set a to row set b, or from row set c to row set d. For these transitions no movement within the row set of origin is *required*, but this type of secondary action can be introduced at the option of the designer, so there is some choice in writing the excitation matrix.

There are other opportunities for modifying the excitation matrix. We note that the entry ③$_2$ in the second column is redundant, in the sense that it cannot be reached by any normal change of either primary or secondary variables. Hence the entries which are made in that

cell of the excitation matrix are entirely optional. Since the entry
$\widehat{3_2}$ cannot be reached, the uncircled entries 2_2 and 7_1 in the same
row cannot be reached and are also redundant. The uncircled
entry 5_2 in the same row cannot be treated optionally because it is
required as an intermediate state in the transition from row **010** to
row **100**.

All remaining circled entries in the flow matrix can be reached
by either secondary or primary action, or both. However, all circled
entries occur in pairs corresponding to adjacent secondary states.
Hence, in writing the excitation matrix one secondary variable can be
given an optional value in each pair. It should be noted, however,
that if we exercise this option with respect to the pair $\widehat{3_1}$ and $\widehat{3_2}$), it
may not be possible to make use of the fact that entry $\widehat{3_2}$ is redundant
in the sense previously described.

We observed that once a destination state within a row set is reached,
no further secondary action is needed in order to obtain the specified
circuit output. The effect of introducing optional entries, where one
secondary variable is common to a pair of circled entries, is to make
one member of each row set a true stable state and the other an unstable state. If this situation occurs, there may be additional secondary action after a destination state is reached and the output is
obtained, which may make the circuit unduly "busy," and the circuit
action somewhat slower for particular sequences. These factors must
be considered in relation to the possible reduction in circuit complexity before options of the type under discussion are exercised.

The preceding assignments illustrate, without being exhaustive, the
more general ways in which secondary states may be applied to the
four-row flow table in which all transitions between pairs of rows are
required. A few additional assignments based on the row-set idea are
given in Fig. 13–37. We note in some that a row set may consist of

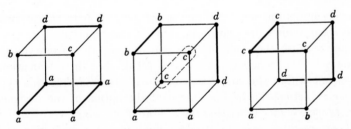

Fig. 13–37. Additional row-set assignments for four-row flow tables.

only a single member. We note also that row sets need not be connected, as is shown in the cube representation in the middle of Fig.

13–37 where row set c contains two non-adjacent secondary states. This situation, of course, was encountered in Assignment 5 where all row sets contain two non-adjacent members. It will be instructive for the student to analyze in further detail the properties of the secondary assignments based on the row sets shown in Fig. 13–37, and the consequences of using them in circuit realization.

13.4 Cyclic Secondary Action

Cyclic secondary action in a sequential circuit can be something which the designer does not intend to have, such as a parasitic oscillation in an amplifier. This discussion, however, relates to secondary cycles that are introduced intentionally. We may use a cycle, for example, as a means for introducing a time delay or, in another situation, we may use a secondary cycle to produce a set of output pulses. Our interest here is not so much in the specific application of secondary cycles as it is in the success or failure of particular secondary assignments to meet the transition requirements imposed by cycles.

In Fig. 13–38 two typical secondary cycles are described. This figure contains eight rows for which an assignment of three secondary

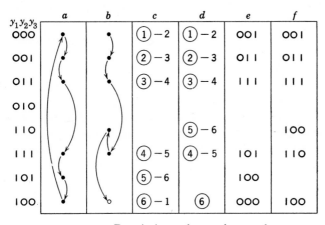

Fig. 13–38. Descriptions of secondary cycles.

variables is given. The first two columns show the cycles diagrammatically. Column a contains a diagram of a continuous cycle, where the various secondary states occupied are indicated by dots, and the transitions between states are indicated by lines carrying arrows. The cycle may begin at any of the secondary states represented by a dot and will continue indefinitely if the primary variables are not changed. In column b an interrupted cycle is illustrated. It may begin at any of the secondary states represented by solid dots, but the longest length of the cycle is found when it begins in the secondary state 000. The cycle terminates when the secondary state reaches 100, as marked by the open circle. A continuous cycle must always involve an even number of secondary states, but an interrupted cycle may involve either an even or odd number of secondary states.

Columns c and d contain descriptions of the cycles in columns a and b, respectively, as they might appear in a flow table or a flow matrix. All but one of the circled entries in these columns have a different meaning than the one we have previously used. Consider, for example, the entries in column c. Each entry consists of a circled number followed by an uncircled number. The entry ①–2 means that the circuit is in the secondary state ① but is to change immediately to secondary state ②. We then look for a ② as the destination of the transition from the first row. The entry ② is found in the second row, but we find it followed by the uncircled number 3, and this is an indication that the secondary state is to be changed immediately to that represented by the entry ③. Hence, each entry consisting of a circled number followed by an uncircled number indicates that the preceding transition directed the secondary state to that represented by the circled number, but that the state is to change immediately to the state represented by the uncircled number. If we trace these entries throughout column c, we find that the secondary system goes successively through states $1, 2, 3, 4, 5$, and 6, and then returns to state 1 where the cycle begins again. This is exactly the action which is shown diagrammatically in column a.

In column d the double entries consisting of a circled number and an uncircled number have exactly the same meaning as in column c. We note, however, that in the last row of column d there is an entry ⑥ which is not followed by an uncircled number. This entry has the usual meaning of a circled number, that is, it represents a stable state and the cycle does not continue beyond this point.

Columns e and f of Fig. 13–38 contain the entries which would be required in an excitation matrix for the cycles described in columns c and d, respectively. Consider some typical entries in column e. The first row of this column corresponds to the secondary state 000, and in column c the circuit is directed to the secondary state represented by entry ②. This circled entry is in the second row, for which the secondary state is 001. Hence, in the first row of column e we enter 001 to direct the transition to the second row. In the second row the transition is to be directed to the secondary state of the third row and we hence find the entry 011 in the second row of column *e.* The final entry at the bottom of column *e* is 000 which requires a secondary transition to the top row, where the cycle begins again. In column *f*, however, we find that the entry in the bottom row is 100, and since this is the same as the secondary state for that row it represents a stable entry and terminates the cycle.

Now consider the flow table shown in Fig. 13–39. This is the same flow table as that in Fig. 13–24 except that the description of a cycle has been entered in the column for $X_1X_2 = 10$, in place of the previous entries. We now note that if we disregard the cycle in the fourth column the remaining three columns of the flow table are sufficient to establish the transition diagram given in Fig. 13–24; that is, only three of the four columns of the flow table are

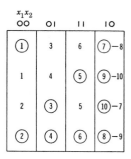

Fig. 13–39. Flow table containing a cycle.

needed to require all possible interrow transitions, and the fourth column cannot impose any new requirements. We might expect then that a secondary assignment which is truly general will be applicable in meeting the requirements of the flow table of Fig. 13–39.

Since the set of assignments studied in the preceding article have already been found to satisfy the first three columns of the flow table, we need investigate only their applicability to the fourth column which contains the cycle. Let us first use Assignment 3, shown in Fig. 13–28, for this purpose. In Fig. 13–40, the "rows" of an excitation matrix

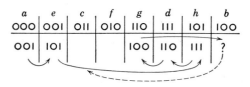

Fig. 13–40. Assignment 3 fails to satisfy a cyclic requirement.

are arranged horizontally and we examine the transitions required to pass through the nodes *a, d, b, c, a,* and so on, as required in Fig. 13–39. According to Assignment 3 we pass from node *a* to node *d* by way of nodes *e* and *h*. The excitation entries for these transitions are given in Fig. 13–40 and arrows show the steps required in going from node *a* to node *d*. Next, we go from node *d* to node *b* by way of node *g*. Again the excitation entries are shown together with arrows to indicate the route, but at node *b* a question mark is entered. Node *b* corresponds to the secondary state 100 and the next point in the cycle is node *c,* corresponding to the secondary state 011. The transition between nodes b and c requires a change of all three secondary variables. Since, however, there is only one other node left available, that is node f, it is evident that no excitation can be entered for the transition from b to c without involving a critical race. Thus, Assignment 3 fails to satisfy the requirement given in the fourth column of Fig. 13–39.

In Fig. 13–41 the same problem is treated using Assignment 4, as described in Fig. 13–29. It may readily be verified that there is no

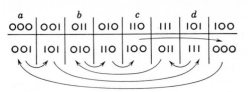

Fig. 13–41.   Cyclic requirement satisfied by Assignment 4.

difficulty in satisfying the requirements of the cycle when this assignment is used.

Figure 13–42 displays graphically the reasons for the failure of Assignment 3 and the success of Assignment 4. In each part of this

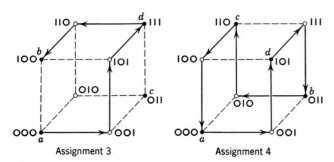

Fig. 13–42.   Cyclic secondary action represented geometrically.

figure the cycle starts at node a and each subsequent change of a secondary variable is indicated by a solid line with an arrow to the next node. All unused edges of the cubes are represented by dotted lines. In the cube representing Assignment 3 it becomes apparent that in order to make the transition from node b to node c it becomes necessary to give contradictory instructions to the secondary system somewhere. For example, it would be quite easy to direct the transition from node b back to node d, but upon arrival there we would find the system had already been directed to go to state 110, and in order to go to node c we would have to give the contradictory instruction to go to state 011. This difficulty is not encountered when Assignment 4 is used, and in fact the cube representation of the path taken during the cycle as given in Fig. 13–42 represents only one of two ways in which this cycle can be handled by Assignment 4. It can readily be verified that Assignment 4 will satisfy the requirements of any four-row cycle.

The limitation on the generality of an assignment because of cycles is not necessarily serious. Assignment 3 fails to handle a cycle represented by the sequence a, d, b, c, a, but it will readily handle the cycles represented by the sequences a, b, c, d, a, or a, b, d, c, a, or a, d, c, b, a. By permutation of the rows of a flow table it is readily possible to transform the a, d, b, c, a sequence into a form which the assignment will satisfy. This permutation does not change in the least the applicability of the assignment to the other three rows of the flow table which contain no cycles.

13.5 Row-Set Assignments for Large Flow Tables

When the number of rows in a flow table becomes large it may be quite difficult to assign secondary states by means of a transition diagram or a map. Nevertheless, the attempt should be made to satisfy the requirements of a flow table by a direct assignment procedure using S_0 secondary variables, and using additional secondary variables only if necessary. Practical problems, of the type that are described by word statements, seem to lead to flow tables that do not require all possible transitions between rows. It is reasonable, therefore, to work first with simple ideas and methods in making secondary assignments. If these methods fail we can then resort to a general type of assignment as described in this article. These assignments apply to arbitrary types of flow tables in which all possible transitions between rows are required. They will certainly satisfy the requirements of practical problems, but they do not necessarily use minimum numbers of secondary variables.

The general assignments to be discussed here will extend the row-set concept to include an indefinitely large number of secondary variables.[*] First, however, it will be desirable to review and extend some of the basic ideas involved, and to define certain terms we will use.

For a given number of secondary variables, S, there are 2^S *states* which we can describe by either algebraic or binary designators. Any two of these states are *adjacent* if their designators differ in the value

---

[*] D. A. Huffman, "A Study of the Memory Requirements of Sequential Switching Circuits," *Technical Report No. 293*, Research Laboratory of Electronics, Massachusetts Institute of Technology, April, 1955.

of only one of the variables. Thus, the state represented by $wxyz$ is adjacent to that represented by $wx'yz$, or using binary designators, state 1111 is adjacent to state 1011.

From the 2^s available secondary states we may select a group containing any number of states, up to 2^s, and call this group a *set*.* Although this selection may be quite arbitrary we are, of course, most interested in those sets which because of their special properties can be used systematically in satisfying secondary assignment requirements.

In Art. 13.3 we found in our study of Assignments 5 and 6 that instead of assigning individual secondary states to each row of a flow table, we could assign a set of secondary states to each row, and we called these row sets. For Assignment 6 each row set contained two adjacent states, and we called each of these a connected row set. We must now broaden the concept of a connected row set.

A *connected set* is one in which *any* two members are contained in a connected sequence. The set represented by the nodes of Fig. 13–43 is a connected set. Each line joining two nodes indicates that they are adjacent, and a sequence of such lines joins every pair of nodes. (A set containing only one member is a connected set.) The same set of states is arranged somewhat differently in Fig. 13–44 by removing the connec-

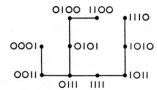

Fig. 13–43. A connected set of states.

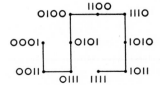

Fig. 13–44. A connected sequence of states.

tion between the adjacent states 0111 and 1111, and by adding the connection between the adjacent states 1100 and 1110. This is still a connected set, but it now has the property that, beginning at state 0001 (or 1111) and following a path along the lines joining nodes, all consecutive pairs of states are adjacent. Any sequence of states which has this property is called a *connected sequence*. It may readily be verified that in a connected set it is always possible to form a connected sequence, using only members of the set, to join any member to any

* Mathematically, the number of states in a set may range from none (the empty set) to all the states (the master set, or space). For secondary assignments we have at least as many sets as there are rows in the flow table and each row set contains at least one state.

other member. Thus, in Fig. 13–43, we may join the states 0101 and 1010 by the connected sequence 0101, 0111, 1111, 1011, and 1010.

The *length* of a connected sequence is equal to the number of changes of variable required to traverse the entire sequence. The *distance* between two states in a connected set is equal to the length of the shortest connected sequence which joins the two states (using only states within the set). If in finding the distance between states 0001 and 1111 we make use of the connected sequence shown in Fig. 13–44, we find that the distance is apparently 9. However, if we make use of all the adjacencies in the set, as shown in Fig. 13–45, it can be seen that there are three different connected sequences, each of length 3, which join these two states.

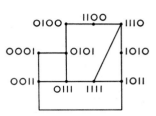

Fig. 13–45. The connected set contains a number of sequences.

It is convenient to extend the concept of adjacency to include adjacent sets. In Fig. 13–46 the solid lines between nodes indicate that A, B, and C are connected sets. By dotted lines, however, we indicate

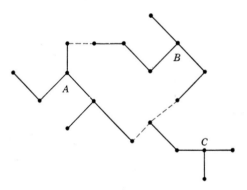

Fig. 13–46. Adjacent connected sets.

that each pair of these sets contains members which are adjacent, so that at the points indicated by these dotted lines it is possible to pass from one set to the other by a single change of variable. The sets A, B, and C are adjacent connected sets.

We have defined a row set as a set of secondary states which is assigned to a particular row in a flow table. In simple problems the row sets may contain only single members and the rows of a flow table may then become identified with individual secondary states. If, however, a set of secondary states containing more than one member is assigned to represent a row, it becomes necessary to associate the flow table row with some aspect of the circuit which includes all the secondary states in the row set. For this purpose we regard the row as representing an *internal state* of the circuit.

The circuit can assume as many internal states as there are rows in its flow table. To any particular internal state, say the ith state, we can assign the ith row set, R_i. We may find it useful or otherwise desirable to assign row sets which are connected sets, but it is not necessary to do so. In Assignment 6 of Art. 13.3 the row sets were connected sets, but in Assignment 5 we used row sets which were not connected. If a row set is not connected, then it may be visualized as being partitioned into two or more sub-sets which are connected sets but no two of which are adjacent. We call these *row sub-sets*. (We must remember here that a single secondary state can constitute a row sub-set.) In Fig. 13–47(a) the row set A consists of the sub-sets A_1 and A_2,

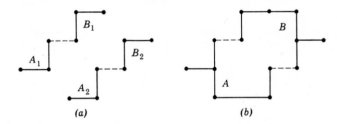

Fig. 13–47. Meshed sets need not be connected sets.

each of which is connected, and the row set B consists of the connected sub-sets B_1 and B_2. A_1 is not adjacent to A_2, and B_1 is not adjacent to B_2.

Whether the row sets assigned to a flow table are connected sets or not, in order to satisfy the requirements of an arbitrary flow table they must be *meshed row sets*. If two row sets R_i and R_j are not connected sets, in order to be meshed row sets each sub-set of R_i must be adjacent to at least one sub-set of R_j, and vice versa. Thus, in Fig. 13–47 the row sets A and B are meshed in both configurations. In part (a), the sub-sets A_1 and B_1 are adjacent, as shown by the dotted connection, and the sub-sets A_2 and B_2 are likewise adjacent. In part (b) of Fig. 13–47 the row sets A and B are both connected sets and are also adjacent sets as indicated by the dotted lines. A group of row sets is said to be *intermeshed* when each pair of the row sets is meshed.

If meshed row sets are used to represent internal states, and if no races are permitted in the excitation matrix, the number of changes of secondary state required to bring about a change of internal state will never exceed the number of members in the largest sub-set of a row set. If the number of members in the largest sub-set is M, the longest connected sequence will have a length $M - 1$. Then, one more secondary change will be required to change the internal state, so the largest number of changes required is $M - 1 + 1 = M$. Hence the largest row sub-set places an upper limit on the number of secondary changes which may be needed to bring about a change of internal state.

A somewhat better appreciation of the row-set concept may perhaps be derived by considering the transition diagram of Fig. 13–48(a),

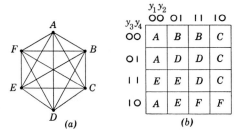

Fig. 13–48. The transition diagram of a six-row flow table and a map of intermeshed row sets which satisfy the transition requirements.

and the secondary assignments in terms of row sets represented by the map of Fig. 13–48(b). The transition diagram represents the requirements of an arbitrary six-row flow table in which it must be possible to direct a transition from each row to any other row. It may readily be verified that the six row sets represented by the map are connected sets, and further examination shows that they are intermeshed row sets. In Fig. 13–49 the row sets assigned in Fig. 13–48(b) are arranged to show how the requirements of the transition diagram of Fig. 13–48(a) are satisfied. Each row set is shown as a set of nodes joined by solid lines to indicate that each row set is a connected set. Broken lines then show the adjacencies between row sets which satisfy the requirements expressed in the original transition diagram. This is not the only intermeshed row-set assignment that can be made for a six-row flow table, but the fact that at least one assignment in four variables exists indicates that no more than four secondary variables need ever be used for a six-row flow table.

In many practical problems it is useful to take advantage of the ideas developed for meeting the secondary requirements of arbitrary flow tables. In Fig. 13–50, for example, a map containing an assignment of eight row sets is shown. These are all connected sets but they do not represent an intermeshed collection. The transition diagram of

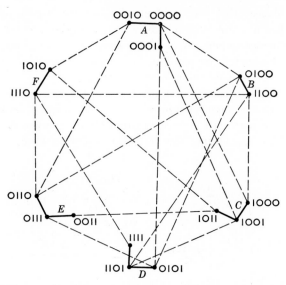

Fig. 13–49. A transition diagram showing connections between intermeshed row sets.

Fig. 13–50(b) shows the transitions which are possible using this assignment. It will be observed that many connections that would be required by an arbitrary flow table are missing, but many practical

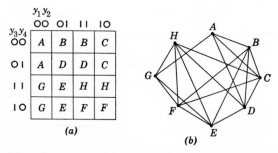

(a)

(b)

Fig. 13–50. Map of a row-set assignment and the transition diagram it satisfies.

problems do not require that all connections be established. We can therefore expect that incomplete meshing of row sets will be a valuable technique.

Huffman* has shown a systematic development of a number of secondary assignment procedures, all based on the row-set concept, which can be enlarged to meet the requirements of a flow table of any size.

* Op. cit.

One of these, which we shall now examine, uses the smallest number of secondary variables which will satisfy the requirements of an arbitrary flow-table.

It is assumed that the rows of the flow table are identified by decimal numbers beginning with zero. A full flow table will have exactly 2^{S_0} rows. A three-quarter flow table, for a given value of S_0, has exactly $0.75\ (2^{S_0})$ rows. A full flow table can always be satisfied by the use of $2S_0 - 1$ secondary variables and a three-quarter flow table can always be satisfied by $2S_0 - 2$ secondary variables.

At the left of Fig. 13–51 an assignment of three secondary variables to four rows of a flow table is given. This may be recognized as Assignment 6 in Art. 13.3. This figure is a map in which some of the cell

	y_1 0	y_1 1
y_2y_3 00	0	1
01	0	1
11	2	2
10	3	3

$S_0 = 2$

	y_1y_2 00	01	11	10
$y_3y_4y_5$ 000	0	1	2	2
001	0	1	3	3
011	0	0	2	3
010	1	1	2	3
110	4	5	4	4
111	4	5	5	5
101	6	6	6	7
100	7	7	6	7

$S_0 = 3$

Fig. 13–51. Intermeshed row-set assignments for four-row and eight-row flow tables.

boundaries have been omitted in order to emphasize the pattern formed by the entries. The row sets are connected and intermeshed. At the right of Fig. 13–51 the assignment has been enlarged so that five secondary variables meet all requirements of an eight-row flow table. The row sets in this assignment contain twice as many members, but again they are connected and intermeshed. It will become evident after study that the pattern of alternating vertical and horizontal groups of row designators established in the assignment for the four-row table is also used in making the assignment for the eight-row flow table.

When we enlarge the assignment to satisfy a sixteen-row flow table, as in Fig. 13–52, it again becomes necessary to double the number of members in each row set. Each horizontal and each vertical group of entries contains four row designators instead of two, but the pattern of alternating vertical and horizontal groups is maintained. If we wish to extend this assignment to a flow table of thirty-two rows we again

$y_4y_5y_6y_7$ \ $y_1y_2y_3$	000	001	011	010	110	111	101	100
0000	0	1	2	3	4	4	4	4
0001	0	1	2	3	5	5	5	5
0011	0	1	2	3	6	6	6	6
0010	0	1	2	3	7	7	7	7
0110	0	0	0	0	4	5	6	7
0111	1	1	1	1	4	5	6	7
0101	2	2	2	2	4	5	6	7
0100	3	3	3	3	4	5	6	7
1100	8	9	10	11	8	8	8	8
1101	8	9	10	11	9	9	9	9
1111	8	9	10	11	10	10	10	10
1110	8	9	10	11	11	11	11	11
1010	12	12	12	12	12	13	14	15
1011	13	13	13	13	12	13	14	15
1001	14	14	14	14	12	13	14	15
1000	15	15	15	15	12	13	14	15

Fig. 13–52. Intermeshed row-set assignment for a 16-row flow table.

double the number of members in each row set and double the number of entries in each vertical and horizontal group.

When a flow table contains only 0.75 (2^{S_0}) rows a modified type of secondary assignment becomes more economical; it is illustrated in Fig. 13–53. At the left is shown an assignment for a six-row flow table, for which $S_0 = 3$. The left half of this map is identical to the map for $S_0 = 2$ in Fig. 13–51. We then have available the entire right half of the map to intermesh two additional row sets. At the right of Fig. 13–53 the map is enlarged to show the secondary assignments for a flow table of twelve rows ($S_0 = 4$). The left half of this map is identical to the map for $S_0 = 3$ in Fig. 13–51, and the right

y_3y_4 \ y_1y_2	00	01	11	10
00	0	1	4	4
01	0	1	5	5
11	2	2	4	5
10	3	3	4	5

$S_0 = 3$

$y_4y_5y_6$ \ $y_1y_2y_3$	000	001	011	010	110	111	101	100
000	0	1	2	2	8	9	8	8
001	0	1	3	3	8	9	9	9
011	0	0	2	3	10	10	10	11
010	1	1	2	3	11	11	10	11
110	4	5	4	4	8	9	10	10
111	4	5	5	5	8	9	11	11
101	6	6	6	7	8	8	10	11
100	7	7	6	7	9	9	10	11

$S_0 = 4$

Fig. 13–53. Intermeshed row-set assignments for "three-quarter" flow tables.

half of the map then becomes available to intermesh four more row sets. The enlargement procedure again depends upon the alternating of vertical and horizontal groups of entries and is a process which is best understood by studying the maps given.

A tabulation of the maximum number of rows that a given number of secondary variables can satisfy is shown in Table 13–1. It must be kept in mind that a given flow table may not require the number of secondary variables listed in Table 13–1, but if a flow table seems to require more than the tabulated number it is certain that a more economical assignment can be achieved.

A possible disadvantage of these intermeshed row set assignments is the time required, in terms of the number of secondary variables which must change, in making some transitions. For example, suppose in Fig. 13–52 that we have just entered row set 11 from row set 3. The secondary state is then represented by 0101100. If we now want to go to row set 7 we must move through all the states in row set 11 until we reach the secondary state 1001110, before we find a point of ad-

Table 13–1

Number of Secondary Variables	Number of Rows in Flow Table
1	2
2	3
3	4
4	6
5	8
6	12
7	16
8	24
9	32
$2S_0 - 2$	$0.75\ (2^{S_0})$
$2S_0 - 1$	2^{S_0}

jacency with row set 7. It will require eight changes of secondary variables to make the transition.

In Assignment 5 of Art. 13.3 all transitions were made by the change of a single secondary variable. Unfortunately, when we attempt to extend this type of assignment to larger flow tables the number of secondary variables required increases very rapidly.

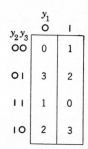

Fig. 13–54. Assignment map corresponding to Assignment 5 ($S_0 = 2$).

In Fig. 13–54 the row sets for Assignment 5 are mapped. Each row set contains two sub-sets and each sub-set contains a single member. For an eight-row flow table the corresponding assignment map is given in Fig. 13–55. Again, the row sets of the assignment are not connected. Each entry in the map represents one of the sixteen sub-sets contained in each row set.

There is an interesting relation between this assignment and the Hamming code which was discussed in Art. 10.5, although there is no error detection or correction feature associated with the secondary assignment. The decimal numbers entered in the map of Fig. 13–55 correspond to the position numbers found by applying the 4–5–6–7, 2–3–6–7, and 1–3–5–7 parity checks on the digits of the secondary-state designators. Thus, for the secondary state $y_1 y_2 y_3 y_4 y_5 y_6 y_7 = 1110100$, these parity checks give the position number 101, or decimal 5, which is the entry in the map corresponding to that secondary state.

It may be verified that each entry in the map is adjacent to one sub-set of each of the other row sets, so every transition can be accomplished by the change of a single secondary variable. In terms of the number of secondary variables, and hence devices, which would be required in a physical circuit, the price paid for the high speed of

$y_4 y_5 y_6 y_7$ \ $y_1 y_2 y_3$	000	001	011	010	110	111	101	100
0000	0	3	1	2	3	0	2	1
0001	7	4	6	5	4	7	5	6
0011	1	2	0	3	2	1	3	0
0010	6	5	7	4	5	6	4	7
0110	3	0	2	1	0	3	1	2
0111	4	7	5	6	7	4	6	5
0101	2	1	3	0	1	2	0	3
0100	5	6	4	7	6	5	7	4
1100	1	2	0	3	2	1	3	0
1101	6	5	7	4	5	6	4	7
1111	0	3	1	2	3	0	2	1
1110	7	4	6	5	4	7	5	6
1010	2	1	3	0	1	2	0	3
1011	5	6	4	7	6	5	7	4
1001	3	0	2	1	0	3	1	2
1000	4	7	5	6	7	4	6	5

Fig. 13–55. A secondary assignment for minimum transition time. $S_0 = 3$.

transition is large. The number of secondary variables required by this type of assignment is $2^{S_0} - 1$. As S_0 increases, the number of secondary variables required thus approaches one secondary variable for each row in the flow table.

13.6 Feedback and Delay

We have been visualizing sequential circuits as constructed in accordance with the schematic diagram of Fig. 12–20. Primary relays are under the direct control of the inputs, secondary relays are controlled by the excitation network, and another network supplies the outputs of the circuit. There is no real need to modify these ideas if we deal only with circuits built on relay contacts, but for a better understanding of sequential circuits built on electronic and solid-state devices it becomes desirable to regard sequential circuits in the manner suggested by the schematic of Fig. 13–56. There is no change in the terminal action of the circuit. The only change is in the concept of how the circuit does its work.

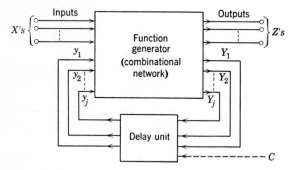

Fig. 13–56. Schematic representation of secondary action in terms of feedback and delay.

In this concept the circuit contains two major features. First, there is a combinational network—the function generator—which has as its inputs the X's and the y's of the circuit. The X's collectively represent the primary state and the y's represent the *present* secondary state. Together, these variables describe the total state of the circuit. The outputs of the function generator are the Z's and Y's. We have been calling the Y's the excitation functions of the secondary relays. We know, however, that the y's must eventually become the same as the Y's, so when they differ we can regard the Y's as being a description of the *next* secondary state.

The second major feature of the diagram in Fig. 13–56 is the box marked "delay unit," for which the inputs are the Y's and the outputs are the y's. Whenever the system is stable the outputs of the delay unit are equal to the inputs. If a change of primary state requires a change in the secondary state, the combinational circuit delivers values of the Y's which describe the next secondary state. After a time delay, the y's change to correspond to the Y's. If the resultant total state is stable, there will be no further change in the Y's. If the total state is unstable, the Y's again change and the action repeats until stability is reached.

In the relay circuits we have been studying, the required time delay is contained in the components and is merely the operate or release times of the relays. The amount of time delay will vary, depending on which particular components are required to respond. A circuit of this type is free-running or *asynchronous,* and its speed of operation is entirely determined within the circuit. On the other hand, we can introduce another input to the delay unit in Fig. 13–56, as indicated by the dotted input marked C. This we may call a *clock* input. Its function is to control the time at which the output of the delay unit can change. Thus in Fig. 13–57 a change of Y is followed by a change

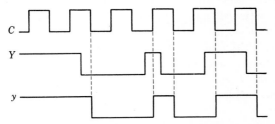

Fig. 13–57.   Time delays in a synchronous circuit.

of y at a time determined by the next change of C. Effectively, the time delay is an escapement device, and a circuit operating in this mode is called *synchronous.*

We shall make extensive use of the feedback-delay concept throughout the next two chapters. We now complete our discussion of relay sequential circuits by examining some of the "universal" circuits which might be designed on the basis of the feedback-delay concept.

In the synthesis of a sequential circuit we first write a primitive flow table and reduce it to a minimum form by the elimination of equivalences and by row merger. Our next problem is to assign a set of secondary variables so that no transition involves a critical race. If we can assume the availability of a delay unit, as indicated in Fig. 13–56, we can perhaps ignore the problem of critical races in designing the combinational part of the circuit, and simply assign secondary states based on S_0 variables. Then the question is, can we design the delay device with the property that it can accept any change of the input Y's and, after a time delay, change the output y's to correspond to the inputs. Note that this requires that the y's change from one state to the next state without momentarily being in an intermediate state.

It will be instructive to design a function generator and a delay unit, in accordance with the schematic circuit of Fig. 13–56, to realize the flow table of Fig. 13–24, which we have been using as a running example. To design the combinational, or function-generator, part of the feedback circuit we first assign a binary-number code to represent the rows of the flow table, as shown in Fig. 13–58. These numbers represent internal states, but they are not secondary-variable assignments, so we designate them as Q_1Q_2. At the inputs of the combinational circuit in Fig. 13–56, Q_1 and Q_2 replace the y's. In effect, Q_1Q_2 describe the present internal state of the circuit by identifying which row of the flow table is being occupied. The input state X_1X_2 and the present internal state Q_1Q_2 together determine what the next internal state will be, that is, the row of the flow table which will be occupied next. Since this is strictly a combinational description, the binary code assigned to identify the rows of the flow table can always be written with no more than S_0 digits.

The output of the combinational circuit (exclusive of the Z's) must describe the next row to be occupied, that is, the destination row. We call this output P_1P_2, replacing the Y's of Fig. 13–56. In Fig. 13–59 P_1 and P_2 are mapped as functions of X_1, X_2, Q_1, and Q_2. The entries

Q_1Q_2 \ x_1x_2	00	01	11	10
00	(1)	3	6	(7)
01	1	4	(5)	(8)
11	2	(3)	5	7
10	(2)	(4)	(6)	8

Fig. 13–58. Flow table with rows described by an arbitrary code.

Q_1Q_2 \ x_1x_2	00	01	11	10
00	00	11	10	00
01	00	10	01	01
11	10	11	01	00
10	10	10	10	01

Fig. 13–59. Map (combinational) for P_1P_2.

P_1P_2 00	01	11	10	Q_1Q_2
(1)	2	3	4	00
1	(2)	3	4	01
1	2	(3)	4	11
1	2	3	(4)	10

Fig. 13–60. A flow table for the delay unit.

which correspond in location to the circled entries of the flow table are the same as the Q_1Q_2 of the rows occupied. This means that wherever an entry in the flow table is stable, the destination row, P_1P_2, is the same as the occupied row, Q_1Q_2. In a map location which corresponds to an uncircled entry in the flow table we must enter the Q_1Q_2 of the row which contains the corresponding circled entry. Thus, in the first row and second column, the flow table (Fig. 13–58) contains the entry

3, and we enter a 11 in the P_1P_2 map (Fig. 13–59) to signify that the next internal state is represented by the 11 row which contains the entry ③. When this map is completed as in Fig. 13–59, we can immediately write P_1 and P_2 as algebraic functions of X_1, X_2, Q_1, and Q_2.

We now have a combinational circuit which, when given a description of the input state and the occupied row, provides a description of the destination row. To complete the feedback we must now design a delay unit which, when given at its inputs the description of the destination row, provides at its outputs the same information after a delay in time. At the input of the delay unit we must permit any change of input variables, and the output must, after a time delay, make the same change without going through any intermediate states.

If we try to treat these requirements as a simple sequential problem we might write the flow table of Fig. 13–60. However, this flow table merges to a single row from which we immediately write $Q_1 = P_1$, and $Q_2 = P_2$. These relations lead to the circuit of Fig. 13–61, in which

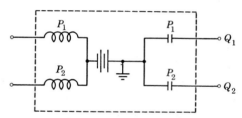

Fig. 13–61.   Delay box based on flow table of Fig. 13–60.

the required delay is represented by the response times of the relays P_1 and P_2. This would be entirely satisfactory if the P's always change one variable at a time. If both P_1 and P_2 change simultaneously, however, there is a race between the two relays, and unless their response times are identical the resulting sequence of Q_1Q_2 values presents false information to the inputs of the function generator.

We can regard the delay circuit as one in which we obtain time delay by requiring the action of some secondary devices in a manner such that any *change of output* occurs because of the change of *a single secondary variable*. To do this we can establish a collection of intermeshed row sets and associate all members of a given row set with a single output state. Then, in response to a change of input, we can move within a row set, without changing the output, until we reach a point of adjacency with the destination row set, where the change of output is made by changing one secondary variable.

Let us try this by using the intermeshed row sets represented by the assignment for $S_0 = 2$ in Fig. 13–51. In writing the flow matrix of Fig. 13–62 we assign the P_1P_2 values to the columns of the matrix, and within each column we designate certain rows which are members of a row set by circling the entries. The outputs associated with the circled entries of a column are identical, and are all equal to the P_1P_2 for that column. Thus, in the 00 column we have the entries ① and ② in rows which are members of the connected set (000, 001). The outputs given for both rows are $Q_1Q_2 = 00 = P_1P_2$.

If we now design the output matrix to obtain maximum delay, the output associated with each row will be constant and equal to the output for the circled entry of that row. Hence, the output is independent of the P_1P_2 values and we can immediately write, from Fig. 13–62,

$$Q_1 = y_2y_3' + y_1y_2' \ (+y_1y_3')$$

$$Q_2 = y_2$$

The expression for Q_1 contains a term in parentheses which is needed only to avoid a static hazard. Time delay is clearly present since Q_1Q_2 are independent of P_1P_2 and require secondary action to be changed.

We can also write an excitation matrix in the usual manner, being careful to make the multiple transitions as indicated by the arrows in Fig. 13–62 so that no false outputs will be produced. The excitation matrix in combination with the expressions for Q_1Q_2 give us the data

$y_1y_2y_3$ \ P_1P_2	00	01	11	10	Q_1Q_2
000	①	3	5	8	00
001	②	3	5	7	00
011	2	③	5	7	01
010	1	3	⑤	8	11
110	1	4	⑥	8	11
111	2	④	6	7	01
101	2	4	6	⑦	10
100	1	4	6	⑧	10

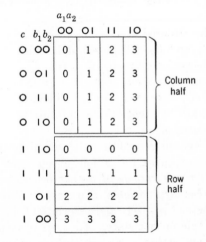

Fig. 13–62. Outputs Q_1Q_2 are constant within each row set.

c b_1b_2 \ a_1a_2	00	01	11	10	
0 00	0	1	2	3	Column half
0 01	0	1	2	3	
0 11	0	1	2	3	
0 10	0	1	2	3	
1 10	0	0	0	0	Row half
1 11	1	1	1	1	
1 01	2	2	2	2	
1 00	3	3	3	3	

Fig. 13–63. Secondary assignment for a four-row flow table, using $2S_0 + 1$ secondary variables.

needed for the design of a "universal" delay box with which we can realize any four-row flow table, in accordance with the feedback-delay concept, by merely designing the associated function generator.

Another type of "universal" design starts with the intermeshed row-set assignment given in Fig. 13–63.* For a four-row flow table the assignment requires five secondary variables or, in general, $2S_0 + 1$ variables. Each row set is connected, but contains a "column half" and a "row half." The upper half of the chart in Fig. 13–63 contains all the column-half parts, and the lower half of the chart contains all the row-half parts. While it is possible to make some changes of internal state without shifting between the upper and lower parts of the chart, the type of transition illustrated in Fig. 13–64 will be used exclusively. In Fig. 13–64(a) a transition starts in a column half and the b variables change, by racing, to the point adjacent to the row half of the destination state, after which a change of the c variable completes the transition. In Fig. 13–64(b) the a variables are allowed to race to a point adjacent to the column half of the destination state, after which a change of the c variable completes the transition. No race within either a column half or a row half is critical. The final part of the transition always requires the change of one variable, which is always the same variable. Since each race involves essentially only one response time (that of the slowest element), the complete transition requires essentially two response times.

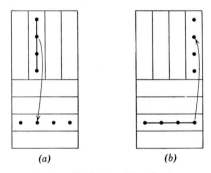

Fig. 13–64. Each transition begins as a non-critical race and ends by the change of a single variable.

The secondary devices are used in the circuit illustrated schematically in Fig. 13–65. The inputs $P_1 P_2$ go to the upper and lower parts of the circuit. Switches T_a and T_b are under the control of the secondary variable c, and the solid lines within the switches correspond to the connections made when $c = 1$. For this condition, P_1 and P_2 are connected to B_1 and B_2, respectively, and we assume that sufficient time is allowed for these secondary devices to respond. We note that the outputs $Q_1 Q_2$ are not derived from $b_1 b_2$, because the switch T_0 is in the position corresponding to $c = 1$.

The outputs $a_1 a_2$ of the secondaries $A_1 A_2$ supply the circuit out-

* Huffman, op. cit.

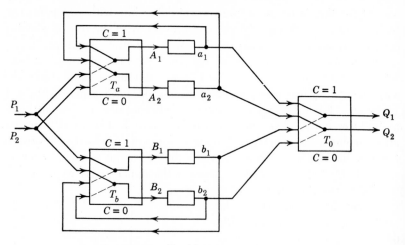

Fig. 13–65.   Double-memory delay unit.

puts $Q_1 Q_2$ through the switch T_0. Also, the $a_1 a_2$ signals feed back through switch T_a to maintain the excitations $A_1 A_2$. These secondary devices are clearly stable because their excitations correspond to their states of operation. We assume for the moment that they are storing, or remembering, the values corresponding to the previous values of $P_1 P_2$, which are in turn the present values of $Q_1 Q_2$.

While $c = 1$, suppose we allow $P_1 P_2$ to change to the next destination state. The secondary devices B_1 and B_2 can race to match the values of P_1 and P_2, respectively, without producing false outputs, because they are disconnected from Q_1 and Q_2. If, after $b_1 b_2$ become equal to $P_1 P_2$, the secondary variable c changes to $c = 0$, all the T switches will change their positions simultaneously. The outputs $Q_1 Q_2$ will be derived from $b_1 b_2$, and the feedback to $B_1 B_2$ will maintain these as stable values. At the same time, the inputs $P_1 P_2$ become connected to $A_1 A_2$, and any subsequent change of input will be stored by the upper secondary devices. In this system, the A secondaries and the B secondaries represent two separate storage systems. One of them is always remembering the last state of the inputs and supplying that state at the output. The other half of the storage is always prepared to accept the next state of the input and to be ready to supply that state to the output when the secondary variable c changes.

It should be clear that the variable c need not be derived from a secondary device within the network, but can be an external clock variable. In this mode of operation we have a *synchronous* circuit, in which the time delay is determined by the clock variable.

It is possible, however, to operate the circuit in the asynchronous mode, in which the time delay is determined by the response times of the secondary devices. One method for doing so proceeds in this manner. We first define a function

$$D_1 = P_1 Q_1' + P_1' Q_1 + P_2 Q_2' + P_2' Q_2$$

This function has the value 1 when

$$P_1 \neq Q_1, \text{ or } P_2 \neq Q_2$$

We next define a function

$$D_2 = (a_1 P_1 + a_1' P_1')(a_2 P_2 + a_2' P_2')c'$$
$$+ (b_1 P_1 + b_1' P_1')(b_2 P_2 + b_2' P_2')c$$

This function has the value 1 when, with $c = 0$, the $P_1 P_2$ are the same as the $a_1 a_2$, or when, with $c = 1$, the $P_1 P_2$ are the same as the $b_1 b_2$.

When $D_1 = 1$ we know that a new destination state $P_1 P_2$ is demanded. When $D_2 = 1$ we know that the half of the memory connected to the $P_1 P_2$ input has responded and is ready to deliver the new stored state to the $Q_1 Q_2$ outputs.

If we now define $D_3 = D_1 D_2$, we can specify that the variable c must *change* its value when $D_3 = 1$. Soon after this change occurs, D_3 again becomes 0 because D_1 and D_2 become 0, so the secondary device C must again become stable. This is a sequential problem for which

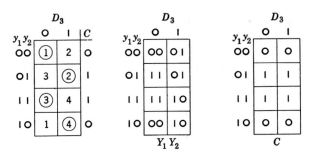

Fig. 13–66. Control of the C relay.

the flow matrix, excitation matrix, and output matrix are developed in Fig. 13–66. From these matrices we can write

$$Y_1 = D_3' y_2 + D_3 y_1 = (D_3 + y_2)(D_3' + y_1)$$

$$Y_2 = D_3' y_2 + D_3 y_1' = (D_3 + y_2)(D_3' + y_1')$$

$$C = y_2$$

These excitation functions can be realized by the circuit shown in Fig. 12–2. It is also apparent from the output function C that the Y_2 relay can serve to provide the variable c directly, without adding a C relay. In the circuit of Fig. 12–2 the variable a must be replaced by D_3. The student may identify which relay in Fig. 12–2 corresponds to relay Y_1 and which to Y_2.

PROBLEMS

13.1 Demonstrate (by deriving a secondary excitation matrix) what minimum number of secondary devices is required in a circuit that has the terminal action described in the flow table shown. Write a concise and accurate word description of the terminal action.

$x_1 x_2$				
OO	OI	II	IO	Z
(1)	5		7	O
(2)	6		7	O
(3)	6		7	I
2	(4)	10		O
3	(5)	10		O
3	(6)	10		I
1		11	(7)	O
1		12	(8)	O
1		12	(9)	I
	4	(10)	8	O
	4	(11)	9	O
	4	(12)	9	I

Problem 13.1.

$x_1 x_2$				
OO	OI	II	IO	Z
(1)	4	5	11	O
12	(2)	5	6	O
7	4	10	(3)	I
1	(4)	5	11	O
9	2	(5)	3	O
7	2	5	(6)	I
(7)	4	10	11	O
12	(8)	5	11	O
(9)	8	5	3	I
1	8	(10)	3	O
7	8	5	(11)	I
(12)	4	10	6	O

Problem 13.2.

13.2 The flow table shown contains a specification of the terminal requirements for a switching circuit. Determine the smallest number of secondary devices which the circuit requires for synthesis, and carry out the following steps to demonstrate this:

    1. Reduce the number of circled entries in the primitive flow table as far as possible (by recognition of equivalence).

2. Minimize the number of rows in the flow table by merging.
3. Assign secondary states to the result of part 2.
4. Write an excitation matrix.

13.3 (a) Determine secondary assignments which meet the requirements of each of the merged flow tables given.

(b) Write the Y-matrix corresponding to each of these assignments.

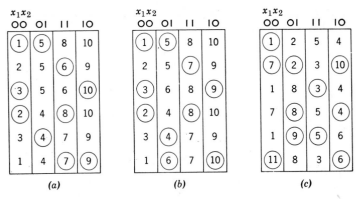

(a) (b) (c)

Problem 13.3.

13.4 For each of the merged flow tables given make a proper assignment of secondary states (i.e., races, if any, are non-critical). Use as few secondary variables as possible.

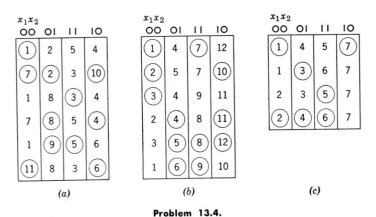

(a) (b) (c)

Problem 13.4.

13.5 Make a proper assignment of secondary response states to each of the flow tables given. Use as few secondary variables as possible.

13.6 For the given four-row merged flow table make an assignment of secondary states which accommodates the required transitions from unstable to stable states and also the cycle corresponding to the input $X_1X_2 = 11$.

x_1x_2

(a)

00	01	11	10
(1)	4	(7)	11
(2)	6	(8)	10
(3)	6	7	(10)
2	(4)	9	10
1	(5)	9	10
3	(6)	7	11
2	6	(9)	11
1	5	7	(11)

x_1x_2

(b)

00	01	11	10
(1)	5	9	(10)
3	(4)	8	(11)
1	(5)	9	(12)
(2)	6	8	(13)
(3)	6	8	10
1	4	(8)	12
3	(6)	(9)	11

x_1x_2

(c)

00	01	11	10
(1)	4	(7)	10
1	(5)	(8)	11
2	(6)	8	(10)
(2)	(4)	9	(11)
3	6	(9)	10
(3)	5	7	(12)

Problem 13.5.

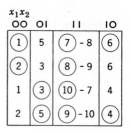

x_1x_2

00	01	11	10
(1)	5	(7) - 8	(6)
(2)	3	(8) - 9	6
1	(3)	(10) - 7	4
2	(5)	(9) - 10	(4)

Problem 13.6.

x_1x_2

(a)

00	01	11	10
(1)	6	2	10
3	5	(4)	9
8	6	(7)	(9)
(3)	(5)	4	10
1	(6)	(2)	9
(8)	5	7	9
3	6	2	(10)

x_1x_2

(b)

00	01	11	10
(3) - 6	(7) - 9	11	(13)
(4) - 5	(8)	11	13
(2) - 1	10	(12)	14
(6) - 4	(9) - 8	12	(14)
(1) - 3	10	(11)	13
(5) - 2	(10)	12	14

Problem 13.7.

13.7 Make proper assignments of secondary response states to the flow tables shown. Use as few secondary variables as possible. Races may be permitted if they are non-critical. Indicate any such races you would permit.

13.8 Make proper assignments of secondary response states to each of the flow tables shown, using as few secondary variables as possible.

$x_1 x_2$

OO	OI	II	IO
(1) -3	(9)	(11)	(16)
(2)	9	12	(17)
(3) -5	10	(13)	(18)
(4) -7	(10)	13	(19)
(5) -6	10	(14)	(20)
(6) -4	9	(12)	(21)
(7) -1	9	(15)	(22)
(8)	10	11	(23)

(a)

$x_1 x_2$

OO	OI	II	IO
(1) -3	(7) -11	(12)	(15)
(2) -4	10	12	15
(3) -5	(8) -7	(13)	(16)
(4) -6	(9) -8	14	15
(5) -2	(10)	13	16
(6) -1	(11) -9	(14)	16

(b)

Problem 13.8.

13.9 The relays A, B, and C are to operate sequentially in accordance with the cycle described in the table shown (0 = relay not operated; 1 = relay operated).

A	B	C
0	0	0
1	0	0
1	1	0
1	1	1
0	1	1
0	1	0
0	0	0

The sequence is to be started by closing the single make contact of a key K and it must begin and end with relays A, B, and C unoperated, as given in the table. Regardless of whether the key K is depressed and held indefinitely, or is depressed only long enough to start the cycle, the relays must go through the sequence once only and then stop. Each repetition of the sequence must require a separate closure of the contact on K.

Design a circuit, containing a minimum number of relays and contacts, that meets these requirements.

13.10 A system for counting road traffic may deliver any one of four possible input sequences to a relay circuit. Each sequence requires a different output response. The input sequences and the corresponding output sequences are:

(a)   Input Sequence: $00 \rightarrow 10 \rightarrow 11 \rightarrow 01 \rightarrow 00$
       Output Sequence: 0000   0000   1000   0000   0000

(b)   Input Sequence: $00 \rightarrow 01 \rightarrow 11 \rightarrow 10 \rightarrow 00$
       Output Sequence: 0000   0000   0100   0000   0000

(c)   Input Sequence: $00 \rightarrow 10 \rightarrow 00 \rightarrow 01 \rightarrow 00$
       Output Sequence: 0000   0000   0010   0000   0000

(d)   Input Sequence: $00 \rightarrow 01 \rightarrow 00 \rightarrow 10 \rightarrow 00$
       Output Sequence: 0000   0000   0001   0000   0000

1. Design a circuit which meets these requirements, using matrix augmentation to obtain the secondary assignment.
2. Repeat the design using Assignment 6 (Art. 13.3) as the secondary assignment.

13.11 A sequential circuit has two inputs and one output. All input changes are permitted. The output is to be ungrounded after every input change of a single variable, and is to be grounded after every change of both input variables.

1. Write a minimum-row flow diagram.
2. Find a set of secondary states that satisfy the flow diagram.
3. Write the flow matrix, the excitation matrix, and the output matrix.
4. Design the excitation and output networks.

13.12 A sequential circuit has two inputs and one output. For a random sequence of input states the output is to remain unchanged following any change of a single input variable, but the output is to change its state whenever the input variables change simultaneously.

1. Prepare a flow table with outputs designated.
2. Find a set of secondary assignments that satisfies the requirements of the flow table.
3. Write the Y matrix.
4. Write a Z matrix which takes advantage of any free choices which are available.

13.13 A relay sequential circuit has two inputs and a single output. Starting with power applied while $X_1 = X_2 = 0$, the output is to be 0 and to remain 0 for any input sequence in which X_1 and X_2 change alternately, and in which each change in X_1 is followed by the same change in X_2. If this pattern is not followed the output is to become 1 and remain thus until power is shut off.

1. Construct the primitive flow table and the merged flow table.
2. Determine secondary assignments which satisfy the flow table.
3. Construct the Y and Z matrices.
4. Write the algebraic expressions for the Y and Z variables.

13.14 In Art. 13.6 a "universal" delay box was designed using the assignment for $S_0 = 2$ given in Fig. 13.51. Any change in the input state P_1P_2 is permitted and after a delay the output state Q_1Q_2 must become the same as the input state. All changes in output must be accomplished without producing any momentary false output.

The partially completed flow tables shown have two different intermeshed row-set assignments as indicated by the circled entries. For each flow table:

1. Derive the complete primitive flow table and its associated output data.
2. Write the matrix which shows the excitation for the secondary devices.
3. Write minimal algebraic expressions for the outputs Q_1 and Q_2.

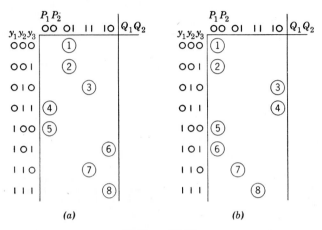

(a)   *(b)*

Problem 13.14.

13.15 A sequential switching circuit is to be built using a delay unit according to the schematic diagram in part (a) of the figure.

The delay unit has two input and two output variables. A particular choice of intermeshed row sets leads to the partially written flow table shown in part (b) of the figure.

Derive:

1. The complete flow table, including output data.
2. A geometric representation of the row-set assignments.
3. The excitation matrix for the secondary devices.
4. Minimal algebraic expressions for the outputs Q_1 and Q_2.

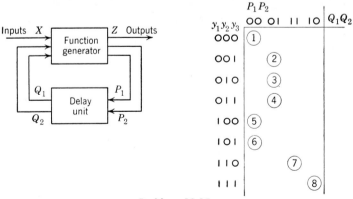

Problem 13.15.

13.16 In another sequential switching circuit, similar schematically to that of Prob. 13.15, the intermeshed row sets in the delay unit consist of the sets (000), (100), (010, 110), and (001, 011, 111, 101).

Complete the requirements of Prob. 13.15 using the indicated secondary assignment.

13.17 By means of a synchronous device (not shown) the ground signal available at the input terminal, X, has the following properties: X is grounded for one second, X is then ungrounded for one second; the cycle is then continuously repeated.

It is desired to create a signal at the output terminal, Z, according to the following specifications: Z is to be grounded for one second; Z is then to be ungrounded for two seconds; the preceding cycle is then to repeat continuously as long as the input cycle continues.

Derive the schematic diagram for a relay switching circuit which will convert the signal at X to the signal at Z. The contact network necessary to generate the signal at Z is to be kept separate from the networks which control relays, and all networks should contain a minimum number of contacts.

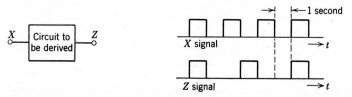

Problem 13.17.

13.18 Repeat the synthesis of Prob. 13.17 under the requirement that all contact networks be free of static hazards. Can the hazard-free circuit be simplified by using a combination of series and shunt control of the secondary relays?

CHAPTER 14

Sequential circuits using electronic and solid-state elements

In Chapter 9 we studied the synthesis of combinational circuits built with various electronic and solid-state components and characterized by the fact that all variables were represented by voltage (or current) levels. In Chapter 12 our study of the synthesis of sequential circuits emphasized the conversion of the sequential problem to one of combinational design. Finally, in Chapter 13 we introduced the feedback-delay concept in the synthesis of sequential circuits. This concept becomes most useful in the treatment of the circuits to be studied in this chapter. The initial steps in the synthesis procedure are not changed, but by applying the ideas of feedback and delay, the final step—the combinational design—is more clearly described.

14.1 Electronic Secondary Devices

Our basic synthesis method for the design of relay sequential circuits contained a step in which a reduced flow table was converted to a flow matrix by an appropriate assignment of secondary states. Each row of the reduced flow table was made to correspond to an internal state, and in the simplest problems each internal state was represented by the response state of one or more secondary devices. In more complex problems one row of the flow table was represented by more than one response state, as we saw in the discussion of row-set assignments. In either event, from the flow matrix we could write excitation functions for the secondary devices.

For relay circuits we visualize a secondary device as illustrated in Fig. 14–1, in which we may apply a ground, representing $Y = 1$, at

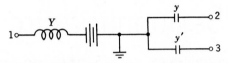

Fig. 14–1. The relay as a secondary device.

terminal 1. When the relay operates in response to this excitation a ground appears on terminal 2 to indicate the response $y = 1$. If the excitation ground at terminal 1 is removed, the relay releases and this is shown by the appearance on terminal 3 of a ground to indicate the response $y' = 1$. We also recognize the fact that the application of the excitation $Y = 1$ does not immediately cause the response $y = 1$, and the removal of the excitation does not immediately cause the response $y' = 1$. We carefully distinguish between the state of excitation and the state of response. When these states are the same, the device is said to be stable; when the states have opposite values, the device is unstable. An important characteristic of the relay as a secondary device is the delay it interposes between changes of excitation and the corresponding changes of response.

One way to approach the problem of synthesizing electronic sequential circuits, in which variables are represented by voltage levels, is to form electronic secondary devices which have characteristics similar to relays. This is by no means a complete answer to the problem of synthesizing such circuits, but it is quite useful as a starting point. For example, in Fig. 14–2(a) an excitation Y is applied to the grid of

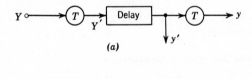

(a)

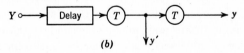

(b)

Fig. 14–2. The triode as a secondary device.

a single triode. The output Y' of this triode is fed through a delay element and then into another triode. We may designate the output of the delay element as the response y', and the output of the second triode is therefore the response y. For all practical purposes, except for the magnitude of the time delay involved, this electronic device is equivalent to the relay device of Fig. 14–1.

It is not strictly necessary that the delay element be placed between the triodes as in Fig. 14–2(a). It is often located in the position indicated in Fig. 14–2(b). This situation commonly occurs when delay is present in the grid circuit of a triode, either because of stray capacitances or because of elements placed in the grid circuit purposely. In Fig. 14–2(b), however, we avoid at this time designating the output of the delay element as the response y. Under appropriate circumstances the output of a delay element thus located may be identified as the response, but this is not necessarily true. We shall see in the next article that the development of response states requires that important gain requirements be satisfied.

In Example 14–1 we repeat a synthesis which we first performed in Art. 12.1 (circuit of Fig. 12–4). The situation is sufficiently simple that we can readily trace the propagation of signals and see that other requirements are satisfied.

Example 14–1

An electronic sequential circuit is to have two inputs, X_1 and X_2, and one output, Z, all of which are to be represented by voltage levels. The output level is to be high ($Z = 1$) when both input levels are high ($X_1 = X_2 = 1$), but only if X_1 is high before X_2. Changes in inputs are to be made one at a time, and all time intervals between input state changes are to be long enough to permit the completion of any secondary state changes that may be required.

A primitive flow table that describes these requirements is given in Fig. 14–3. Note that this table provides for the output to be high whenever the input state $X_1X_2 = 11$ follows the input state $X_1X_2 = 10$, and not otherwise, but there is no restriction on how the input state $X_1X_2 = 10$ is reached.

x_1x_2				
OO	**OI**	**II**	**IO**	**Z**
①	4	–	2	0
1	–	3	②	0
–	4	③	2	1
1	④	5	–	0
–	4	⑤	2	0

Fig. 14–3. Primitive flow table, Example 14–1.

Two minimum-row mergers of the primitive flow table are possible. One of these, with an assignment of secondary states, is given as the flow matrix of Fig. 14–4(a), and the corresponding excitation matrix is shown as Fig. 14–4(b). No separate output matrix is given since the output is high only for the total state represented by the entry ③, and for this the output function may be written immediately as $Z = x_1x_2y'$.

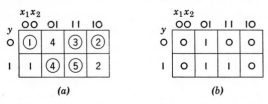

(a)   (b)

Fig. 14–4. (a) Flow matrix and (b) excitation matrix derived from flow table of Fig. 14–3.

From the excitation matrix we write

$$Y = x_1'x_2 + x_2y$$

We note, however, that since

$$Z' = x_1' + x_2' + y$$

$$x_2Z' = x_1'x_2 + x_2y = Y$$

These relations lead to the circuit of Fig. 14–5. One Multiply gate, M_1, forms the product, $Z = x_1x_2y'$, and another Multiply gate, M_2,

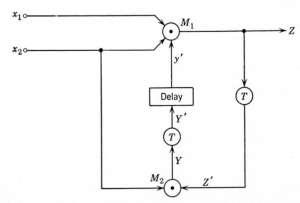

Fig. 14–5. An electronic realization of the circuit described by the flow matrix of Fig. 14–4.

forms the product, $Y = x_2Z'$. One triode forms the complement Z' and another triode forms the complement Y'. The response y' is then obtained, after a time delay, from Y'. We observe that, starting at the output of the Multiply gate M_1, there is a path which leads through a triode, then through the Multiply gate M_2, through the second triode, through the delay element, and back to one of the inputs of the gate M_1. This is a feedback loop which contains delay and loop gain (from the two triodes). In the next article we shall see that gain is always required in a feedback loop in a sequential circuit. In Art. 14.4 we shall study in more detail how time delay influences the operation of sequential circuits. For the circuit considered in this example we can readily see that if the time delay in the feedback loop is made sufficiently large, relative to the time delays in other signal paths, the circuit will operate in accordance with its flow-matrix and output-matrix description.

Let us examine the operation of this circuit in response to the input sequence $X_1X_2 = 00 \rightarrow 10 \rightarrow 11$. With $X_1X_2 = 00$ the output of Multiply gate M_1 is 0, so $Z = 0$. Although $Z' = 1$, the output of Multiply gate M_2 is 0 because $X_2 = 0$. Hence $Y = 0$, $Y' = 1$, and in the steady state, $y' = 1$. This is a stable state in which $Y = 0$ and $y = 0$. In the next step of the sequence, $X_1X_2 = 10$, only the input X_1 changes. Since X_2 remains at 0, the outputs of both M_1 and M_2 remain at 0 and there is no change in secondary state. This corresponds to the transition from entry ① to entry ② in Fig. 14–4(a), and the total state remains stable.

Next we consider the input transition $X_1X_2 = 10 \rightarrow 11$. Just before this change, at gate M_1 the inputs X_1 and y' are both equal to 1, and at gate M_2, $Z' = 1$. Therefore, at both M_1 and M_2, provided no other inputs change when X_2 changes from 0 to 1, the gate outputs change from 0 to 1. However, the output of gate M_1 is connected through a triode to an input of gate M_2. Hence, when the output of M_1 changes from 0 to 1, the Z' input to gate M_2 must change from 1 to 0, and the output of M_2 should remain at 0. This is the action which will occur at M_2 if the change of X_2 reaches that gate at the same time as the change of Z', or later. If, however, the change of X_2 influences the gate M_2 before Z' can change to the 0 value, the output Y of M_2 will go through the sequence $0 \rightarrow 1 \rightarrow 0$ instead of remaining at 0. If there is no time delay in the remainder of the feedback loop it is then possible for y' to drop immediately to 0 and thereby cause a momentary change in the output. This situation is the electronic counterpart of the static hazards in relay contact networks which we studied in Art. 12.7. Physically, the hazard is present because the change in X_2 influences the gate M_2 both directly and by way of the feedback loop. If the propagation times of these two effects differ, there may be a momentary fluctuation in the output of M_2, even though the transition from entry ② to entry ③ in the flow matrix of Fig. 14–4(a) involves no change of secondary state.

If the magnitude of the time delay in the feedback loop is large enough, the secondary state will not respond to the momentary fluctuation in the output of gate M_2. The duration of this fluctuation is equal to the *difference* in the delay times in the two paths through which the change in X_2 reaches the inputs of M_2. Hence if the delay element of the feedback loop introduces a time delay larger than the difference in the two signal propagation times, it acts effectively as a low-pass filter and no change in y' occurs.

The source of the static hazard in this example is shown by a study of the maps in Fig. 14–6. We first wrote the excitation function,

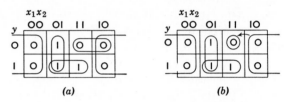

(a)   (b)

Fig. 14–6. Lift sets and drop sets in the excitation function of Example 14–1, (a) as originally written and (b) as realized in Fig. 14–5.

$Y = x_1'x_2 + x_2y$, and in this form the terms of the function represent the lift sets (see Art. 9.2) indicated in Fig. 14–6(a). When we factor the function and write $Y = x_2(x_1' + y)$, the terms in this form represent the drop sets indicated in Fig. 14–6(a). However, the circuit of Fig. 14–5 was derived from the excitation function written in the form

$$Y = x_2Z' = x_2(x_1' + x_2' + y)$$

$$= x_1'x_2 + x_2y$$

Although the lift sets are those specified originally, the drop sets x_2 and $(x_1' + x_2' + y)$ are those shown in Fig. 14–6(b). We see that the transition marked by the arrow does not take place *within* a drop set, so there exists the possibility that the excitation will momentarily have the value 1 instead of remaining at 0, as x_2 changes from 0 to 1. We have already seen that this hazard indeed occurs if the effect of the x_2 change propagates over one path faster than it does over another path. This, of course, is the electronic analogue of the hazard found in contact networks when normally open and normally closed contacts do not change state at the same instant.

As in contact networks, it is always possible to design the electronic combinational network so that no static hazards arise. When a transmission is to remain at the value 1 during the change of a single input variable, the states before and after the input change must be contained within at least one lift set. When the transmission is to remain at the value 0 during the change of a single input variable, the states before and after the input change must be contained within at least one drop set.

In the circuit of Fig. 14–7, the excitation function Y is derived from a Multiply gate having the inputs x_2 and $(x_1' + y)$; these correspond

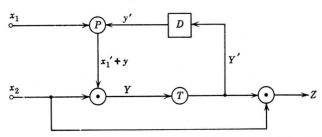

Fig. 14–7. A circuit in which the lift sets and drop sets of Fig. 14–6(a) are present.

exactly to the drop sets of Fig. 14–6(a). Moreover, if $x_1 = 0$ and $x_2 = 1$, or if $x_2 = 1$ and $y = 1$, the excitation $Y = 1$. The sets $x_1'x_2$ and x_2y are, by definition, lift sets and they correspond exactly to the lift sets of Fig. 14–6(a). The network of Fig. 14–7 hence contains no static hazards. The student may readily verify that the network is free of static hazard regardless of the magnitude of the time delay in the feedback loop (represented by a box containing the letter D). Specifically, even though the delay D is reduced to zero, the network will behave in accordance with the flow table and without momentary false output or excitation. This is not a general statement. It is true of this particular network, and we shall see in Art. 14.4 that it is possible to predict when delay in a feedback loop is necessary and when it is not.

It is instructive to emphasize the nature of the feedback loop in another way. In Fig. 13–56 we showed how a sequential circuit could be regarded as a combinational circuit which delivered, in addition to other outputs, a set of excitation functions. These functions, after suitable time delays, became the secondary response functions and were returned to the combinational circuit as inputs. In this example there is only one excitation function and hence only one feedback loop. In Fig. 14–8 the circuit of Fig. 14–5 has been redrawn so that the combinational circuit is enclosed within the dashed-line boundary and the feedback passes through a delay element.

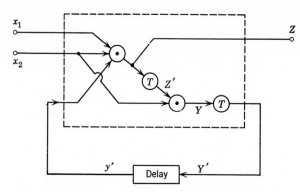

Fig. 14–8. The circuit of Fig. 14–5 redrawn to emphasize the feedback-delay path.

14.2   Physical Requirements

In Example 14–1 we wrote the excitation function $Y = x_1'x_2 + x_2y$. A symbolic realization of the circuit, with the output function omitted, is given in Fig. 14–9. It may be verified that this circuit is free of

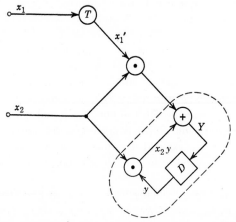

Fig. 14–9. The circuit of Example 14–1 realized by the use of basic gates (output omitted).

static hazard. We are interested in examining the portion of the circuit contained within the dotted line, particularly when this portion is realized by the use of diode gates as in Fig. 14–10.

Consider the behavior of the circuit of Fig. 14–10 when $x_1 = x_2 = 1$. For these inputs, $Y = (0 \cdot 1) + (1 \cdot y) = y$. This equation is satisfied either by $Y = y = 0$ or by $Y = y = 1$. Hence, for the particular input conditions given there are two stable states, which correspond to the entries ③ and ⑤ in the flow matrix of Fig. 14–4.

Let us assume in Fig. 14–10 that 1 is represented by the 50-volt level and 0 is represented by zero voltage. Numerical values of the voltages for gate excitations and for the input levels corresponding to $x_1 = x_2 = 1$ are marked at appropriate positions in the circuit diagram and enclosed in parentheses. The question now is, what voltage levels represent Y and y.

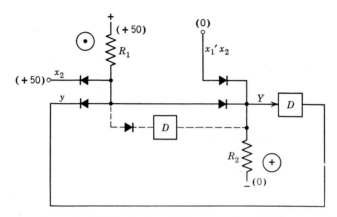

Fig. 14–10.   A portion of the circuit of Fig. 14–9 using a diode-gate realization.

Let us consider first the relative values of the gate resistors R_1 and R_2. Since the Add gate is a load on the Multiply gate we must make $R_2 \gg R_1$. Then Y and y are at their high levels and we satisfy the relation $Y = y = 1$. But, because of the feedback connection, the Multiply gate is also a load on the Add gate, and the situation requires that $R_1 \gg R_2$. For this condition Y and y are at their low levels and we have $Y = y = 0$. These are obviously contradictory requirements. If we make $R_1 = R_2$ to resolve the contradiction, then Y and y are each represented by a 25-volt level.

This circuit is composed entirely of passive elements and there is no reason why we should expect it to have more than one point of equilibrium for the input conditions given. That point of equilibrium is determined entirely by the relative values of R_1 and R_2. The feedback path indicated in the diagram is meaningless. The circuit is exactly the same if we remove the feedback path and insert the path shown in dotted lines. Except for the time-delay element indicated, the dotted path is identical to the connection already present which represents $x_2 y$.

In order to have binary equilibrium states we must introduce gain in every feedback loop. In Fig. 14–11 a portion of a sequential circuit is shown, at the left, in which only a single feedback loop is indicated and

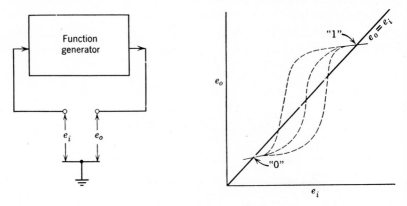

Fig. 14–11. Binary equilibrium states are possible only if there is gain in the feedback loop.

all other inputs and outputs of the combinational function generator are omitted. If the feedback loop is broken as shown we can measure the input e_i and the output e_o and plot the open-loop e_o versus e_i characteristic. We now ask what is required of this open-loop characteristic in order to have binary equilibrium conditions when the loop is closed and $e_o = e_i$.*

In the graph at the right of Fig. 14–11 we draw a solid line at an angle of 45° to represent the closed loop condition $e_o = e_i$. Two points are marked on this line, corresponding to the voltage levels which represent logical 0 and logical 1. At each of these points a short section of an open-loop curve of e_o vs. e_i is drawn in solid lines. At each of these points of intersection the slope of the open-loop curve must be less than the slope of the closed-loop curve in order to have a stable operating point. It may readily be verified that any tendency to "drift" away from either of these equilibrium points sets up voltage unbalance around the loop which is in the direction to correct the "drift."

In any physical system the two sectors of the open-loop curve must be joined by some sort of line which connects the right-hand part of

---

* This discussion is adapted from a formal proof given by S. H. Unger, "A Study of Asynchronous Logical Feedback Networks," Doctoral dissertation, Department of Electrical Engineering, Massachusetts Institute of Technology, June, 1957.

the 0 sector to the left-hand part of the 1 sector. The dotted lines in the graph of Fig. 14–11 suggest the range of variation which might be found in these connecting links. Regardless of how the connection between the two sectors is actually made, the link must contain a region in which the slope is greater than unity. In other words, the open-loop characteristic must be that of an amplifier with gain greater than unity. Furthermore, at the point where this link crosses the closed-loop line the slope of the open-loop curve is greater than that of the closed-loop curve and the circuit therefore cannot be in stable equilibrium at this crossing point when the loop is closed. The voltage level will always change until either the intersection corresponding to 0 or that corresponding to 1 is reached.

These considerations apply to every feedback loop present in a sequential circuit. This does not mean that there must be a separate amplifier in each feedback loop, because sometimes more than one loop can share a single amplifier. Each feedback loop, however, if broken must show an open-loop characteristic which has gain. (We were not concerned with the problem of gain in relay sequential circuits because each relay can participate in the control of a substantial amount of energy through a contact network, and each relay is hence an amplifier.)

An important characteristic of the electromagnetic relay is the time delay it introduces between its excitation and its response. This is a built-in property of the device which ensures freedom from a type of hazard to be considered in Art. 14.4. In contrast, electronic devices are characterized by high-speed response. One disadvantage of this is that stray delays due to constructional features of a circuit may require the introduction of compensating delays.

There is a conservative approach to the problem of introducing delays which assures the proper operation of any sequential switching circuit provided certain other conditions are satisfied.* These are as follows:

(a) The combinational function generator, when the circuit is arranged as in Fig. 13–56, must be free of static hazard;
(b) Only one input variable at a time changes;
(c) No critical races are present in the secondary assignments.

In the combinational function generator part of the circuit there will always be a distribution in the magnitudes of the time delays which occur between input changes and output changes. Let D be the longest such delay and d be the shortest delay that ever occurs. Unger shows

* S. H. Unger, op. cit.

that if the three conditions listed are satisfied, and if each feedback loop contains a delay having a magnitude at least equal to $D - d$, the circuit will always perform as described in its flow and output matrices.

Let the network initially be in a stable state and let a single input variable change. If this input change causes no change in any of the secondary excitation functions there can be no incorrect operation of the circuit. If, however, a secondary excitation changes, there must be a delay of at least d units between the input change and the resulting change in the secondary excitation. There will now be an additional delay of at least $D - d$ units in the feedback path for which the exci-tation changed. Hence, after the original input change there is a delay of at least $D - d + d = D$ units before a secondary response can cause another change at the input of the combinational function generator. Since D is the maximum possible delay in the function generator, the minimum of $D - d$ delay in each feedback path assures that the function generator responds completely to an input change before it receives a new signal due to a change of secondary state. If a single change of primary state causes a succession of secondary state changes, each change of secondary state in turn finds the function generator ready to receive it.

This is exactly what happens in relay sequential circuits designed so that the three basic conditions are satisfied. Each relay responds with a delay many times the required minimum delay in magnitude. This is, of course, a highly conservative design from the standpoint of delay, but there is little that can be done to reduce the response times of relays. In electronic circuits, however, the problem is usually one of introducing the right amount of delay in the right place. We shall see later that sometimes no delay is required except perhaps for purposes of smoothing. But in any sequential circuit designed with a hazard-free combinational circuit, operated without critical races, and having input variables restricted to change only one at a time, the introduction of at least $D - d$ units of delay in each feedback loop is sufficient to assure operation in accordance with the flow table.

14.3 Analysis of Electronic Sequential Circuits

We have already studied the basic steps in the analysis of sequential switching circuits using relays. Much of that procedure is exactly the same for electronic sequential circuits. The points of difference are, however, sufficiently important to warrant a brief discussion.

Let us consider the simple situation represented by the circuit in Fig. 14–12. This circuit has a single feedback loop and we assume that the switching elements used provide gain in the loop. One question that immediately arises is whether any secondary device can be recognized. Neither of the gates is wholly under the control of the primary variables. Each gate has one primary variable as an input and both gates are contained within the feedback loop. We simply cannot distinguish anything corresponding clearly to either a primary device or a secondary device in this circuit. In electronic circuits we cannot expect always to be able to allocate duties to particular devices as we did in relay circuits.

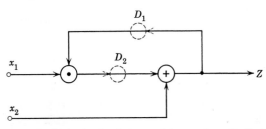

Fig. 14–12. A single feedback loop with two hypothetical delays.

When we attempt to use the feedback-delay concept to analyze the circuit, we find that the circuit as originally drawn does not have a specific time delay indicated. If a delay element is explicitly present in a feedback loop we can designate the input to that element as an excitation function and the output as a response. If no time delay element is indicated we can use the artifice of introducing a hypothetical delay as an aid to analysis. This, however, may involve the dilemma illustrated in Fig. 14–12 in which we see that there are two possible locations within the loop where the hypothetical delay may be introduced. It becomes important then to examine the effect, if any, of changing the position of the delay element in the feedback loop.

If we introduce a hypothetical delay element at the point shown as D_1, and then consider the input to this element as the excitation Y and the output as the response y, we can write $Y = x_2 + x_1 y$, and $Z = Y$. If the delay is in the position corresponding to D_2, we write $Y = x_1(x_2 + y)$ and $Z = x_2 + y$.

In Fig. 14–13(a) the upper map shows the excitation and output functions corresponding to the delay in the D_1 position. The output function values are those enclosed in parentheses. Below the excitation (output) matrix, the flow matrix is given. The corresponding maps for the delay in the D_2 position are given in Fig. 14–13(b).

Examination shows immediately that these matrices are quite different in appearance. If, however, the input variables are restricted so that they change only one at a time, the terminal action described by the matrices will be identical, except for small differences in the timing of output changes. Hence, if changes of input variables are thus restricted, we can choose either position in Fig. 14–12 for the location of the delay.

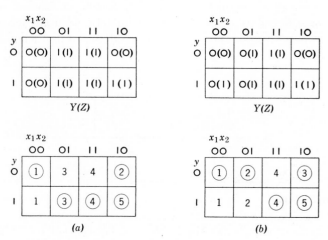

Fig. 14–13. Excitation (output) matrices and flow matrices corresponding to two positions of the delay element in Fig. 14–12.

If the two input variables are allowed to change simultaneously it is possible for the location of the delay to influence the terminal action of the circuit. Suppose we build two versions of the circuit in Fig. 14–12 which differ only in the position of the delay element. We start by placing both circuits in the state corresponding to entry ①, for which the output is 0, and then allow the input to make the change $x_1 x_2 = 00 \rightarrow 01$. The circuit having the flow matrix of Fig. 14–13 (a) responds by going to the entry ③, for which the output is 1, and the circuit having the flow matrix of Fig. 14–13 (b) responds by going to entry ② for which the output also is 1. Now let the input variables make the change $x_1 x_2 = 01 \rightarrow 10$. The first circuit changes from entry ③ to entry ⑤ and the output remains 1. The second circuit changes from entry ② to entry ③ and its output goes from 1 to 0. Thus the two circuits do not have identical terminal action under all possible changes of input variables.

This is an ambiguity which can be resolved only by obtaining more information. No process of analysis can discover merely from a circuit diagram what the circuit is supposed to do under these conditions. In order to complete an analysis, it would be necessary to know the magnitudes, or at least the relative magnitudes, of all time delays in the circuit. When we insert delays in feedback loops to obtain secondary action, we assume that they are the dominant delays of the circuit.*

Example 14–2

Analyse the electronic circuit of Fig. 14–14 by writing the excitation, output, and flow matrices. Assume that the delay elements indicated introduce the dominant time delays in the circuit. Input variables are to be allowed to change only one at a time.

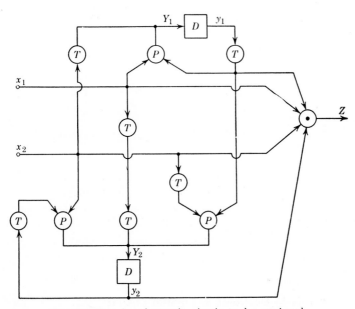

Fig. 14–14. An electronic circuit to be analyzed.

Two feedback loops are present in this circuit. The inputs and outputs of the delay elements in these loops are marked with the excitation variables Y_1, Y_2, and the response variables, y_1, y_2, respectively. The corresponding excitation functions can then be written

$$Y_1 = x_2'(x_1' + y_1)$$

$$Y_2 = x_1(x_2' + y_2)(x_2 + y_1)$$

and the output function is $Z = x_1 x_2 y_1' y_2$.

---

* We assume in this discussion that the delay is a pure time delay which shifts a wave form in time without altering its form. In the engineering of actual circuits, however, due account must be taken of the fact that the networks used for delay purposes also alter wave shape. These effects may not be troublesome in circuits working with voltage levels unless the distortion becomes serious

The excitation matrix is drawn in Fig. 14–15(a) and the flow matrix in Fig. 14–15(b). No output matrix is necessary since the output is 1 only for the state represented by the entry ④. We observe, however, that if the output is allowed to have the high value as early as possible, we can enter $Z = 1$ for the state represented by the uncircled 4 entry. If this is done, then $Z = x_1x_2y_2$.

(a)

y_1y_2 \ x_1x_2	00	01	11	10
00	10	00	00	00
01	10	00	01	00
11	10	00	01	11
10	10	00	00	11

(b)

y_1y_2 \ x_1x_2	00	01	11	10
00	6	①	②	③
01	6	1	④	3
11	6	1	4	⑤
10	⑥	1	2	5

Fig. 14–15. Excitation matrix and flow matrix derived by analysis of the circuit of Fig. 14–14.

The terminal action of this circuit is such that the output becomes high if and only if the input passes through the sequence $x_1x_2 = 00 \rightarrow 10 \rightarrow 11$. Once the high output has been obtained, any subsequent input change will cause the output to become low and it will remain low until the input again passes through the prescribed sequence. This circuit is an electronic equivalent of the relay circuit of Fig. 12–5.

14.4 Hazards in Electronic Sequential Circuits

From our study of combinational electronic circuits we know that the type of hazard known as a static hazard can be avoided by providing in the circuit design all the lift sets and drop sets needed to ensure that whenever the output is required to remain constant during the change of a single input variable, the input change will occur within a lift set or a drop set. In Example 14–1 we synthesized the circuit of Fig. 14–5 and found there was a static hazard in it because one of the drop sets required to prevent the hazard was not present. By introducing sufficient delay and smoothing action in the secondary response

enough to blur the distinction between the binary levels corresponding to "high" and "low." We have also seen that when static hazards are present the presence of some filtering action in the delay element serves to minimize the effects of momentary false transmission values.

the effect of the hazard could be avoided. A better solution was illustrated by the circuit of Fig. 14–7 in which the hazard was avoided by including all the required lift sets and drop sets. In this circuit, no delay element is needed at all. The delay element shown in the circuit diagram is merely a formal way of designating the secondary excitation and response locations used in the synthesis.

We can always design a circuit to eliminate static hazard. But the speed of response of electronic circuits renders them susceptible to another form of hazard which Unger calls an *essential hazard*.* This form of hazard is most readily recognized by close examination of the flow matrix. It is important that it be recognized and that it be taken into account in synthesis, because it can cause not merely a momentary malfunction but rather a complete failure of the circuit to operate in accordance with the specifications of the flow matrix.

We will assume that: (a) input variables change one at a time; (b) secondary assignments contain no critical race conditions; and (c) the combinational part of the circuit is free of static hazards. In the circuit to be synthesized here we will omit the output network and assume that if the circuit operates in accordance with the given flow matrix the correct outputs will be obtained.

The circuit is described by the flow matrix of Fig. 14–16(a). Blank entries in this matrix indicate that the corresponding input states

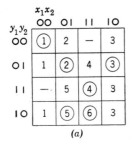

Fig. 14–16. Flow matrix and excitation matrix of a circuit to be synthesized.

cannot be reached from a stable entry by changing a single input variable. In writing the excitation matrix of Fig. 14–16(b) these blank positions are treated as points at which the excitation values are optional, and the values actually entered in the excitation matrix are chosen to simplify the combinational circuit. Excitation functions which contain all the lift sets and drop sets required to avoid static

* S. H. Unger, op. cit.

hazard are

$$Y_1 = x_1 x_2 + x_2 y_1 = x_2 (x_1 + y_1)$$

$$Y_2 = x_1 y_1' + x_2 y_1' + x_1 y_2$$

$$= (x_1 + x_2)(y_1' + y_2)(x_1 + y_1')$$

An electronic circuit to realize these functions is given schematically in Fig. 14–17. The delay elements D_1 and D_2 are associated with Y_1

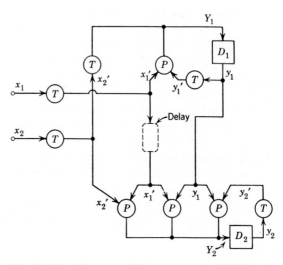

Fig. 14–17. Circuit to illustrate an essential hazard.

and Y_2, respectively. A dotted construction indicates a possible delay element in the line supplying x_1' to the lower pentodes, but for the moment let us assume that this delay is not present.

We now consider the situation when the circuit is in the state represented by the entry ② and the input state changes from 01 to 11. Initially, the secondary state is $y_1 y_2 = 01$. Before the input change is made, the excitation Y_1 is low because the inputs, x_1' and y_1', to the upper pentode are both high. In the lower group of tubes, the low value of x_2' holds one pentode output high and the low value of y_1 holds the outputs of the other two pentodes high.

When x_1 changes from 0 to 1, x_1' changes from 1 to 0 and the upper pentode becomes cut off. Since the upper triode is already cut off ($x_2' = 0$), the output Y_1 rises. In the lower group of tubes, when x_1' changes from 1 to 0, at least one input to each pentode remains low, so all the pentodes remain cut off and Y_2 remains high, even though the change of Y_1 causes y_1 to rise. Thus the change of input values from 01 to 11 causes the secondary state to change from 01 to 11 and the circuit makes the transition to the state represented by the entry ④ as required by the flow matrix.

Let us now assume that a large delay (larger than D_1) is introduced at the point shown by the dotted construction in the connection between x_1' and the lower group of pentodes in Fig. 14–17. Because of this delay the change of x_1' from 1 to 0 appears at the upper pentode some time before it appears at the lower pentodes. If the change of y_1 from 0 to 1 reaches the lower pentodes before the change of x_1', the middle pentode in the lower group receives a 1 on both input grids. Hence it conducts and drops the output Y_2 to the 0 level. This change in turn causes y_2' to rise and, in combination with $y_1 = 1$, causes the right-hand pentode in the lower group to conduct. When the change of x_1' finally reaches the lower tubes, the secondary state is 10 instead of 11. Therefore, instead of making the transition from state ② to state ④, the circuit goes from state ② to state ⑥—a serious malfunction indeed.

This difficulty is the consequence of a difference in delay times in the propagation of a change of primary variable. Effectively, we tell one secondary excitation function generator that a primary variable has changed, but we do not tell another secondary excitation function generator about the change until after the first function generator has already completed its response. Obviously, this is a shabby way to treat the circuit, but we are discussing electronic circuits in which stray delays may be longer than secondary response times. The problem does not arise in relay circuits because the secondary response times are large compared with delays in the propagation of primary changes.

Let us review the sequence of events with the aid of the flow matrix of Fig. 14–16(a). Starting with the circuit in the state represented by the entry ②, we change the input variable x_1 from 0 to 1. According to the flow matrix, this input change should make the circuit go to the state represented by the entry ④. However, the change of input state is at the moment recognized only by the part of the circuit which generates the secondary excitation Y_1. A delay in the transmission of the change of x_1 leaves the circuit that generates Y_2 uninformed. Hence, when Y_1 changes from 0 to 1 and the response y_1 also changes from 0 to 1, the circuit that generates the excitation Y_2 becomes aware of a secondary state $y_1 y_2 = 11$ but at its other inputs the primary state is still $x_1 x_2 = 01$. In other words, this part of the circuit acts as though the total state were that represented by the entry 5 (uncircled). Its response is to change to the state represented by the entry ⑤ through Y_2 changing from 1 to 0 and the secondary state thus changing to

$y_1 y_2 = 10$. When the change in the input x_1 finally reaches the Y_2 function generator the damage has already been done and the circuit goes to the state represented by the entry ⑥ instead of that represented by the entry ④.

Unger has stated a rule which enables us to locate an essential hazard by direct examination of a flow matrix. He defines an essential hazard as "the existence of a state S_0 and an input variable x, such that starting with the system in the state S_0, three consecutive changes in x bring the system to a state other than the one arrived at after the first change in x."

If we refer to Fig. 14–16(a) we see that this situation is present with respect to the state ② and the change of input variable x_1. If we start with the state ② and change x_1 three times, the first change takes the system to the state ④, the second change to the state ⑤, and the third change to the state ⑥. After the first change, the system is in the state ④ but after the third change it is in the state ⑥, and according to Unger's test an essential hazard exists. The section of the flow matrix in Fig. 14–16(a) involved in the essential hazard is redrawn as Fig. 14–18(a). Only the two columns involved in the primary

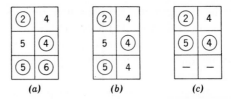

(a)   *(b)*   *(c)*

Fig. 14–18. Modifications of the flow matrix of Fig. 14–16(a) which avoid the essential hazard.

change and the three rows involved in the secondary change are indicated. In parts (b) and (c) of Fig. 14–18 are shown some possible variations of the pattern which do not contain the essential hazard of Fig. 14–18(a). In Fig. 14–18(b), the first change of input variables takes the system from the state ② to the state ④, the second change to the state ⑤, and the third change back to the state ④. A similar sequence of events takes place in Fig. 14–18(c). Since in both these patterns the state reached after the third change of the input variable is the same as the state reached after the first change there is no essential hazard present. In Fig. 14–19 a group of patterns is shown which represent all possible responses to three consecutive changes of a single input variable. The first four of these patterns contain no essential hazards but patterns 5 and 6 both contain an essential hazard. It is interesting to note that flow tables written for the design of binary counting circuits operating on voltage levels invariably contain patterns similar to pattern 6 in Fig. 14–19.

Although we observe, as in Fig. 14–18, that a slight modification in a flow table pattern can avoid an essential hazard, we cannot make these slight modifications in the synthesis of actual circuits. The question is how to design a circuit so that the hazard causes no trouble. From the discussion of the detailed operation of the circuit in Fig. 14–17 we see that when an essential hazard is present, a change of an input variable is followed by a change of a secondary variable and the secondary variable change propagates through the circuit faster than the input change that caused it. The remedy for the essential hazard condition is to delay the change of the secondary variable which is required to change first,

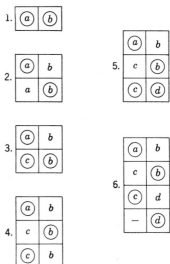

Fig. 14–19. Flow table patterns corresponding to three successive changes of one input variable.

long enough to allow the initial primary-variable change to reach all circuit elements effected by it. In the circuit of Fig. 14–17, the delay element D_1 must hence be larger than any stray delay in the part of the new circuit which connects the input x_1 to the lower group of pentodes.

14.5 Some Synthesis Examples

In Example 12–1 we performed the synthesis of a clamp-gate circuit using relays. It will be instructive to repeat this synthesis using electronic elements. In Fig. 14–20 the flow matrix and the excitation matrix are presented. In the primitive flow table the output is 1 for the states ②, ④, and ⑥. Hence, we can write either $Z = Y$ or $Z = y$,

y	$x_1 x_2$ 00	01	11	10
0	①	③	4	⑤
1	②	3	④	⑥

y	$x_1 x_2$ 00	01	11	10
0	0	0	1	0
1	1	0	1	1

Fig. 14–20. Flow matrix and excitation matrix of a clamp-gate circuit.

depending on the output values assigned to the unstable states. For
the excitation function we write

$$Y = x_1 x_2 + x_2'y \ (+ x_1 y)$$

$$= (x_1 + x_2')(x_2 + y) \cdot (x_1 + y)$$

In the first form the term $(x_1 y)$ is a lift set required to avoid static
hazard in the transition from state ④ to state ⑥, or vice versa. In the
second form the term $(x_1 + y)$ is a drop set required to avoid a static
hazard in the transition between state ① and state ③.

None of the two-row patterns in Fig. 14–19 involves an essential
hazard, so this is one question that need not concern us when a circuit
to be synthesized is described by a two-row flow matrix.

If we are prepared to accept a momentarily false value of Y, and
to avoid improper circuit response by the use of smoothing and delay,
the circuit of Fig. 14–21 realizes the excitation function in the form

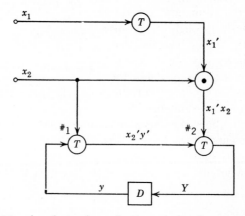

Fig. 14–21. An electronic realization of the clamp-gate circuit.

$Y = (x_1 + x_2')(x_2 + y)$. We note that the input variable x_2 effects
the output Y of triode pair No. 2 by way of two paths. In one path
the term $x_2'y'$ is developed and in the other path the term $x_1'x_2$. Consider the circuit in state ① where $x_1 = x_2 = y = 0$. The inputs to
triode pair No. 2 are $x_2'y' = 1$ and $x_1'x_2 = 0$. One triode is conducting
and hence $Y = 0$. Now let the circuit input change from 00 to 01,
corresponding to the transition from state ① to state ③. The inputs to the triode pair No. 2 make the changes $x_2'y' = 1 \to 0$ and
$x_1'x_2 = 0 \to 1$. The triode which was formerly conducting cuts off, and
the triode formerly cut off begins to conduct. Hence, after the input
change, Y is again 0, but if the grid input $x_2'y'$ changes from 1 to 0

before the grid input $x_1'x_2$ changes from 0 to 1, both triodes will be momentarily cut off and there will be a momentary rise in Y.

We can, of course, avoid getting this momentary false value of Y by adding the drop set $(x_1 + y)$ in the realization of Y. Since $x_1 = y = 0$ throughout the transition, the presence of this term ensures that Y remains 0 as x_2 changes. However, it is more economical in this instance to introduce a delay element of a type which will smooth out the effect of the brief rise in the value of Y. A small capacitance across the y input to triode pair No. 1 is probably sufficient.

It is interesting now to take the section of the circuit in Fig. 14–21 which contains the two triode pairs, and their inputs and outputs, and redraw that section using actual circuit elements instead of logical symbols. This is done in Fig. 14–22 where we see that two of the triodes are connected in the familiar Eccles-Jordan circuit and the other two triodes act as puller inputs.

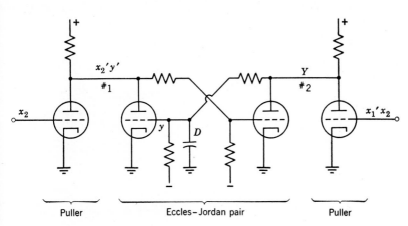

Fig. 14–22. A part of Fig. 14–21 showing circuit elements.

Although in this instance the end result of the logical process of synthesis is a well-known, conventional circuit, the mode of operation of the Eccles-Jordan pair in Fig. 14–22 is not conventional. Usually these circuits are operated in a manner such that the plate voltages have complementary values. In this circuit, the left-hand tube has its plate voltage represented by $x_2'y'$, and the right-hand plate voltage is represented by $Y = (x_1 + x_2')(x_2 + y)$. These are certainly not complementary functions, and it may readily be verified that in the state represented by ③ in the flow matrix, where $x_1 = 0$, $x_2 = 1$, $y = 0$, both plate voltages are low. In this condition, both puller tubes are conducting and both triodes in the Eccles-Jordan pair are cut off.

The Eccles-Jordan bistable pair is a basic configuration which is widely used in electronic switching. We need not plan to introduce the bistable pair into a circuit, however, because the feedback required in sequential circuits leads to this circuit form if it is needed. In the synthesis of switching circuits with pulse inputs, however, we do make direct use of toggle circuits, usually called flip-flops, and these depend for their operation on some form of a bistable pair. It will be interesting, therefore, to undertake the synthesis of a flip-flop.

A simple flip-flop, of the set-reset type, has two inputs, x_1 and x_2, and two outputs, Z_1 and Z_2. The output is always either 01 or 10. When the level of either input is raised, with the other input low, the correspondingly numbered output level is to rise, or remain raised. When both inputs are low, one output remains high, corresponding to the input which last was at the high value. The inputs can never have the value 11, and the input transitions $01 \rightleftharpoons 10$ are not permitted.

A primitive flow table which satisfies these requirements is given in Fig. 14–23(a). This merges to the two-row form which is completed

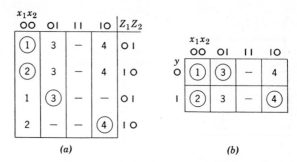

Fig. 14–23. Primitive flow table and flow matrix for a set-reset flip-flop.

as a flow matrix in Fig. 14–23(b). In the excitation matrix of Fig. 14–24 there are two blank entries. We can hence write four different excitation functions, depending on what values are chosen for the

Fig. 14–24. Excitation matrix and partially completed output matrix for the flip-flop.

blank entries. The most interesting of these are

$$Y = x_2'(x_1 + y) \qquad \text{(0 entered in both blank cells)}$$

$$Y = x_1 + x_2'y \qquad \text{(1 entered in both blank cells)}$$

A number of alternative function forms for Z_1 and Z_2 are possible as we see in the partially completed output matrix of Fig. 14–24. In addition to those in the blank entries, the output values corresponding to unstable entries are also to be specified. In making these choices there is always the restriction that Z_1 and Z_2 must have complementary values. We will postpone the completion of this matrix until the remainder of the combinational design is finished. It may be noted, however, that $Z_1 = Y$ and $Z_2 = Y'$, or $Z_1 = y$ and $Z_2 = y'$, are both indicated as possibilities by appropriate completion of the output matrix.

In Fig. 14–25(a), the flip-flop circuit is shown as derived from the excitation function $Y = x_2'(x_1 + y)$. The complement of the alternate

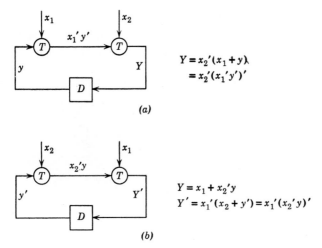

Fig. 14–25. Flip-flop circuits as derived from two forms of the excitation function.

excitation function $Y = x_1 + x_2'y$ is $Y' = x_1'(x_2 + y')$, and this leads to the circuit of Fig. 14–25(b). Since both excitation functions are free of static hazards there is no need for a delay element in either of these circuits. When the indicated delay elements are removed the two circuits in Fig. 14–25 are indistinguishable. Their symmetry is emphasized by the arrangement shown in Fig. 14–26.

Except for the symbols designating variables, and the smoothing capacitance, the electrical circuit represented by the symbolic diagram of Fig. 14–26 is the same as that in Fig. 14–22. We can simplify the circuit by performing some of the operations with passive elements. We first write the excitation function in the form $Y = x_1 + x_2'y = x_1 + (x_2 + y')'$. If we use Add gates and triodes the circuit may be drawn as in Fig. 14–27. All branches of the diagram are marked to show the

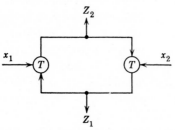

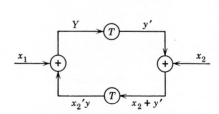

Fig. 14–26. Symbolic diagram of the flip-flop circuit with delay elements removed.

Fig. 14–27. The flip-flop circuit using add gates at the inputs.

variables represented but it will be evident that the circuit is again symmetrical in structure and that the choice of the output that represents Y is arbitrary.

In the diagram of Fig. 14–28 the electrical circuit is given, using resistance gates to realize the Add gates in the symbolic diagram.

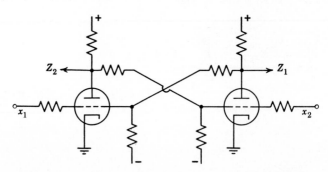

Fig. 14–28. Circuit schematic derived from Fig. 14–27.

This will be recognized as a familiar form of the flip-flop circuit without puller tubes. Outputs are taken from the plate terminals as indicated (voltage dividers in the output circuits are omitted).

The next example is a conventional synthesis which is interesting, however, in the contrasts between two alternate solutions.

Example 14–3

We are to synthesize an electronic sequential circuit which has a single output and two inputs. Only one of the inputs can change at a time. Every time x_2 *changes*, and only at those times, the output is to assume the value of x_1 and hold that value until x_2 again changes.

A primitive flow table and its merger diagram are given in Fig. 14–29. We note that the merger diagram is a closed figure which joins all eight

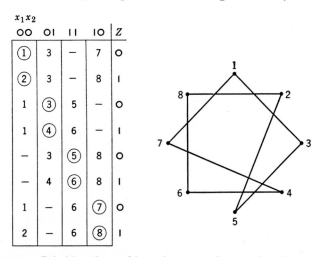

$x_1 x_2$

	OO	OI	II	IO	Z
①	3	—	7	O
②	3	—	8	I
1	③	5	—	O
1	④	6	—	I
—	3	⑤	8	O
—	4	⑥	8	I
1	—	6	⑦	O
2	—	6	⑧	I

Fig. 14–29. Primitive flow table and merger diagram for Example 14–3.

of the nodes. There are hence two possible minimum-row mergers, represented by the sets (a) $(1, 3)$, $(5, 2)$, $(8, 6)$, $(4, 7)$, and (b) $(1, 7)$, $(4, 6)$, $(8, 2)$, $(5, 3)$. When these mergers are made we obtain the reduced flow tables of Fig. 14–30 (a) and (b), respectively. Secondary

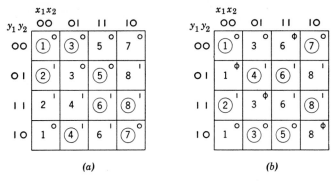

(a)   *(b)*

Fig. 14–30. Flow matrices derived from the two minimum-row mergers of Fig. 14–29.

states are also shown for these tables, but it should be noted that the table of Fig. 14–30(b) can be realized without races with any assignment of secondary states based on two secondary variables.

Output values are superposed on the flow matrices by marking the values in the upper right-hand corner of each cell. In the matrix of Fig. 14–30(a), after the outputs associated with stable states are entered it is found that all outputs for unstable states are fixed by the existence of transitions for which no output changes are permitted. In the matrix of Fig. 14–30(b) the outputs for half of the unstable states can be chosen optionally. One set of choices leads to the output $Z = y_2$.

If we examine the flow matrices for essential hazards we find that there are none present in either matrix. Hence, if we realize excitation functions which are free of static hazards the final synthesis need not contain delay elements.

$y_1 y_2$ \ $x_1 x_2$	00	01	11	10
00	00	00	01	10
01	01	00	01	11
11	01	10	11	11
10	00	10	11	10

$y_1 y_2$ \ $x_1 x_2$	00	01	11	10
00	00	10	01	00
01	00	01	01	11
11	11	10	01	11
10	00	10	10	11

(a)   (b)

Fig. 14–31.   Excitation matrices derived from the flow matrices of Fig. 14–30.

The excitation matrices are presented in Fig. 14–31. For the matrix of Fig. 14–31(a) the excitation functions in hazard-free form are

$$Y_1 = x_1 x_2' + x_2 y_1 + x_1 y_1$$

$$= (x_1 + x_2)(x_1 + y_1)(x_2' + y_1)$$

$$Y_2 = x_1 x_2 + x_2' y_2 + x_1 y_2$$

$$= (x_1 + x_2')(x_1 + y_2)(x_2 + y_2)$$

and the output function, from Fig. 14–30(a), is

$$Z = x_2 y_1 + x_2' y_2 + y_1 y_2$$

$$= (x_2 + y_2)(x_2' + y_1)(y_1 + y_2)$$

While the output function from Fig. 14–30(b) is quite simple, the excitation functions from Fig. 14–31(b) are considerably more complex than those hitherto given. We hence will continue the synthesis using the excitation and output functions derived from Figs. 14–30(a) and 14–31(a).

It is convenient in designing the circuit to write the complementary excitation functions

$$Y_1' = (x_1' + x_2)(x_2' + y_1')(x_1' + y_1')$$

$$Y_2' = (x_1' + x_2')(x_2 + y_2')(x_1' + y_2')$$

These lead directly to the circuit shown in Fig. 14–32. Electronic elements are used to realize the excitation functions and there is hence

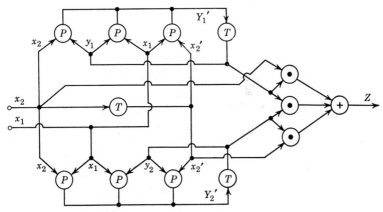

Fig. 14–32. Electronic sequential circuit as synthesized in Example 14–3.

the required gain in both feedback loops. The output function is generated by gates and these may be diode gates.

It is important to observe that the two excitation functions in this circuit operate independently of each other. In the algebraic expressions for the excitations each is a function of the input variables and of its own response, but neither contains the other response as a variable. It is only in the output function that both secondary response variables appear. This is a situation in which it can readily be seen that it is physically impossible to have an essential hazard. When there is no functional dependence of one secondary excitation on another secondary response it becomes immaterial, so far as secondary action is concerned, whether there is delay in the propagation of a primary-variable change.

14.6 Other Switching Devices in Sequential Circuits

Regardless of the nature and characteristics of the switching elements to be used in a sequential circuit operating on voltage or current levels, once we have written the excitation and output functions the first problem is to design a combinational circuit that realizes those functions. We then provide feedback paths, with or without delay elements, to furnish the response variables required as inputs to the combinational network. Finally, we must ascertain whether each feedback loop has gain, either from the elements used in the combinational network or from amplifiers introduced for that purpose.

Semiconductor diodes have an extremely large range of application in switching circuits. With the need for gain in a feedback loop clearly recognized we can apply diodes with confidence in the realization of the combinational parts of the circuit. Diodes operate compatibly in sequential circuits in which loop gain is supplied by electronic tubes, transistors, or magnetic amplifiers. Combinations with transistors and with magnetic elements are becoming especially attractive. These circuits are entirely static, their power requirements are low, and the physical size is small.

We have already examined the combinational properties of transistors. Since they can supply gain there is no problem in using them to realize sequential circuits in accordance with the methods discussed in this chapter.

It will be interesting now to examine a new switching device—the cryotron*—which is especially promising as an element in extremely compact switching circuits. This device takes advantage of the phenomenon of superconductivity, which is a property of many metals and alloys. A piece of superconductive material at ordinary room temperature has a definite electrical resistance which may be small but is not zero in value. At a certain very low temperature the resistance of a superconductor drops to zero. Tantalum, for example, becomes a superconductor at a temperature of 4.4°K. At a slightly lower temperature, 4.2°K for tantalum, it becomes possible to control the superconductivity by the application of a small magnetic field (50 to 100 oersteds). With no magnetic field applied the resistance of the superconductive material is zero. If the magnetic field strength is gradually increased a critical value is reached beyond which the superconductive material regains its normal resistance. It should be emphasized that the effect is not one in which the resistance of the material is decreased to a low value; the resistance of a superconductor becomes *zero* at its low-temperature transition point if no magnetic field is present.

The required low temperature is obtained by immersing the entire

---

* D. A. Buck, "The Cryotron—A Superconductive Computer Component," *Proc. I.R.E.*, Vol. 44, No. 4, April 1956, pp. 482–493.

device in liquid helium. By making all the control windings and the interconnections of superconducting materials, and immersing the entire switching circuit in liquid helium, we avoid introducing resistances between the switching elements, and the total power requirement becomes very small.

As described by Buck, a typical cryotron is a piece of tantalum wire, one inch long and 0.009 inch in diameter, on which is wound a single layer of insulated niobium wire of 0.003-inch diameter. The central tantalum wire is called the *gate* and the wire wound on it is called a control winding. At normal room temperature the resistance of the gate described is about 0.01 ohm. Because of the low impedance levels found in assembled cryotron circuits the power supply is a current source. With a constant-current input supplied to the circuit, switching can be accomplished by providing paths of zero resistance for the 1's of transmission and complementary paths to by-pass the supply current for the 0's of transmission. A monitoring cryotron, with suitable output measuring equipment, can be used to detect the presence of current in one path or another of the switching circuit.

We can study the basic switching action with the aid of the circuit in Fig. 14–33. Two cryotrons, A and A', have their control windings

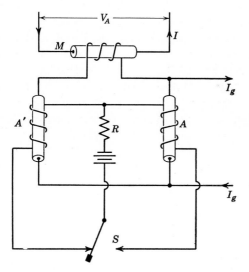

Fig. 14–33. The cryotron as a complementing device.

connected in a circuit with the transfer switch S so that control current passes through one of the control windings but not the other. The resistance R limits the control current. The gates of these two cryotrons are supplied in parallel by the constant current I_g. Gate current leaving the A' cryotron passes through the *control* winding of the monitoring cryotron M. The gate current, I_m, of the monitor is supplied from another constant current source.

If the control winding A' is energized its gate is resistive and the gate of the A cryotron has zero resistance. Consequently *all* the gate current I_g passes through the A gate and *none* passes through the A' gate. Hence the current in the control winding of monitor M is zero and its gate has zero resistance. The voltage V_A at the output of the monitor is zero because the monitor gate current is passing through a zero resistance.

If the control winding of cryotron A is energized the gate current I_g passes through gate A' and also through the control winding of the monitor M. With its control winding energized the gate of the monitor becomes resistive and the output voltage V_A rises.

In cryotron circuits switching variables are represented by current levels. There will either be the full current of the constant-current source flowing, or there will be zero current. These levels represent 1 and 0, respectively. An individual cryotron has a transmission which is the complement of the variable represented by the current in its control winding. If the input variable A has the value 1, the gate current is 0, and vice versa. The gate current represents the transmission of the cryotron and we can write $T = A'$. Thus the individual cryotron behaves like a relay with a single, normally closed contact.

In the circuit of Fig. 14–33 it may readily be verified that the output of the monitor cryotron represents the variable A. The need for using both A and A' cryotrons arises from the fact that although the ratio of a normal gate resistance to its superconductive resistance is infinite, the difference between the two values is small. If we try to detect and use the small change in resistance the result will be unsatisfactory from the standpoint of representing binary variables. When, however, two parallel resistances are supplied by a constant current, the current divides so that the ratio of the currents in the two paths is the reciprocal of the resistance ratio. Thus, the parallel connection of two paths representing complementary functions is our means of using resistance ratio instead of resistance difference to represent binary variables. It should be noted here that the operation of a cryotron is independent of the direction of the current through its gate and through its control winding. Because it is bilateral in operation the cryotron is not restricted to use in series-parallel circuits.

A simple combinational circuit is shown in Fig. 14–34 in which the output voltage V_T of the monitor M is to represent the transmission function $T = A + B'C$. In the upper part of the circuit we provide a zero-resistance path for the gate current which will control the monitor output. The cryotron gates are connected as though they were contacts, that is, with a series connection representing multiplication and a parallel connection representing addition, but the control windings are excited by the complements of the variables given in the

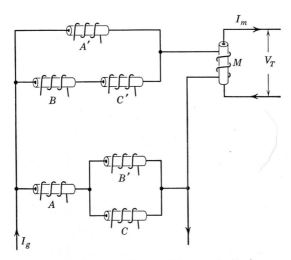

Fig. 14–34. Cryotron combinational circuit.

transmission function. This is the kind of circuit we would have to use if we were working with relays which had only normally closed contacts. In order to have zero current through the control winding of the monitor when $T = 0$, we provide a lower path in which the flow of gate current represents the complementary transmission $T' = A'(B + C')$.

Buck has shown that the cryotron can be designed to have current and power gain. In this type of circuit the feedback necessary for sequential switching must be a feedback of current, so the loop gain requirement is satisfied. Since all interconnections between cryotrons are superconductive, including the feedback connections, and since all control windings are also superconductive, the feedback current can be used in more than one control winding.

Time delay in the response of a cryotron is essentially that represented by the time constant of the control circuitry. If sequential circuits using cryotrons are designed as though they were to be built using relays with normally closed contacts only, and if all necessary precautions are taken in the design to avoid static hazards and races,

the normal delays present in the control circuits of the cryotrons will
provide proper sequential action.

A simple set of feedback connections is illustrated in Fig. 14–35.
This circuit is based on Example 14–1 in which

$$Y = x_2 (x_1' + y)$$

$$Y' = x_2' + x_1 y'$$

In the circuit diagram we have omitted the control windings on cryotrons which receive primary variables as inputs. The gate current

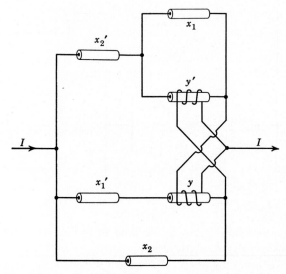

Fig. 14–35. Feedback in a cryotron sequential circuit.

which passes through the upper path represents the excitation Y and
this current is fed back as the control current of the cryotron y in the
lower path. The gate current of the lower path represents the excitation Y' and this current is fed back to the control winding of the cryotron y' in the upper path. The other terminals of the control windings
on y and y' are joined to form the return path to the constant-current
source. It is necessary, of course, to supply suitable input and output
circuits to complete a synthesis but this requires only appropriate combinational design.

It may be thought somewhat fanciful to consider operating an entire
switching circuit in liquid helium. However, the production and
storage of liquid helium has become an efficient and relatively inex-
pensive matter. As an indication of the practicability of the method,

Buck has estimated that the necessary cryotrons and interconnections for a large-scale digital computer can be built in about one cubic foot of space and would consume about one-half watt of power. Both the quantity of liquid helium required in the reservoir and the loss of helium due to heating can therefore be quite small.

PROBLEMS

14.1 The circuits shown are both electronic sequential switching circuits. Each has two inputs, X_1 and X_2, and a single output, Z.
   1. Starting from the initial condition $X_1 = X_2 = Z = 0$, derive for each circuit the output sequence resulting from the following sequence of input states X_1, X_2: 00, 10, 11, 01, 11, 10, 00, 01, 00.
   2. Give a word description of the terminal action of each circuit.

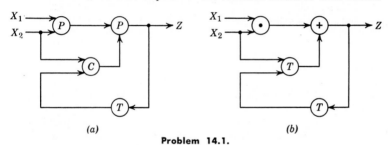

(a)   (b)

Problem 14.1.

14.2 It has been determined that a vacuum-tube switching circuit will meet its terminal requirements if its single secondary excitation is the function $Y = x_1' (y + x_2)$ and if its single output is the function $Z = x_1'x_2'y'$.

Starting with the triode chain shown as a "secondary device," design one physical realization of the circuit (using vacuum tubes in the combinational networks).

In the final circuit diagram all obviously unnecessary tubes should be eliminated. Show in this diagram the algebraic expressions for the voltage at each terminal of each tube, and show at what location delay would be inserted if it is necessary for proper circuit operation.

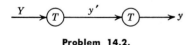

Problem 14.2.

14.3 Synthesize a switching circuit with electron tubes and rectifiers, corresponding to the terminal requirements listed in the flow table shown. Your de-

x_1x_2				
00	01	11	10	Z_1Z_2
–	3	①	2	00
6	–	1	②	01
7	③	1	–	10
7	–	1	④	10
6	⑤	1	–	01
⑥	5	–	2	01
⑦	3	–	4	10

Problem 14.3.

rived schematic diagram is to show the algebraic nature of all voltages and the exact location of all secondary delay points.

The voltages X_1 and X_2 (but not their complements) are available from low impedance sources. Your derived circuit is to utilize as few grids as possible.

14.4 The electronic escapement circuit shown has the property that the output Z becomes equal to the input X_1 when X_2 changes from "low" to "high." At all other times Z retains the level it had when X_2 last changed from "low" to "high." Assume that X_1 cannot change when X_2 is rising.

1. Derive the primitive flow table.
2. Derive two (or more) different types of minimum-row merged flow table.
3. Obtain at least four major variations of the possible electronic realizations, using only triode and pentode vacuum-tube gates, and diode adding and multiplying circuits.
4. Draw the complete circuit diagram (including diode load resistors, plate load resistors, etc.) of the simplest circuit found.

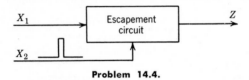

Problem 14.4.

14.5 Design a two-input, one-output electronic sequential circuit for which the output is 1 at the end of the input sequence $X_1X_2 = 00, 01, 11$ and which maintains this output for all input variations until the input completes the sequence $X_1X_2 = 11, 01, 00$ at which time the output is to become 0. At most, a single input variable is changing state at any time. Realize the secondary excitation functions separately and each with as few grids as possible. Indicate any static hazards that may be present.

14.6 Design a d-c coupled electronic circuit having two level inputs and one level output, with the following terminal action: the output level is high if and only if both input levels are high and if at the preceding input state both input levels were low.

Obtain a minimal realization of the circuit using only triodes and rectifiers. Particular effort is to be made to minimize the number of triodes necessary. (Two triodes and seven rectifiers are sufficient.) Show in the schematic diagram the location of the secondary delay point(s).

14.7 An electronic sequential circuit is to have two voltage-level inputs, X_1 and X_2, and one voltage-level output, Z. Changes of input state will always occur one variable at a time. The output signal must indicate which input variable *changed* last. Specifically, whenever X_1 *changes* Z is to become *or remain* 0, and whenever X_2 *changes* Z is to become *or remain* 1.

1. Write a primitive flow table and reduce it to a minimum-row form.
2. Determine a secondary-variable assignment and write the excitation and output matrices.
3. Design an electronic network with all variables, including the output, marked. Assume that the input voltages and their complements are available, but the synthesis is to minimize the

number of grids required exclusive of those used to obtain input complements. The only logical elements to be used are triodes and pentodes. Show that the solution involves no static hazard.

14.8 The diagram shown is a representation of a direct-coupled electronic circuit with level inputs and outputs. You are to consider the effect of delay at two points, A and B, in the feedback loop. For the purposes of this problem assume that there is no delay except at these points.

1. Derive the flow table and Z matrix if there is delay at A but not at B.
2. Derive the flow table and Z matrix if there is delay at B but not at A. What is the "steady-state" behavior of this circuit?
3. Derive the flow table and Z matrix if there are delays at both A and B. Discuss the relationship of these results to those of parts 1 and 2.
4. Resynthesize the circuit of part 1 in an economical form using only diode gates and a minimum number of plate-loaded triodes. (Two grids and six diodes are sufficient.)

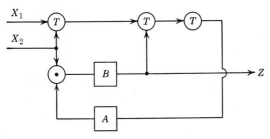

Problem 14.8.

14.9 Simplify the given sequential circuit by resynthesis, using only triodes and pentodes.

14.10 Synthesize a minimal form of the voltage-level electronic sequential circuit shown. Assume no double change of input variables can occur, and that when the power is first turned on the primary variables X_1 and X_2, and the secondary y variables are all 0.

The final circuit is to be free of static hazards.

14.11 The output of a factory consists of two kinds of opaque cylindrically shaped objects which differ in external characteristics only in the fact that one kind of object is 19.8 inches long and the other has a length of 20.2″. Through a mistake someone has put some of the "long" objects into a storage bin which should have in it only "short" objects:

To sort out the long objects in the bin it is decided to load a rapidly moving conveyor belt with these objects and to arrange that each object passes before two narrow beams of light which are spaced 20.0 inches apart, as shown, and which in turn shine into two photocell units, P_1 and P_2. Each photocell is arranged so that when its corresponding light beam is *interrupted* by an object on the belt the output of the photocell is a *low voltage*; but when the light beam reaches the photocell unit its output voltage is high. It is also known that objects on the conveyor belt may be spaced as little as two inches apart, but no less.

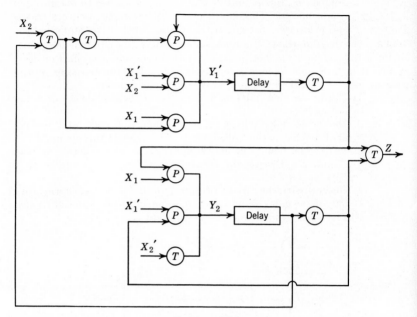

Problem 14.9.

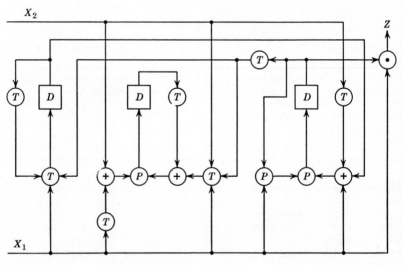

Problem 14.10.

You are to derive an electronic switching circuit which has as its two input voltages the voltages from the photocell units. (Assume that only single changes of input state are possible.) The single output voltage from the switching circuit is to be high if and only if both light beams are being interrupted by the same *long* object. Only vacuum tubes are to be used in your realization and the output voltage is to be taken either from a plate-loaded triode (or triodes in parallel) or from a cathode-follower. The schematic diagram of the circuit should be marked to show (1) the algebraic description of each voltage, and (2) the location of each time-delay element.

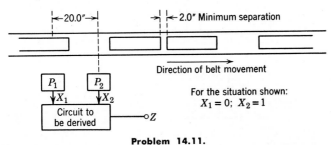

For the situation shown:
$$X_1 = 0; \quad X_2 = 1$$

Problem 14.11.

14.12 Design an electronic sequential circuit that meets the requirements of Problem 12.10. Use the most effective selection of triodes, pentodes, and rectifiers to obtain a minimal network. If hazards are present determine what circuit changes are required to be hazard free.

14.13 In the flow tables shown, assume that the input state can change in only one variable at a time. List all the essential hazards in each flow table. Describe each hazard by stating the entry that represents the initial state and the input variable that must change.

(a)

$y_1 y_2$ \ $x_1 x_2$	00	01	11	10
00	①	2	⑤	7
01	3	②	5	⑦
11	③	④	⑥	8
10	1	—	6	⑧

(b)

$y_1 y_2$ \ $x_1 x_2$	00	01	11	10
00	①	2	5	⑧
01	6	②	3	—
11	⑥	4	③	7
10	1	④	⑤	⑦

Problem 14.13.

CHAPTER 15

Pulsed
sequential
circuits

High-speed, digital computing machines, with their sensational advances in design and in applications, offer eloquent testimony to the power of the pulse. In this chapter we extend the concepts and methods we have developed for the synthesis of sequential circuits using levels to represent variables, to the design of circuits in which variables are represented by pulses. There are many types of pulse circuits, using many types of components. Our objective in this discussion is to establish principles and methods that are sufficiently powerful and flexible to be applicable and effective in any pulse switching situation.

15.1 Flow Tables for Circuits with Pulse Inputs

It will be useful to start by examining a specific problem of synthesis. As an example, let us consider the design of a circuit, as in Fig. 15–1, for which the required performance and the conditions of operation are:

1. All inputs, and the output, are pulses.

2. The shapes of input pulses and their durations are assumed to be compatible with the components and circuits used.

3. There must be a minimum time interval between successive pulses which we will call the *resolution time* of the circuit.

4. An output pulse is to be obtained if and only if pulses occur at the inputs in the order indicated in Fig. 15–1, that is, in the sequence

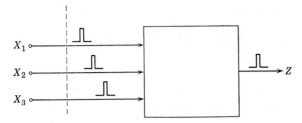

Fig. 15–1. A circuit to be synthesized.

X_1, X_2, X_3. To get another output pulse the specified sequence must be repeated.

5. The output pulse is to occur simultaneously with the input pulse X_3, but otherwise no two pulses occur simultaneously.

Items 1, 4, and 5 in this list specify primarily points of logical design. Items 2 and 3 pertain primarily to engineering requirements. For the purposes of this discussion we will assume that engineering requirements have been satisfied.

One way to regard a pulse is to think of it as consisting of two changes of voltage or current level. If we take this view we can write a flow table similar to those we have already learned to write, as shown in Fig. 15–2. Since item 5 in the specifications given indicates that there can be only one input pulse at a time, the flow table contains fewer columns than those we usually write. The input changes which occur always start in the column 000; then there is a change of a single variable to, say, 010 for a change of X_2, and the primary state again returns to 000 before any further change can occur. We need not provide columns in the flow table for all possible combinations of $X_1X_2X_3$. As we see in Fig. 15–2, only the columns corresponding to the input states 000, 100, 010, and 001 are needed.

In the abbreviated table there are many blank entries, and hence many optional choices of secondary excitation values. These result from the fact that for circled entries in the

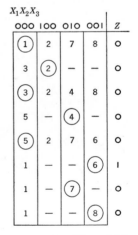

$X_1X_2X_3$

000	100	010	001	Z
①	2	7	8	0
3	②	—	—	0
③	2	4	8	0
5	—	④	—	0
⑤	2	7	6	0
1	—	—	⑥	1
1	—	⑦	—	0
1	—	—	⑧	0

Fig. 15–2. Flow table derived by treating pulses as changes of level.

columns other than 000, the only possible transition is back to the 000 column. If we were to continue to use this form of flow table for the synthesis of pulse circuits the columns which are not included could also be used to enter optional choices of values in writing excitation functions.

Suppose we think of the inputs X_1, X_2, and X_3 as pulses which are of quite short duration relative to the minimum time interval between successive pulses. For example, the pulse duration might be one millisecond and the interval between one pulses second. It is evident, then, from an examination of the flow table that most of the time the circuit is in one of the states represented by the entries ①, ③, or ⑤, all of which are in the column representing the input state 000. The other circled entries in the table represent states which are occupied only briefly. During the change from state ⑤ to state ① by way of state ⑥, we briefly raise the output level and thus produce an output pulse. The high output level is associated with the entry ⑥, but if we were to construct an output matrix we would surely assign the 1 value also to the state represented by uncircled 6 (inspection shows that this entry would still be present in a reduced flow table after merger).

If we can use secondary elements that change state (in some sense which at the moment we do not define) in response to a pulse input, we can regard the circuit state as that represented by a combination of secondary states. There would be no primary devices, and the secondary state would be the total state of the circuit. It then becomes useful to visualize the circuit operation in response to input pulses by means of a flow diagram as given in Fig. 15–3. In this type of diagram the nodes represent circuit states and the branches which connect nodes represent the transitions between states. Each branch is marked to show what pulse causes the transition represented and what output response is caused. We have here used Z_0 to stand for $Z = 0$ and Z_1 to stand for $Z = 1$. Between the nodes S_1 and S_2 there is a branch marked X_2,Z_0. This means that an X_2 pulse causes the transition and that there is no output pulse during the change. If the next pulse is X_3, however, the circuit is driven to the state represented by node S_3. The branch indicating this change is marked X_3,Z_1. There is hence an output pulse associated with this transition.

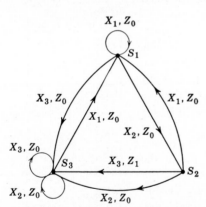

Fig. 15–3. A flow diagram for the circuit to be synthesized.

In constructing this type of diagram we do not necessarily know at the outset how many nodes are required. As a starting point, let us begin with the lower left-hand node and say that if, with the circuit in that state, an X_1 pulse is received, we have established the first part of the sequence required to obtain an output. From this node, which is marked S_3, a branch leads to the node marked S_1. The branch is marked X_1,Z_0 to indicate that an X_1 pulse causes the transition and that there is no output pulse. It is possible, though, that while the circuit is in the state represented by node S_3, an X_2 pulse or an X_3 pulse might be received. No matter what the rest state of a circuit is we must always indicate its response to any allowable input action. In the preceding discussion we have taken state S_3 as a starting point in establishing a sequence which produces an output. If there is either an X_2 pulse or an X_3 pulse we want the circuit to stay in state S_3 so that it can make the transition to state S_1 when an X_1 pulse arrives to start the specified X_1, X_2, X_3 sequence. Hence we show two closed loops at the node representing state S_3, indicating that if either the X_2 or the X_3 pulse is received the circuit remains in state S_3 and no output is produced.

State S_1 is reached by an X_1 pulse from state S_3. If the circuit is in state S_1 and another X_1 pulse is received, the circuit must remain in that state because any X_1 pulse can be the beginning of the specified sequence. However, if an X_3 pulse is received the circuit must return to state S_3, as shown by the branch marked X_3,Z_0, to be prepared for another X_1 pulse.

If an X_2 pulse is received while the circuit is in state S_1 it represents the second pulse in the specified sequence, so the transition marked X_2,Z_0 is directed to state S_2. At state S_2 we must again examine the consequences of all possible inputs. Of course, if the input pulse X_3 is received we show a transition back to the state S_3, and an output pulse is indicated for this transition because it represents the completion of the specified sequence. The transition back to the state S_3 is clearly indicated because the circuit is then prepared to receive an X_1 pulse and thus begin a new sequence. If, with the circuit in state S_2, an X_1 pulse is received, it represents a failure to complete the required sequence and the transition marked X_1,Z_0 takes the circuit back to the state S_1. This action is clearly appropriate because any X_1 pulse can begin the specified sequence. If, with the circuit in the state S_2, a second X_2 pulse is received, it represents an interruption of the specified sequence and the transition marked X_2,Z_0 directs the circuit back to the state S_3 so that it will be ready to begin a new sequence.

The flow diagram is not a necessary step in the synthesis of a pulse circuit but it is a useful means for visualizing circuit performance and for making sure that all possible transitions are included. The information contained in the flow diagram may be summarized in the modified flow table of Fig. 15-4. In this table each column heading identifies the input pulse received and each row represents a rest state of the circuit.

	X_1	X_2	X_3	$y_1 y_2$
S_1	S_1, Z_0	S_2, Z_0	S_3, Z_0	0 0
S_2	S_1, Z_0	S_3, Z_0	S_3, Z_1	0 1
S_3	S_1, Z_0	S_3, Z_0	S_3, Z_0	1 1
	—	—	—	1 0

Fig. 15–4. A modified flow table contains the same information as the flow diagram.

The numbering of the row states is entirely arbitrary. Each entry in the table shows the destination state and the output to be obtained, in response to the input pulse represented by the column under which the entry is made. We observe in the flow table that in the column under X_1 the destination is always the state S_1, and we might therefore identify that state as the one occupied by the circuit at the beginning of the specified sequence. If the circuit is in the state S_1 and an X_2 pulse is received it is directed to go to the state S_2 without producing an output. Hence, state S_2 represents the state of the circuit when the first two pulses required in the sequence have been received. If the circuit is in state S_2 and an X_3 pulse is received it is directed to the state S_3 and an output pulse is indicated. The state S_3 is reached after any X_3 pulse, and after any X_2 pulse, except an X_2 pulse which occurs while the circuit is in the state S_1. The state S_3 is hence the state occupied by the circuit either at the conclusion of the specified sequence, or after any X_2 or X_3 pulse which is not a part of the specified sequence. It requires only three secondary states to obtain proper circuit performance for any sequence of inputs. We note both in the flow table and in the flow diagram that the circuit output pulse is associated only with transitions between rest states and not with the states themselves.

We now allow the states S_1, S_2, and S_3 to be identified with the states of some secondary devices. The assignment of secondary states is arbitrary and we begin with the assignment shown at the right of the table in Fig. 15-4.

We will now draw a new matrix which will show at each entry which secondary device or devices must *change* state when an input pulse corresponding to that column is received. In writing the entries we enter 1 if a secondary change is required and 0 if no change is required. For example, in the flow table the entry in the second row of the X_2 column directs the circuit to go to state S_3. This requires the secondary state to change from 01 to 11. In the transition matrix of Fig. 15–5 the corresponding entry is 10, indicating that the variable y_1 changes and y_2 does not change when the secondary state changes from 01 to 11.

We now examine the secondary device represented by Fig. 15–6. It is shown as having a pulse input τ, and outputs y and y' which are complementary voltage levels. There is a time delay indicated in the device to signify that the output voltage levels change some time *after* the input pulse is received. In this type of device the output levels *change* after every input pulse.

$y_1 y_2$	X_1	X_2	X_3
1. OO	OO	O I	I I
2. O I	O I	I O	I O'
3. I I	I I	OO	OO
I O	(I O)	(O I)	(O I)

$\tau_1 \tau_2$

Fig. 15–5. A transition matrix for the flow table of Fig. 15–4.

The primary input variables and the τ variables which provide the inputs to the secondary devices are all pulse variables. We allow 1 to mean that a pulse is present and 0 to mean that there is no pulse. The d-c levels at the secondary outputs are treated as before.

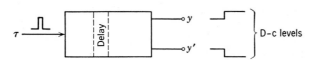

Fig. 15–6. One type of toggle, or flip-flop, device. Its outputs change after each input pulse.

Suppose we consider two of these secondary devices connected in the feedback circuit of Fig. 15–7. The combinational network is one in which the d-c levels of the secondary response variables control gates which permit pulses from the X_1, X_2, and X_3 inputs to pass to or to be blocked from the outputs represented by Z, τ_1, and τ_2. In response to pulses at the τ_1, τ_2 outputs the corresponding secondary devices change state and after a time delay the secondary response variables change the pattern of open and closed gates.

The matrix we have written in Fig. 15–5 describes the secondary changes which must occur in response to the indicated primary input pulses. This matrix therefore describes the τ_1, τ_2 excitations of the secondary devices. We proceed to write these functions by noting, for example, that in the X_1 column τ_1 is 1 for the secondary states 11 and

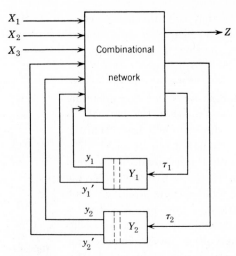

Fig. 15–7. Feedback circuit using τ toggles.

10 (the entry shown in the 10 state in parentheses is an optional entry). Hence, we say that there must be a τ_1 pulse if there is an X_1 pulse, and if $y_1 = 1$. This gives us the term $X_1 y_1$ which is the first term in the expressions which follow for τ_1, τ_2, and Z. The remaining terms in the functions for excitation pulses and for the output pulse are obtained in a similar manner.

$$\tau_1 = X_1 y_1 + X_2 y_1{}' y_2 + X_3 y_1{}'$$

$$\tau_2 = X_1 y_2 + X_2 y_2{}' + X_3 y_2{}'$$

$$Z = X_3 y_1{}' y_2$$

A circuit which realizes these functions is given in Fig. 15–8. We observe that each Multiply gate receives voltage *levels* from the secondary output responses, and receives *pulses* from the circuit inputs. If any Multiply gate has high level inputs when its circuit input line is pulsed, a τ pulse reaches the secondary device by way of the Add gate.

The flow matrix given in Fig. 15–4 is somewhat more elaborate than it need be. A simplified form is illustrated in Fig. 15–9(a). At the right of each row is placed the arbitary number which identifies the secondary state. The entries in each column describe the circuit action in response to an input pulse at the terminal associated with that column. Each entry consists of two numbers, the first of which shows the destination state and the second shows what output, if any, is associated with the indicated transition. In this type of flow table we omit the

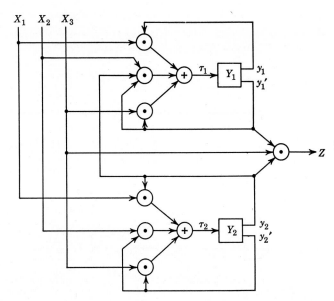

Fig. 15–8. Circuit synthesized from the transition matrix of Fig. 15–5.

letters S and Z and use as entries the numbers which in Fig. 15–4 were
the subscripts of those letters.

If the flow matrix of Fig. 15–9(a) is compared with that of Fig. 15–4
it will be found that the secondary state assigned to the third row is
changed from 11 to 10. For this new assignment, the combined excitation and output matrix is given in Fig. 15–9(b). Optional values selected are again enclosed in parentheses. An output pulse is indicated
by a 1 in the upper right-hand corner of the appropriate cell and it
should be noted that the output entry is optional for the secondary

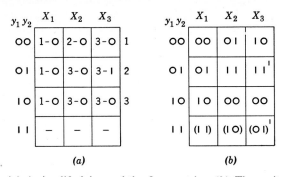

	X_1	X_2	X_3	
$y_1 y_2$				
00	1-0	2-0	3-0	1
01	1-0	3-0	3-1	2
10	1-0	3-0	3-0	3
11	–	–	–	

(a)

	X_1	X_2	X_3
$y_1 y_2$			
00	00	01	10
01	01	11	11'
10	10	00	00
11	(11)	(10)	(01)'

(b)

Fig. 15–9. (a) A simplified form of the flow matrix. (b) The excitation matrix
derived after a change in the secondary assignment.

state $y_1y_2 = 11$. From this matrix we write the excitation and output functions

$$\tau_1 = X_1y_1 + X_2y_2 + X_3y_1{}'$$

$$\tau_2 = X_1y_2 + X_2y_1{}' + X_3y_2$$

$$Z = X_3y_2$$

The circuit corresponding to these functions is given in Fig. 15–10. It contains only eighteen gate inputs in comparison with the circuit of Fig. 15–8 which contains twenty-two gate inputs. This number is used

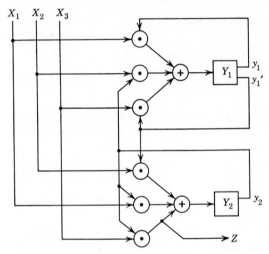

Fig. 15–10. The number of gate inputs has been reduced by changing the secondary assignment.

as a rough measure of circuit complexity since it usually corresponds to the number of grids, diodes, or bases used in an actual circuit. It is apparent that sometimes even a slight change in the assignment of secondary values can considerably alter the complexity of a pulse circuit.

In both the flow matrices of Figs. 15–5 and 15–9 we permitted excitation entries which required two secondary values to change, a race condition which we must be certain is not critical. In Fig. 15–9(b) let us examine the entry in the X_3 column and the second row. We see that the X_3 pulse is required to produce an output pulse and to provide excitation pulses to both secondary devices. Although this calls for a race between the secondary devices there need be no circuit hazard as a result. The timing of events is given in Fig. 15–11. We first observe that the Z, τ_1, and τ_2 pulses are all synchronous with the

X_3 input pulse. There must be sufficient delay in the response of the secondary devices to be sure that these pulses are delivered. The secondary response occurs *after* all pulse propagation requirements in the state of origin are satisfied. We also note that it is not necessary for the delay in the two secondary devices to be the same. In Fig. 15–11 we see that y_1 changes from 0 to 1 before y_2 changes from 1 to 0. For a short period the secondary state is $y_1 y_2 = 11$, but at this time there is no other circuit activity and it is therefore a harmless event. Although the secondary delays need not be equal, the next input pulse must not arrive before the slowest secondary device has reached its destination state. These secondary delays impose a minimum time interval between input pulses that we call the resolution time of the circuit. If inputs arrive at time intervals smaller than the resolution time, the secondary devices do not have time to respond and the circuit will not operate correctly. We will examine this problem more completely in Art. 15.4.

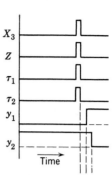

Fig. 15–11. Race conditions in pulse circuits need not cause circuit malfunction.

15.2 Secondary Devices

The example treated in the preceding article brought out the need for a secondary device which would respond to a pulse at its input terminals by changing state, and which would remain in that state until another pulse ordered another change. The bistable pair, or toggle, or flip-flop, are names for the kind of secondary device which meets these requirements. We synthesized a flip-flop in Art. 14.5, and we also saw that in the synthesis of level circuits flip-flop configurations appear in circuits without any attempt to introduce them. In designing pulse circuits, however, we use the pattern of feedback shown in Fig. 15–7 in which toggle devices are introduced as essential elements.

The state of a toggle is indicated by the d-c voltage levels at its output terminals. These levels are complementary and the values interchange when the toggle changes state. The output levels may be used as circuit outputs or as gate inputs to control and direct the propagation of pulses.

It is important that the relation between pulse duration and toggle response illustrated in Fig. 15–11 be maintained. When a toggle changes state after the input pulse which initiated the change is gone we can use feedback in the manner indicated in Fig. 15–7 without placing restrictions on the form of the excitation functions. If the response time of the toggle is shorter than the pulse duration we must make sure, for example, that no toggle output variable appears in its own excitation function.

We have already used the type of toggle which we call the τ flip-flop. Its response to pulses at its single input terminal is to change state after each pulse. In writing its excitation function we must supply an input pulse each time the flow matrix requires a change in the secondary variable represented by the toggle response.

Another type of toggle device, and probably the most widely used type, is called the set-reset flip-flop. It is represented by the diagram in Fig. 15–12. An input pulse is applied to either of the two input terminals Y_α and Y_β, but never to both simultaneously. The two outputs y_α and

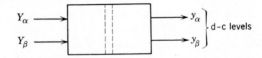

Fig. 15–12.   Excitation and response symbols for a set-reset flip-flop.

y_β are d-c voltage levels which have complementary values. These levels may, of course, be used in forming circuit outputs or they may be used as inputs to gates for the control of pulse propagation within the circuit. The basic mode of operation of the set-reset flip-flop is that after any input pulse the corresponding output level rises or remains high. Thus, $y_\alpha = 1$ after $Y_\alpha = 1$, and $y_\beta = 1$ after $Y_\beta = 1$.

It is convenient to describe the state of a set-reset flip-flop by the value of the level at y_α. There is no need to specify y_β also because $y_\beta = (y_\alpha)'$. It is necessary, however, to specify both Y_α and Y_β. A set-reset flip-flop has the important characteristic that if it is not required to change state in response to a circuit input pulse, we have the choice of blocking the pulse from the flip-flop input or of applying the pulse to the input which last received a pulse. As we shall see in Art. 15.3 this leads to numerous optional entries in writing excitation matrices. Using

Table 15–1.   Excitation of Set-Reset Flip-Flop

Required Response of y_α	Input Pulses Required Y_α	Y_β
$0 \rightarrow 0$	0	ϕ
$0 \rightarrow 1$	1	0
$1 \rightarrow 0$	0	1
$1 \rightarrow 1$	ϕ	0

the state of y_α to describe the state of the flip-flop and changes, if any, which are required, we can tabulate the required excitations as shown.

We note in Table 15–1 that both Y_α and Y_β must be specified. For the $0 \to 0$ transition, we have the option of applying a pulse to the Y_β input or not, but we must be sure to block the pulse from the Y_α input. In the next line of the table we have no choice at all, for Y_α must receive a pulse and Y_β must not receive a pulse.

It is interesting to note that by the addition of suitable gates we can convert one type of flip-flop to another. In Fig. 15–13 the output

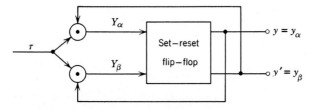

Fig. 15–13. Conversion of a set-reset flip-flop to a τ flip-flop.

levels of a set-reset flip-flop control Multiply gates at the inputs so that the flip-flop changes state after each input pulse. In its terminal action this combination behaves exactly like a τ flip-flop. In Fig. 15–14

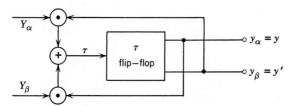

Fig. 15–14. Conversion of a τ flip-flop to a set-reset flip-flop.

pulses received from two sources are applied through gates to the input of a τ flip-flop so that at its terminals the combination behaves like a set-reset flip-flop.

Two other types of toggles have received some attention in pulse switching circuits. The first of these, as shown in the diagram of Fig. 15–15, combines the properties of the τ flip-flop with those of the

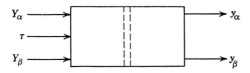

Fig. 15–15. A three-input flip-flop.

set-reset type. If a pulse is applied to the Y_α or the Y_β terminal the device acts like a set-reset flip-flop. If a pulse is applied to the τ input the flip-flop changes state. In Table 15–2 the required and the optional excitation values are summarized.

Table 15–2. Excitation of the Three-Input Flip-Flop

Required Response of y_α	Input Pulses Required Y_α	τ	Y_β
$0 \rightarrow 0$	0	0	ϕ
$0 \rightarrow 1$	$\begin{bmatrix} \phi \\ 1 \end{bmatrix}$	$\begin{matrix} 1 \\ \phi \end{matrix}$	$\begin{bmatrix} 0 \\ 0 \end{bmatrix}$
$1 \rightarrow 0$	$\begin{bmatrix} 0 \\ 0 \end{bmatrix}$	$\begin{matrix} 1 \\ \phi \end{matrix}$	$\begin{bmatrix} \phi \\ 1 \end{bmatrix}$
$1 \rightarrow 1$	ϕ	0	0

As we see from this tabulation there is a wide variety of optional excitation in the control of the three-input flip-flop. When the flip-flop is required to change state, there are three optional excitation patterns, and when it is required to hold its state there are two optional excitations. It is especially important, of course, to block pulses wherever a 0 is entered in the table.

Schematically, the other type looks exactly like a set-reset flip-flop. With respect to pulses applied to either Y_α or Y_β inputs alone, it behaves like a set-reset type. If however a pulse is applied to both the Y_α and Y_β inputs, the device changes state and thus behaves like a τ flip-flop. Its required and optional excitation patterns are summarized in Table 15–3.

Table 15–3. Excitation of the Two-Input Combination Flip-Flop

Required Response of y_α	Input Pulses Required Y_α	Y_β
$0 \rightarrow 0$	0	ϕ
$0 \rightarrow 1$	1	ϕ
$1 \rightarrow 0$	ϕ	1
$1 \rightarrow 1$	ϕ	0

We see from Table 15–3 that every required response of this device can be obtained with a choice of two excitation patterns. Moreover, there are only two situations which require that a pulse be blocked.

15.3 Synthesis of Sequential Circuits Using Toggle Devices

For this type of synthesis our general problem is first to write a flow table of the type studied in Art. 15.1, then to assign secondary states to the rows of the flow table, and finally to prepare an excitation matrix which provides the circuit action described in the flow table. From this matrix and the output matrix we write the excitation and output functions directly.

The feedback circuit of Fig. 15–7 shows the form of the circuit to be designed if we use τ flip-flops. The student may readily substitute set-reset type flip-flops in this circuit with, of course, provision for applying Y_α and Y_β excitation inputs to all flip-flops.

In making secondary-state assignments we will assume that input pulses are of short duration compared to the response times of the secondary devices, and that the time intervals between pulses are sufficient to allow all secondary responses to be completed before another pulse arrives. Under these conditions secondary assignments can be quite arbitrary. In fact, we can try alternate assignments to see if the combinational circuit can be simplified. We will examine in the next article the management of circuits in which these favorable conditions do not prevail.

In the examples which follow we will omit the step taken in Art. 15.1 of writing a flow table in terms of the successive levels represented by a pulse. Instead we will go directly to flow tables of the form illustrated in Fig. 15–4 and Fig. 15–9. It will be desirable at first to draw flow diagrams, as in Fig. 15–3, to visualize circuit action more clearly. In all flow tables and flow diagrams the only states shown are stable secondary states. Transitions from one stable state to another are initiated by pulses of short duration. Outputs may be pulses associated with the transitions, or may be levels associated with the stable states, or both.

Example 15–1

A circuit has two inputs, X_1 and X_2, and a single output Z. The variables X_1, X_2, and Z are pulse variables for which the value 0 means "no pulse present" and the value 1 means "pulse present." Input pulses appear on only one input at a time and the time interval between input pulses is always greater than the resolution time of the circuit.

There is to be an output pulse coincident with any X_2 pulse which follows exactly two, consecutive X_1 pulses. We wish to realize this circuit using either τ flip-flops or set-reset flip-flops.

Our first problem is to describe in some way the states of the circuit which are to be represented by the secondary variables. There must be at least the three states represented by the nodes in Fig. 15–16. If the pulse sequence consists of the pulses X_2-X_1-X_1-X_2-X_1-X_1-X_2, and if this pattern is repeated indefinitely, the circuit will make the transitions indicated by the arrows. The subsequence X_2-X_1-X_1-X_2 is required in order to produce an output pulse. We must have an initial X_2 pulse (at which time there may or may not be an output pulse) in order to begin counting X_1 pulses. If we then have exactly two X_1 pulses

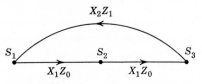

Fig. 15–16. A partial flow diagram, Example 15–1.

followed by an X_2 pulse, we produce an output pulse.

Clearly, any valid flow diagram must contain at least the partial diagram of Fig. 15–16, but it must also provide *at each node* a description of circuit action if either input is pulsed.

At node S_1 we show only the response to a pulse on X_1, so we must decide what the circuit does if there is a pulse on X_2. Since *any* X_2 pulse can be the start of the sequence $X_2\text{-}X_1\text{-}X_1\text{-}X_2$ there is no reason to direct the circuit away from state S_1, so in Fig. 15–17 the X_2 pulse at S_1 is indicated by a closed loop returning to S_1.

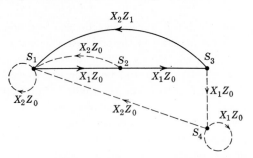

Fig. 15–17. Completed flow diagram, Example 15–1.

At node S_2 we must again decide what to do if a pulse is received on X_2. Previous reasoning indicates that any X_2 pulse can start the output-producing sequence. We hence show in Fig. 15–17 a transition from S_2 to S_1 caused by an X_2 pulse, and there is a 0 output.

In Fig. 15–16 we show that an X_2 pulse directs the circuit from state 3 back to state 1, and that there is an output associated with this transition. We have not, however, shown what happens if the circuit is in state 3 and receives an X_1 pulse. Can we direct the circuit back to either state 1 or state 2 in this event? Clearly we cannot, for that would permit state 3 to be reached again by receiving additional X_1 pulses, and it would then be possible to obtain an output at an X_2 pulse which followed more than two consecutive X_1 pulses.

An X_1 pulse received while the circuit is in state 3 must lead to a new state 4 which is indicated by the node S_4 in Fig. 15–17. We complete the flow diagram by indicating that the circuit remains in state 4 if another X_1 pulse is received and returns to state 1 if an X_2 pulse is received. The output is 0 for all transitions except for that initiated by the X_2 pulse from state 3 back to state 1.

We have here used the flow diagram to visualize all possible pulse sequences and to define circuit response. Looking back we now can see that the X_2 pulse clears the circuit of all memory of any previous X_1 pulses. State 1 can be entered only by X_2 pulses and every X_2 pulse returns the circuit to that state. We could therefore construct a flow table from the following descriptions of the meanings of each state; moreover, we see that we must provide exactly the number of states listed.

State 1—there has been no X_1 pulse since the last X_2 pulse.

State 2—there has been one X_1 pulse since the last X_2 pulse.

State 3—there have been two consecutive X_1 pulses since the last X_2 pulse.

State 4—there have been more than two consecutive X_1 pulses since the last X_2 pulse.

$y_1 y_2$	X_1	X_2	
00	2-0	1-0	1
01	3-0	1-0	2
11	4-0	1-1	3
10	4-0	1-0	4

Fig. 15–18. Flow matrix for Example 15–1.

From these statements we can write immediately the flow table of Fig. 15–18. State numbers are at the right of each row. The entries under each pulse designation show first the destination state and then the associated output. In the X_1 column each destination state is the next higher number state until we reach state 4 where no further change of state occurs. In the X_2 column all pulses return the circuit to state 1 and the transition which starts at state 3 produces an output.

An arbitrary secondary response assignment is given at the left of the flow table. This is used in Fig. 15–19 to write excitation matrices

$y_1 y_2$	X_1	X_2
00	0 1	00
01	1 0	0 1
11	0 1	1 1'
10	00	1 0

$\tau_1 \tau_2$

$y_{1\alpha} y_{2\alpha}$	X_1	X_2
00	0φ,1 0	0φ,0φ
01	1 0,φ0	0φ,0 1
11	φ0,0 1	0 1,0 1'
10	φ0,0φ	0 1,0φ

$Y_{1\alpha} Y_{1\beta} , Y_{2\alpha} Y_{2\beta}$

Fig. 15–19. Excitation matrices for τ flip-flops and for set-reset flip-flops.

for two kinds of flip-flops. A typical entry in the $\tau_1 \tau_2$ matrix is that for state 2 in the X_1 column. The flow matrix specifies state 3 as the destination state. For state 2 the secondary state is $y_1 y_2 = 01$, and for state 3, $y_1 y_2 = 11$. This requires y_1 to change but not y_2. Hence the entry in the $T_1 T_2$ matrix is 10.

The matrix at the right of Fig. 15–19 shows the Y_α and Y_β excitations required for set-reset flip-flops. We must remember that these entries do not indicate the changes of state to be made but describe the actual secondary response values required at the destination state. We do take advantage, however, of the options provided in Table 15–1. Thus in the transition from state 2 to state 3, the secondary change required is $y_{1\alpha} y_{2\alpha} = 01 \rightarrow 11$. To change $y_{1\alpha}$ from 0 to 1 we *must* provide the excitation $Y_{1\alpha} Y_{1\beta} = 10$. Since $y_{2\alpha}$ does not change we could enter $Y_{2\alpha} Y_{2\beta} = 00$, but, as we saw in Table 15–1, a repetition of the pulse on $Y_{2\alpha}$ does not change the state, so we enter $Y_{2\alpha} Y_{2\beta} = \phi 0$ and repeat the pulse if that helps simplify the circuit. Thus we find the composite entry in the X_1 column, second row, of the matrix is $10, \phi 0$.

From the $\tau_1 \tau_2$ matrix we write the excitation and output functions

$$\tau_1 = X_1 y_1' y_2 + X_2 y_1$$

$$\tau_2 = X_1 y_1' y_2' + X_1 y_1 y_2 + X_2 y_2$$

$$Z = X_2 y_1 y_2$$

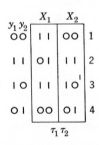

Fig. 15–20. Simplification of excitation functions by change of secondary assignments.

From the $Y_{1\alpha} Y_{1\beta}$, $Y_{2\alpha} Y_{2\beta}$ matrix we write the excitation and output functions

$$Y_{1\alpha} = X_1 y_{2\alpha}$$

$$Y_{1\beta} = X_2$$

$$Y_{2\alpha} = X_1 y_{1\beta}$$

$$Y_{2\beta} = X_1 y_{1\alpha} + X_2$$

$$Z = X_2 y_{1\alpha} y_{2\alpha}$$

The excitation functions for the set-reset flip-flops are reasonably simple, but those for the τ flip-flop version seem relatively complex. In Fig. 15–20 an arbitrary reassignment of secondary variables has been made and new entries prepared. This matrix yields the functions

$$\tau_1 = X_1 y_2' + X_2 y_1$$

$$\tau_2 = X_1 y_1 + X_1 y_2' + X_2 y_2$$

$$Z = X_2 y_1 y_2'$$

A circuit using set-reset flip-flops to meet the requirements of this example is given in Fig. 15–21. The circuit using τ flip-flops in Fig. 15–22 operates in accordance with the matrix of Fig. 15–20. The student

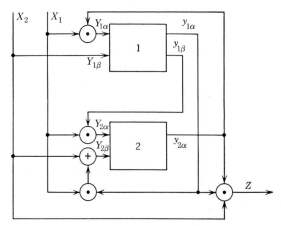

Fig. 15–21. Realization of required circuit using set-reset flip-flops.

will find it helpful in developing an understanding of the physical operation of these circuits to assume a sequence of input pulses, begin-

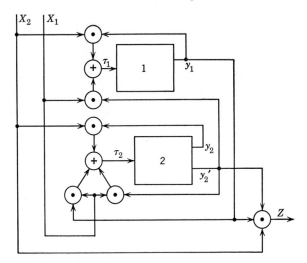

Fig. 15–22. Circuit of Example 15–1, using τ flip-flops.

ning with an X_2 pulse, and trace the propagation of each pulse through the network. The element used most often in developing the excitation functions is the Multiply gate. In Fig. 15–23 we see that the propaga-

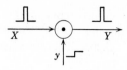

Fig. 15–23. The multiply gate in pulse switching.

tion of a pulse through a Multiply gate is controlled by the d-c level obtained from a flip-flop response.

Example 15–2

In Fig. 15–24 a circuit is shown with two pulse inputs, X and C, and one pulse output Z. The C input is a "clock" input. As we see in Fig. 15–24 the C pulses occur at uniform frequency. The X pulses occur between C pulses and there may be either one or two X pulses, as shown, between clock pulses. The time interval between pulses is always greater than the resolution time of the circuit.

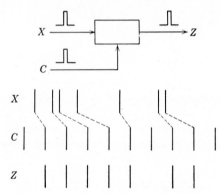

Fig. 15–24. Circuit to be synthesized, Example 15–2.

An output pulse is to be obtained for each X pulse received, but at the time of the next clock pulse. If more than one X pulse arrives between clock pulses, the circuit is to store the information and deliver

$y_{1\alpha} y_{2\alpha}$	X	C	
OO	1 - O	0 - O	0
O I	2 - O	0 - I	1
I I	3 - O	1 - I	2
I O	3 - O	2 - I	3

Fig. 15–25. Flow table with secondary assignment of set-reset flip-flops.

$y_{1\alpha} y_{2\alpha}$	X	C
OO	Oϕ, I O	Oϕ, Oϕ
O I	I O, ϕO	Oϕ, O I^{I}
I I	ϕO, O I	O I, ϕO^{I}
I O	ϕO, Oϕ	ϕO, I O^{I}

$Y_{1\alpha} Y_{1\beta}, Y_{2\alpha} Y_{2\beta}$

Fig. 15–26. Excitation matrix for set-reset flip-flops.

an output pulse at the next available clock pulse. We specify further that the circuit need store up to three X pulses only. A sequence of

X pulses and the resulting output pulses is shown in Fig. 15–24. Dotted lines indicate at which clock pulse each X pulse is read out. The circuit is to be designed using set-reset flip-flops.

For this design no flow diagram is needed. The circuit need only have states which represent: no X pulses stored, one X pulse stored, two X pulses stored, and three X pulses stored. If we identify these states by the numbers 0, 1, 2, and 3, we write the flow table of Fig. 15–25. An assignment of secondary response states is given with the flow table and we can hence write the excitation matrix of Fig. 15–26. The excitation and output functions are

$$Y_{1\alpha} = X y_{2\alpha}$$

$$Y_{1\beta} = C y_{2\alpha}$$

$$Y_{2\alpha} = X y_{1\beta} + C y_{1\alpha}$$

$$Y_{2\beta} = X y_{1\alpha} + C y_{1\beta}$$

$$Z = C(y_{1\alpha} + y_{2\alpha})$$

The circuit realizing these functions is drawn in Fig. 15–27.

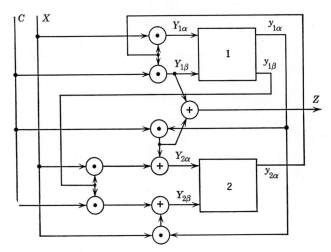

Fig. 15–27. Circuit synthesized in Example 15–2.

Sometimes we find it desirable to reduce the number of gates by using more flip-flops than are necessary. If in the flow table of Fig. 15–25 we replace the two-variable secondary assignment by a three-variable secondary assignment, reading from top to bottom, of 000, 001, 011, 111, we can rewrite the excitation matrix, as in Fig. 15–28. We now have not only the optional entries that are explicitly written in the excitation

$y_{1\alpha}\, y_{2\alpha}\, y_{3\alpha}$	X	C
000	Oϕ, Oϕ, 1 O	Oϕ, Oϕ, Oϕ
001	Oϕ, 1 O, ϕO	Oϕ, Oϕ, O1
011	1 O, ϕO, ϕO	Oϕ, O1, ϕO
111	ϕO, ϕO, ϕO	O1, ϕO, ϕO

$$Y_{1\alpha}\, Y_{1\beta},\; Y_{2\alpha}\, Y_{2\beta},\; Y_{3\alpha}\, Y_{3\beta}$$

Fig. 15–28. Excitation matrix with a redundant flip-flop.

matrix, but also four additional optional values because only four of the eight combinations of the three secondary variables are being used.

For example, let us determine the excitation $Y_{1\alpha}$. All entries in the C column are 0 so we need be concerned only with the X pulse. An excitation pulse at the $Y_{1\alpha}$ input is required when the secondary state is 011 and there is an X pulse, and the excitation pulse is optional when the X pulse occurs while the secondary state is 111. If we use only these provisions, and choose the optional value as 1, we write $Y_{1\alpha} = Xy_{2\alpha}y_{3\alpha}$. However, the secondary combinations 010 and 110 are among those that never appear, and we can assign the value 1 to these combinations also. When we group all the secondary combinations for which an X pulse must or may produce a $Y_{1\alpha}$ pulse we have simply $Y_{1\alpha} = Xy_{2\alpha}$. The entire group of excitations and the output function, after we have taken advantage of all options, are:

$$Y_{1\alpha} = Xy_{2\alpha} \qquad Y_{2\alpha} = Xy_{3\alpha} \qquad Y_{3\alpha} = X$$

$$Y_{1\beta} = C \qquad Y_{2\beta} = Cy_{1\beta} \qquad Y_{3\beta} = Cy_{2\beta}$$

$$Z = Cy_{3\alpha}$$

The circuit which realizes these functions is given in Fig. 15–29. It contains a total of five gates, in contrast with the nine gates of Fig. 15–27.

The construction of a flow table sometimes involves rather subtle difficulties. In the example that follows we can present an argument to justify either of two flow tables. It requires a special test to prove that one of them is wrong.

Example 15–3

A circuit with two inputs, X_1 and X_2, and two outputs, Z_1 and Z_2, receives pulses on only one input terminal at a time. Output pulses appear on only one output terminal at a time and these pulses are coincident with input pulses.

There must be an output pulse for every input pulse. A consecutive group of X_1 pulses is to cause a consecutive group of Z_1 pulses, and a consecutive group of X_2 pulses is to cause a consecutive group of Z_2 pulses. However, if any group of Z_1 pulses starts, at its termination it must contain an odd number of pulses; and if any group of Z_2 pulses starts, at its termination it must contain an even number of pulses. For this example consider zero an even number. Z_1 and Z_2 pulses are never to appear simultaneously.

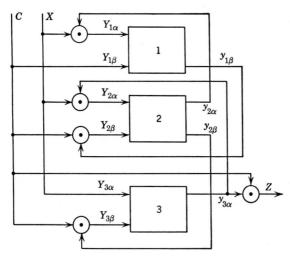

Fig. 15–29. Reduction in the number of gates by adding a redundant flip-flop.

It is not difficult to identify the states which must be represented by the secondary devices. These states designate whether the last output pulse was on Z_1 or Z_2 and whether it was an odd or even numbered member of its group. In Fig. 15–30 the abbreviated description "Even Z_1," applied to state 1, means that after the most recent output pulse there is an even-numbered group of Z_1 pulses. The remaining state descriptions are of similar character.

We start the construction of the flow table by making the entries shown in Fig. 15–30(a). When the input consists of a consecutive group of X_1 pulses the circuit alternately occupies state 2 and state 1, and each transition is accompanied by the output $Z_1Z_2 = 10$. When the input is a consecutive group of X_2 pulses the circuit alternately occupies state 3 and state 4, and the output at each transition is $Z_1Z_2 = 01$.

In Fig. 15–30(b) we have added the full entries in row 3 of the X_1 column and in row 2 of the X_2 column. At any time that a series of X_2 pulses has been accompanied by an even number of Z_2 pulses, a pulse on the X_1 input should immediately produce a Z_1 output pulse. Accordingly the entry in row 3 of the X_1 column directs the circuit to state 2, signifying an odd number of Z_1 pulses in the group, and requires the output 10. Similarly, the Z_1 group can be terminated when the number of pulses is odd, so the entry in row 2 of the X_2 column directs the circuit to state 4, signifying an odd number of pulses in the Z_2 group, and requires the output 01.

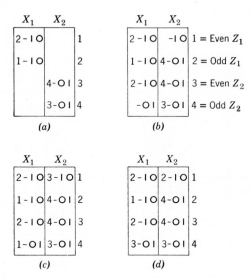

Fig. 15–30. Development of the flow table, Example 15–3.

There remain to be specified the entries in row 4 of the X_1 column and row 1 of the X_2 column. The situation in state 4 is that there is an odd number of pulses in the Z_2 group. No matter which input is pulsed next, the output must be a Z_2 pulse, since the group cannot be terminated until the number of pulses is even. In Fig. 15–30(b) we have hence entered the output 01, but the destination state is not specified. Likewise, in state 1 the Z_1 group contains an even number of pulses, and since this number must be odd before the group can terminate, we enter the output 10, even though the input is X_2.

Consider now the unspecified destination state in row 4 of the X_1 column. The X_1 pulse produces a Z_2 output, thereby making the Z_2 group even. But since it did not produce a Z_1 output, the Z_1 group also is even (zero is considered an even number). We might therefore specify state 1 (Z_1 even) or state 3 (Z_2 even) as the destination state. Likewise, in row 1 of the X_2 column, where the X_2 pulse produces a Z_1 output, we can direct the transition to state 3 (Z_2 even) or to state 2

(Z_1 odd). These two sets of entries are carried out in Fig. 15–30(c) and Fig. 15–30(d), respectively.

For most input sequences that might be applied, both flow tables specify the same output sequence. But if we apply the input sequence X_1-X_2-X_1-X_2-X_1-X_2, and so on, with the alternation of inputs continuing, we find a difference. With this input applied to the table of Fig. 15–30(c), the output sequence settles down to Z_1-Z_1-Z_2-Z_2-Z_1-Z_1-Z_2-Z_2, and so forth. This sequence contains even-numbered groups of Z_1 pulses and hence is false. With the same input sequence applied to the flow table of Fig. 15–30(d), two output sequences are possible, both of which are correct. If, starting in state 2, the first of the alternating input pulses is X_1, we obtain a continuous group of Z_1 pulses. But if we start in state 3 and apply an X_2 pulse first, the output is a continuous series of Z_2 pulses. In the first instance each X_1 pulse arrives when the Z_1 group is already odd in number, so this pulse changes the circuit to the "Z_1 even" state. The X_2 pulse that follows must hence produce another Z_1 pulse to make the number odd, and the cycle continues. A continuous group of Z_2 pulses in the second instance arises because the X_2 pulse always makes the Z_2 group odd and the next X_1 pulse must make it even.

Using the flow table of Fig. 15–30(d), we prepare the excitation and output matrices of Fig. 15–31. From these we write the functions

$$Y_{1\alpha} = X_2 y_{2\alpha}$$

$$Y_{1\beta} = X_1 y_{2\alpha}$$

$$Y_{2\alpha} = X_1 y_{2\beta} + X_2 y_{2\beta}$$

$$Y_{2\beta} = X_1 y_{1\beta} y_{2\alpha} + X_2 y_{2\alpha}$$

$$Z_1 = X_1 (y_{1\beta} + y_{2\alpha}) + X_2 y_{1\beta} y_{2\beta}$$

$$Z_2 = X_1 y_{1\alpha} y_{2\beta} + X_2 (y_{1\alpha} + y_{2\alpha})$$

The final circuit for this example should be drawn by the student. Note that the function $Y_{1\alpha}$ appears as a term in the expression for $Y_{2\beta}$,

$y_{1\alpha} y_{2\alpha}$	X_1	X_2			$y_{1\alpha} y_{2\alpha}$	X_1	X_2
OO	Oϕ, I O	Oϕ, I O	1		OO	I O	I O
O I	Oϕ, O I	I O, O I	2		O I	I O	O I
I I	O I, ϕO	ϕO, O I	3		I I	I O	O I
I O	ϕO, I O	ϕO, I O	4		I O	O I	O I

$Y_{1\alpha} Y_{1\beta}, Y_{2\alpha} Y_{2\beta}$ $\qquad\qquad$ $Z_1 Z_2$

Fig. 15–31. Excitation and output matrices, Example 15–3.

and again in Z_2. Once a term is developed it can be used wherever needed, assuming that we do not build up an excessive number of stages of diode gates. Before a circuit of this type is built, of course, the arbitrary assignment of secondaries should be reviewed to see whether the assignment used in Fig. 15–31 gives a reasonably economical result, or whether it can be improved by modification.

15.4   The "Half-Pulse" Hazard

We have, generally speaking, considerable freedom in making secondary assignments for pulse circuits. That freedom, however, is not unlimited. In this article we discuss one important restriction which must be respected when making secondary assignments.

Consider the situation illustrated in Fig. 15–32. At a time when the secondary state is $y_1y_2 = 00$, a pulse is received on the X_1 input. The secondary devices respond by changing to the state $y_1y_2 = 01$. Some time after this response a pulse is received on the X_2 input, after which both secondary devices change and the state becomes $y_1y_2 = 10$. We note also that the secondary response is not instantaneous. The changes are completed during a finite time interval after the termination of the pulses which originate them.

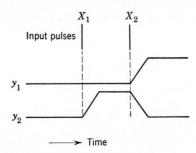

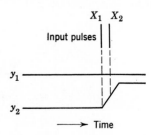

Fig. 15–32. Both secondary devices change state in response to the X_2 pulse.

Fig. 15–33. The time interval between input pulses is less than the secondary response time.

We now consider the situation illustrated in Fig. 15–33, in which the two input pulses arrive in rapid succession. In fact, the X_2 pulse arrives while the y_2 secondary device is still responding to the X_1 pulse. Under these circumstances any circuit output in response to the X_2 pulse may be attenuated severely. This reduced signal is known as a *half-pulse*.

In Fig. 15–32 we see that a pulse at the input X_2 is the signal for a change in state of both secondary variables. If, because the X_2 pulse follows too closely after the X_1 pulse, a half-pulse type of driving signal is applied to the two flip-flops simultaneously, one of several things may happen.

1. If the driving signal is above a certain threshold value, both flip-flops will make the transition to their new states and the circuit response will be normal.

2. If the signal strength is below a certain threshold value, neither flip-flop will make the transition to the new state. Effectively, the circuit behaves as though the input pulse never occurred. Sometimes this defect can be accepted, but usually a complete loss of an input signal is a serious matter.

3. For intermediate values of signal strength one of the flip-flops will change state and the other will not. In general this is a completely unacceptable situation.

Whenever, due to the close spacing of input pulses, it is possible to have a half-pulse signal, we must be sure to make secondary assignments such that the half-pulse signal is not used to originate a change of state of more than one secondary device. Furthermore, the circuit design must otherwise provide that no information is lost if a half-pulse is below the threshold required to produce normal response. We illustrate these points by the design of a pulse synchronizer.

After we have indulged in some deliberately bad design, the circuit shown in Fig. 15–34 is "suggested" as a pulse synchronizer to operate

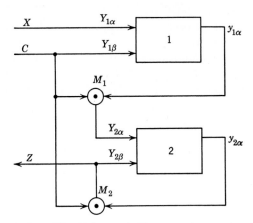

Fig. 15–34. Circuit "suggested" as a pulse synchronizer.

in accordance with the following specifications. The circuit has two inputs and one output. The input C is a clock pulse of constant frequency. The input on X is a pulse which occurs at random times with respect to the clock pulse. An output pulse Z is to occur during the second clock pulse after an X pulse. The clock frequency is such that consecutive X pulses will always be separated by at least three C pulses.

It is further specified that if an X pulse precedes a clock pulse by less than the response time of the secondary devices, it will be satisfactory to consider that this X pulse occurred *after* the clock pulse rather than before it. That is, we may delay the output required by the X pulse but we must not lose it.

We now examine the operation of the circuit of Fig. 15–34 to see whether it meets these specifications. First consider the operation when the random X pulse is not too close to the C pulse, and assume that both flip-flops are in the 0 state as the result of at least three clock pulses since the last X pulse. When another X pulse arrives it sets the No. 1 flip-flop in the 1 state, since this pulse goes directly to the $Y_{1\alpha}$ input. When the next clock pulse is received it goes directly to the $Y_{1\beta}$ input of the No. 1 flip-flop and, by way of gate M_1, to the $Y_{2\alpha}$ input of the No. 2 flip-flop. The gate M_1 transmits the clock pulse because the level $y_{1\alpha}$ is high. In response to this clock pulse both flip-flops change state, No. 1 going to the 0 state and No. 2 going to the 1 state. With the level $y_{2\alpha}$ high, gate M_2 can transmit, so the second clock pulse goes through this gate to form the output Z and also to pulse the input $Y_{2\beta}$ of flip-flop No. 2, thus restoring it to the 0 state. Both flip-flops are now back in the 0 state and the circuit is ready to receive another X pulse.

This circuit has two poor features of design. If an X pulse and a clock pulse happen to occur simultaneously, both inputs of flip-flop No. 1 receive pulses. But even if we could be sure that X and C pulses would never occur simultaneously there still is serious difficulty. If an X pulse precedes a clock pulse by a short time interval, the full-amplitude clock pulse may be able to initiate a return of the No. 1 flip-flop to the 0 state, but the clock pulse arriving at gate M_1 may find the level $y_{1\alpha}$ only partly changed to the 1 state. Hence, the pulse reaching input $Y_{2\alpha}$ may be a half-pulse which is insufficient to set that flip-flop in the 1 state. In that event the effect of the X pulse is entirely lost and the circuit performance is not in accordance with specifications.

To analyze this circuit we first write the excitation and output functions

$$Y_{1\alpha} = X$$

$$Y_{1\beta} = C$$

$$Y_{2\alpha} = Cy_{1\alpha}$$

$$Y_{2\beta} = Cy_{2\alpha} = Z$$

These functions are mapped in the excitation matrix shown in Fig. 15–35. In order to draw the flow matrix of Fig. 15–36 we first note that the effect of a successive group of clock pulses is to place the circuit in the

$y_{1\alpha}\,y_{2\alpha}$	X	C
O O	I O, O O	O I , O O
O I	I O, O O	O I , O I$'$
I I	I O, O O	O I , I I$'$
I O	I O, O O	O I , I O

$$Y_{1\alpha}\,Y_{1\beta},\ Y_{2\alpha}\,Y_{2\beta}$$

Fig. 15–35. Excitation matrix for the circuit of Fig. 15–34.

$y_{1\alpha}\,y_{2\alpha}$	X	C	
O O	4– O	1– O	1 No X-pulse received
O I	—	1– I	2 Read out and reset
I I	—	—	3
I O	—	2– O	4 One X-pulse received

Fig. 15–36. Flow matrix for circuit of Fig. 15–34.

00 secondary state. In Fig. 15–36 we identify this as the state in which no X pulse has been received. Next we observe that the excitation shown in Fig. 15–35 directs the circuit to state 4 after an X pulse is received. Because there must be at least three clock pulses after every X pulse the circuit will always return to state 1 before another X pulse is received. Hence the only entry in the X column of the flow matrix shows a transition from state 1 to state 4, with no output. All other entries in that column are blank because the circuit can be in no other state when an X pulse arrives.

When the circuit is in state 4 it means that an X pulse has been received and the first clock pulse must prepare the circuit to transmit an output pulse at the second clock pulse. In the excitation matrix we see that from state 4 the excitation causes a transition to state 2 when the first clock pulse is received, and there is no output on this transition. The excitation in state 2 returns the circuit to state 1 when the second clock pulse arrives, and there is an output associated with this final transition. The excitation shown for state 3 in the C column is meaningless because the circuit can never occupy this state. Accordingly we enter a blank in the C column for state 3 of the flow matrix.

We can now see in the flow matrix that the half-pulse hazard arises because the first clock pulse after an X pulse is required to initiate the transition from state 4 to state 2. This involves a change of the secondary state from 10 to 01, and it is this multiple change of secondary variables that must be avoided.

Let us see how a new synthesis can avoid the hazard. In Fig. 15–37 a flow matrix is written in which, with the circuit initially in state 1, an X pulse causes a transition to state 2 with no output. The first clock pulse that follows the X pulse then directs a transition to state 3, with

$y_{1\alpha} y_{2\alpha}$	X	C	
OO	2-O	1-O	1
OI	—	3-O	2
II	—	1-I	3
IO	—	—	4

$y_{1\alpha} y_{2\alpha}$	X	C
OO	OΦ, IO	OΦ, OΦ
OI	— —	IO, ΦO
II	— —	OI, OI
IO	— —	— —

$$Y_{1\alpha} Y_{1\beta}, \quad Y_{2\alpha} Y_{2\beta}$$

Fig. 15–37. Flow and excitation matrices that avoid the half-pulse hazard.

no output. In assigning secondary variables we are careful to make this critical transition by the change of a single secondary variable, that is, from 01 to 11. The next clock pulse returns the circuit to state 1 and delivers an output pulse. This transition, of course, requires a change of both secondary variables, but it is associated with the *second* clock pulse after the X pulse and the half-pulse hazard exists only with respect to the *first* clock pulse.

In the excitation matrix also shown in Fig. 15–37, there are many entries which have optional values. The options available in applying pulses to the flip-flop inputs (Table 15–1) are indicated in the usual manner. In addition, the dashes entered in the X column indicate that no X pulse can be received while the circuit is in any of those states and these dashes are hence optional entries. The dashes in the bottom row of the C column can also be used as optional entries because the circuit never occupies that state at all. These fixed and optional entries lead to the following excitation and output functions.

$$Y_{1\alpha} = Cy_{1\beta}y_{2\alpha}$$

$$Y_{1\beta} = Y_{2\beta} = Z = Cy_{1\alpha}$$

$$Y_{2\alpha} = X$$

The circuit which realizes these functions is shown in Fig. 15–38. For convenience in arranging the circuit, flip-flop No. 2 is shown at the top and No. 1 at the bottom. With both flip-flops initially in the 0 state, the circuit action is as follows. When an X pulse is received it sets flip-flop No. 2 to the 1 state and thereby raises the level of $y_{2\alpha}$ at gate M_2. At this same gate the input $y_{1\beta}$ is already at the high level. The first clock pulse, after the X pulse, passes through gate M_2 and sets flip-flop No. 1 to the 1 state. After this transition the level $y_{1\alpha}$ at gate M_1 is high, so the next clock pulse passes through gate M_1, returns both flip-flops to the 0 state, and produces an output pulse.

Suppose the interval between the X pulse and the first clock pulse is so small that the level of $y_{2\alpha}$ at gate M_2 has not fully changed. The clock pulse which follows may or may not set flip-flop No. 1 to the 1 state. But if it fails to do so on the first clock pulse after the X pulse, the next clock pulse will find the level $y_{2\alpha}$ at gate M_2 at its high value and the clock pulse will accordingly be transmitted through the gate. Another clock pulse (the third) then completes the required circuit action by resetting both flip-flops to the 0 state and producing an output pulse. Effectively, the circuit behaves as though the X pulse followed the first clock pulse rather than preceding it. The output is obtained one clock interval late but it is not lost.

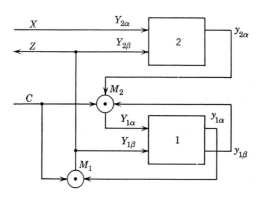

Fig. 15–38. The redesigned pulse synchronizer.

There is one curious redundancy in this circuit. The input $y_{1\beta}$ at gate M_2 is not needed, because at no time during the circuit operation does it exert any influence. The level $y_{2\alpha}$ is sufficient to control the clock pulse at the gate M_2, but algebraically the excitation $Y_{1\alpha}$ contains the dependence on $y_{1\beta}$. This term would be needed as written if it were possible for an X pulse to cause a transition other than to state 2. Algebraic manipulation does not indicate that the term is redundant but physically we can see that it does no harm to remove the $y_{1\beta}$ input to the gate M_2.

15.5 Magnetic Core Circuits

In Art. 9.7 we discussed the design of combinational circuits built on magnetic cores and having pulse inputs and pulse outputs. To design sequential circuits upon these components we use the feedback diagram illustrated in Fig. 15–39. The function generator in this circuit is again a combinational circuit. It delivers the circuit outputs and the secondary excitations as pulses at the time of the phase 1 advance pulse, A_1. All combinational core circuits will be synthesized by the output-composite method illustrated in Fig. 9–58.

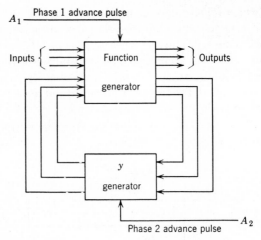

Fig. 15–39. Feedback circuit using pulsed magnetic cores.

For secondary devices we use cores, taking advantage of the fact that a core will remain in either of its two states indefinitely until it is switched to the other state. Excitation pulses are read into the secondary cores by the phase 1 advance pulse. Response pulses are read out of the secondary cores and into the function-generator cores by the phase 2 advance pulse, A_2. At the time of the A_2 pulse, circuit inputs also enter the function-generator cores, and the circuit is ready for the next cycle of operation. Because the A_1 and A_2 advance pulses are sources of energy, and supply output energy sufficient to set load cores, the requirement that there be gain in the feedback loop is readily satisfied.

We shall use the convention that an advance pulse resets a core to its 0 state. If an input pulse sets the core to the 1 state, the next advance pulse applied therefore resets it to the 0 state. In diagrams drawn with mirror symbols a core will be considered in the 0 state when it is magnetized in the downward direction.

Although the core as a secondary device is very simple, it brings up problems we have not encountered before. We note that a core can act much like a set-reset flip-flop except that its output is hidden. We must apply an advance pulse in order to read the state represented by the core. But in this process we reset all the cores and the information stored in them is lost. Consequently if we want to have a secondary state remain unchanged during a succession of advance pulses, we must provide in the excitation functions terms which regenerate the state. Effectively, if no change of circuit input occurs a secondary state then circulates continuously as the two-phase advance pulses shuttle it back and forth between the cores of the function generator and the cores of the y generator in Fig. 15–39.

A synthesis similar to that performed in Example 15–2 will serve to show the modifications we must make in our procedure to design pulsed sequential circuits using cores. The circuit we will design has two inputs, X_1 and X_2, and one output. An input pulse, if it occurs, is always applied at the time of the A_2 advance pulse, and only one input line is pulsed at a time. There need not necessarily be an input pulse at each A_2 pulse. An output pulse is to be obtained for each X_1 pulse received, but only after the next X_2 pulse is received. If more than one X_1 pulse arrives between X_2 pulses, the circuit is to store the information and provide output pulses at the next available X_2 pulses, but the circuit need not store more than three X_1 pulses.

Since input pulses do not occur at every possible input time, we must write a flow table that provides for the continuation of a secondary state when neither input receives a pulse. In Fig. 15–40 entries in the X_1 and the X_2 columns provide for the required circuit action and outputs if input pulses are received. In the column for the condition $X_1X_2 = 00$, $(X_1'X_2' = 11)$, the entries require that the excitation pulses delivered prevent any change of state when no input pulses are received. The excitation-output matrix required by this flow table is given in Fig. 15–41.

$y_1 y_2$	$X_1'X_2'$	X_1	X_2	
00	0 - 0	1 - 0	0 - 0	0
01	1 - 0	2 - 0	0 - 1	1
11	2 - 0	3 - 0	1 - 1	2
10	3 - 0	3 - 0	2 - 1	3

Fig. 15–40. Flow table with a column to prevent change of state when there is no input pulse.

$y_1 y_2$	$X_1'X_2'$	X_1	X_2
00	00-0	01-0	00-0
01	01-0	11-0	00-1
11	11-0	10-0	01-1
10	10-0	10-0	11-1

$Y_1 Y_2 - Z$

Fig. 15–41. Excitation-output matrix derived from flow table of Fig. 15–40.

In writing excitation and output functions from this matrix we must keep in mind the restriction imposed by the fact, discussed in Art. 9.7, that the advance-pulse current must never be permitted to divide among two or more paths. This restriction requires us, in realizing combinational circuits with only a single output, to write transmission functions so that all terms are disjunctive. In the situation we now face we must realize three different functions without permitting the advance pulse current to divide. In the X_2 column, Fig. 15–41, the entry in the fourth row is 11–1, indicating that pulses are to appear at all three outputs. This requires a three-way division of the advance current if we merely set up three output circuits on one set of cores.

If the required multiple outputs are used to set other cores, a procedure suggested by Rosenfeld* can be considered. For the three outputs Y_1, Y_2, and Z, there are seven combinations of values which contain one or more 1's. Six of these seven possible output combinations appear in the matrix of Fig. 15–41. We write a function for the realization of each combination separately. Since only one of these combinations can appear at a time all the output-combination functions are therefore disjunctive and can be realized without requiring the advance-pulse current to divide among multiple paths.

In the following tabulation the function subscript used is the decimal equivalent of the binary number that describes the output combination.

$Y_1 Y_2 Z$	Output Function
0 0 1	$f_1 = X_2 y_1' y_2$
0 1 0	$f_2 = X_1' X_2' y_1' y_2 + X_1 y_1' y_2'$
0 1 1	$f_3 = X_2 y_1 y_2$
1 0 0	$f_4 = X_1' X_2' y_1 y_2' + X_1 y_1$
1 1 0	$f_6 = X_1' X_2' y_1 y_2 + X_1 y_1' y_2$
1 1 1	$f_7 = X_2 y_1 y_2'$

We now note that we can recover the original non-disjunctive outputs from

$$Y_1 = f_4 + f_6 + f_7$$

$$Y_2 = f_2 + f_3 + f_6 + f_7$$

$$Z = f_1 + f_3 + f_7$$

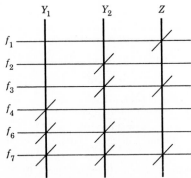

Fig. 15–42. Disjunctive output combinations combined to set output cores.

The core circuit of Fig. 15–42 uses the output-combination functions f_1 to f_7 as setting inputs for cores which represent Y_1, Y_2, and Z. Only one input line at a time receives a pulse and this pulse passes through windings on all cores which should be set for that particular output combination.

When, at the time of the advance pulse A_2, the $y_1 y_2$ values are to be transferred back to the input of the function generator, we have another

* See Reference 18 in the Bibliography at the end of Chapter 9.

multiple-output situation when we must transmit $y_1 y_2 = 11$. To generate these as two simultaneous outputs would require the A_2 pulse current to divide between two paths. Hence we must again generate the separate output combinations corresponding to $y_1 y_2 = 01, 10$, and 11 by a circuit which realizes the output-combination functions $f_1 = y_1' y_2$, $f_2 = y_1 y_2'$, and $f_3 = y_1 y_2$. These disjunctive outputs are then combined as setting functions on the y_1 and y_2 cores in the function generator by a circuit similar to that of Fig. 15–42.

The need for realizing multiple outputs in terms of a set of output combinations is a discouraging aspect of the use of cores in the synthesis of sequential circuits. Each output combination requires a separate combinational circuit of one of the types described in Art. 9.7. If all the circuits could be carried on one set of cores the situation would be acceptable, but another restriction makes it difficult, in general, to accomplish this. This restriction is that no core may furnish forward-polarized windings for more than one output. Consider the circuit segment of Fig. 15–43 in which windings on the X core supply forward potential for the outputs XY' and XY. When $X = 1$ and $Y = 0$, advance-pulse current flows to the XY' output of the upper path, but none flows in the lower path where the backward voltage of the Y'

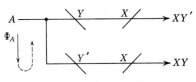

Fig. 15–43. Circuit to illustrate a design restriction.

winding opposes the forward voltage of the X winding. However, if we designate the number of turns in an advance winding by N_a, the number of turns in a forward winding by N_f, and the advance-pulse current by I, the net magnetomotive force acting on core X is $(N_a - N_f)I$, and that acting on core Y' is $N_a I$. Because the magnetomotive force acting on core Y' is greater than that applied to core X, the Y' core tends to switch faster. Hence, at a time when the Y' core has completed its switching and no backward potential is present in the lower path, there still will be forward potential induced in the winding on the X core. During the remainder of the switching time the advance-pulse current will divide between the two paths. This division leads to the hazard that the load core supplied by the upper path may not be completely set and that the spurious current in the lower path may partially set the load core supplied by that output. This situation, of course, cannot be accepted, and we must therefore avoid it in our design.

In designing a function generator to realize the output combinations f_1 to f_7 it will be necessary to set some cores to represent the complements of one or more of the input variables X_1, X_2, y_1, and y_2. The winding and input arrangements for doing so are indicated in Fig. 15–44 for the input X_1. A unit pulse sets the core to the 1 state, and if $X_1 = 0$,

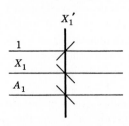

Fig. 15–44. Arrangement of windings on a core representing the complement of an input variable.

the advance pulse A_1 resets the core to the 0 state and reads out $X_1' = 1$. If $X_1 = 1$ the X_1 pulse opposes the unit pulse and the core is not set. Hence the advance pulse will find the core already in the 0 state and will read out $X_1' = 0$. It should be noted that if the unit pulse in this circuit cannot be coincident with the X_1 pulse, we must be sure that the unit pulse arrives first.

We shall use the output-composite method, described in Art. 9.7, for the synthesis of the required combinational circuit. This method has the advantage that variation in the time of arrival of input pulses causes no difficulty, provided they arrive before the advance pulse A_1, and not sooner than the unit pulse, if complementary cores are to be set.

In the chart of Fig. 15–45 the columns show for headings the variables represented by each core. Each row contains crosses to show the

	X_1	X_1'	X_2	X_2'	y_1	y_1'	y_2	y_2'
f_1		⊗				×	×	
f_2	×		×			⊗	×	
	×					⊗		×
f_3			×		⊗	×		
f_4		⊗		×	×			×
	⊗				×			
f_6	×			×	×		⊗	
	×					×	⊗	
f_7			×		×			⊗

Fig. 15–45. Chart used for the selection of forward-polarized windings in the multiple-output circuit.

variables present in each product term. Horizontal lines have been drawn to separate the different output combinations. Encircled crosses indicate a core chosen to carry a forward-polarized winding. Our objective is to place the encircled crosses in different columns so that no two output combinations are supplied by the same forward winding. We can, however, use a common forward potential for different terms in the same output combination. Thus we use y_1' in both paths of f_2, and we use y_2 in both paths of f_6. In the first trial selection, y_1 was used in both paths of f_4, but that made it necessary to provide a duplicate core for some variable in either f_1 or f_3, since only one of these could use a forward winding on the X_2 core. Hence the f_4 terms are given forward windings on X_1 and X_1', and the forward winding on y_1 is used in developing the output combination f_3. All crosses without circles should be shifted to the columns headed by their complementary variables to show directly which cores carry backward-polarized windings. To avoid excessive detail these shift indications are omitted in Fig. 15–45, but their effect is taken into account in the circuit diagram of Fig. 15–46. Detached mirror symbols are used in this circuit dia-

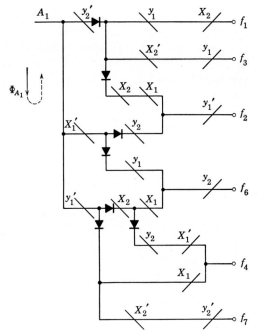

Fig. 15–46. Generation of output combinations. These outputs are the inputs to like-numbered terminals in Fig. 15–42.

gram of the output-combination network. The arrow symbol at the left indicates that the A_1 advance pulse magnetizes all cores downward, corresponding to the 0-state.

To complete the synthesis it is necessary to provide another multiple-output circuit to supply the disjunctive output combinations $Y_1'Y_2$, Y_1Y_2', and Y_1Y_2 which serve to set the y_1, y_1', y_2 and y_2' cores. Since there are three output combinations, three cores are needed in order to provide a separate forward potential for each output. We note in Fig. 15–42 that the Y_1 core has only three setting windings on it, but the Y_2 core has four windings. We hence require fewer setting windings if we add a $Y_1{}'$ core, using the method of Fig. 15–44 to do the complementing. The required unit pulse must occur before the f_4, f_6, and f_7 pulses, and it sets the $Y_1{}'$ core upward. The windings which receive an f_4, f_6, or f_7 pulse are in the direction to reset the core downward. It will be instructive for the student to verify the details of this design by completing the circuit in accordance with Fig. 15–39.

Some simplification of these multiple-output circuit designs can be achieved in this synthesis if we can eliminate the need for circulating secondary-state information during periods when there is no change at the inputs. If, after each input pulse, there is just one A_1 and one A_2 pulse, the new state will be stored and remain stored in the y cores awaiting the next input pulse. The $X_1{}'X_2{}'$ column of the excitation-output matrix could then be eliminated, and all product terms derived from that column would vanish.

Let us examine the circuit of Fig. 15–47. We assume that cores 1 and 2 are initially in the 0 state. The A_1 pulse cannot reset core 1 so there

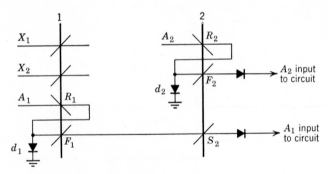

Fig. 15–47. Circuit for control of advance pulses.

will be no forward potential induced in the winding F_1 and the A_1 pulse is by-passed through the diode d_1. Similarly in core 2 there is no path for the pulse A_2 through the forward winding F_2, so the A_2 pulse is by-passed through the diode d_2. Now, if there is a pulse on either X_1 or X_2, core 1 is set. Pulse A_1 then takes the path through the advance winding R_1 which resets core 1, through the forward winding F_1, then through the winding S_2 which sets core 2, and continues as the A_1 pulse-input to the circuit. With core 2 now set, the next A_2 pulse passes through winding R_2 to reset the core, then through winding F_2 because of the forward potential induced in it, and continues as the

A_2 pulse-input to the circuit. Each advance pulse in this process resets its core to the 0 state and there can hence be no further advance pulses delivered to the circuit until there is another circuit input on X_1 or X_2 to initiate the advance-pulse sequence once again.

When sequential circuits are built on cores used as magnetic amplifiers, such as the Ramey type discussed in Art. 9.7, we can treat inputs and outputs as though they were voltage levels, but because there is a half-cycle lag in each core it becomes necessary to take account of relative phase angles. Phase relations in these circuits are as defined in Fig. 15-48. Reset and gate voltages are a-c and of opposite phase.

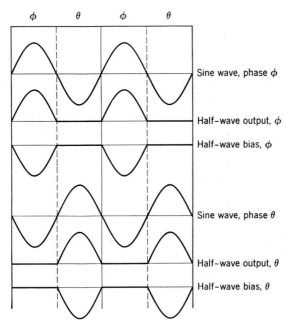

Fig. 15–48. Phase relations in circuits using Ramey magnetic amplifiers.

When an amplifier output becomes the input of another device containing an amplifier, the reset voltage supply of the second amplifier must be of the same phase as that of the half-wave d-c that appears at its input. Likewise, any bias voltage applied to an impedance-correction circuit must be of the same phase as the a-c voltage which supplies that part of the circuit.

Since an Add gate contains rectifiers only, a signal does not change phase in passing through it. Multiply gates and Complement gates, however, contain cores, and a half-cycle phase shift occurs in each of them. The symbols shown in Fig. 15–49 are used rather widely in representing circuits built with these elements.

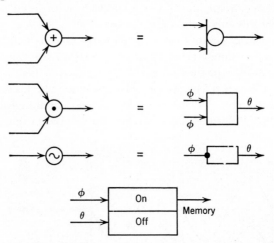

Fig. 15–49. Symbols used in magnetic-amplifier circuits.

The memory circuit, shown symbolically in Fig. 15–49, is constructed in accordance with the circuit diagram of Fig. 15–50. It contains the two Add gates, A_1 and A_2, and the two Complement gates, C_1 and C_2.

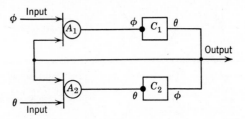

Fig. 15–50. Structure of the memory circuit.

The Complement gates operate in opposite phases in order to be compatible with the two input phases. Their outputs join to form the common output of the circuit, and the output is connected back to one input of each Add gate. Suppose we make the ϕ input high and the θ input low. The output of $C_1(\theta)$ is low and that of $C_2(\phi)$ is high. Thus the output consists of half-wave direct current of ϕ phase. This is fed back to the A_1 input and permits the circuit to remain in this state if the external signal is removed. If the high input is applied to A_2 in the θ phase, the output will be a half-wave direct current of θ phase and the feedback again makes the circuit stable. If both inputs become high the output is 0 in both phases because the complement of each input appears at the output. If the inputs are both high, and both are removed simultaneously, the next output is unpredictable, because it depends upon which of the two complementing gates first fails to reset. The excitation in which both inputs are high can be very useful, however, if the change of input from 11 to 00 cannot occur. If the input changes from 11 by way of either 01 or 10, the output is, of course, fully determined by the input.

Although this memory device may be used in a manner similar to the use of the set-reset flip-flop in the design of sequential circuits, we may also use the feedback-delay method without providing a memory device. Consider, for example, the clamp-gate synthesis performed in Example 12–1. From the excitation and the output matrices of Fig. 12–18 (left-hand pair) we may write

$$Y = (X_1 + X_2')(X_1 + y)(X_2 + y)$$

$$Z = Y \text{ or } y$$

In Fig. 15–51 these functions are realized using magnetic amplifier elements.* We note that a half-cycle delay is needed after Y is generated,

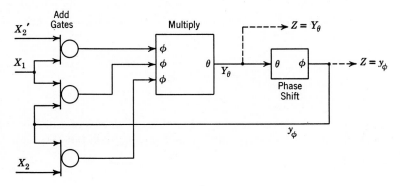

Fig. 15–51. The clamp-gate synthesis by direct feedback with delay.

to make the phase of y coincident with the phase of the Multiply gate input.

When the memory circuit of Fig. 15–50 is used as a secondary device its excitation treatment can be similar to that used for various types of flip-flops. Its required and optional excitations for all possible responses are shown in Table 15–4.

* Cynthia H. P. Hsiao, "Sequential Switching Circuits Built with Magnetic Amplifiers," Master's thesis, Department of Electrical Engineering, Massachusetts Institute of Technology, February, 1958.

Table 15–4.   Excitation of Magnetic Amplifier Memory Circuit

Required Response of y_ϕ	Inputs Y_ϕ	Y_θ
$0 \rightarrow 0$	0	ϕ
$0 \rightarrow 1$	1	0
$1 \rightarrow 0$	0	1
$1 \rightarrow 1$	ϕ	0

Applying the memory circuit to the synthesis of the clamp-gate circuit, we repeat in Fig. 15–52 the flow table of the clamp-gate circuit, and use

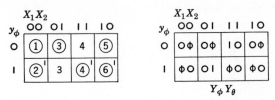

Fig. 15–52. Excitation matrix using the magnetic memory circuit.

Table 15–4 to complete the excitation matrix. After taking advantage of the available optional excitations, we write the excitation and output functions,

$$Y_\phi = X_1 X_2$$

$$Y_\theta = X_1' X_2$$

$$Z = y_\phi$$

The circuit which realizes these functions is shown in Fig. 15–53. It is remarkable in that it appears to have no feedback, but this simply

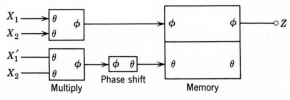

Fig. 15–53. Clamp-gate circuit synthesized from excitation matrix of Fig. 15–52.

is a consequence of the symbols used. The feedback is actually present in the memory circuit itself.

If we can permit the memory circuit to have a high excitation on both input terminals, there is somewhat more freedom of excitation than is shown in Table 15–4. For the response $y_\phi = 0 \rightarrow 0$, we can apply as inputs $Y_\phi Y_\theta = 00$, 01, or 11; and for the response $y_\phi = 1 \to 0$, we can apply as inputs either 01 or 11. In the synthesis under consideration, the circuit inputs never change in more than one variable at a time, and the high excitation of both inputs of the memory circuit is therefore allowable. The additional options thus available do not help us much in improving the excitation matrix of Fig. 15–52, but if the assignment of y_ϕ values in the flow matrix is reversed, the additional options may be used to write the excitation and output functions in the form

$$Y_\phi = X_2$$

$$Y_\theta = X_1 X_2$$

$$Z = y_\phi{}'$$

These functions lead to the circuit shown in Fig. 15–54. We note that this circuit requires a complementing gate which also introduces a

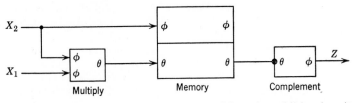

Fig. 15–54. Simplified clamp-gate circuit derived by using additional excitation options.

phase shift. In Fig. 15–53 we used a simple phase shift unit which did not complement the signal. It must be remembered that a shift in time phase does not produce a complement; there must be a change of state.

In this article we have considered relatively simple examples to illustrate synthesis procedures for magnetic core circuits. These examples, however, serve to emphasize the breadth of application of basic switching circuit concepts to logical design using many kinds of components. As new types of two-valued components are developed we can expect procedures similar to those discussed to be applicable in the design of new types of switching circuits.

PROBLEMS

15.1 Design a circuit which has the terminal action of the 3-input flip-flop specified in text Table 15–2, page 630:
    1. Using the τ flip-flop as the basic device.
    2. Using the set-reset flip-flop as the basic device.

15.2 In Problem 15.1 substitute the 2-input flip-flop, specified in text Table 15–3, for the 3-input flip-flop.

15.3 For each of the pulse sequential circuits described construct the flow diagram and the flow table. Assign the secondary variables and determine both τ and $Y_{\alpha,\beta}$ functions for the realization of the circuits using τ flip-flops and set-reset toggles, respectively.

Assume all input pulses are separated by at least the response times of the circuits.

1. A two-input one-output pulse sequential circuit has an output pulse coincident with the second X_2 pulse following an X_1 pulse. Not more than one X_1 pulse ever occurs between two X_2 pulses.
2. A three-input two-output pulse sequential circuit has an output pulse, Z_1, coincident with each X_2 pulse directly preceded by an X_1 pulse, and has an output pulse Z_2, for all X_2 pulses which form an uninterrupted sequence following an X_3 pulse.
3. A two-input one-output pulse-level sequential circuit has a level output of 1 which is originated by an X_1 pulse and is returned to 0 by the next X_1 pulse, provided that an X_2 pulse has not occurred in the meantime, in which event the output level can be returned to 0 only by another X_2 pulse. An X_2 pulse cannot originate an output level of 1.

15.4 A pulse sequential circuit has a single output and two inputs. One input receives clock pulses and the other input receives X pulses which are intermittent but never occur simultaneously with the clock pulse. There is to be an output pulse at each clock pulse which follows two accumulated X pulses.

Synthesize a minimal circuit using set-reset flip-flops.

15.5 The three inputs of a sequential circuit receive separate pulses X_1, X_2, X_3, which are always spaced by at least the resolution time of the circuit.

The single output is to deliver a pulse at each input pulse which completes one of the sequences $X_1 \rightarrow X_2 \rightarrow X_3$, or $X_2 \rightarrow X_3 \rightarrow X_1$, or $X_3 \rightarrow X_1 \rightarrow X_2$.

1. Prepare a flow table, including outputs, which satisfies the requirements.
2. Make an assignment of secondary values such that the output is controlled by a single flip-flop.
3. Prepare the appropriate excitation matrix for a realization using τ flip-flops.
4. Write the excitation equation for the flip-flop which controls the output.

15.6 A pulse sequential circuit has two pulsed inputs, X and C, and an output at which the voltage level is to change. The C input represents clock

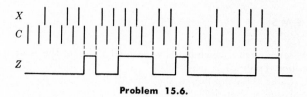

Problem 15.6.

pulses which are at constant frequency. If any X pulse appears it will be midway between clock pulses.

The output voltage level, Z, is to rise at the time of the clock pulse which follows the second pulse in a group of at least two consecutive X pulses, and is to fall at the second clock pulse after the last X pulse in a group. The sketch given illustrates typical input-output relations.

1. Write a flow table and from it write the excitation and output matrices for a circuit using τ flip-flops.
2. Design the circuit.

15.7 An electronic sequential circuit is to be designed using set-reset type toggles as the secondary devices. The two circuit inputs, X and C, are pulses which never occur simultaneously. The C pulse occurs periodically as shown in the diagram. The X pulse can appear (if it does appear) only singly and midway between two successive C pulses. The single level output, Z, is high in the interval between two successive C pulses if and only if the preceding interval contained an X pulse.

1. Derive a minimum-row flow table and output data for the circuit specified.
2. Derive a complete excitation matrix showing for which situations a toggle input can be chosen arbitrarily.
3. Derive an economical circuit using only set-reset toggles and diode gates.

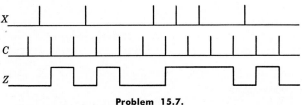

Problem 15.7.

15.8 Design one element of a counter which registers pulses to the number base four. As indicated in the figure there is one pulse input X and one pulse output Z. There are four voltage-level outputs, "0," "1," "2," "3," only one of which is high at any time. Each input pulse is to advance the high, voltage-level output from "0" to "1," "1" to "2," "2" to "3," and then back to level "0." As the voltage level advances, the level at the previously "high" output returns to "low."

Each time the voltage-level output advances from "3" to "0" there is to be an output Z pulse, synchronous with the X pulse that caused the advance. (This Z pulse is a "carry" pulse to the next higher stage of the counter.)

1. Write a flow table showing all *outputs*.

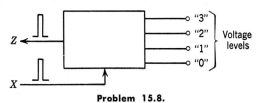

Problem 15.8.

    2. Write the excitation and output functions, using set-reset flip-flops.

    3. Draw the indicated circuit.

15.9 An electronic circuit has three inputs and one output. The inputs (X_1, X_2, X_3) are pulses which are always separated by more than the resolution time of the circuit. The output is to be a voltage level which is either "high" $(Z = 1)$ or "low" $(Z = 0)$.

The output is to become 0 or remain 0 for each X_3 pulse which immediately follows an X_1 pulse.

The output is to become 1 or remain 1 for each X_3 pulse which immediately follows an X_2 pulse.

The output is to *change* for each X_1 pulse that immediately follows an X_2 pulse.

For any other input sequence the output must remain constant.

    1. Construct a flow table showing all transitions and outputs.

    2. Using τ flip-flops, assign secondary states so that the output is derived from a single flip-flop.

    3. Write the expressions for the τ excitations and for the output.

15.10 Repeat Problem 15.9, using set-reset flip-flops instead of τ flip-flops.

15.11 A pulse sequential circuit has two inputs, X_1 and X_2, and two outputs Z_1 and Z_2. All input pulses occur at equally spaced intervals of time and a pulse will occur on either X_1 or X_2, but not both, at each time interval.

Whenever there are two or more consecutive pulses on either input lead, there is to be the same number of consecutive pulses on the corresponding output lead. Output pulses, if they appear, are to be synchronous with input pulses.

Note that in the steady state the circuit is *always* in the condition of having received at least one pulse.

    1. Write a flow table for steady-state operation, that is, one that does *not* include a state to represent "no input received." Show all outputs on the flow table and describe what each state represents.

    2. Synthesize the circuit, using set-reset flip-flops.

15.12 A two-input, two-output circuit receives input pulses which never occur simultaneously. Output pulses appear on only one output terminal at a time and these pulses are coincident with input pulses.

A consecutive group of X_1 pulses is to cause a consecutive group of Z_2 pulses, and a consecutive group of X_2 pulses is to cause a consecutive group of Z_1 pulses. However, if any group of Z_1 pulses starts, at its termination it must contain an even number of pulses, and if any group of Z_2 pulses starts, at its termination it must contain an odd number of pulses. For this problem, treat zero as an even number. Z_1 and Z_2 pulses are never to appear simultaneously, but there must be either a Z_1 or a Z_2 pulse at each input pulse.

    1. Prepare a flow table, including outputs, which satisfies these conditions.

    2. Write the secondary excitation equation(s) using the set-reset type of flip-flop.

    3. Write the equations for the outputs.

    4. Draw a schematic of the required network.

Binary numbers

A number, N, may be expressed in the form

$$N = a_0 r^0 + a_1 r^1 + a_2 r^2 + \ldots + a_n r^n$$

where

r = the base, or the radix of the number system,

$a_0, a_1, a_2, \ldots, a_n$ are the number digits having values between 0 and $(r - 1)$.

Thus, when we write a *decimal* number, say 1629, we are actually writing it in an abbreviated form, since

$$1629 = 9 \times 10^0 + 2 \times 10^1 + 6 \times 10^2 + 1 \times 10^3$$

We note that in the decimal system the only digits used are those between 0 and 9. If we use a radix $r < 10$, we need use only the familiar digits from 0 to $(r - 1)$. If $r > 10$, we must devise new digits to represent 10, 11, 12, $\ldots$, $(r - 1)$.

Methods for changing a number expressed in terms of one radix to its equivalent in terms of any other radix are discussed in numerous books on ordinary algebra. We will consider here only the decimal equivalents of binary numbers and the binary equivalents of decimal numbers.

A number written in the base 2 has the form

$$N_2 = a_0 2^0 + a_1 2^1 + a_2 2^2 + a_3 2^3 + \ldots + a_n 2^n$$

$$= a_0 + a_1(2) + a_2(4) + a_3(8) + \ldots + a_n(2^n)$$

The coefficients $a_0, a_1, a_2, \ldots, a_n$ can have only the values 0 and 1, since $(r - 1) = 2 - 1 = 1$.

If we divide N_2 by the radix 2, each power of 2 is reduced by one and there will be a remainder, a_0. If $N_2/2$, with the remainder a_0 discarded, is again divided by 2, we obtain the remainder a_1. By continuing this process of detaching a previous remainder and dividing by 2, we obtain a succession of remainders which are the coefficients $a_0, a_1, a_2, \ldots, a_n$. When these coefficients are arranged in the order

$$a_n \ldots a_2 a_1 a_0$$

we have the conventional form of the binary number, with the highest-order digit at the left and successively lower-order digits to the right.

Thus, we may change the decimal number 1629 to its binary coefficient by the successive divisions

		Remainder
$1629/2 =$	$814 +$	1
$814/2 =$	$407 +$	0
$407/2 =$	$203 +$	1
$203/2 =$	$101 +$	1
$101/2 =$	$50 +$	1
$50/2 =$	$25 +$	0
$25/2 =$	$12 +$	1
$12/2 =$	$6 +$	0
$6/2 =$	$3 +$	0
$3/2 =$	$1 +$	1
$1/2 =$	$0 +$	1

When the column of remainders is read from the bottom up and arranged in conventional order, we write the binary equivalent of 1629 as 11001011101.

Another method, which is sometimes more rapid, is to subtract powers of 2 from the decimal number, starting wtih the highest power that can be subtracted, and continuing with the lower powers in decreasing order. Each time a power of 2 can be subtracted, a digit 1 is entered in the binary equivalent. If a power of 2 cannot be subtracted, the digit 0 is entered. Let us find the binary equivalent of decimal 101 by this method.

$$
\begin{array}{rl}
101 & \qquad 64 = 2^6 \qquad \text{can be subtracted} \\
-64 & \\
\hline
37 & \\
-32 & \qquad 32 = 2^5 \qquad \text{can be subtracted} \\
\hline
5 & \\
-4 & \qquad 4 = 2^2 \qquad \text{can be subtracted} \\
\hline
1 & \\
-1 & \qquad 1 = 2^0 \qquad \text{can be subtracted} \\
\hline
0 &
\end{array}
$$

We note that we could not subtract 2^4, 2^3, or 2^1, so the binary equivalent of decimal 101 is written 1100101.

The transformation of a binary number to its decimal equivalent is accomplished simply by adding the powers of 2 corresponding to the digit positions which contain 1's in the binary representation. Thus, we write for the decimal equivalent of 1100101, $64 + 32 + 4 + 1 = 101$.

In Appendix 5 a decimal-binary conversion table is given for the range from 0 to 127.

Sum
modulo two

In this book operations using the sum modulo two, or ring sum, are not discussed. The general literature of switching circuits does, however, contain scattered references to such operations. The following summary of postulates and theorems will enable the student to relate sum modulo two operations on binary variables to the processes of switching algebra.*

Sum modulo two is expressed by the symbol $\oplus$

Postulates

$$(1) \quad 0 \oplus 0 = 0$$
$$(2) \quad 1 \oplus 1 = 0$$
$$(3) \quad 0 \oplus 1 = 1 \oplus 0 = 1$$

Theorems

$$(4) \quad X \oplus 0 = X$$
$$(4') \quad X \oplus 1 = X'$$
$$(5) \quad X \oplus X = 0$$
$$(5') \quad X \oplus X' = 1$$
$$(6) \quad X \oplus X \oplus \ldots \oplus X = 0, \text{ if the number of terms is even}$$
$$(6') \quad X \oplus X \oplus \ldots \oplus X = X, \text{ if the number of terms is odd}$$
$$(7) \quad X \oplus Y = Y \oplus X$$

* From "Notes for a Seminar on Switching Circuits," by D. A. Huffman. Presented at Lincoln Laboratory, Massachusetts Institute of Technology, 1955.

(8) $(X \oplus Y) \oplus Z = X \oplus (Y \oplus Z) = X \oplus Y \oplus Z$

(9) $X \oplus Y = Z$ implies $\begin{cases} X \oplus Z = Y \\ Y \oplus Z = X \\ X \oplus Y \oplus Z = 0 \end{cases}$

(10) $XY \oplus XZ = X(Y \oplus Z)$

But, $(X + Y) \oplus (X + Z) \neq X + (Y \oplus Z)$

$(X \oplus Y) + (X \oplus Z) \neq X \oplus (Y + Z)$

$(X \oplus Y) \cdot (X \oplus Z) \neq X \cdot (Y \oplus Z)$

(11) $X \oplus Y = XY' + X'Y = (X + Y)(X' + Y')$

The numbers of functions of *n* variables

A function of n binary variables may be formed by selecting members of a standard sum from the set of $N = 2^n$ combinations of the n variables. If a function thus formed is to contain M terms, the number of possible selections is given by

$$_N C_M = \frac{N!}{M!(N - M)!}$$

This is the formula from which we find the number of combinations of N things taken M at a time. If we evaluate this formula for all values of M from zero to N, we obtain the binomial coefficients for the order N.

These coefficients are tabulated for $n = 2, 3$, and 4, or $N = 4, 8$, and 16. For a given n the sum of the coefficients is the total number of possible functions, and this sum equals 2^{2^n}.

Table of Binomial Coefficients

n	N	$M =$ 0	1	2	3	4	5	6	7	8
2	4	1	4	6	4	1				
3	8	1	8	28	56	70	56	28	8	1
4	16	1	16	120	560	1820	4368	8008	11440	12870

n	N	$M =$ 9	10	11	12	13	14	15	16
2	4								
3	8								
4	16	11440	8008	4368	1820	560	120	16	1

Classes
of functions
# of three variables

If in the function $A'C + BC'$ we make the substitutions $A = C'$ and $A' = C$, we obtain the function $AB + A'C$. In a list of the 256 functions of three variables, these would appear to be two different functions. They are, however, related through a substitution of variables.

A systematic study of these transformations* shows that there are only 22 *different* functions of three variables, including $f = 0$ and $f = 1$. In the following table a representative function from each of the different classes of functions is given and the number of terms in the corresponding standard sum is shown.

---

*See Reference 9 in the Bibliography at the end of Chapter 3. This reference also contains an Appendix which is an exhaustive classification of the functions of four variables.

Functions of Three Variables

Class		Number of Terms in Standard Sum
1.	0	0
2.	ABC	1
3.	$ABC + A'B'C' = (A + B')(B + C')(A' + C)$	2
4.	$ABC + AB'C' = A(BC + B'C')$	2
5.	$ABC + ABC' = AB$	2
6.	$S_2(A,B,C)$	3
7.	$AB'C' + BC$	3
8.	$A(B + C)$	3
9.	A	4
10.	$S_{2,3}(A, B, C)$	4
11.	$AB + A'C$	4
12.	$A'BC + A(B' + C')$	4
13.	$S_{0,2}(A, B, C)$	4
14.	$BC + B'C'$	4
15.	$A + BC$	5
16.	$(A + B' + C')(B + C)$	5
17.	$S_{0,1,3}(A, B, C)$	5
18.	$A + B$	6
19.	$(A + B + C)(A + B' + C')$	6
20.	$(A + B + C)(A' + B' + C') = AB' + BC' + A'C$	6
21.	$A + B + C$	7
22.	1	8

Decimal-binary conversion table

Decimal Number	Binary Number	Index	Decimal Number	Binary Number	Index
0	0	0	23	10111	4
1	1	1	24	11000	2
2	10	1	25	11001	3
3	11	2	26	11010	3
4	100	1	27	11011	4
5	101	2	28	11100	3
6	110	2	29	11101	4
7	111	3	30	11110	4
8	1000	1	31	11111	5
9	1001	2	32	100000	1
10	1010	2	33	100001	2
11	1011	3	34	100010	2
12	1100	2	35	100011	3
13	1101	3	36	100100	2
14	1110	3	37	100101	3
15	1111	4	38	100110	3
16	10000	1	39	100111	4
17	10001	2	40	101000	2
18	10010	2	41	101001	3
19	10011	3	42	101010	3
20	10100	2	43	101011	4
21	10101	3	44	101100	3
22	10110	3	45	101101	4

Decimal Number	Binary Number	Index	Decimal Number	Binary Number	Index
46	101110	4	87	1010111	5
47	101111	5	88	1011000	3
48	110000	2	89	1011001	4
49	110001	3	90	1011010	4
50	110010	3	91	1011011	5
51	110011	4	92	1011100	4
52	110100	3	93	1011101	5
53	110101	4	94	1011110	5
54	110110	4	95	1011111	6
55	110111	5	96	1100000	2
56	111000	3	97	1100001	3
57	111001	4	98	1100010	3
58	111010	4	99	1100011	4
59	111011	5	100	1100100	3
60	111100	4	101	1100101	4
61	111101	5	102	1100110	4
62	111110	5	103	1100111	5
63	111111	6	104	1101000	3
64	1000000	1	105	1101001	4
65	1000001	2	106	1101010	4
66	1000010	2	107	1101011	5
67	1000011	3	108	1101100	4
68	1000100	2	109	1101101	5
69	1000101	3	110	1101110	5
70	1000110	3	111	1101111	6
71	1000111	4	112	1110000	3
72	1001000	2	113	1110001	4
73	1001001	3	114	1110010	4
74	1001010	3	115	1110011	5
75	1001011	4	116	1110100	4
76	1001100	3	117	1110101	5
77	1001101	4	118	1110110	5
78	1001110	4	119	1110111	6
79	1001111	5	120	1111000	4
80	1010000	2	121	1111001	5
81	1010001	3	122	1111010	5
82	1010010	3	123	1111011	6
83	1010011	4	124	1111100	5
84	1010100	3	125	1111101	6
85	1010101	4	126	1111110	6
86	1010110	4	127	1111111	7

Index